GENERAL ARITHMETIC FOR SCHOOLS

is issued in the following styles:

ORDINARY EDITION

COMPLETE, *with* and *without answers.*
PARTS I, II, III, *separately, with answers perforated.*
PARTS I and II, *bound together, without answers.*
PARTS II and III, *bound together, with answers.*

EDITION WITH APPENDIX

COMPLETE, *with* and *without answers.*
PARTS I, II, III, *separately, with* and *without answers.*
PARTS I and II, *bound together, without answers.*
PARTS II and III, *bound together,* with whole of appendix
   to PARTS I–III, *with* and *without answers.*

LONDON: G. BELL AND SONS, LTD

GENERAL ARITHMETIC
FOR SCHOOLS

G. Bell and Sons Ltd
Portugal Street, London, W.C. 2

Calcutta, Bombay & Madras
Orient Longmans Ltd

GENERAL ARITHMETIC
FOR SCHOOLS

BY

CLEMENT V. DURELL, M.A.

AUTHOR OF "A NEW GEOMETRY FOR SCHOOLS," "SCHOOL CERTIFICATE
ALGEBRA," "GENERAL MATHEMATICS," ETC.

LONDON

G. BELL AND SONS, LTD

1951

First published 1936
Reprinted 1936 (*twice*), 1937 (*twice*), 1938, 1939, 1940 (*twice*),
1941, 1942 (*twice*), 1943, 1944, 1945, 1946, 1947,
1948, 1949, 1950, 1951

Printed in Great Britain by
NEILL & CO. LTD., EDINBURGH

PREFACE

THE character of this book has been determined by the belief that the primary object in the teaching of elementary arithmetic is to secure accuracy. In pure computation, the less a pupil has to think, the more likely is it that mistakes will be avoided, but this state can only be reached by ample practice in fundamental processes. For this reason, numerous straightforward exercises have been included.

The book is designed for pupils from the age of 11 plus up to School Certificate standard, and is divided into three parts. In the early stages where explanations of processes are always given by the teacher, the bookwork is confined to simple statements of definitions and rules and illustrative examples; in the later chapters the treatment is sufficiently detailed for the pupil to be able to read ahead by himself.

A number of exercises are headed "oral" or "for class discussion"; these are constructed so that the working can be done mentally and are intended to accustom the pupil to the *routine of the argument*: it is suggested that these exercises should be taken *viva-voce*, but that all pupils should be required to write down the answers.

The examples in the other exercises are classified under three heads:

(A) *Minimum course :* plain numbers.
> These examples cover all *essential points* of the work and have been graded carefully. They may be done entire by all pupils.

(B) *Extra practice :* numbers enclosed in brackets.
> These examples provide extra practice, if needed; they are parallel to those in A and do *not* extend the ground covered.

(C) *Advanced :* asterisked numbers.
> These examples bring out the finer points of the work under consideration and are intended for those pupils who run ahead of the class.

For the convenience of teachers who prefer to make their own selection, these groups are not printed separately, the examples being arranged in order of difficulty.

A new feature which it is believed will be found useful is the inclusion of 3-*minute and* 4-*minute oral-practice exercises* at the ends of Parts I, II.   Additional drill practice is provided by the comprehensive *Tests in Computation* and more miscellaneous work by the *Revision Papers* at the end of each Part.

Although accuracy is of primary importance, the subject naturally offers considerable scope for developing power of expression and thought; the miscellaneous examples at the end of most chapters are intended to serve this purpose.

An **Appendix** to each Part has been compiled, containing (i) drill exercises, (ii) additional revision papers, (iii) parallel exercises of all important exercises in the main book, and for convenience of reference numbered in the same way except for a distinguishing (*a*). The main purpose is to provide material for a revision course in a systematic form, but it will also be of use to those who like to have a very large supply of examples at their disposal. *The book may be obtained with or without this appendix.*

The author has followed closely the recommendations of the recent report on the teaching of Arithmetic issued by the *Mathematical Association*, and some quotations from that Report will be found in the text.   In cases where there is considerable divergence of opinion (*e.g.* in multiplication of decimals), each of the methods in general use has been explained.   Use has also been made of various practical suggestions in the *Board of Education* pamphlet (No. 101, 1934) on Senior School Mathematics.

CONTENTS

NOTE. This Arithmetic is issued complete and also in parts and combinations of parts. There are two editions : (i) Ordinary Edition ; (ii) Edition with Appendix of additional examples. A full list of styles will be found on page ii. The following is the Table of Contents of the whole book.

PART II

[Pages 129–272]

PART III

[Pages 273–412]

CONTENTS

APPENDIX

[Pages 413–572]

TABLES

LENGTH

British

12 inches (in.) = 1 foot (ft.).
3 feet = 1 yard (yd.).
22 yards = 1 chain (ch.).
10 chains = 1 furlong (fur.).
8 furlongs = 1 mile (mi.).

220 yards = 1 furlong.
1760 yards = 1 mile.

100 links = 1 chain.
5½ yards = 1 pole (p.), rod, perch.
40 poles = 1 furlong.
4 inches = 1 hand.
6 feet = 1 fathom.
600 feet = 1 cable.
1 knot = 1 nautical mile per hour.
= about 6080 feet per hour.

Metric

10 *milli*metres (mm.) = 1 *centi*metre (cm.).
10 centimetres = 1 *deci*metre (dm.).
10 decimetres = 1 metre (m.).
10 metres = 1 *deka*metre (Dm.).
10 dekametres = 1 *hecto*metre (Hm.).
10 hectometres = 1 *kilo*metre (Km., km.).

Approximate equivalents

1 inch = 2·540 cm.
1 yard = 0·9144 m.
1 mile = 1·6093 Km.
1 metre = 39·37 in.
= 1·0936 yd.
1 Km. = 0·62₁4 mi.
= about ⅝ mi.

AREA

144 (or 12²) sq. inches = 1 sq. foot.
9 (or 3²) sq. ft. = 1 sq. yard.
484 (or 22²) sq. yd. = 1 sq. chain.
10 sq. ch. = 1 acre (ac.)
640 acres = 1 sq. mile.

30¼ (or 5½ × 5½) sq. yd. = 1 sq. pole (p.).
40 sq. poles = 1 rood (r.).
4 roods = 1 acre.
4840 sq. yards = 1 acre.
10,000 (or 100²) sq. links = 1 sq. chain.

100 (or 10²) sq. mm. = 1 sq. cm.
100 (or 10²) sq. cm. = 1 sq. dm.
100 (or 10²) sq. dm. = 1 sq. m.
and so on.

1 are (a.) = 1 sq. dekametre.
100 centiares (ca.) = 1 are.
100 ares = 1 hectare (Ha.).

Approximate equivalents

1 sq. in. = 6·4516 sq. cm.
1 sq. cm. = 0·15500 sq. in.
1 acre = 0·4047 Ha.
1 are = 119·6 sq. yd.
1 hectare = 2·471 ac. (about 2½ ac.).

VOLUME

1728 (or 12³) cu. inches = 1 cu. foot. | 1000 (or 10³) cu. mm. = 1 cu. cm.
    27 (or 3³) cu. feet   = 1 cu. yard. | (c.c.),
      1 cu. in. ≏ 16·387 cu. cm. | and so on.
                                     | 1 cu. cm. ≏ 0·061024 cu. in.

CAPACITY

4 gills   = 1 pint (pt.). | 10 *centi*litres (cl.) = 1 *deci*litre (dl.).
2 pints   = 1 quart (qt.). | 10 decilitres   = 1 litre (l.),
4 quarts   = 1 gallon (gall.). | and so on.
2 gallons = 1 peck (pk.). |
4 pecks   = 1 bushel (bush.). | 1 litre = 1 cu. dm. = 1000 c.c.
8 bushels = 1 quarter (qr.). |

Gills are used only for liquids; pecks, bushels, quarters are used only for dry measures.

Approximate equivalents

1 gallon = 277·3 cu. in. = 4·546 cu. dm. = 4·546 litres.
1 cu. ft. =   6·23 gall. = 28·32 cu. dm. = 28·326 litres.
1 litre   = 61·03 cu. in. = 1·76 pints (about 1¾ pints).

WEIGHT

Avoirdupois

16 ounces (oz.) = 1 pound (lb.).
    28 lb. = 1 quarter (qr.).
      4 qr. = 1 hundredweight (cwt.).
20 cwt. = 1 ton (t.).

14 lb. = 1 stone (st.).
112 lb. = 1 cwt.
2240 lb. = 1 ton.
100 lb. = 1 cental.

Metric

10 milligrams (mg.) = 1 *centi*gram (cg.).
10 centigrams = 1 *deci*gram (dg.).
10 decigrams = 1 gram (gm.).
10 grams   = 1 *deka*gram (Dg.).
10 dekagrams = 1 *hecto*gram (Hg.).
10 hectograms = 1 *kilo*gram (Kg.).
1000 kilograms = 1 metric ton or tonne.

1 c.c. of water (at 4° C.) weighs 1 gram.
1 litre of water (1 cu. dm.) weighs 1 kilogram.
1 cu. ft. of water weighs 62·3 lb. approx. (about 1000 oz.).
1 gallon of water weighs 10 lb. (a pint of water weighs a pound and a quarter).

Approximate equivalents

1 kg. = 2·205 lb. (about 2¼ lb.); 1 metric ton = 0·9842 ton.
1 lb. = 0·4536 kg.; 1 ton = 1·016 metric tons.

Troy Weight (precious metals)	Apothecaries' Weight (drugs)
24 grains (gr.) = 1 pennyweight (dwt.).	20 grains = 1 scruple.
	3 scruples = 1 drachm.
20 dwt. = 1 ounce.	8 drachms = 1 ounce.

The Troy grain and ounce are the same weights as the Apothecaries' grain and ounce. There is no Troy pound or Apothecaries' pound.

1 oz. avoirdupois = 437½ grains; 1 ounce troy = 480 grains.

NUMBER

12 units = 1 dozen.	**Writing Paper**
12 dozen = 1 gross.	24 sheets = 1 quire.
20 units = 1 score.	20 quires = 1 ream.

TIME

60 seconds (60″) = 1 minute (1′).	365 days = 1 common year.
60 minutes = 1 hour (hr.).	366 days = 1 leap year.
24 hours = 1 day.	12 months = 1 year.
7 days = 1 week.	10 years = 1 decade.
14 days = 1 fortnight.	100 years = 1 century.

"Thirty days hath September,
April June and November.
All the rest have thirty-one,
Excepting February alone,
Which has but twenty-eight days clear,
And twenty-nine in each leap year."

Note. A leap year is a year whose date is divisible by 4, unless it is also divisible by 100. If the date is divisible by 100, the year is not a leap year unless it is divisible by 400. For example, 1936 was a leap year because 1936 is divisible by 4, and 2000 will be a leap year because 2000 is divisible by 400, but 1900 was not a leap year because 1900 is not divisible by 400.

MONEY

4 farthings = 1 penny (d.).	**French**
12 pence = 1 shilling (s.).	100 centimes (c.) = 1 franc (fr.).
20 shillings = 1 pound (£1) or sovereign.	
	American
1 florin = 2s.	100 cents = 1 dollar ($).
1 half-crown = 2s. 6d.	
1 crown = 5s.	**Spanish**
1 guinea = 21s.	100 centimos = 1 peseta (pta.).
	Italian
	100 centesimi = 1 lira (*pl.* lire).

FORMULÆ

Percentage

(i) $\dfrac{a}{b} = \dfrac{100a}{b}$ per cent.; a is $\dfrac{100a}{b}$ per cent. of b.

(ii) If P is increased by r per cent., it becomes $P\left(1 + \dfrac{r}{100}\right)$.

(iii) For a gain of r per cent., C.P. : S.P. $= 100 : (100 + r)$.

(iv) If the *simple interest* on £P for T years at r per cent. p.a. is £I,

$$I = \frac{PRT}{100};$$

$$P = \frac{100 \times I}{RT}, \qquad R = \frac{100 \times I}{PT}, \qquad T = \frac{100 \times I}{PR}.$$

(v) If the amount at *compound interest* of £P for n years at r per cent. p.a. is £A,

$$A = PR^n \quad \text{where} \quad R = 1 + \frac{r}{100};$$

$$\log P + n \log R = \log A.$$

Mensuration

(i) Area of Parallelogram $=$ base $\times$ height.

(ii) Area of Triangle $= \frac{1}{2}$ base $\times$ height.
$$= \sqrt{\{s(s-a)(s-b)(s-c)\}}$$
where a, b, c are the lengths of the sides and $s = \frac{1}{2}(a + b + c)$.

(iii) Volume of Prism $=$ base-area $\times$ height.

(iv) Volume of Pyramid $= \frac{1}{3}$ base-area $\times$ height.

(v) For a circle, radius r,
$$\text{circumference} = 2\pi r; \quad \text{area} = \pi r^2.$$

(vi) For a circular cylinder, radius r, height h,
$$\text{area of curved surface} = 2\pi rh; \quad \text{volume} = \pi r^2 h.$$

(vii) For a circular cone, radius r, height h, slant height l,
$$\text{area of curved surface} = \pi rl; \quad \text{volume} = \frac{1}{3}\pi r^2 h;$$
$$l^2 = r^2 + h^2.$$

(viii) For a sphere, radius r,
$$\text{area of surface} = 4\pi r^2; \quad \text{volume} = \frac{4}{3}\pi r^3.$$

PART I

CHAPTER I

USE OF PRIME FACTORS

Factors. Since $24 = 8 \times 3$, 8 and 3 are each called **factors** of 24, and 24 is called a **multiple** of 8, also a multiple of 3.

Any number, of which 2 is a factor, is called **even**; numbers which are not even are called **odd**. Thus 2, 4, 6, 8, . . . are even, and 1, 3, 5, 7, . . . are odd.

EXERCISE 1 (Oral)

Express as the product of *two* factors in as many ways as possible :
1. 12. **2.** 18. **3.** 28. **4.** 30. **5.** 36. **6.** 60. **7.** 96. **8.** 108.

Complete the following :—

9. $63 = 7 \times \ldots$ **10.** $72 = 8 \times \ldots$ **11.** $75 = 5 \times \ldots$

12. $132 = 11 \times \ldots$ **13.** $144 = 9 \times \ldots$ **14.** $112 = 7 \times \ldots$

15. $42 = 2 \times 3 \times \ldots$ **16.** $84 = 4 \times 3 \times \ldots$ **17.** $180 = 5 \times 9 \times \ldots$

18. $120 = 8 \times 3 \times \ldots$ **19.** $154 = 11 \times 2 \times \ldots$ **20.** $140 = 7 \times 4 \times \ldots$

21. Find the multiples of 7, which are less than 50.

22. Find the multiples of 12, which are less than 70.

23. Find the even multiples of 13, which are less than 100.

24. Find the odd multiples of 17, which are less than 100.

Tests of Divisibility

(1) A number is divisible by **2** if its last digit is even.

It is divisible by **4** if the number formed by the last two digits is divisible by 4.

It is divisible by **8** if the number formed by the last three digits is divisible by 8.

A

1

(2) A number is divisible by **5** if the last digit is 5 or 0. It is divisible by **10** if the last digit is 0.

(3) A number is divisible by **3** if the sum of its digits is divisible by 3; it is divisible by **9** if the sum of its digits is divisible by 9.

(4) A number is divisible by **11** if the sum of the digits in the odd places and the sum of the digits in the even places are equal or differ by a multiple of 11.

Also it should be noted that a number is divisible by **6** if it is divisible both by 2 and by 3, and is divisible by **12** if it is divisible both by 4 and by 3; and so on. There is no simple test for divisibility by 7.

Further, a number is divisible by **25** if the number formed by the last two digits is divisible by 25; and it is divisible by **125** if the number formed by the last three digits is divisible by 125.

EXERCISE 2 (Oral)

Which of the following numbers are divisible by the first number :—

1. 4; 712, 822, 14780, 59376, 716834, 26308.

2. 8; 67344, 89020, 95752, 4567128.

3. 5; 852, 1435, 687930, 4182806, 2793485.

4. 3; 261, 705, 1433, 2655, 101001.

5. 9; 432, 873, 606, 7857, 8427, 30708, 54669.

6. 11; 3267, 814, 6425, 7282, 1001, 33333, 909183.

7. 6; 744, 543, 7134, 9258, 8060, 51234.

8. 12; 4128, 4242, 9456, 3147, 71562.

9. 25; 71850, 34685, 107075, 418255.

10. 33; 28512, 47058, 52492, 82632, 73282.

Find all the possible values of the missing digits in Nos. 11–15:

11. 7*3, 1*43, 60*18 are divisible by 3.

12. 83*, 95*2, 70*4 are divisible by 4.

13. 8*7, 4*75, 7123*5 are divisible by 9.

14. 6*2, 7*81, 919*8 are divisible by 11.

15. 396*5, 4875*, 2948** are divisible by 25.

Prime Numbers. A number is called **prime** if it is divisible only by itself and 1.

Thus 2, 3, 5, 7, 11, 13, 17, . . . are prime numbers. Any number, which is not prime, can be expressed as the product of two or more prime numbers, that is in **prime factors.**

For example, $600 = 6 \times 10 \times 10 = (2 \times 3) \times (2 \times 5) \times (2 \times 5)$
$$= 2 \times 2 \times 2 \times 3 \times 5 \times 5.$$

Index Notation. For brevity,

2×2 is written 2^2, called "2 squared" or "the square of 2";

$2 \times 2 \times 2$ is written 2^3, called "2 cubed" or "the cube of 2";

$2 \times 2 \times 2 \times 2$ is written 2^4, called "2 to the power 4" or "the 4th power of 2";

and so on.

Similarly for other numbers, $3 \times 3 \times 3 \times 3 \times 3$ is written 3^5, called 3 to the power 5.

In the symbol 3^5, 5 is called the *index*; it denotes the number of factors in the product $3 \times 3 \times 3 \times 3 \times 3$.

When expressing a number in prime factors, it is best at first to proceed systematically. Take the prime numbers in ascending order 2, 3, 5, 7, 11, . . . and divide as often as possible by anyone before passing on to the next.

Example 1. Express 5148 in prime factors :

$$5148 = 2 \times 2574 = 2 \times 2 \times 1287$$
$$= 2 \times 2 \times 3 \times 429 = 2 \times 2 \times 3 \times 3 \times 143$$
$$= 2 \times 2 \times 3 \times 3 \times 11 \times 13$$
$$= 2^2 \times 3^2 \times 11 \times 13.$$

Alternatively the working may be set out as follows :—

$$
\begin{array}{r|r}
2 & 5148 \\
2 & 2574 \\
3 & 1287 \\
3 & 429 \\
11 & 143 \\
\hline
& 13
\end{array}
$$

$\therefore\ 5148 = 2 \times 2 \times 3 \times 3 \times 11 \times 13$
$= 2^2 \times 3^2 \times 11 \times 13.$

EXERCISE 3

State which of the following numbers are prime, and express the others in prime factors, using the index notation :—

1. 24.	**2.** 32.	**[3]** 35.	**4.** 37.	**[5]** 75.
6. 125.	**[7]** 43.	**8.** 111.	**[9]** 104.	*10. 139.
*11. 182.	**12.** 198.	**13.** 101.	**[14]** 207.	*15. 294.
[16] 300.	**17.** 315.	**[18]** 438.	**[19]** 450.	**20.** 528.
*21. 588.	**[22]** 648.	*23. 693.	*24. 754.	**25.** 868.
[26] 1111.	*27. 3432.	*28. 3528.	*29. 3773.	*30. 6032.

Factors and Brackets

The expression $(2 \times 3) \times 5$ equals 30 and may be written in any of the forms, $2 \times 3 \times 5$, 6×5, 2×15, 10×3; it is *not* equal to the expression $(2 \times 5) \times (3 \times 5)$. This statement must not be confused with the fact that $(2 + 3) \times 5 = (2 \times 5) + (3 \times 5)$.

The expression $(20 \times 30) \div 10$ equals 60 and may be written in either of the forms 2×30, 20×3; it is *not* equal to the expression $(20 \div 10) \times (30 \div 10)$. This statement must not be confused with the fact that $(20 + 30) \div 10 = (20 \div 10) + (30 \div 10)$.

The value of an expression like $(12 \times 25) \div 15$ is found by successive short division :

$$(12 \times 25) \div \ 3 = 4 \times 25$$
$$\therefore \ (12 \times 25) \div 15 = (4 \times 25) \div 5 = 4 \times 5.$$

$(12 \times 25) \div 15$ is written in the form, $\frac{12 \times 25}{15}$, and the working is arranged as shown in Example 2.

Example 2 (i)	**Example 2 (ii)**
$\dfrac{12 \times 25}{15} = \dfrac{4 \times 25}{5}$	$\dfrac{135 \times 119}{105} = \dfrac{27 \times 119}{21}$ (divide by 5)
$= 4 \times 5$	$= \dfrac{9 \times 119}{7}$ (divide by 3)
$= 20.$	$= 9 \times 17 = 153.$

EXERCISE 4 (Nos. 1–12, Oral)

State the values of :

1. $(4 + 3) \times 2$; $(4 \times 3) \times 2$.

2. $(2 + 5) \times 3$; $(2 \times 5) \times 3$.

3. $(8 + 12) \div 4$; $(8 \times 12) \div 4$.

4. $(10 + 15) \div 5$; $(10 \times 15) \div 5$.

5. One-third of (6×9).

6. One-tenth of (40×50).

Express as the product of two factors in three ways:

7. $(4 \times 6) \times 2$.   **8.** $(5 \times 7) \times 3$.   **9.** $(7 \times 11) \times 5$.

10. 10 times (3×7).   **11.** 6 times (7×10).   **12.** 12 times (3×7).

Find the values of:

13. $(4 \times 6) \div 2$.   **14.** $(20 \times 25) \div 5$.   **[15]** $(8 \times 24) \div 8$.

16. $(8 \times 6) \div (4 \times 3)$.   **17.** $(100 \times 80) \div (10 \times 10)$.

[18] $(20 \times 30 \times 40) \div 10$.   **[19]** $(10 \times 20 \times 30) \div (10 \times 10)$.

*20. $(21 \times 15 \times 2) \div (5 \times 7)$.   **21.** $(12 \times 8 \times 6) \div (6 \times 4 \times 3)$.

22. $\frac{8 \times 15}{6}$.   **[23]** $\frac{10 \times 21}{14}$.   **24.** $\frac{33 \times 30}{18}$.   **[25]** $\frac{42 \times 28}{24}$.

26. $\frac{49 \times 9}{21}$.   **[27]** $\frac{36 \times 35}{45}$.   **28.** $\frac{84 \times 33}{77}$.   **[29]** $\frac{15 \times 64}{96}$.

30. $\frac{8 \times 27}{12 \times 6}$.   **[31]** $\frac{20 \times 36}{8 \times 9}$.   **[32]** $\frac{28 \times 9}{7 \times 12}$.   **33.** $\frac{21 \times 16}{14 \times 6}$.

34. $\frac{33 \times 8}{11 \times 6}$.   ***35.** $\frac{63 \times 32}{28 \times 3}$.   ***36.** $\frac{55 \times 105}{33 \times 7}$.   ***37.** $\frac{121 \times 42}{22 \times 77}$.

Laws of Indices

Example 3. Express in the index notation, $5^2 \times 5^4$.

$$5^2 \times 5^4 = (5 \times 5) \times (5 \times 5 \times 5 \times 5)$$
$$= 5 \times 5 \times 5 \times 5 \times 5 \times 5, \quad \text{six factors,}$$
$$= 5^6.$$

Similarly, if we write out in full the expression $7^4 \times 7^5$, we obtain $7 \times 7 \times 7 \times \ldots \times 7$, where there are $(4+5)$ factors, and this is written 7^9; $\therefore 7^4 \times 7^5 = 7^9$.

These results are special cases of the general rule that, if x, p and q are any numbers,

$$x^p \times x^q = x^{p+q}.$$

This formula is sometimes expressed shortly by the words: "in multiplication, *add* the indices"; but it must be remembered that this applies only to the product of powers of the same number; it cannot be applied to the product $2^4 \times 3^5$.

Example 4. Express in the index notation, $5^6 \div 5^2$.

$$5^6 \div 5^2 = \frac{5 \times 5 \times 5 \times 5 \times 5 \times 5}{5 \times 5} = 5 \times 5 \times 5 \times 5,$$

that is, $5^6 \div 5^2 = 5^{6-2} = 5^4$.

This result is a special case of the general rule that if p and q are any numbers such that p is greater than q,

$$x^p \div x^q = x^{p-q}.$$

This formula is sometimes expressed shortly by the words: "in division, *subtract* the indices"; but it must be remembered that this only applies to powers of the same number.

Example 5. Express in the index notation, $8 \times 10 \times 12 \times 15$.

Reduce each number to its prime factors,

$$8 \times 10 \times 12 \times 15 = 2^3 \times (2 \times 5) \times (2^2 \times 3) \times (3 \times 5)$$
$$= 2^3 \times 2 \times 2^2 \times 3 \times 3 \times 5 \times 5 = 2^6 \times 3^2 \times 5^2.$$

EXERCISE 5

Express in prime factors (a, b being prime) using the index notation:

1. $3 \times 3 \times 3 \times 3 \times 3$.   **2.** $5 \times 5 \times 5 \times 5$.   ***3.** $a \times a \times a \times a \times a \times a$.

4. $2^2 \times 2^3$.   **[5]** $3^2 \times 3^4$.   **6.** 5×5^3.   **[7]** $6^4 \times 6^4$.

8. $2^5 \div 2^2$.   **[9]** $3^6 \div 3^2$.   **10.** $5^5 \div 5$.   **[11]** $7^8 \div 7^4$.

12. $2^4 \times 2^3 \times 2$.   **13.** $3^5 \times 3^2 \times 3^4$.   **14.** $5^4 \times 5^6 \div 5^2$.

*15. $10^2 \times 10^4 \div 1000$.   ***16.** $7^6 \div (7^2 \times 7^3)$.   ***17.** $2^4 \times 2^8 \div 2$.

18. $3 \times 3 \times 5 \times 5 \times 5$.   **[19]** $5 \times 7 \times 5 \times 7 \times 7 \times 7$.

*20. $a \times b \times a \times b \times a$.   **21.** 2×12.   **[22]** 9×15.   **23.** $2^3 \times 18$.

[24] $3^3 \times 6^2$.   **25.** $4 \times 6 \times 9$.   ***26.** $12 \times 16 \times 18$.   **[27]** $10 \times 20 \times 25$.

*28. $2^3 \times 4 \times 18$.   ***29.** $2^5 \times 3^4 \times 6^3$.   ***30.** $4 \times 18 \times 21^2$.

Powers and Roots

The **square root** of a given number is that number whose square is equal to the given number.

Thus 7 is the square root of 49 because $7^2 = 49$. The symbol for "square root" is $\sqrt{}$ (derived from r), we therefore write

$$\sqrt{(49)} = 7.$$

The **cube root** of a given number is that number whose cube is equal to the given number.

Thus 2 is the cube root of 8 because $2^3 = 8$.

The symbol for "cube root" is $\sqrt[3]{}$, we therefore write

$$\sqrt[3]{8} = 2.$$

The fourth root, fifth root, etc., of a number are defined in a similar way and are denoted by $\sqrt[4]{}$, $\sqrt[5]{}$, etc.

Example 6. Express in powers of prime factors,

    (i) the square of $2^4 \times 3 \times 5^3$;   (ii) the cube of $3^2 \times 5^4$.

(i) $(2^4 \times 3 \times 5^3) \times (2^4 \times 3 \times 5^3) = 2^4 \cdot 2^4 \times 3 \cdot 3 \times 5^3 \cdot 5^3$;

        $\therefore (2^4 \times 3 \times 5^3)^2 = 2^8 \times 3^2 \times 5^6$.

(ii) $(3^2 \times 5^4) \times (3^2 \times 5^4) \times (3^2 \times 5^4) = 3^2 \cdot 3^2 \cdot 3^2 \times 5^4 \cdot 5^4 \cdot 5^4$;

        $\therefore (3^2 \times 5^4)^3 = 3^6 \times 5^{12}$.

Example 7. Express in powers of prime factors,

(i) the square root of $3^6 \times 5^2 \times 7^4$; (ii) the cube root of $2^9 \times 3^6 \times 5^3$.

(i) $(3^3 \times 5 \times 7^2) \times (3^3 \times 5 \times 7^2) = 3^6 \times 5^2 \times 7^4$,

        $\therefore \sqrt{(3^6 \times 5^2 \times 7^4)} = 3^3 \times 5 \times 7^2$.

(ii) $(2^3 \times 3^2 \times 5) \times (2^3 \times 3^2 \times 5) \times (2^3 \times 3^2 \times 5) = 2^9 \times 3^6 \times 5^3$,

        $\therefore \sqrt[3]{(2^9 \times 3^6 \times 5^3)} = 2^3 \times 3^2 \times 5$.

The argument used in Example 7 shows that if a number is expressed in powers of *prime* factors, its square root is obtained by halving each index; if any index is odd, there is no exact square root. Similarly, its cube root is obtained by dividing each index by 3; if any index is not a multiple of 3, there is no exact cube root.

Example 8. Find the square root of 7056.

$$7056 = 2 \times 3528 = 2^2 \times 1764 = 2^3 \times 882 = 2^4 \times 441$$
$$= 2^4 \times 3 \times 147 = 2^4 \times 3^2 \times 49 = 2^4 \times 3^2 \times 7^2;$$
$$\therefore \sqrt{(7056)} = 2^2 \times 3 \times 7 = 84.$$

Note. As soon as the process is understood, the working may be abbreviated by dividing in succession by factors which are perfect squares:

$$7056 = 4 \times 1764 = 4^2 \times 441 = 4^2 \times 9 \times 49;$$
$$\therefore \sqrt{7056} = 4 \times 3 \times 7 = 84.$$

EXERCISE 6

Write down in index form:

1. The squares of (i) 2^4;   (ii) $3^3 \times 5^2$;   *(iii) $5^4 \times 7^3 \times 11$.

2. The cubes of (i) 3^2;   (ii) $5^3 \times 7$;   *(iii) $5^2 \times 7^4 \times 11^3$.

3. The square roots of (i) 2^6;   (ii) 4^4;   *(iii) 3^{16}.

4. The square roots of (i) $2^4 \times 5^2$;   (ii) $3^6 \times 7^4$;   *(iii) $2^8 \times 5^4 \times 7^6$.

5. The cube roots of (i) 2^6;   *(ii) 3^{27};   *(iii) $3^{12} \times 5^6 \times 7^3$.

Write down the values of:

6. $\sqrt{(4 \times 9)}$.   **[7]** $\sqrt{(25 \times 64)}$.   8. $\sqrt{(49 \times 36 \times 121)}$.   *9. $\sqrt[3]{(27 \times 64)}$.

Find the square roots of:

10. 196.   **[11]** 729.   **12.** 1764.   **[13]** 2916.   **14.** 3969.

[15] 5625.   **16.** 9604.   ***17.** 12544.   ***18.** 50176.   ***19.** 53361.

Find the cube roots of:

20. 2744.   **[21]** 21952.   ***22.** 91125.

*23. Find the length of the side of a square whose area is equal to that of a rectangle 80 yd. long, 45 yd. wide.

*24. Find the length of the side of a square field 10 acres in area. [1 acre = 4840 sq. yd.]

*25. Find the length of the edge of a cube whose volume is equal to that of a rectangular block, 12 in. by 9 in. by 2 in.

Find the least integers by which the following numbers must be multiplied to give perfect squares, and find the square roots of the products obtained:—

26. $3^3 \times 5^2$.   **[27]** $2^6 \times 7^3 \times 11$.   **28.** 294.   ***29.** 5544.

Find the least integers by which the following numbers must be multiplied to give perfect cubes, and find the cube roots of the products obtained:—

30. $2^4 \times 3^2$.   **[31]** $2^7 \times 3 \times 5^8$.   **32.** 360.   ***33.** 2352.

It is proved in algebra that $a^2 - b^2 = (a+b)(a-b)$; verify this if $a=5$, $b=3$, and if $a=9$, $b=4$, and use this fact to express in prime factors:

*34. $23^2 - 17^2$.   ***35.** $38^2 - 9^2$.   ***36.** $147^2 - 93^2$.   ***37.** $28^2 - 16$.

Highest Common Factor

A number which is a factor of two or more given numbers is called a *common factor* of these numbers.

The greatest number which is a common factor of two or more given numbers is called their **highest common factor** or for short their **H.C.F.**

EXERCISE 7 (Oral)

Write down the H.C.F. of:

1. 10, 15. **2.** 12, 30. **3.** 12, 30, 40. **4.** 6, 10, 14.

5. 21, 35. **6.** 27, 45, 63. **7.** 6, 18. **8.** 10, 21.

9. 40, 60, 80. **10.** 4, 9. **11.** 14, 35, 56. **12.** 7, 14, 20.

Write down in prime factors the H.C.F. of:

13. $2^3 \times 3^2, 2^2 \times 3^4$. **14.** $2 \times 3^3 \times 5, 2^2 \times 3^2 \times 7$.

15. $2^4 \times 3 \times 5^3, 2^2 \times 3^3 \times 5 \times 7$. **16.** $2^4 \times 3^2 \times 5^2, 2^2 \times 3^3 \times 7^2$.

17. $2^2 \times 3^4 \times 5^3 \times 11, 2^4 \times 3^3 \times 5^2 \times 7, 2^3 \times 3^2 \times 5 \times 7 \times 11$.

18. $2^4 \times 3^2 \times 5^3, 3^4 \times 5^2 \times 7^2, 5^4 \times 7^3 \times 11^2$.

The H.C.F. can be found by expressing each number as the product of powers of *prime* factors.

Example 9. Find the H.C.F. of 84, 180, 264.

$$84 = 4 \times 21 = 2^2 \times 3 \times 7;$$
$$180 = 9 \times 20 = 2^2 \times 3^2 \times 5;$$
$$264 = 8 \times 33 = 2^3 \times 3 \times 11.$$

The highest power of 2 which is a factor of each number is 2^2; the highest power of 3 which is a factor of each number is 3; there is no other common factor.

$$\therefore \text{ the H.C.F. is } 2^2 \times 3, \text{ that is 12.}$$

Any common factor of two numbers is also a factor of their difference.

For example, since 5 is a factor of 70 and of 55, it is also a factor of 70 − 55, because

$$70 - 55 = (14 \text{ fives}) - (11 \text{ fives}) = 3 \text{ fives.}$$

Hence in looking for common factors of two numbers it is only necessary to consider factors of their difference.

For example, any common factors of 406 and 371 must be factors of 406 − 371, that is 35, and can therefore only be 5 and 7; 5 is obviously not a factor; and by trial we find that 7 is a common factor.

This fact is also used in the following process for finding the H.C.F. of two numbers which cannot be expressed easily in prime factors.

Example 10.   Find the H.C.F. of 9271 and 19783.

First divide 19783 by 9271,

$$
\begin{array}{r}
2 \\
9271\overline{)19783} \\
18542 \\
\hline
1241
\end{array}
$$

Next divide 9271 (the first divisor) by the remainder 1241,

$$
\begin{array}{r}
7 \\
1241\overline{)9271} \\
8687 \\
\hline
584
\end{array}
$$

Next divide 1241 (the second divisor) by the remainder 584,

$$
\begin{array}{r}
2 \\
584\overline{)1241} \\
1168 \\
\hline
73
\end{array}
$$

Next divide 584 (the third divisor) by the remainder 73,

$$
\begin{array}{r}
8 \\
73\overline{)584} \\
584 \\
\hline
\end{array}
$$

This completes the process because the division is exact.   The last divisor 73 is the H.C.F.

∴ the H.C.F. of 9271 and 19783 is 73.

The working may be arranged concisely as follows :—

The process must terminate eventually because successive divisors decrease steadily; but if the last divisor is 1, the only common factor of the two numbers is 1, and in this case the numbers are said to be "prime to one another" or "co-prime."

$$
\begin{array}{r|r|r|l}
7 & 9271 & 19783 & 2 \\
 & 8687 & 18542 & \\
\hline
8 & 584 & 1241 & 2 \\
 & 584 & 1168 & \\
\hline
 & & 73 &
\end{array}
$$

EXERCISE 8

Find by prime factors the H.C.F. of :

1. 60, 126.   [2] 168, 189.   **3.** 245, 385.   [4] 756, 2205.

5. 24, 42, 78.   [6] 65, 78, 104.   **7.** 108, 162, 270.

[8] 546, 882, 924.   *9. 440, 715, 935.   *10. 784, 1232, 1904.

*11. 189, 882, 1071.   *12. 756, 1764, 2268.   *13. 7875, 21560.

14. 84, 144, 264, 360, 420.   [15] 105, 147, 231, 252, 294.

Find by the division method the H.C.F. of :

16. 361, 589.   [17] 527, 1333.   **18.** 703, 1387.

[19] 2419, 2993.   **20.** 2914, 3782.   [21] 1457, 2773.

*22. 6887, 9301.   *23. 51641, 67913.   *24. 21779, 24737.

Least Common Multiple

A number which is a multiple of two or more given numbers is called a *common multiple* of these numbers.

The least number which is a common multiple of two or more given numbers is called their *least common multiple* or for short their **L.C.M.**

EXERCISE 9 (Oral)

1. Name 5 multiples of 6, and name 4 multiples of 8. What is the L.C.M. of 6 and 8?

2. Name 3 multiples of 15 which are also multiples of 10. What is the L.C.M. of 15 and 10?

Write down the L.C.M. of:

3. 4, 10. **4.** 8, 10. **5.** 4, 12. **6.** 6, 9.

7. 7, 14. **8.** 9, 12. **9.** 10, 12. **10.** 12, 24.

11. 2, 3, 4. **12.** 4, 6, 9. **13.** 4, 14, 21. **14.** 30, 40, 60.

Write down in index form the L.C.M. of:

15. $2^2 \times 3$, $2^3 \times 5$.   **16.** $2^2 \times 3^4$, $2^3 \times 3^2$.   **17.** $2^4 \times 5$, 3^2.

18. 2×3^3, $2^2 \times 3^2$, $2^4 \times 3$.   **19.** $2^3 \times 3^4$, $2^2 \times 3^5$, $2^4 \times 3^3$.

The L.C.M. can be found by expressing each number as the product of powers of *prime* factors.

Example 11. Find the L.C.M. of 48, 56, 105, 225.

$$48 = 3 \times 16 = 2^4 \times 3; \qquad 56 = 8 \times 7 = 2^3 \times 7;$$
$$105 = 5 \times 21 = 3 \times 5 \times 7; \qquad 225 = 9 \times 25 = 3^2 \times 5^2.$$

Every common multiple of these numbers must have 2, 3, 5, 7 as factors, and each of these factors must occur to as high a power as it occurs in any of the numbers. The highest power of 2 is 2^4, the highest power of 3 is 3^2, the highest power of 5 is 5^2, and the highest power of 7 is 7^1;

$$\therefore \text{ the L.C.M. is } 2^4 \times 3^2 \times 5^2 \times 7, \text{ that is } 25200.$$

Note. It is usually more convenient to keep the L.C.M. in factors than to multiply it out.

EXERCISE 10

Express in prime factors the L.C.M. of:

1. $2^2 \times 3^3$, $2^4 \times 3^2$.   **[2]** $2^3 \times 3^2$, $2^2 \times 5$.   **3.** 2^5, $2^2 \times 3 \times 5^2$.

[4] $2^4 \times 3^2$, $3^4 \times 5$, $2^5 \times 5$.   **5.** $3^3 \times 5^2 \times 7$, $3^2 \times 5^4 \times 7^3$, $3 \times 7 \times 11$.

6. 6, 10, 15.   **[7]** 9, 21, 35.   **8.** 12, 15, 18.

[9] 16, 28, 84.   **10.** 18, 24, 56.   **[11]** 26, 40, 104.

12. 32, 84, 40.   **[13]** 25, 55, 75.   **14.** 36, 63, 77.

*15. 39, 117, 169.   ***16.** 132, 165, 220.   ***17.** 720, 1260, 1350.

*18. 21, 33, 63, 121.   ***19.** 36, 64, 96, 100.   ***20.** 21, 45, 63, 81.

*21. 12, 18, 24, 30, 36, 42.   ***22.** 14, 22, 24, 28, 32, 34.

MISCELLANEOUS EXAMPLES

EXERCISE 11

1. Find the largest number which is a factor of each of the numbers 504, 792, 1080.

[2] Find the smallest number which is a multiple of each of the numbers 54, 63, 105.

3. What is the least sum of money which is an exact number of half-crowns and an exact number of florins?

[4] What is the least length of tape which can be cut up exactly both into equal strips 1 ft. 3 in. long and into equal strips 1 ft. 6 in. long?

5. Either by striding 30 in. or by striding 32 in., I take an exact number of steps to walk across a road. Find the least width of the road.

[6] Divide the L.C.M. of 20, 24, 36 by their H.C.F.

*7. Lines are drawn so as to divide a rectangle, 1 ft. 8 in. long, 1 ft. wide, into equal squares. Find the least possible number of squares.

8. Three bells toll at intervals of 4, 6, 9 seconds respectively. They start together; after what time will they next toll together?

*9. Find the smallest sum of money which can be divided into an exact number of shares either of 6d. each or of 8d. each or of 1s. 3d. each or of 1s. 8d. each.

10. The rims of the wheels of a tractor and van are 7 ft. and 5 ft. 3 in. long respectively. What is the least distance in which both make an exact number of turns?

[11] Three bells toll at intervals of 36 sec., 40 sec., 48 sec. respectively. They start together; after how many minutes will they next toll together?

*12. Telegraph poles occur at intervals of 84 yd. along a road, and heaps of stones are deposited at intervals of 60 yd. The first heap is at the foot of the first pole. How far along the road is the next heap which lies at the foot of a pole?

13. Three people take steps of lengths 30 in., 36 in., 40 in. respectively. They start off together each with the right foot; how far have they gone before they are next in step, each with the right foot?

14. Four bells toll at intervals of 40 sec., 45 sec., 60 sec., 75 sec. respectively. They start together; after how many minutes will they next toll together?

*15. A rectangular block, 6 in. by 12 in. by 15 in., is cut up into an exact number of equal cubes. Find the least possible number of cubes.

*16. A hearth measuring 4 ft. 8 in. by 10 ft. 6 in. is paved with equal square tiles. Find the largest size of a tile if only whole tiles are used, and find the number of such tiles that are required.

*17. Find the least number such that the remainder is 5 when it is divided either by 10 or by 15 or by 18.

*18. What is the least number of steps in a staircase if when I go up 2 steps at a time, 3 steps at a time, or 4 steps at a time, there is always 1 odd step at the top?

*19. The total weight of a certain number of equal packets is 24 lb. 12 oz.; and when some more of the same weight are added the total weight is 33 lb. 12 oz. Find the greatest possible weight of a packet.

*20. What pair of numbers between 100 and 130 have 14 as their H.C.F.?

*21. If 90, 146, and 230 are each divided by the same number, the remainder is 6. What is the greatest possible value of the divisor?

*22. The H.C.F. of 3240, 3600, and a third number is 36, and their L.C.M. is $2^4 \times 3^5 \times 5^2 \times 7^2$. Find the third number.

*23. Three men A, B, C go round a circular track one mile in circumference, in the same direction and starting together from the same place. A bicycles at 352 yd. per minute, B runs at 220 yd. per minute, C walks at 132 yd. per minute. After how many minutes will they first be together again at the starting-point?

CHAPTER II

SIMPLE AREAS AND VOLUMES

Area. A rectangle 4 in. long, 3 in. wide can be divided into
(4×3) squares, each of side 1 in.; we therefore say that its area
is (4×3) sq. in.; the shape of the rectangle is
described by saying that it measures "4 inches
by 3 inches."

If each side of a rectangle is 3 in. long, the
rectangle is said to be 3 *inches square*. The
rulings in the diagram show that a rectangle
APQD, 3 in. square, can be divided into (3×3) squares each of
side 1 in.; its area is therefore 9 sq. in.

EXERCISE 12 (Oral)

1. Draw freehand diagrams to show how many squares, each of
side 1 in., are contained in (i) a rectangle 3 in. long, 2 in.
broad; (ii) a square of side 4 in.

How many squares each of side 1 in. are contained in the following
rectangles?

2. 5 in. high, 3 in. wide.   **3.** 4 in. by 6 in.

4. A square of side 6 in.   **5.** A square of side 1 ft.

6. How many square inches are there in 1 sq. ft.?

How many squares each of side 1 ft. are contained in the following
rectangles?

7. 4 ft. broad, 7 ft. long.   **8.** 8 ft. high, 12 ft. wide.

9. A square of side 5 ft.   **10.** A square of side 1 yd.

11. How many square feet are there in 1 sq. yd.?

Find the areas of the following rectangles :—

12. 5 in. long, 2 in. broad.   **13.** 6 in. high, 10 in. wide.

14. 7 in. by 3 in.   **15.** A square of side 4 in.

16. 8 in. square.   **17.** 10 in. square.

18. 5 ft. long, 4 ft. wide. **19.** 10 ft. long, 8 ft. high.

20. A square of side 7 ft. **21.** 9 ft. square.

22. 1 yd. long, 2 ft. broad. **23.** 1 ft. long, 7 in. wide.

24. A square of side 7 ch. **25.** A square of side 10 mi.

26. How many square chains are there in 1 sq. mi.?

27. The area of a rectangle, 1 fur. by 1 ch., is called an **acre**. How many square chains are there in 1 acre?

The examples in Exercise 12 illustrate the following statement :—

The number of units in the area of a rectangle is equal to the product of the number of units in its length and the number of units in its breadth.

This rule is usually *abbreviated* as follows :—

Area of Rectangle = length × breadth.

Using the notation of Algebra, we say that if a rectangle is *l* ft. long, *b* ft. broad, its area A sq. ft. is given by the formula,

$$A = l \times b.$$

This formula can also be written in either of the following ways :—

$$l = A \div b = \frac{A}{b}; \qquad b = A \div l = \frac{A}{l},$$

where A, *l*, *b* are numbers, *not* quantities.

These facts are often stated in words in the *abbreviated* forms,

Breadth of Rectangle = Area ÷ length ;
Length of Rectangle = Area ÷ breadth.

The **Perimeter** of a figure bounded by straight lines is the sum of the lengths of the sides.

For example, the perimeter of a field is the total length of the fence which encloses it.

Since the opposite sides of a rectangle are equal, the perimeter of a rectangle is twice the sum of its length and breadth; if a rectangle is *l* ft. long, *b* ft. broad, its perimeter P ft. is given by the formula, $P = 2(l + b)$.

Example 1. A strip of carpet is 4 ft. wide, 5 yd. long. Find its area.

The carpet is 4 ft. wide, 15 ft. long;

∴ area of carpet = (4 × 15) sq. ft., = 60 sq. ft.

Example 2. The area of a rectangular courtyard, 30 yd. long, is 450 sq. yd. Find its breadth and perimeter.

Breadth of courtyard $= (450 \div 30)$ yd.

$\qquad = 15$ yd.

$\therefore$ perimeter of courtyard $= 2(30 + 15)$ yd.

$\qquad = (45 \times 2)$ yd., $= 90$ yd.

EXERCISE 13

Find the areas of the rectangles in Nos. 1–10 :

1. 8 in. long, 15 in. broad.   [**2**] 100 yd. long, 60 yd. wide.

3. 5 yd. wide, 10 ft. high.   **4.** 15 yd. square.

[**5**] 17 ft. by 13 ft.   **6.** 1 ch. by 5 yd., in square yards.

7. 2 fur. by 5 ch., in square chains.

[**8**] 2 ft. by 1 ft. 3 in., in square inches.

*9. 1 ft. 6 in. by 1 ft. 8 in., in square inches.

*10. 8 yd. 1 ft. by 16 yd. 2 ft., in square feet.

[**11**] Find the area of a window 4 ft. wide, 6 ft. high.

12. Find the area of the floor of a room 24 ft. long, 15 ft. wide.

13. Find the area in square inches of a plank 5 in. wide, 4 ft. long.

[**14**] Find the area of a courtyard 45 yd. long, 50 ft. wide.

*15. How many square feet are there in 2 sq. yd.? Illustrate your answer by a sketch.

*16. 1 acre = 10 sq. ch.; how many square yards are there in 1 acre?

Find the breadths and perimeters of the rectangles in Nos. 17–22 :

17. Area 48 sq. in., length 8 in.   [**18**] Area 108 sq. yd., length 12 yd.

19. Area 10 sq. yd., length 6 ft.   [**20**] Area 1 sq. ft., length 16 in.

21. Area 6 sq. ft., height 27 in.   [**22**] Area 10 sq. yd., height 10 ft.

23. The perimeter of a rectangle is 30 in., and its breadth is 6 in.; find its length and its area.

24. The perimeter of a football ground 120 yd. long is 400 yd.; find the area in square yards.

[**25**] The perimeter of a rectangle is 2 ft., and its length is 7 in.; find its breadth and area.

26. The area of a rectangular field is 4840 sq. yd.; it is 55 yd. wide. Find its perimeter.

*27. 20 sq. ft. of cloth are cut into strips 3 in. wide; find the total length of the strips in feet.

*28. Find the cost of a carpet 8 yd. long, 10 ft. wide, at 2s. per square foot.

Land Measurement. If each side of a square is 1 ch. long, its area is 1 sq. ch.; but 1 ch. = 22 yd., therefore the area of this square is (22×22) sq. yd., = 484 sq. yd.

$$\begin{array}{r} 22 \\ 22 \\ \hline 44 \\ 44 \\ \hline 484 \end{array}$$

$$\therefore 1 \text{ sq. ch.} = \mathbf{484 \text{ sq. yd.}}$$

If a rectangle measures 1 fur. (10 ch.) by 1 ch., its area is 10 sq. ch., = 4840 sq. yd., and this area is called 1 **acre** (ac.).

$$\therefore 1 \text{ acre} = 10 \text{ sq. ch.} = \mathbf{4840 \text{ sq. yd.}}$$

Areas of fields and estates are usually expressed in acres. A full-sized Association football ground measures 120 yd. by 80 yd., therefore its area is 9600 sq. yd., which is a little less than 2 acres. This fact is useful when estimating by eye an area in acres.

Similarly, since 1 mi. = 80 ch., the area of 1 sq. mi. is 6400 sq. ch.; but 10 sq. ch. = 1 acre;

$$\therefore 1 \text{ sq. mi.} = \mathbf{640 \text{ acres.}}$$

Example 3. The area of a rectangular field is 10 ac.; its breadth is 200 yd. Find its length.

The area of the field = (4840×10) sq. yd.; and the breadth = 200 yd.;

$$\therefore \text{ the length} = (48400 \div 200) \text{ yd.} = 242 \text{ yd.}$$

Example 4. A carpet 15 ft. long, 12 ft. wide is laid in a room 20 ft. square. Find the area of the floor left uncovered.

$$\text{Area of floor} = (20 \times 20) \text{ sq. ft.} = 400 \text{ sq. ft.}$$
$$\text{Area of carpet} = (15 \times 12) \text{ sq. ft.} = 180 \text{ sq. ft.}$$
$$\therefore \text{ area of part uncovered} = (400 - 180) \text{ sq. ft.} = 220 \text{ sq. ft.}$$

Example 5. Find the area of the given figure, where all corners are right-angled and dimensions are given in inches.

Divide the figure into rectangles A, B, C.

The width of B is $(8 - 6)$ in., *i.e.* 2 in.
Area of rect. A = (8×3) sq. in. = 24 sq. in.;
area of rect. B = (2×5) sq. in. = 10 sq. in.;
area of rect. C = (10×4) sq. in. = 40 sq. in.;
$\therefore$ total area = 74 sq. in.

Example 6.   A lawn 30 yd. long, 16 yd. wide is surrounded by a path 2 yd. wide.   Find the area of the path.

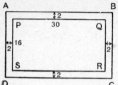

PQRS represents the rectangular lawn, and ABCD represents the outer edge of the path.

Since PQ = 30 yd., and since the path is 2 yd. wide,

AB = (30 + 2 + 2) yd. = 34 yd.;

similarly AD = (16 + 2 + 2) yd. = 20 yd.

∴ area ABCD = (34 × 20) sq. yd. = 680 sq. yd.,

and area PQRS = (30 × 16) sq. yd. = 480 sq. yd.

∴ area of path = area ABCD − area PQRS

= (680 − 480) sq. yd. = 200 sq. yd.

Note. It is better to find the area of the path by the subtraction method than by dividing it up into separate rectangles.

Example 7.

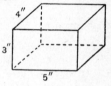

An open box (no lid) is 5 in. long, 4 in. wide, 3 in. high. Find the area of the total external surface.

The external surface is made up as follows :—

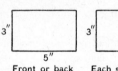

Front or back   Each side face   Base

The total area of the front and back is (2 × 3 × 5) sq. in., = 30 sq. in.;

the total area of the two side faces is (2 × 3 × 4) sq. in., = 24 sq. in.;

the area of the base is (4 × 5) sq. in., = 20 sq. in.;

∴ area of total external surface = (30 + 24 + 20) sq. in. = 74 sq. in.

EXERCISE 14

Find in acres the areas of the rectangular fields, Nos. 1–3 :

1. 5 ch. by 4 ch.   **2.** 220 yd. by 44 yd.   *3. 4 fur. square.

4. How many square chains are there in 2 ac., 10 ac.?

5. How many square yards are there in 5 ac., 100 ac.?

6. How many acres are there in 2 sq. mi., half a square mile?

7. A rectangular 5-acre field is 100 yd. wide; find its length and perimeter.

Find the areas of the figures, Nos. 8–11, where all corners are right-angled and *dimensions are given in inches*.

Divide the figures into rectangles; No. 8 *two* rectangles, Nos. 9–11 *three* rectangles. Set out the working clearly as in Example 5.

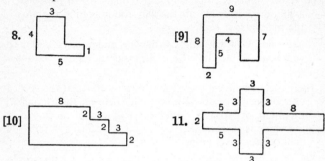

Find the areas of the shaded parts of the figures, Nos. 12–15, by *subtracting* one or more areas from another area. All corners are right-angled and *dimensions are given in feet*.

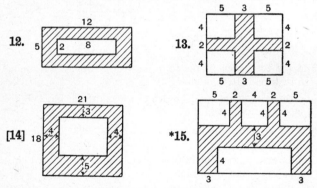

Make freehand sketches showing the data of Nos. 16–22, and find the required areas.

16. A carpet 12 ft. by 10 ft. is laid in a room 15 ft. square. Find the area of the part of the floor left uncovered.

[17] A carpet 16 ft. by 9 ft. is laid in a room 18 ft. long, 12 ft. wide. Find the area of the part of the floor left uncovered.

18. A picture 18 in. by 15 in. is mounted on a card 2 ft. long, 1 ft. 6 in. wide; what area of the card is uncovered?

[19] A lawn 10 yd. by 8 yd. is surrounded by a path 1 yd. wide. Find the area of the path.

[20] A picture 30 in. by 24 in. is mounted on a card so that there is a margin 3 in. wide all the way round. Find the area of the margin.

21. A courtyard is 40 yd. long, 24 yd. wide, and a paved path 3 yd. wide runs round the edge of it, inside it. Find the area of the path.

*22. There are four flower beds, each 10 ft. by 10 ft., at the corners of a square with grass paths 4 ft. wide between them (compare the figure of No. 13). Find the total area of the grass. If the whole is surrounded by a gravel path 6 ft. wide, find the area of the gravel path.

23. The diagram represents the four walls of a rectangular room, folded out flat, dimensions in feet. Find the total area of the four walls.

8	Long wall	Short wall	Long wall	Short wall
	18	14	18	14

[24] Find the total area of the four walls of a room, 15 ft. long, 10 ft. wide, 7 ft. high. [Make a sketch as in No. 23.]

25. Find the total area of the four walls of a room, 21 ft. long, 16 ft. broad, 10 ft. high.

26. Find the area of the total surface of a rectangular block, 8 in. long, 5 in. wide, 4 in. high.

[27] Find the area of the total surface of a rectangular block, 9 in. square, 6 in. high.

[28] Find the area of the total external surface of a closed box 12 in. long, 7 in. wide, 6 in. high.

29. The diagram represents the base and sides of an *open* tank, dimensions in feet. Find the area of the total external surface.

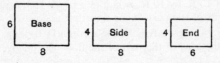

6	Base	4	Side	4	End
	8		8		6

[30] Make freehand sketches, as in No. 29, to show the faces of a closed rectangular box, 12 in. long, 9 in. wide, 6 in. high, and find the total area of the surface of the box.

31. Find the area of the total external surface of an *open* box (*i.e.* without a lid), 15 in. long, 8 in. wide, 10 in. high.

*32. Find the area of thin sheeting required for making an *open* cistern (*i.e.* without a lid), 5 ft. long, 3 ft. wide, 4 ft. deep.

*33. Repeat No. 24 for a room *l* ft. long, *b* ft. wide, *h* ft. high.

*34. Repeat No. 32 for an open cistern *l* ft. long, *b* ft. wide, *h* ft. deep.

Volume. A solid like an ordinary brick, each face of which is a rectangle, is called a **rectangular solid** or **cuboid**; and if each face is a square, the solid is called a **cube**.

A cube, each edge of which is 1 in. long, is called a cubic inch block or, for short, a **cubic inch.**

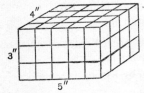

By using cubic inch blocks, we can build up cuboids of various sizes. The diagram represents a cuboid 5 in. long, 4 in. broad, 3 in. high. This cuboid contains $(5 \times 4) \times 3$ cubic inch blocks; so we say its *volume* is $(5 \times 4 \times 3)$ cubic inches (cu. in.). The shape of the cuboid is described by saying that it measures "5 in. by 4 in. by 3 in."

This form of argument can be used to show that the number of units of volume of any cuboid is obtained by multiplying together the numbers of units in the length, breadth, and height. This rule is *abbreviated* as follows :—

Volume of cuboid = length × breadth × height.

Further, by using the formula for the area of a rectangle, this rule may be stated in the *abbreviated* form :

Volume of cuboid = (area of base) × height.

Using the notation of Algebra, we say that if a cuboid is *l* in. long, *b* in. broad, *h* in. high, its volume V cu. in. is given by the formula,

$$V = l \times b \times h.$$

Hence also $\qquad h = V \div (l \times b),$

and this fact may be stated in the *abbreviated* form,

Height of cuboid = Volume ÷ (area of base)

Example 8. The internal measurements of a tank are 10 ft. by 8 ft. by 5 ft.; find how much water the tank can hold.

The volume of the tank is $(10 \times 8 \times 5)$ cu. ft.;
∴ the tank can hold 400 cu. ft. of water.

Example 9. The volume of a rectangular solid is 240 cu. in.; it is 8 in. long and 5 in. broad, find its height.

The area of the base $= (8 \times 5)$ sq. in. $= 40$ sq. in.
∴ height of solid $=$ volume $\div$ (area of base)
$\qquad = (240 \div 40)$ in. $= 6$ in.

EXERCISE 15

[*Nos.* 1–11 *are intended for oral work*]

How many cubic inch blocks are required to build up rectangular solids having the following dimensions?

1. 5 in. by 8 in. by 7 in.   **2.** 4 in. by 6 in. by 1 ft.
[**3**] A 3-in. cube.   *****4.** A 2-ft. cube.

How many cubic inch blocks can be packed into rectangular boxes of the following internal dimensions?

5. 4 in. by 7 in. by 9 in.   [**6**] 5 in. by 1 ft. by 1 ft. 6 in.

Find the volumes of the following cuboids :—

7. 4 ft. by 8 ft. by 3 ft.   [**8**] 1 yd. by 2 ft. by 4 ft.
[**9**] 1 yd. by 2 ft. by 1 ft.   **10.** 1 ft. 3 in. by 1 ft. 4 in. by 1 in.

*****11.** How many (i) 2-in. cubes, (ii) 6-in. cubes can be packed into a box 1 ft. by 1 ft. by 1 ft., internal measurements?

12. The volume of a rectangular block is 720 cu. in.
    (i) Find its height if its length is 15 in. and breadth is 6 in.
    (ii) Find its length if its breadth is 9 in. and height is 4 in.
    (iii) Find its height if the area of the base is 45 sq. in.

[**13**] The volume of a rectangular tank is 432 cu. ft.
    (i) Find its height if the base is 4 yd. square.
    (ii) Find its breadth if its length is 3 yd. and height is 8 ft.
    (iii) Find its length if the area of the end face is 16 sq. ft.

14. A rectangular tank 8 ft. long, 6 ft. wide, 10 ft. high contains water to a depth of 7 ft. How much more water will it hold?

*15. A rectangular block of lead, 1 ft. by 10 in. by 9 in., is melted and recast into a cuboid 8 in. high, 5 in. wide. Find its length.

*16. How many cubic feet of water must be pumped into a swimming-bath 80 ft. long, 15 yd. wide, to raise the water-level 2 ft.?

*17. A rectangular tank 9 ft. by 8 ft., and 5 ft. deep (internal measurements), contains water to a depth of 3 ft. How many concrete blocks measuring 6 in. by 6 in. by 4 in. can be put into the tank before the water overflows?

*18. The water in the tank in No. 17 is run off into an empty tank 18 ft. long, 6 ft. wide; what will be the depth of the water in the second tank?

Volume of Material used in making a Box

Suppose the external dimensions of a closed wooden box are 10 in. by 9 in. by 6 in., and that the wood is 1 in. thick. The volume of the material is found by subtracting the *internal* volume (*i.e.* the volume of space inside the box) from the *external* volume.

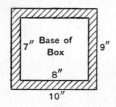
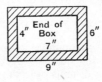

The diagrams show that

$$\text{internal length} = (10 - 1 - 1) \text{ in.} = 8 \text{ in.},$$
$$\text{internal breadth} = (9 - 1 - 1) \text{ in.} = 7 \text{ in.},$$
$$\text{internal height} = (6 - 1 - 1) \text{ in.} = 4 \text{ in.};$$
$$\therefore \text{ internal volume} = (8 \times 7 \times 4) \text{ cu. in.} = 224 \text{ cu. in.};$$
$$\text{but total external volume} = (10 \times 9 \times 6) \text{ cu. in.} = 540 \text{ cu. in.};$$
$$\therefore \text{ volume of wood} = (540 - 224) \text{ cu. in.} = 316 \text{ cu. in.}$$

If this box has no lid,

$$\text{internal height} = (6 - 1) \text{ in.} = 5 \text{ in.},$$
$$\therefore \text{ internal volume} = (8 \times 7 \times 5) \text{ cu. in.} = 280 \text{ cu. in.};$$
$$\therefore \text{ volume of wood} = (540 - 280) \text{ cu. in.} = 260 \text{ cu. in.}$$

Volume of Solid of uniform Cross-section

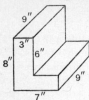

The diagram represents a solid 9 in. long so shaped that, if any cut is made through it at right angles to its length, the surface exposed to view is always the same size and shape, in this example an **L** shape; this surface is called the *cross-section* of the solid, and the solid is said to be of *uniform* cross-section. Solids of uniform cross-section are of common occurrence, *e.g.* a new pencil, a water-pipe, a bar of chocolate or a stick of Yarmouth rock, a ruler, a flight of steps, a lean-to shed, etc.

The **L**-shaped solid in the diagram can be built up by using cubic inch blocks.

By dividing the cross-section into two rectangles, we see that its area is

$$\{(8 \times 3) + (2 \times 4)\} \text{ sq. in., } = 32 \text{ sq. in.}$$

Therefore 32 cu. in. blocks are required for each inch in the length of the solid.

$$\therefore \text{ volume of solid} = (32 \times 9) \text{ cu. in.} = 288 \text{ cu. in.}$$

Here, the number of units of volume has been found by multiplying the number of units of area of the cross-section by the number of units of length, and a similar argument may be used for finding the volume of any solid of uniform cross-section. The rule may be stated in the *abbreviated* form,

Volume of solid of uniform cross-section = (area of cross-section) × length.

Note. **Cross-area** is a convenient abbreviation for area of cross-section.

EXERCISE 16

Find the internal dimensions of *closed* wooden boxes of the following external dimensions, and find the volume of space in each box:

1. 12 in. by 9 in. by 8 in.; wood 1 in. thick.

[2] 10 in. by 8 in. by 6 in.; wood half an inch thick.

Find the internal dimensions of *open* wooden boxes of the following external dimensions, and find the volume of water each box will hold :—

[3] 10 in. by 7 in.; 9 in. high; wood 2 in. thick.

4. 9 in. by 6 in.; 10 in. high; wood 1 inch thick.

Find the amount of wood used in making *closed* wooden boxes of the following external dimensions :—

5. 16 in. by 12 in. by 9 in.; wood 1 in. thick.

[6] 1 ft. by 9 in. by 5 in.; wood half an inch thick.

Find the amount of wood used in making *open* wooden boxes of the following external dimensions :—

[7] 20 in. by 15 in.; 10 in. high; wood 1 in. thick.

8. 2 ft. by 18 in.; 1 ft. high; wood 2 in. thick.

*9. Find the area of the inside surface of an *open* box made of wood 1 in. thick if the box is 10 in. long, 9 in. wide, 8 in. high, measured externally.

*10. A closed box, 8 in. by 7 in. by 6 in., has a coating of asbestos all round it, half an inch thick. What amount of asbestos is used? [The external surface is also a cuboid.]

The solids represented in the following diagrams are composed of rectangular blocks, dimensions in inches.

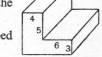

11. Find the area of the total surface of the given L-shaped solid.

12. Find the volume of the given L-shaped solid.

*13. What are the dimensions of the smallest cuboid from which the given L-shaped solid can be carved, and what is the volume of the portion which must be cut away?

[14] Find the area of the total surface of the given T-shaped solid.

[15] Find the volume of the given T-shaped solid.

16. The area of the internal cross-section of a jar which contains 54 cu. in. of water is 6 sq. in.   Find the depth of the water.

17. If 15 cu. in. of water are poured into a bottle of uniform cross-section, the water level rises 3 in.   Find the area of the cross-section of the bottle.

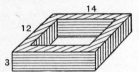

*18. The sides of the given wooden collar are 2 in. thick.   Find (i) the area of the top surface of the collar, (ii) the volume of the wood used.

*19. The diagram represents the cross-section of a solid, 10 in. long; the corners are right-angled and the dimensions are given in inches. Find (i) the area of the cross-section, (ii) the volume of the solid.

CHAPTER III

EASY UNITARY METHOD

Direct Variation

Example 1.   If 4 buns cost one shilling, find the cost of 7 buns.

> 4 buns cost 12d.
> ∴ 1 bun costs $\frac{12}{4}$d., =3d.
> ∴ 7 buns cost 3d. × 7, =21d., =1s. 9d.

Always express the data by a *proper sentence*, and arrange it so that the quantity which is to be found comes **at the end of the sentence.**

Example 2. If 50 cigarettes cost half a crown, find the cost of 80 cigarettes of the same kind.

> 50 cigarettes cost 30d.
> ∴ 10 cigarettes cost $\frac{30}{5}$d., =6d.
> ∴ 80 cigarettes cost 6d. × 8, =48d., =4s.

Note.   In this argument, 10 cigarettes are taken as the unit; 10 is the H.C.F. of 50 and 80.   It is unnecessary to find the cost of 1 cigarette. *Always choose as large a unit as possible.*

EXERCISE 17 (Class Discussion)

[Assume that the rates are uniform]

1. A man earns 2s. an hour. How much does he earn in 3 hr.? in 5 hr.?

2. If 1 lb. of sugar costs 3d., find the cost of 8 lb., of 12 lb.

3. A man walks at the rate of 120 yd. a minute. How far does he walk in 4 min.? in 10 min.?

4. 1 chain = 22 yards; how many yards are there in 5 chains?

5. If 7 lb. of tea cost 14s., find the cost of 10 lb.

6. If 2 tablets of soap cost 6d., find the cost of 5 tablets.

7. My watch loses 20 sec. in 4 days, how much does it lose in 1 week?

8. 30 tablets of Aspirin cost 6d.; how many can I buy for 10d.?

9. A train travels 75 yd. every 5 sec.; how far does it go in 12 sec.?

10. 6 copies of *The Times* cost one shilling; how many copies can I buy for half a crown?

11. 6 similar notebooks weigh 30 oz.; what is the weight of 5 of them?

12. A dance band plays 4 tunes in 36 min.; how long does a programme of 10 tunes last, at the same rate?

13. If 12 envelopes cost 6d., how many can be bought for 1s. 3d.?

14. My car uses 8 gall. of petrol for 200 mi.; how far will it run on 5 gall.?

15. If 20 cigarettes cost 1s., find the cost of 50 cigarettes at the same rate.

16. 5 equal bags of flour weigh 35 lb.; how many bags are required for 56 lb. of flour?

17. 12 tennis balls cost 15s.; how many can I buy for £1?

18. 8 boys eat 12 lb. of butter a week. How much butter will 10 boys eat in a fortnight?

EXERCISE 18

[Assume that the rates are uniform]

1. If 6 peaches cost 2s., find the cost of 4 peaches.

2. I can walk 3 mi. in 45 min.; how long do I take to walk 5 mi. at the same rate?

3. A car uses 6 gall. of petrol for 144 mi.; how far will it run with 5 gall.?

[4] For 4d. I can buy 12 envelopes; how many can I buy for 1s. 3d.?

[5] 2 dozen dried eggs cost 3s.; find the cost of 5 dozen.

6. 4 lb. of Gorgonzola cost 5s.; find the cost of 3 lb.

7. A hotel bill for 10 days is £7, 10s.; what is the charge for 1 week at the same rate?

[8] The fare for 8 mi. is 1s.; what is the fare for 22 mi. at the same rate?

9. 21 lb. of freezing-salts cost 1s. 6d.; find the cost of 7 lb., of 56 lb.

10. In 20 min. a train travels 15 mi.; how far does it go in 4 min., in 12 min., at the same rate?

*11. If 40 mi. is represented on a map by a line 16 in. long; what length on the map represents 5 mi., 25 mi.?

[12] A man saves £12 in 40 weeks; how long does it take him to save (i) £3, (ii) £21 at the same rate?

[13] A lorry uses 15 gall. of petrol for 250 mi.; how much will it use for (i) 50 mi., (ii) 350 mi.?

14. If 84 French francs are worth £1, what is the value of 700 French francs?

15. If 10 lb. of coffee costs 15 shillings, how much can be bought for a guinea?

*16. A faulty cyclometer records 36 mi. for a journey of 42 mi. What does it record for 63 mi.?

*17. The shadow of a man 6 ft. high is 10 ft. long at the same time that the shadow of a telegraph pole is 35 ft. long. Find the height of the pole.

*18. A bankrupt who owes £550 only possesses £150. How much does a man to whom he owes £44 receive?

19. A carpet, 10 ft. by 7 ft., costs £14. Find the cost of a carpet of the same quality, 15 ft. by 8 ft.

[20] A thin metal sheet, 2 ft. by 3 ft., weighs 4 oz. Find the weight of 1 sq. yd. of a sheet of the same kind.

*21. If 100 cu. in. of copper weigh 30 lb., find the weight of a rectangular block of copper 1 ft. long, 6 in. wide, 5 in. high.

*22. In a sale the price of a table is reduced from 28s. to 21s.; find the sale price of a chair, originally £1, if reduced at the same rate.

*23. If 4 in. on a map represent 1 mi., what area on the map represents 9 sq. mi.?

*24. If 16 in. on a map represents 40 mi., what area on the map represents 25 sq. mi.?

Inverse Variation

Example 3. 3 men can weed a field in 8 days. How long will 4 men take, if all work at the same rate?

3 men can weed the field in 8 days;

  (but 1 man will take 3 times as long as 3 men take);

  ∴ 1 man can weed the field in 8 days × 3, =24 days;

  (but 4 men will take one-quarter of the time 1 man takes);

  ∴ 4 men can weed the field in 24 days ÷ 4, =6 days.

Note. The sentences in brackets show the reasoning which must be done *mentally*; they should not be written down.

Example 4. A certain sum of money is sufficient to pay the wages of 12 men for 15 days. For how many days is it sufficient for 10 men, if all receive the same daily wages?

  12 men can be paid for 15 days;

  ∴ 1 man can be paid for (15 × 12) days, =180 days;

  ∴ 10 men can be paid for (180 ÷ 10) days, =18 days.

The unitary-method argument can only be used in cases of direct or inverse variation.

For example, if a football team scores 4 goals in 1 match, it is absurd to argue that it will score 40 goals in 10 matches.

In examples where the unitary-method argument *can* be used, it is always necessary to consider whether the quantity at the end of the sentence is *increased* or *decreased* by the change made in the quantity at the beginning of the sentence.

In Exercises 19–21, if the unitary-method argument cannot be used, say so, and give the reason, but no other answer.

EXERCISE 19 (Oral)

[Assume that the rates are uniform unless this assumption is contrary to common sense]

1. 6 men can mow a field in 3 days; how long will it take 1 man? 2 men? 9 men?

2. 4 men can dig a trench in 5 days; how long will it take 1 man? 2 men? 10 men?

3. At 6 mi. an hour, a man takes 4 hr. for a journey; how long will he take at 1 mi. an hour? 3 mi. an hour? 12 mi. an hour?

4. A man runs 100 yd. in 10 sec.; how long will he take to run 1000 yd.?

5. Four taps running at the same rate fill a tank in 12 min.; how long will it take with 1 tap? 2 taps? 3 taps?

6. Two men can whitewash a ceiling in 120 min.; how long will it take 1 man? 3 men? 120 men?

7. The oats in a bin will feed 9 horses for 10 days; how long will they feed 3 horses? 15 horses?

8. The sun dries 6 towels on a clothes line in 30 min.; how long does it take to dry 1 towel? 8 towels?

9. A certain number of tennis balls have to be packed in boxes. If 6 balls are packed in a box, 10 boxes are required; how many boxes are used with 12 balls in each box? 4 balls in each box?

10. 2 in. of rain fall in 3 days; how much rain falls in 12 days?

11. A 10 horse-power car can do a certain journey in 3 hr.; how long will it take a 40 horse-power car?

12. I have enough money for my holiday to spend £8 a week for 6 weeks. How long will it last if I spend £4 a week? £12 a week?

EXERCISE 20

[Assume that the rates are uniform unless this assumption is contrary to common sense]

1. A man packs 20 boxes of peaches with 18 in each box; how many boxes are needed if only 12 are put in each box?

2. At 30 mi. an hour a train takes 6 hr. for a journey; how long will it take at 36 mi. an hour?

3. A haystack is large enough to feed 12 horses for 15 days; how long will it last 20 horses?

[4] 15 men can mend a road in 24 days; how long will it take 9 men to mend it?

***5.** From the top of a tower, 1 man can see a distance of 10 mi.; how far can 5 men see?

6. 12 men can build a wall in 15 days; how long would it take 20 men to do so?

[7] A gardener ties up 54 bunches of flowers with 10 in each bunch. How many bunches would there be if he put 12 in each bunch?

***8.** I spend some money on $1\frac{1}{2}$d. stamps and receive 12 rows with 18 in each row. How many rows should there be if there are 8 in each row?

***9.** A boy is 5 ft. high when 12 years old. What will be his height when he is 24 years old?

10. Six equal pumps working together empty a tank in 28 min.; how long will it take if only 4 pumps are working?

***11.** A swimming-bath can be filled in 10 hr. by 6 equal pumps working together. How many pumps are working together if the bath is filled in 15 hr.?

[12] I have enough money to spend 18 shillings a day for 40 days; how long will my money last if I spend 15 shillings a day?

MISCELLANEOUS EXAMPLES

EXERCISE 21

[Assume that the rates are uniform unless this assumption is contrary to common sense]

1. If 12 balls cost 15 shillings, find the cost of 8 balls.

2. If 10 men can repair a road in 18 days, how long will 15 men take?

[3] A man earns £35 in 10 weeks; how long will he take to earn £56 at the same rate of pay?

[4] A watch gains 48 sec. in 10 days; what will it gain in 15 days?

5. A steamer, doing 12 knots, takes 15 days for a journey. How long will it take at 10 knots? [1 knot = 1 nautical mile per hour.]

6. 20 tins of boot polish cost 4s. 2d.; find the cost of 2 dozen tins.

[**7**] A car, which runs 24 mi. to the gallon of petrol, uses 5 gall. for a journey; how much does a car, which runs 30 mi. to the gallon, use for the same journey?

*****8.** A man weighs 10 stone when he is 20 years old; what will he weigh when he is 60?

*****9.** On a certain map 2 in. represent 1 mi.; what area does 20 sq. in. on the map represent?

10. The railway fare for 20 mi. is half a crown; what is the fare for 36 mi.?

11. A tin sheet, 20 in. by 42 in., weighs 6 oz.; find the weight of a tin sheet, 35 in. by 60 in., of the same material and thickness.

[**12**] If 4 cu. in. of copper weigh 21 oz., find the weight of a rectangular block of copper, 2 in. by 3 in. by 4 in.

13. The greatest safe load for a lift is 12 men each weighing 15 stone. How many people, each weighing 10 stone, can it take safely?

*****14.** A batsman scores 10 runs in his first over; what does he score in his first 5 overs?

15. 3 turns of the winder of my watch keep it going for 12 hr. What is the effect of 5 turns?

*****16.** When the temperature rises by 72° Fahrenheit, it rises 40° Centigrade. What is the fall in degrees Centigrade corresponding to a fall of 45° Fahrenheit?

*****17.** A cartwheel, perimeter 12 ft., makes 120 revolutions in going from A to B. How many revolutions does a carriage wheel, perimeter 9 ft., make in going from A to B and back again?

*****18.** 3 similar lamps burn 4 gall. of oil in 100 hr.; how much oil will 5 such lamps burn in 60 hr.?

CHAPTER IV

FRACTIONS: ADDITION AND SUBTRACTION

Common Fractions. If 1d. is divided into 4 equal parts, each part is written as $\frac{1}{4}$d., and 3 of these parts as $\frac{3}{4}$d.

$\frac{3}{4}$ is called a *vulgar* or *common fraction* or simply a **fraction**; 4 is called the **denominator** of the fraction, it is the number of parts into which the unit is divided; 3 is called the **numerator** of the fraction, it is the number of parts taken.

$$\text{Fraction} = \frac{\text{Numerator}}{\text{Denominator}}$$

EXERCISE 22 (Oral)

Write down the values of:

1. One-quarter of 1s.
2. One-third of 1s.
3. One-sixth of 1s.
4. Three-quarters of 1s.
5. Two-thirds of 1s.
6. Five-sixths of 1s.
7. One-half of 1 lb.
8. One-quarter of 1 lb.
9. One-eighth of 1 lb.
10. Two-quarters of 1 lb.
11. Three-quarters of 1 lb.
12. Six-eighths of 1 lb.
13. One-fifth of 1 hr.
14. One-tenth of 1 hr.
15. One-twentieth of 1 hr.
16. Two-fifths of 1 hr.
17. Four-tenths of 1 hr.
18. Eight-twentieths of 1 hr.

Write as fractions:

19. Four-fifths.
20. Seven-tenths.
21. Five-twelfths.
22. One-ninth.
23. Four-sevenths.
24. Eight-fifteenths.
25. Write in words $\frac{3}{4}$, $\frac{4}{5}$, $\frac{3}{10}$.
26. Write in words $\frac{5}{7}$, $\frac{4}{9}$, $\frac{7}{20}$.

Write down the values of:

27. $\frac{1}{2}$ of £1.
28. $\frac{1}{4}$ of £1.
29. $\frac{1}{5}$ of £1.
30. $\frac{2}{4}$ of £1.
31. $\frac{3}{4}$ of £1.
32. $\frac{4}{5}$ of £1.
33. $\frac{1}{6}$ of 1 hr.
34. $\frac{3}{8}$ of 1 hr.
35. $\frac{5}{6}$ of 1 hr.
36. $\frac{1}{8}$ of 1 day.
37. $\frac{3}{8}$ of 1 day.
38. $\frac{4}{8}$ of 1 day.
39. $\frac{1}{7}$ of 1 wk.
40. $\frac{4}{7}$ of 1 wk.
41. $\frac{7}{7}$ of 1 wk.
42. $\frac{1}{5}$ of £2.
43. $\frac{1}{3}$ of 2 ft.
44. $\frac{2}{3}$ of 1 ft.
45. $\frac{2}{3}$ of 2 ft.
46. $\frac{1}{8}$ of 3 lb.

B

3

47. $\frac{3}{8}$ of 3 lb.   **48.** $\frac{2}{3}$ of 1 yd.   **49.** $\frac{3}{5}$ of 1 ton.   **50.** $\frac{7}{12}$ of 1 hr.

51. $\frac{4}{11}$ of 1 ch.   **52.** $\frac{3}{8}$ of 1 gall.   **53.** $\frac{11}{12}$ of 1 day.   **54.** $\frac{3}{16}$ of 2 lb.

55. $\frac{7}{20}$ of 1 min.   **56.** $\frac{1}{20}$ of 1 mi.   **57.** $\frac{4}{9}$ of 1 yd.   **58.** $\frac{3}{8}$ of 2 tons.

Take a rectangular sheet of paper (long and narrow) and fold it in half with a firm crease.   Shade one of the halves.

Fold the paper again so as to divide it into 4 equal parts; then the shaded area contains 2 of these parts and is therefore $\frac{2}{4}$ of the sheet; thus $\frac{2}{4}=\frac{1}{2}$.   Repeat the process, dividing the sheet into 8 equal parts; this shows that $\frac{4}{8}=\frac{1}{2}$; and so on.

Thus $\frac{1}{2}=\frac{2}{4}=\frac{4}{8}=\frac{8}{16}= \cdots$

Draw on a squared blackboard or on squared paper a rectangle,

3 units wide, 5 units high, and divide it into 3 equal columns, and shade 2 of them. The shaded area, see fig. (i), is $\frac{2}{3}$ of the whole rectangle.   Fig. (ii) represents the same rectangle divided into 15 equal parts, and the shaded area contains 10 of these parts; thus $\frac{10}{15}=\frac{2}{3}$.

(i)   (ii)

In the same way it can be shown that

$$\frac{2}{3}=\frac{4}{6}=\frac{6}{9}=\frac{8}{12}=\frac{12}{18}= \cdots$$

This may also be illustrated by finding in inches the lengths of these fractions of a line 1 yd. long.

Hence we have the following rule :—

The value of a fraction is not altered by multiplying, or dividing, the numerator and denominator by the same number.

For example, $\frac{1}{2}=\frac{5}{10}$, $\frac{3}{7}=\frac{12}{28}$, $\frac{40}{90}=\frac{4}{9}$;
    and $\frac{3}{3}=\frac{1}{1}=1$, $\frac{15}{3}=\frac{5}{1}=5$.

Example 1.   What fraction is 9d. of 2s.?

2s. =24d. | It is shorter to say,
∴ 1d. =$\frac{1}{24}$ of 2s. | 9d. =3 threepences,
∴ 9d. =$\frac{9}{24}$ of 2s. | 2s. =8 threepences,
∴ 9d. =$\frac{3}{8}$ of 2s. | ∴ 9d. is $\frac{3}{8}$ of 2s.

EXERCISE 23 (Oral)

What fraction is :

1. 3d. of 1s.   **2.** 4d. of 1s.   **3.** 9d. of 1s.

4. 10s. of £1.   **5.** 4s. of £1.   **6.** 6s. of £1.

7. 20s. of £1.   **8.** 12s. of £1.   **9.** 8 hr. of 1 day.

10. 20 hr. of 1 day.   **11.** 20 min. of 1 hr.   **12.** 18 min. of 1 hr.

13. 4 oz. of 1 lb.   **14.** 12 oz. of 1 lb.   **15.** 9 in. of 1 yd.

16. 27 in. of 1 yd.   **17.** 30 in. of 1 yd.   **18.** 8 cwt. of 1 ton.

19. 6 pt. of 1 gall.   **20.** 8 lb. of 1 st.   **21.** 6 sq. ft. of 1 sq. yd.

Complete the following :—

22. $\dfrac{1}{2} = \dfrac{\cdots}{6} = \dfrac{\cdots}{14} = \dfrac{9}{\cdots} = \dfrac{10}{\cdots}$.   **23.** $\dfrac{3}{4} = \dfrac{\cdots}{8} = \dfrac{9}{\cdots} = \dfrac{\cdots}{20} = \dfrac{21}{\cdots}$.

24. Express each of the fractions $\dfrac{1}{2}, \dfrac{2}{3}, \dfrac{3}{4}, \dfrac{5}{6}$ in the form $\dfrac{\cdots}{12}$.

Express as simply as possible :

25. $\dfrac{4}{6}$.   **26.** $\dfrac{6}{10}$.   **27.** $\dfrac{5}{10}$.   **28.** $\dfrac{9}{12}$.   **29.** $\dfrac{10}{15}$.   **30.** $\dfrac{5}{5}$.

31. $\dfrac{8}{18}$.   **32.** $\dfrac{16}{24}$.   **33.** $\dfrac{30}{40}$.   **34.** $\dfrac{18}{30}$.   **35.** $\dfrac{10}{35}$.   **36.** $\dfrac{24}{32}$.

37. $\dfrac{27}{36}$.   **38.** $\dfrac{35}{42}$.   **39.** $\dfrac{18}{45}$.   **40.** $\dfrac{26}{52}$.   **41.** $\dfrac{45}{63}$.   **42.** $\dfrac{25}{65}$.

43. $\dfrac{54}{72}$.   **44.** $\dfrac{63}{81}$.

Write down the value of x in the following equations :—

45. $\dfrac{2}{3} = \dfrac{x}{6}$.   **46.** $\dfrac{x}{4} = \dfrac{24}{32}$.   **47.** $\dfrac{7}{10} = \dfrac{x}{30}$.   **48.** $\dfrac{6}{15} = \dfrac{2}{x}$.   **49.** $\dfrac{9}{21} = \dfrac{30}{x}$.

Lowest Terms.   If the numerator and denominator of a fraction have a common factor (other than 1), we have seen that the fraction can be simplified by dividing the numerator and denominator by this factor.   If we divide by the *highest* common factor, no further reduction is possible, and the resulting fraction is then said to be in its *lowest terms*.

Example 2.   Reduce $\dfrac{84}{210}$ to its lowest terms.

$$84 = 7 \times 12 = 2^2 \times 3 \times 7; \quad 210 = 10 \times 21 = 2 \times 3 \times 5 \times 7;$$

$$\therefore \ \dfrac{84}{210} = \dfrac{2^2 \times 3 \times 7}{2 \times 3 \times 5 \times 7} = \dfrac{2}{5}.$$

In practice, however, *it is easier to make the reduction in steps.*

$\dfrac{84}{210} = \dfrac{12}{30}$ (dividing above and below by 7)

$\qquad = \dfrac{2}{5}$ (dividing above and below by 6).

$$\dfrac{\overset{2}{\cancel{12}}}{\underset{5}{\cancel{30}}} \ \dfrac{\overset{\overset{2}{\cancel{12}}}{\cancel{84}}}{\underset{\underset{5}{\cancel{30}}}{\cancel{210}}} = \dfrac{2}{5}.$$

Time is saved by crossing out or "cancelling"; **but this must be done neatly.**

EXERCISE 24

Reduce to their lowest terms:

1. $\frac{48}{60}$.   [2] $\frac{27}{108}$.   3. $\frac{60}{156}$.   [4] $\frac{45}{162}$.   5. $\frac{55}{120}$.

[6] $\frac{21}{77}$.   7. $\frac{35}{105}$.   [8] $\frac{25}{175}$.   9. $\frac{154}{198}$.   [10] $\frac{99}{264}$.

11. $\frac{105}{147}$.   [12] $\frac{168}{480}$.   13. $\frac{345}{405}$.   [14] $\frac{192}{448}$.   15. $\frac{52}{546}$.

[16] $\frac{231}{476}$.   *17. $\frac{252}{1728}$.   *18. $\frac{648}{972}$.   *19. $\frac{665}{1190}$.   *20. $\frac{253}{460}$.

*21. $\frac{539}{1001}$.   *22. $\frac{1176}{1386}$.   *23. $\frac{1716}{2904}$.   *24. $\frac{1015}{1827}$.

Example 3. Arrange in ascending order of magnitude (that is to say, the smallest first, then the next smallest, and so on)

$$\tfrac{2}{3}, \tfrac{3}{4}, \tfrac{7}{10}, \tfrac{13}{20}.$$

The *least common multiple* of the denominators 3, 4, 10, 20 is 60. Express each fraction so that its denominator is 60:

$$\tfrac{2}{3} = \tfrac{40}{60}, \quad \tfrac{3}{4} = \tfrac{45}{60}, \quad \tfrac{7}{10} = \tfrac{42}{60}, \quad \tfrac{13}{20} = \tfrac{39}{60};$$

Arranging these in ascending order of magnitude, we have:

$$\tfrac{39}{60}, \tfrac{40}{60}, \tfrac{42}{60}, \tfrac{45}{60}, \quad \text{that is} \quad \tfrac{13}{20}, \tfrac{2}{3}, \tfrac{7}{10}, \tfrac{3}{4}.$$

Thus to compare two or more fractions, re-write them so that all have the *same denominator*; this is called expressing them with a **common denominator**.

EXERCISE 25

Which fraction is the greater in the following pairs?

1. $\frac{2}{3}, \frac{1}{2}$.   2. $\frac{2}{3}, \frac{5}{8}$.   3. $\frac{3}{8}, \frac{1}{2}$.   [4] $\frac{4}{5}, \frac{7}{10}$.

[5] $\frac{3}{4}, \frac{4}{5}$.   6. $\frac{3}{4}, \frac{5}{7}$.   [7] $\frac{7}{8}, \frac{11}{12}$.   8. $\frac{7}{10}, \frac{11}{15}$.

[9] $\frac{5}{6}, \frac{7}{8}$.   10. $\frac{4}{9}, \frac{5}{12}$.   *11. $\frac{4}{27}, \frac{2}{15}$.   *12. $\frac{5}{13}, \frac{13}{48}$.

*13. $\frac{2}{25}, \frac{3}{35}$.   *14. $\frac{5}{21}, \frac{7}{30}$.   *15. $\frac{3}{10}, \frac{5}{16}$.   *16. $\frac{4}{33}, \frac{5}{42}$.

Arrange in ascending order of magnitude:

17. $\frac{2}{3}, \frac{1}{2}, \frac{3}{5}$.   [18] $\frac{3}{4}, \frac{5}{8}, \frac{2}{3}$.   [19] $\frac{2}{3}, \frac{5}{6}, \frac{7}{9}$.   20. $\frac{1}{2}, \frac{1}{3}, \frac{5}{8}, \frac{5}{12}$.

*21. $\frac{5}{6}, \frac{13}{18}, \frac{11}{12}, \frac{8}{9}$.   *22. $\frac{5}{12}, \frac{3}{8}, \frac{7}{16}$.   *23. $\frac{5}{9}, \frac{11}{21}, \frac{4}{7}$.   *24. $\frac{7}{36}, \frac{2}{11}, \frac{13}{66}$.

Arrange in descending order of magnitude:

25. $\frac{5}{9}, \frac{1}{2}, \frac{7}{12}$.   [26] $\frac{1}{20}, \frac{2}{35}, \frac{3}{70}$.   [27] $\frac{3}{22}, \frac{4}{33}, \frac{7}{54}$.

28. $\frac{1}{15}, \frac{2}{25}, \frac{3}{50}, \frac{7}{100}$.   *29. $\frac{1}{3}, \frac{7}{24}, \frac{2}{7}, \frac{9}{28}$.   *30. $\frac{2}{9}, \frac{7}{30}, \frac{17}{72}, \frac{13}{60}$.

Fractions and Division

$3 \div 4$ is written $\frac{3}{4}$; $\frac{3}{4}$ is called a **proper fraction**.

$11 \div 4$ is written $\frac{11}{4}$; $\frac{11}{4}$ is called an **improper fraction** because the numerator is *greater* than the denominator.

$\frac{12}{4} = \frac{3}{1} = 3$; 3 is called an **integer** or **whole number**.

$\frac{11}{4} = \frac{8}{4} + \frac{3}{4} = 2 + \frac{3}{4}$, this is written $2\frac{3}{4}$ and is called a **mixed number** because it is the sum of a whole number and proper fraction.

Example 4. Express $\frac{23}{5}$ as a mixed number.

$$\frac{23}{5} = 4 + \frac{3}{5} = 4\frac{3}{5}.$$

$5 \underline{)23}$
$4 \quad rem.\ \textbf{3.}$

Example 5. Express $3\frac{5}{8}$ as an improper fraction.
Multiply 3 by 8, add 5 to the result, $3\frac{5}{8} = \frac{29}{8}$.

EXERCISE 26 (Oral)

Express as mixed or whole numbers :

1. $\frac{7}{3}$.   **2.** $\frac{8}{2}$.   **3.** $\frac{9}{5}$.   **4.** $\frac{12}{2}$.   **5.** $\frac{13}{4}$.

6. $\frac{15}{5}$.   **7.** $\frac{17}{6}$.   **8.** $\frac{30}{7}$.   **9.** $\frac{27}{8}$.   **10.** $\frac{50}{11}$.

11. $\frac{18}{4}$.   **12.** $\frac{15}{6}$.   **13.** $\frac{30}{12}$.   **14.** $\frac{51}{9}$.   **15.** $\frac{100}{12}$.

Express as improper fractions :

16. $1\frac{3}{4}$.   **17.** $3\frac{1}{3}$.   **18.** $1\frac{5}{7}$.   **19.** $3\frac{3}{5}$.   **20.** $4\frac{2}{7}$.

21. $6\frac{1}{8}$.   **22.** $5\frac{4}{9}$.   **23.** $1\frac{3}{16}$.   **24.** $2\frac{5}{12}$.   **25.** $9\frac{6}{11}$.

Write down the values of :

26. $\frac{2s.}{6}$.   **27.** $\frac{6d.}{4}$.   **28.** $\frac{10d.}{8}$.   **29.** $\frac{18\ in.}{12}$.

30. $\frac{9\ lb.}{6}$.   **31.** $\frac{14\ lb.}{4}$.   **32.** $\frac{11\ lb.}{8}$.   **33.** $\frac{£8}{5}$.

EXERCISE 27

Express as mixed or whole numbers :

1. $\frac{60}{13}$.   **2.** $\frac{97}{15}$.   [3] $\frac{100}{21}$.   [4] $\frac{125}{22}$.   **5.** $\frac{50}{18}$.   [6] $\frac{70}{16}$.

7. $\frac{145}{15}$.   [8] $\frac{144}{18}$.   **9.** $\frac{143}{13}$.   [10] $\frac{211}{17}$.   *11. $\frac{340}{23}$.   *12. $\frac{420}{38}$.

*13. $\frac{942}{31}$.   *14. $\frac{826}{49}$.   *15. $\frac{407}{37}$.   *16. $\frac{777}{39}$.   **17.** $\frac{585}{55}$.   **18.** $\frac{1000}{101}$.

Express as improper fractions :

19. $9\frac{3}{5}$.   [20] $11\frac{5}{6}$.   **21.** $14\frac{2}{7}$.   **22.** $13\frac{8}{11}$.   [23] $15\frac{5}{8}$.

[24] $17\frac{3}{13}$.   *25. $12\frac{19}{23}$.   *26. $24\frac{7}{25}$.   *27. $10\frac{47}{74}$.   *28. $3\frac{101}{103}$.

Addition. Express the fractions so that they have a *common denominator*. Give the answer in its *lowest terms*.

Example 6. Simplify $\frac{1}{5} + \frac{1}{6} + \frac{3}{10}$.

$\frac{1}{5} + \frac{1}{6} + \frac{3}{10} = \frac{6}{30} + \frac{5}{30} + \frac{9}{30}$	The L.C.M. of the denominators
$= \frac{20}{30}$	5, 6, 10 is 30.
$= \frac{2}{3}$.	Reduce $\frac{20}{30}$ to its lowest terms.

EXERCISE 28

[*Numbers 1–12 are suitable for oral work*]

Simplify:

1. 2 sevenths + 3 sevenths.   2. 2 ninths + 5 ninths.

3. 2 ninths + 4 ninths.   4. 7 tenths + 7 tenths.

5. $\frac{4}{11} + \frac{5}{11}$.   6. $\frac{1}{8} + \frac{1}{8}$.   7. $\frac{2}{15} + \frac{8}{15}$.   8. $\frac{9}{16} + \frac{3}{16}$.

9. $\frac{7}{20} + \frac{1}{20}$.   10. $\frac{10}{21} + \frac{4}{21}$.   11. $\frac{1}{24} + \frac{1}{24}$.   12. $\frac{7}{27} + \frac{11}{27}$.

13. $\frac{1}{2} + \frac{1}{4}$.   14. $\frac{1}{3} + \frac{1}{6}$.   [15] $\frac{1}{5} + \frac{3}{10}$.   16. $\frac{13}{18} + \frac{1}{9}$.

17. $\frac{1}{2} + \frac{1}{3}$.   [18] $\frac{2}{5} + \frac{1}{7}$.   [19] $\frac{2}{11} + \frac{3}{5}$.   20. $\frac{4}{9} + \frac{3}{11}$.

21. $\frac{1}{2} + \frac{1}{4} + \frac{1}{6}$.   [22] $\frac{1}{3} + \frac{1}{6} + \frac{2}{9}$.   23. $\frac{1}{4} + \frac{3}{8} + \frac{1}{12}$.

[24] $\frac{2}{5} + \frac{3}{10} + \frac{4}{15}$.   25. $\frac{5}{12} + \frac{1}{4} + \frac{3}{10}$.   [26] $\frac{2}{9} + \frac{4}{15} + \frac{3}{10}$.

27. $\frac{1}{4} + \frac{11}{48} + \frac{3}{16}$.   *28. $\frac{2}{9} + \frac{1}{36} + \frac{3}{8}$.   *29. $\frac{11}{32} + \frac{1}{6} + \frac{11}{96}$.

*30. $\frac{3}{10} + \frac{1}{12} + \frac{9}{20}$.   *31. $\frac{2}{21} + \frac{1}{14} + \frac{5}{42}$.   *32. $\frac{3}{20} + \frac{4}{25} + \frac{7}{50}$.

Example 7. Simplify $\frac{3}{5} + \frac{5}{6} + \frac{9}{10}$.

$\frac{3}{5} + \frac{5}{6} + \frac{9}{10} = \frac{18}{30} + \frac{25}{30} + \frac{27}{30}$	The L.C.M. of 5, 6, 10 is 30.
$= \frac{18+25+27}{30}$	Give the answer as a *mixed number*, do *not* leave it as an
$= \frac{70}{30} = \frac{7}{3}$	improper fraction. The first
$= 2\frac{1}{3}$.	step can be omitted.

Example 8. Simplify $\frac{8}{7} + \frac{7}{12} + 2\frac{5}{14} + \frac{15}{4}$.

Expression $= 1\frac{1}{7} + \frac{7}{12} + 2\frac{5}{14} + 3\frac{3}{4}$	In *addition*, first express any improper fraction as a mixed
$= 6 + \frac{12+49+30+63}{84}$	number, then add up all the whole numbers and write the
$= 6\frac{154}{84} = 7\frac{70}{84}$	fractions with a common denominator.
$= 7\frac{10}{12} = 7\frac{5}{6}$.	$\frac{154}{84} = 1\frac{70}{84}$.

EXERCISE 29

Simplify :

1. $\frac{3}{4}+\frac{3}{4}$.   2. $2\frac{1}{2}+1\frac{1}{4}$.   3. $\frac{3}{7}+\frac{4}{7}$.   [4] $\frac{7}{10}+\frac{3}{10}$.

5. $\frac{7}{8}+\frac{5}{8}$.   [6] $1\frac{5}{12}+1\frac{1}{12}$.   7. $\frac{1}{4}+2\frac{1}{12}$.   8. $1\frac{3}{8}+1\frac{5}{6}$.

[9] $\frac{3}{4}+3\frac{1}{4}$.   10. $1\frac{7}{18}+1\frac{11}{18}$.   [11] $\frac{13}{24}+\frac{17}{24}$.   12. $2\frac{2}{9}+1\frac{11}{18}$.

13. $\frac{3}{4}+\frac{5}{8}+\frac{1}{2}$.   [14] $\frac{2}{3}+\frac{5}{6}+\frac{2}{4}$.   15. $1\frac{1}{2}+2\frac{5}{8}+\frac{3}{20}$.

[16] $\frac{3}{7}+3\frac{3}{8}+\frac{5}{14}$.   17. $\frac{5}{4}+\frac{5}{6}+\frac{4}{9}$.   [18] $\frac{5}{8}+\frac{21}{10}+\frac{13}{20}$.

19. $1\frac{3}{4}+\frac{4}{5}+2\frac{7}{10}$.   [20] $2\frac{1}{8}+3\frac{5}{12}+1\frac{2}{9}$.   [21] $\frac{11}{6}+\frac{16}{15}+\frac{47}{20}$.

*22. $1\frac{7}{42}+2\frac{5}{18}+\frac{4}{15}$.   *23. $\frac{6}{8}+\frac{12}{15}+\frac{19}{20}$.   *24. $5\frac{4}{9}+\frac{8}{15}+1\frac{11}{20}$.

*25. $\frac{5}{12}+1\frac{11}{24}+2\frac{6}{32}$.   [26] $\frac{13}{22}+2\frac{1}{4}+\frac{8}{33}$.   *27. $\frac{10}{21}+1\frac{3}{28}+2\frac{5}{6}$.

*28. $\frac{19}{15}+\frac{23}{25}+\frac{7}{30}$.   *29. $\frac{37}{22}+\frac{21}{6}+\frac{89}{55}$.   *30. $\frac{7}{16}+\frac{3}{140}+\frac{3}{2800}$.

31. $\frac{1}{2}+\frac{2}{3}+\frac{3}{4}+\frac{4}{5}+\frac{19}{20}$.   [32] $\frac{2}{3}+\frac{1}{6}+\frac{5}{9}+\frac{11}{12}+\frac{17}{18}$.

Subtraction

Example 9. Subtract $1\frac{8}{15}$ from $3\frac{7}{10}$.

$$3\frac{7}{10}-1\frac{8}{15}=2+\frac{7}{10}-\frac{8}{15}$$
$$=2+\frac{21-16}{30}$$
$$=2\frac{5}{30}=2\frac{1}{6}.$$

First deal with the whole numbers, and write the fractions with a common denominator.

Answer in lowest terms.

Example 10. Subtract $2\frac{3}{4}$ from $8\frac{1}{3}$.

$$8\frac{1}{3}-2\frac{3}{4}=6+\frac{1}{3}-\frac{3}{4}$$
$$=6\frac{4-9}{12}$$
$$=5\frac{16-9}{12}$$
$$=5\frac{7}{12}.$$

We cannot subtract 9 from 4; take 1 of the 6 whole numbers and change it into $\frac{12}{12}$; this gives 5 whole numbers and $\frac{16-9}{12}$ instead of $\frac{4-9}{12}$.

Example 11. Simplify $\frac{77}{12}-\frac{32}{21}$.

$$\frac{77}{12}-\frac{32}{21}=6\frac{5}{12}-1\frac{11}{21}$$
$$=5\frac{35-44}{84}$$
$$=4\frac{119-44}{84}$$
$$=4\frac{75}{84}=4\frac{25}{28}.$$

In *subtraction*, first express any improper fraction as a mixed number, then deal with the whole numbers.

$$\begin{array}{r} 35 \\ 84 \\ \hline 119 \end{array}$$

Change 1 of the 5 whole numbers into $\frac{84}{84}$.

EXERCISE 30 (Oral)

Simplify:

1. $\frac{5}{6} - \frac{1}{6}$. 2. $\frac{7}{8} - \frac{3}{8}$. 3. $\frac{8}{9} - \frac{5}{9}$. 4. $\frac{7}{12} - \frac{1}{12}$.

5. $1 - \frac{1}{2}$. 6. $1 - \frac{1}{3}$. 7. $1 - \frac{3}{4}$. 8. $1 - \frac{2}{7}$.

9. $2 - \frac{1}{4}$. 10. $2 - \frac{5}{8}$. 11. $3 - \frac{4}{7}$. 12. $4 - \frac{3}{10}$.

13. $\frac{3}{4} - \frac{1}{2}$. 14. $\frac{5}{6} - \frac{1}{3}$. 15. $\frac{7}{8} - \frac{3}{4}$. 16. $\frac{7}{10} - \frac{1}{5}$.

17. $\frac{9}{14} - \frac{1}{7}$. 18. $\frac{11}{15} - \frac{2}{5}$. 19. $3 - 1\frac{4}{7}$. 20. $6 - 4\frac{7}{20}$.

21. $2\frac{3}{4} - \frac{1}{4}$. 22. $4\frac{7}{8} - 1\frac{1}{4}$. 23. $5\frac{7}{10} - 1\frac{2}{5}$. 24. $4\frac{9}{10} - 4\frac{2}{5}$.

25. $1\frac{1}{4} - \frac{3}{8}$. 26. $1\frac{1}{8} - \frac{5}{6}$. 27. $2\frac{3}{8} - \frac{5}{8}$. 28. $3\frac{1}{5} - \frac{3}{5}$.

29. $3\frac{1}{3} - 1\frac{5}{6}$. 30. $5\frac{1}{8} - 2\frac{1}{2}$. 31. $4\frac{3}{10} - 1\frac{4}{5}$. 32. $5\frac{5}{12} - 3\frac{3}{4}$.

EXERCISE 31

Simplify:

1. $\frac{1}{3} - \frac{1}{4}$. [2] $\frac{1}{4} - \frac{1}{6}$. 3. $\frac{2}{3} - \frac{1}{4}$. 4. $\frac{4}{5} - \frac{2}{3}$.

[5] $\frac{2}{3} - \frac{1}{2}$. [6] $\frac{7}{8} - \frac{3}{10}$. 7. $\frac{5}{8} - \frac{7}{12}$. [8] $\frac{7}{12} - \frac{9}{16}$.

9. $\frac{2}{15} - \frac{1}{30}$. [10] $\frac{5}{42} - \frac{1}{21}$. 11. $\frac{11}{12} - \frac{4}{15}$. [12] $\frac{7}{10} - \frac{12}{35}$.

13. $2\frac{4}{7} - \frac{6}{7}$. [14] $3\frac{2}{11} - \frac{8}{11}$. 15. $4\frac{3}{10} - \frac{7}{10}$. [16] $6\frac{3}{14} - 2\frac{11}{14}$.

17. $4\frac{1}{6} - 1\frac{2}{3}$. [18] $3\frac{1}{6} - 1\frac{4}{9}$. 19. $6\frac{7}{12} - 3\frac{5}{8}$. [20] $5\frac{3}{16} - 1\frac{7}{12}$.

*21. $5\frac{3}{10} - 4\frac{7}{15}$. *22. $8\frac{3}{8} - 5\frac{4}{5}$. 23. $5\frac{1}{14} - 3\frac{8}{21}$. [24] $\frac{97}{30} - \frac{17}{12}$.

*25. $\frac{99}{16} - \frac{107}{24}$. *26. $\frac{187}{45} - \frac{34}{25}$. *27. $3\frac{1}{42} - \frac{23}{21}$. *28. $\frac{335}{81} - \frac{25}{18}$.

Addition and Subtraction. In addition and subtraction sums, improper fractions should be expressed at once as mixed numbers.

Example 12. Simplify $\frac{23}{4} - \frac{17}{6} - \frac{23}{15} + \frac{87}{20}$.

The expression
$$= 5\frac{3}{4} - 2\frac{5}{6} - 1\frac{8}{15} + 4\frac{7}{20}$$
$$= (5 - 2 - 1 + 4) + (\frac{3}{4} - \frac{5}{6} - \frac{8}{15} + \frac{7}{20})$$
$$= (5 + 4 - 2 - 1) + (\frac{3}{4} + \frac{7}{20} - \frac{5}{6} - \frac{8}{15})$$
$$= (9 - 3) + \frac{45 + 21 - 50 - 32}{60}$$
$$= 6\frac{66 - 82}{60} = 5\frac{126 - 82}{60}$$
$$= 5\frac{44}{60} = 5\frac{11}{15}.$$

In the working opposite, the order of the terms has been changed so that the terms to be subtracted come together at the end; but when the process is understood, this rearrangement need not be made:

The expression
$$= 5\frac{3}{4} - 2\frac{5}{6} - 1\frac{8}{15} + 4\frac{7}{20}$$
$$= 6\frac{45 - 50 - 32 + 21}{60} = 6\frac{66 - 82}{60}$$
$$= 5\frac{126 - 82}{60} = 5\frac{44}{60} = 5\frac{11}{15}.$$

EXERCISE 32

Simplify :

1. $\frac{1}{2} - \frac{1}{6} + \frac{1}{3}$.   **2.** $\frac{3}{4} + \frac{1}{2} - \frac{5}{8}$.   **3.** $1 - \frac{1}{2} - \frac{1}{6}$.

*4. $4\frac{9}{20} + \frac{7}{12} - 1\frac{13}{15}$.   **[5]** $\frac{7}{10} - \frac{2}{5} + 2\frac{1}{2}$.   **6.** $3\frac{5}{6} - \frac{1}{9} - 1\frac{1}{12}$.

[7] $1\frac{1}{3} - \frac{5}{6} - \frac{1}{2}$.   **[8]** $3\frac{1}{4} - \frac{7}{12} - \frac{1}{3}$.   **9.** $4\frac{7}{10} - \frac{7}{15} - 2\frac{5}{6}$.

[10] $4\frac{5}{6} - 1\frac{4}{5} - \frac{2}{3}$.   **11.** $4 - \frac{3}{10} - 1\frac{8}{15}$.   **[12]** $4\frac{3}{4} - 1\frac{3}{5} - \frac{9}{10}$.

13. $\frac{7}{4} + \frac{19}{7} - \frac{17}{14}$.   **[14]** $\frac{16}{7} + \frac{13}{8} - \frac{39}{28}$.   ***15.** $3\frac{7}{8} - 1\frac{3}{10} - 1\frac{13}{24}$.

16. $5\frac{11}{12} - 1\frac{1}{8} - 1\frac{5}{12}$.   ***17.** $2\frac{5}{12} - 1\frac{19}{60} + 2\frac{11}{40}$.   ***18.** $\frac{21}{5} - \frac{12}{7} - \frac{25}{14}$.

19. $2\frac{1}{7} + 4\frac{5}{8} - 3\frac{9}{14} + 1\frac{1}{4}$.   **[20]** $\frac{23}{5} - \frac{17}{15} - \frac{25}{9} - \frac{2}{45}$.

*21. $6\frac{7}{12} - 1\frac{7}{22} - 1\frac{1}{5} - \frac{2}{11}$.   ***22.** $8\frac{1}{3} - 1\frac{1}{9} - 2\frac{2}{17} - \frac{5}{51}$.

Problems involving Fractions

Example 13. What fraction of a cake remains when $\frac{5}{9}$ of the cake has been eaten?

Suppose the cake is divided into 9 equal slices, then 5 of the slices have been eaten and therefore $(9 - 5)$ slices, $=4$ slices, remain.

But each slice is $\frac{1}{9}$ of the cake, $\therefore$ $\frac{4}{9}$ of the cake remains.

Or we may say : when $\frac{5}{9}$ of the cake has been eaten,

$(1 - \frac{5}{9})$ of the cake remains, that is $\frac{4}{9}$ of the cake remains.

Example 14. I read $\frac{2}{9}$ of a book on Friday, $\frac{1}{3}$ of it on Saturday, and the rest, 160 pages, on Sunday. How many pages are there in the book?

On Friday and Saturday I read $(\frac{2}{9} + \frac{1}{3})$ of the book, $=\frac{5}{9}$ of the book;
$\therefore$ on Sunday I read $(1 - \frac{5}{9})$ of the book, $=\frac{4}{9}$ of the book.

4 ninths of the book is 160 pages,

$\therefore$ 1 ninth of the book is $(160 \div 4)$ pages, $=40$ pages,

$\therefore$ the whole book is (40×9) pages, $=360$ pages.

EXERCISE 33

1. I buy a cake and eat $\frac{7}{12}$ of it; what fraction of the cake remains?

2. The weights of 3 parcels are $2\frac{3}{4}$ lb., $1\frac{5}{16}$ lb., $\frac{7}{8}$ lb. respectively; find their total weight.

3. A can contains 2 gall. of water. How much must I pour out to leave $\frac{5}{8}$ of a gallon?

[4] From a stick $10\frac{1}{4}$ in. long, a piece $6\frac{5}{8}$ in. long is cut off; what length remains?

5. I buy 18 oranges, but $\frac{2}{9}$ of them are bad; how many are fit to eat?

[6] A piece of flannel $8\frac{3}{10}$ in. long shrinks after washing to a length of $7\frac{5}{8}$ in.; how much shorter is it?

7. Add $\frac{2}{3}$ to the difference of $3\frac{1}{2}$ and $1\frac{1}{8}$.

[8] Subtract $1\frac{3}{4}$ from the sum of $2\frac{1}{8}$ and $3\frac{5}{8}$.

9. I use 20 tons of fuel (coal and coke) in a year; $\frac{3}{10}$ of this is coke; how many tons of coal do I use?

10. When I have travelled 6 miles, I have done $\frac{2}{7}$ of my journey. What is the length of the journey?

[11] After using $\frac{3}{8}$ of the coal I bought, 15 tons remain; how many tons did I buy?

12. The perimeter of a rectangular tile is 15 in.; it is $4\frac{3}{4}$ in. long; find its width.

13. $\frac{2}{5}$ of a school are boys, what fraction of the school consists of girls? If there are 165 girls, what is the number of boys?

[14] After spending $\frac{4}{9}$ of his money, a boy has 15s. left; how much had he at first?

[15] I increase my stride from $\frac{3}{4}$ of a yard to $\frac{5}{8}$ of a yard. What is the increase (i) as a fraction of a yard, (ii) in inches?

*16. A, B and C buy a business; A pays $\frac{9}{20}$ of the cost price, B pays $\frac{7}{20}$ of it; what fraction of it does C pay? If C pays £700, what did the business cost?

*17. A cargo of 600 tons of coal is shared between A, B, C, D. A receives $\frac{1}{3}$ of it; B and C each take $\frac{4}{15}$ of it. How many tons does D get?

*18. A new road is paid for by 4 towns, A, B, C, D; A pays $\frac{1}{3}$ of the cost, B and C each pay $\frac{1}{4}$ of the cost. What fraction of the cost does D pay? What did the road cost if D paid £8000?

*19. A tank is one-third full. After drawing off 7 gall. it is just one-quarter full. How much will the tank hold?

*20. One tap can fill a bath in 6 min. What fraction of the bath can it fill in 1 min.? Another tap can fill the bath in 3 min. What fraction of the bath is filled in 1 min. when both taps are running? How long will it take to fill the bath if both taps are running?

*21. One tap can fill a bath in 10 min., and another tap in 15 min. How long does it take to fill the bath if both taps are running?

*22. Two men can mow a field in 8 days; one of them could do so by himself in 12 days; how long would the other man take by himself?

CHAPTER V

FRACTIONS: MULTIPLICATION AND DIVISION

Multiplication by an Integer and by a Unit Fraction.

Example 1	Example 2
$\frac{2}{9} \times 4 = \frac{2}{9} + \frac{2}{9} + \frac{2}{9} + \frac{2}{9}$	$\frac{4}{5} \times \frac{1}{3} = \frac{1}{3}$ of $\frac{4}{5}$
$= \frac{8}{9}.$	$= \frac{4}{15}.$
Thus $\frac{2}{9} \times 4 = \frac{2 \times 4}{9}.$	Thus $\frac{4}{5} \times \frac{1}{3} = \frac{4}{5 \times 3}.$

EXERCISE 34 (Oral)

Write down the values of:

1. $\frac{3}{4}$ in. $\times 2$.
2. $\frac{3}{4}$ in. $\times 3$.
3. $\frac{3}{4}$ in $\times 4$.
4. $(\frac{2}{3} \times 4)$s.

5. $(\frac{2}{3} \times 6)$s.
6. $(\frac{3}{4} \times 6)$s.
7. $(\frac{3}{8} \times 2)$ lb.
8. $(\frac{3}{8} \times 5)$ lb.

9. $(\frac{5}{6} \times 3)$ lb.
10. $\frac{3}{10} \times 3$.
11. $\frac{3}{10} \times 5$.
12. $\frac{1}{8} \times 8$.

13. $1\frac{1}{4} \times 3$.
14. $1\frac{1}{3} \times 4$.
15. $1\frac{1}{3} \times 3$.
16. $3\frac{2}{3} \times 12$.

17. $\frac{3}{4} \times 12$.
18. $\frac{5}{8} \times 12$.
19. $\frac{1}{2}$ of 7d.
20. 5d. $\times \frac{1}{2}$.

21. $(9 \times \frac{1}{2})$d.
22. $\frac{1}{4}$ of 5s.
23. 3s. $\times \frac{1}{4}$.
24. $(4 \times \frac{1}{3})$s.

25. $\frac{1}{5}$ of 8 in.
26. $(7 \times \frac{1}{5})$ in.
27. $(5 \times \frac{1}{5})$ in.
28. $\frac{1}{9}$ of 15 oz.

29. $(12 \times \frac{1}{9})$ oz.
30. $(18 \times \frac{1}{9})$ oz.
31. $\frac{2}{3} \times \frac{1}{7}$.
32. $\frac{7}{4} \times \frac{1}{5}$.

33. $1\frac{4}{7} \times \frac{1}{4}$.
34. $6 \times \frac{1}{6}$.
35. $2\frac{1}{3} \times \frac{1}{10}$.
36. $2\frac{1}{4} \times \frac{1}{6}$.

Multiplication by any Fraction

The product of two (proper or improper) fractions is a fraction whose numerator is the product of the numerators and whose denominator is the product of the denominators.

If a *mixed number* occurs in a product, begin by expressing it as an improper fraction.

If "**of**" occurs between two fractions, replace it by $\times$.

Simplify products of fractions by dividing above and below by any common factors *before multiplying up*.

Example 3

$$1\tfrac{5}{7} \times 1\tfrac{1}{3} = \frac{\overset{4}{\cancel{12}}}{7} \times \frac{4}{\cancel{3}}$$

$$= \tfrac{16}{7}$$

$$= 2\tfrac{2}{7}.$$

Example 4

$$1\tfrac{5}{6} \times 4 = \frac{11}{\cancel{6}} \times \frac{\overset{2}{\cancel{4}}}{1}$$

$$= \frac{22}{3}$$

$$= 7\tfrac{1}{3}.$$

Example 5. Simplify $\tfrac{3}{11}$ of $1\tfrac{5}{6}$.

$$\tfrac{3}{11} \text{ of } 1\tfrac{5}{6} = \frac{\overset{1}{\cancel{3}}}{\cancel{11}} \times \frac{\overset{11}{\cancel{11}}}{\cancel{6}}$$

$$= \tfrac{1}{2}.$$

First divide above and below by 11, this leaves $\tfrac{3}{6}$. Next divide above and below by 3, the quotient of the numerator is 1, and *this must be written down.*

Example 6. Simplify $1\tfrac{1}{5} \times 2\tfrac{1}{3} \times \tfrac{5}{14}$.

$$1\tfrac{1}{5} \times 2\tfrac{1}{3} \times \tfrac{5}{14} = \frac{\overset{2}{\cancel{6}}}{\underset{1}{\cancel{5}}} \times \frac{7}{\cancel{3}} \times \frac{\overset{1}{\cancel{5}}}{\underset{2}{\cancel{14}}}$$

$$= \tfrac{1}{1} = 1$$

Cancelling leads to the quotients 1, 1 of the numerator and denominator, and *these must be written down.*

EXERCISE 35

Simplify :

1. $\tfrac{3}{7} \times \tfrac{2}{5}$.   **2.** $\tfrac{2}{5} \times \tfrac{3}{4}$.   **[3]** $\tfrac{4}{9} \times \tfrac{3}{5}$.   **[4]** $\tfrac{4}{7} \times \tfrac{5}{8}$.

5. $\tfrac{5}{8} \times 8$.   **[6]** $(\tfrac{3}{4})^2$.   **7.** $(\tfrac{2}{3})^3$.   **[8]** $\tfrac{7}{9}$ of $\tfrac{3}{14}$.

9. $\tfrac{10}{27}$ of $\tfrac{9}{35}$.   **[10]** $\tfrac{14}{21} \times \tfrac{15}{10}$.   **11.** $2\tfrac{1}{4} \times 5\tfrac{1}{3}$.   **[12]** $2\tfrac{4}{7} \times 4\tfrac{2}{3}$.

13. $\tfrac{3}{10}$ of $\tfrac{5}{12}$.   **[14]** $2\tfrac{5}{8}$ of $2\tfrac{2}{7}$.   **15.** $3\tfrac{8}{9} \times 3\tfrac{6}{7}$.   ***16.** $\tfrac{4}{63} \times \tfrac{21}{32}$.

17. $\tfrac{2}{3} \times \tfrac{6}{7} \times \tfrac{3}{4}$.   **18.** $\tfrac{1}{2}$ of $\tfrac{1}{3} \times \tfrac{1}{4}$.   **[19]** $\tfrac{4}{15} \times \tfrac{7}{12} \times \tfrac{25}{21}$.

20. $\tfrac{3}{7} \times \tfrac{5}{9} \times \tfrac{21}{5}$.   **[21]** $2\tfrac{1}{2} \times 1\tfrac{1}{4} \times \tfrac{8}{75}$.   **22.** $1\tfrac{1}{3} \times 1\tfrac{2}{7} \times 1\tfrac{1}{4}$.

*23. $3\tfrac{1}{16} \times \tfrac{14}{25}$ of $2\tfrac{1}{7}$.   **24.** $(2\tfrac{1}{2})^2 \times 1\tfrac{3}{5}$.   **[25]** $\tfrac{2}{5}$ of $(1\tfrac{1}{4})^2$.

*26. $4\tfrac{1}{8} \times \tfrac{14}{17} \times 1\tfrac{13}{21}$.   ***27.** $6\tfrac{1}{9} \times \tfrac{8}{13} \times 1\tfrac{17}{22}$.   ***28.** $\tfrac{1}{4}$ of $(2\tfrac{1}{2} \times \tfrac{4}{5})^2$.

Division by an Integer. $\tfrac{5}{4} \div 3$ is the same as $\tfrac{1}{3}$ of $\tfrac{5}{4}$, this equals $\tfrac{5}{4} \times \tfrac{1}{3}$. The number $\tfrac{1}{3}$ is called the **reciprocal** of 3 ; hence the rule : **To divide by an integer, multiply by its reciprocal.**

Division by a Fraction

$$\tfrac{4}{3} \div \tfrac{5}{7} = (\tfrac{4}{3} \times 3 \times 7) \div (\tfrac{5}{7} \times 3 \times 7)$$
$$= (4 \times 7) \div (5 \times 3)$$
$$= \tfrac{4 \times 7}{5 \times 3} = \tfrac{4}{3} \times \tfrac{7}{5}.$$

$\tfrac{7}{5}$ is called the **reciprocal** of $\tfrac{5}{7}$; hence the rule: *To divide by a fraction, multiply by its reciprocal;* in other words,

To divide one fraction by another (proper or improper) fraction, turn the second fraction upside down and multiply.

In division, as in multiplication, mixed numbers should be expressed as improper fractions.

Example 7	**Example 8**	**Example 9**
$3\tfrac{1}{3} \div 5 = \tfrac{10}{3} \div \tfrac{5}{1}$	$1\tfrac{5}{6} \div \tfrac{1}{4} = \dfrac{11}{\underset{3}{6}} \times \dfrac{\overset{2}{4}}{1}$	$3\tfrac{2}{5} \div 3\tfrac{3}{4} = \dfrac{\overset{4}{12}}{\underset{5}{35}} \times \dfrac{\overset{2}{14}}{\underset{7}{7}}$
$= \tfrac{10}{3} \times \tfrac{1}{5}$	$= \tfrac{22}{3}$	$= \tfrac{8}{5}$
$= \tfrac{2}{3}.$	$= 7\tfrac{1}{3}.$	$= 1\tfrac{3}{5}.$

EXERCISE 36 (Oral)

1. Divide $\tfrac{1}{2}$ by 3, 4, 5. **2.** Divide $\tfrac{1}{3}$ by 2, 3, 6.

3. Divide $\tfrac{3}{4}$ by 3, 4, 5. **4.** Divide $\tfrac{4}{9}$ by 2, 3, 12.

5. Divide $\tfrac{12}{25}$ by 4, 5, 8. **6.** Divide $\tfrac{9}{13}$ by 2, 3, 9.

7. Divide $1\tfrac{1}{2}$ by 3, 4, 6. **8.** Divide $2\tfrac{1}{4}$ by 3, 6, 9.

Write down the values of:

9. $3 \div \tfrac{1}{2}.$ **10.** $2 \div \tfrac{1}{3}.$ **11.** $5 \div \tfrac{1}{4}.$ **12.** $7 \div \tfrac{1}{5}.$

13. $1 \div \tfrac{1}{3}.$ **14.** $1 \div \tfrac{1}{10}.$ **15.** $1 \div \tfrac{2}{3}.$ **16.** $1 \div 1\tfrac{1}{2}.$

17. $\tfrac{1}{3} \div \tfrac{1}{2}.$ **18.** $\tfrac{1}{3} \div \tfrac{1}{6}.$ **19.** $\tfrac{1}{12} \div \tfrac{1}{9}.$ **20.** $\tfrac{1}{2} \div \tfrac{1}{2}.$

21. $\tfrac{2}{3} \div \tfrac{2}{5}.$ **22.** $\tfrac{3}{4} \div \tfrac{4}{5}.$ **23.** $\tfrac{5}{8} \div \tfrac{2}{3}.$ **24.** $\tfrac{2}{9} \div \tfrac{4}{3}.$

25. Write down the reciprocals of (i) 7; (ii) $\tfrac{4}{3}$; (iii) $\tfrac{2}{5}$; (iv) $\tfrac{1}{6}$; (v) $1\tfrac{1}{2}$; (vi) $3\tfrac{1}{3}$.

EXERCISE 37

Simplify:

1. $1\frac{1}{3} \div \frac{2}{5}$.　　**2.** $\frac{2}{3} \div 1\frac{1}{6}$.　　**[3]** $1\frac{1}{9} \div 2\frac{1}{12}$.　　**4.** $\frac{5}{16} \div 2\frac{1}{12}$.

5. $1 \div 2\frac{3}{4}$.　　**[6]** $1 \div (\frac{1}{3})^2$.　　**7.** $\frac{3}{8} \div \frac{3}{8}$.　　***8.** $3\frac{3}{14} \div 1\frac{4}{21}$.

*9. $1\frac{11}{15} \div 7\frac{4}{5}$.　　**10.** $1\frac{11}{45} \div 10\frac{1}{9}$.　　**[11]** $\frac{25}{15} \div 1\frac{2}{3}$.　　***12.** $\frac{28}{48} \div 4\frac{5}{18}$.

13. $\dfrac{2\frac{1}{3}}{1\frac{1}{4}}$.　　**[14]** $\dfrac{\frac{15}{7}}{1\frac{1}{7}}$.　　**15.** $\dfrac{\frac{14}{27}}{\frac{35}{36}}$.　　**[16]** $\dfrac{\frac{1}{12}}{\frac{1}{18}}$.　　**17.** $\dfrac{1}{\frac{5}{7}}$.　　**18.** $\dfrac{\frac{1}{5}}{7}$.

[19] $\dfrac{5}{3\frac{1}{3}}$.　　**[20]** $\dfrac{3\frac{1}{7}}{11}$.　　**21.** $\dfrac{1\frac{1}{5}}{\frac{2}{3}}$.　　**[22]** $\dfrac{4\frac{1}{3}}{3\frac{1}{4}}$.　　**23.** $\dfrac{\frac{4}{7}}{\frac{7}{4}}$.　　***24.** $\dfrac{2\frac{7}{10}}{7\frac{1}{5}}$.

25. $2\frac{2}{3} \times 3\frac{1}{3} \div 2\frac{4}{5}$.　　**[26]** $1\frac{4}{13} \times 7\frac{4}{5} \div 11\frac{1}{3}$.　　**27.** $2\frac{2}{7} \div (1\frac{4}{11} \times 2\frac{4}{9})$.

[28] $1\frac{7}{20} \times \frac{8}{63} \div \frac{6}{35}$.　　***29.** $\frac{33}{14} \times 12\frac{2}{8} \div 13\frac{1}{5}$.　　***30.** $\frac{7}{9} \times 4\frac{19}{20} \div 19\frac{1}{4}$.

Brackets. In simplifying expressions which contain " of " and the signs $+$, $-$, $\times$, $\div$, operations involving " of ", $\times$ and $\div$ must be performed before those involving $+$ and $-$, unless otherwise indicated by brackets.

Example 10	**Example 11**
$\frac{3}{4} \times \frac{2}{9} + \frac{1}{3} \div 2\frac{1}{2}$	$\frac{3}{4}$ of $(\frac{2}{9} + \frac{1}{3}) \div 2\frac{1}{2}$
$=(\frac{3}{4} \times \frac{2}{9}) + (\frac{1}{3} \times \frac{2}{5})$	$=\frac{3}{4} \times (\frac{2+3}{9}) \div \frac{5}{2}$
$=\frac{1}{6} + \frac{2}{15}$	$=\frac{3}{4} \times \frac{5}{9} \times \frac{2}{5}$
$=\frac{5+4}{30} = \frac{9}{30} = \frac{3}{10}$.	$=\frac{1}{6}$.

Note. The notation $\frac{2}{3} \div \frac{4}{5}$ of $\frac{6}{7}$ means $\frac{2}{3} \div (\frac{4}{5} \times \frac{6}{7})$, that is, in operations involving " of ", $\times$, $\div$, the " of " implies a bracket, but *this notation should be avoided.*

Expressions such as $24 \div 6 \times 2$ are ambiguous and *should never be used.* Brackets must be inserted to make the meaning clear: $24 \div (6 \times 2)$ means $24 \div 12$ and $(24 \div 6) \times 2$ means 4×2.

EXERCISE 38

Simplify:

1. $\frac{1}{2} + \frac{1}{3} \times \frac{1}{4}$.　　**2.** $(\frac{1}{2} + \frac{1}{3}) \times \frac{1}{4}$.　　**[3]** $(\frac{1}{2} + \frac{1}{4}) \times \frac{1}{3}$.　　**4.** $(\frac{2}{3} - \frac{1}{2}) \times \frac{2}{3}$.

5. $\frac{2}{3} - \frac{1}{2} \times \frac{2}{3}$.　　**[6]** $\frac{1}{3} + \frac{1}{6} \times \frac{1}{2}$.　　**7.** $1\frac{3}{4} - \frac{1}{2} \div \frac{1}{3}$.　　**[8]** $(\frac{3}{5} + \frac{1}{3}) \div \frac{2}{3}$.

[9] $\frac{3}{5} + \frac{2}{5} \div \frac{4}{5}$.　　**10.** $\frac{1}{3} \times \frac{1}{2} + \frac{1}{4} \times \frac{1}{5}$.　　**11.** $\frac{1}{3} \times (\frac{1}{2} + \frac{1}{4}) \times \frac{1}{5}$.

12. $\frac{1}{3} \times (\frac{1}{2} + \frac{1}{4} \times \frac{1}{5})$.　　**[13]** $(\frac{1}{3} \times \frac{1}{2} + \frac{1}{4}) \times \frac{1}{5}$.　　**14.** $\frac{2}{3} \times \frac{1}{4} - \frac{1}{12} \div \frac{1}{2}$.

15. $\frac{2}{3} \times (\frac{1}{4} - \frac{1}{12} \div \frac{1}{2})$.　　**[16]** $\frac{2}{3} \times (\frac{1}{4} - \frac{1}{12}) \div \frac{1}{2}$.　　**[17]** $(\frac{2}{3} \times \frac{1}{4} - \frac{1}{12}) \div \frac{1}{2}$.

18. $\frac{1}{2}$ of $4\frac{2}{3} - \frac{1}{3}$ of $6\frac{1}{5}$.　　**[19]** $\frac{1}{2} - \frac{1}{3} \div (\frac{1}{4} + \frac{5}{12})$.　　**20.** $(\frac{1}{2} + \frac{1}{3}) \times \frac{1}{5} - \frac{1}{6}$.

[21] $3\frac{3}{4} \div (2\frac{1}{2} + 3\frac{1}{4})$.　　　　**22.** $1\frac{5}{6} + \frac{1}{3}$ of $(3\frac{1}{2} - 2\frac{1}{4})$.

[23] $5\frac{1}{3} \times 4\frac{1}{2} - 3\frac{1}{4} \times 3\frac{5}{8}$.

[24] $(3\frac{1}{4} - 1\frac{1}{2}) \div (2\frac{5}{6} - \frac{1}{2})$.

*25. $1\frac{1}{4} \times 7 \div (12\frac{7}{12} - 11\frac{1}{3})$.

*26. $(\frac{2}{5} + \frac{1}{7}) \div (\frac{1}{5} - \frac{1}{8})$.

*27. $(1\frac{2}{3} - 1\frac{1}{2}) \div (3\frac{1}{2} - 2\frac{2}{3})$.

*28. $8\frac{1}{2} - 4\frac{2}{3} - 1\frac{1}{6} \times \frac{2}{5} + \frac{3}{5}$.

*29. $(\frac{1}{4} - \frac{1}{8}) \div (\frac{1}{2} + \frac{1}{4} \div \frac{1}{3})$.

*30. $2\frac{1}{3} - \frac{1}{3} \times 3\frac{1}{2} + 1\frac{7}{8} \div 1\frac{1}{4} - 3 \div (\frac{3}{4} \times 1\frac{1}{2})$.

Expression of one Quantity as a Fraction of another

Example 12. Express 8s. 9d. as a fraction of $1\frac{1}{2}$ guineas.

8s. 9d. $= 8\frac{3}{4}$s.; $1\frac{1}{2}$ guineas $= \frac{3}{2} \times 21$s.

∴ required fraction

$$= 8\frac{3}{4} \div \frac{3 \times 21}{2}$$

$$= \frac{35}{4} \times \frac{2}{3 \times 21} = \frac{5}{18}.$$

Alternatively, express each sum in threepences:

8s. 9d. $= (8 \times 4 + 3)$ threepences

$= 35$ threepences,

$1\frac{1}{2}$ guineas $= 31$s. 6d.

$= 126$ threepences;

∴ required fraction $= \frac{35}{126} = \frac{5}{18}$.

Example 13. Express 2 cwt. 40 lb. as a fraction of 2 tons 13 cwt. 4 lb. Reduce each quantity to lb.

cwt.	lb.	tons	cwt.	lb.
2	40	2	13	4
112	224	20	40	5936
224 lb.	264	40 cwt.	53	5940
			112	
			53	
			53	
			106	
			5936 lb.	

∴ required fraction $= \frac{264}{5940}$

$$= \frac{24}{540} = \frac{2}{45}$$

EXERCISE 39

Express the first number or quantity as a fraction of the second:

1. $3\frac{3}{4}$; $12\frac{1}{2}$.   2. $7\frac{1}{3}$; $8\frac{1}{4}$.   [3] $2\frac{2}{15}$; $4\frac{4}{5}$.   [4] $3\frac{17}{20}$; $12\frac{2}{3}$.

*5. $8\frac{1}{6}$; $19\frac{1}{4}$.   *6. $10\frac{5}{6}$; $19\frac{4}{8}$.   7. 6s. 8d.; £1.   8. 3s. 9d.; £1.

[9] 16s. 8d.; £5.   10. 3s. 6d.; 2s. 4d.

[11] 8s. 9d.; 6s. 3d.   12. £1 7s.; £2 5s.

13. 8s. 2d.; £1 11s. 6d.   [14] £1 2s. 6d.; £5 5s.

15. £1 8s. 4d.; 11s. 8d.   [16] 12s. 3d.; £1 2s. 9d.

17. 2 ft. 8 in.; 3 yd. 1 ft.   [18] 3 yd. 2 in.; 14 yd. 2 ft.

19. 6 lb. 4 oz.; 2 qr. 14 lb.   *20. 3 qr. 15 lb.; 2 cwt. 7 lb.

21. 4 fur. 20 yd.; 1 mi. 240 yd.

*22. 1 ch. 1 yd. 1 ft.; 14 ch. 9 yd. 1 ft.

*23. £1 6s. 3d.; £5 16s. 8d. ***24.** £2 1s. 3d.; £3 13s. 4d.

Problems involving Fractions. The unitary method can be applied to problems involving fractions, just as with whole numbers.

Example 14. (i) If 5 yd. of silk cost 15s., find the cost of 4 yd.

(ii) If $\frac{3}{4}$ yd. of silk costs 3s. 9d., find the cost of $\frac{2}{3}$ yd.

(i)	(ii)
5 yd. cost 15s.	$\frac{3}{4}$ yd. costs $3\frac{3}{4}$s.
$\therefore$ 1 yd. costs $(15 \div 5)$s., $= 3$s.	$\therefore$ 1 yd. costs $(3\frac{3}{4} \div \frac{3}{4})$s., $= (\frac{15}{4} \times \frac{4}{3})$s.
$\therefore$ 4 yd. cost (3×4)s., $= 12$s.	$\therefore$ $\frac{2}{3}$ yd. costs $(\frac{15}{4} \times \frac{4}{3} \times \frac{2}{3})$s., that is $\frac{10}{3}$s., or 3s. 4d.

In the working of (ii), 1 yd. costs *more* than $\frac{3}{4}$ yd.; division by the proper fraction $\frac{3}{4}$ causes an increase. Also $\frac{2}{3}$ yd. costs *less* than 1 yd.; multiplication by the proper fraction $\frac{2}{3}$ causes a decrease.

Example 15. A boy has 4s. 8d.; what fraction of this is left after he has spent 3s. 4d.?

He starts with 56d. and then spends 40d.; this leaves 16d.

$\therefore$ $\frac{16}{56}$ of his money is left; $\therefore$ $\frac{2}{7}$ of his money is left.

Example 16. After a boy has spent $\frac{5}{9}$ of his money, he has 6s. left; how much had he at first?

After spending $\frac{5}{9}$ of his money, $\frac{4}{9}$ of his money is left.

$\therefore$ $\frac{4}{9}$ of his money is 6s.

$\therefore$ $\frac{1}{9}$ of his money is $\frac{6}{4}$s.

$\therefore$ $\frac{9}{9}$ of his money is $(\frac{6}{4} \times \frac{9}{1})$s., $= \frac{27}{2}$s.;

$\therefore$ he had 13s. 6d. at first.

Example 17. How many $\frac{3}{4}$-lb. packets can be made up from 40 lb. of tea, and how much remains?

The number of packets is the number of times $\frac{3}{4}$ lb. is contained in 40 lb.

$\therefore$ number of packets $= 40 \div \frac{3}{4} = 40 \times \frac{4}{3} = \frac{160}{3} = 53\frac{1}{3}$;

$\therefore$ 53 complete packets can be made up, and this leaves enough tea for $\frac{1}{3}$ of a packet, that is $\frac{1}{3}$ of $\frac{3}{4}$ lb., $= \frac{1}{4}$ lb.

$\therefore$ 53 packets can be made up, and $\frac{1}{4}$ lb. of tea remains.

4

EXERCISE 40

1. A boy's stride is 30 in.; what fraction is this of 1 yd.?

2. What fraction is $2\frac{1}{4}$d. of a shilling?

[3] Express 12s. 6d. as a fraction of £1 10s.

4. 1 pt. of water weighs $1\frac{1}{4}$ lb.; find the weight of (i) 1 gall., (ii) $\frac{3}{4}$ gall. of water.

[5] What must be added to $\frac{2}{3}$ to make $\frac{3}{4}$?

6. Find the area of a mat $4\frac{1}{2}$ ft. long, $2\frac{2}{3}$ ft. wide.

[7] There are 480 pupils in a school. If there are 270 boys, find what fraction of the school consists of girls.

8. If $\frac{1}{2}$ lb. of tea costs 10d., find the cost of 2 lb. of tea.

[9] Find the cost of $\frac{3}{4}$ lb. of tobacco at 15s. a lb.

*10. The product of two numbers is 10; one of them is $3\frac{3}{4}$, what is the other?

[11] A man sleeps $7\frac{1}{2}$ hr. every day; for what fraction of each day is he awake?

12. How many $\frac{3}{4}$-lb. packets can be made up from 15 lb. of tea?

*13. By what must $5\frac{1}{4}$ be multiplied to make $3\frac{1}{2}$?

[14] In a black and white tile, the area of the white portion is $5\frac{1}{2}$ sq. in., and of the black portion is $2\frac{3}{4}$ sq. in.; what fraction of the surface of the tile is white?

15. Find the volume of a rectangular block $3\frac{3}{4}$ in. long, $3\frac{1}{5}$ in. wide, $1\frac{1}{2}$ in. high.

16. How many jars, each of which holds $7\frac{1}{2}$ lb. of jam, can be filled from a vessel containing 210 lb. of jam?

17. The area of the floor of a room, $11\frac{1}{4}$ ft. wide, is 180 sq. ft.; find the length of the room.

*18. Which of the expressions, $\dfrac{3}{4\frac{1}{2}}$ and $\dfrac{2}{3\frac{1}{4}}$, is the greater, and by how much?

[19] A man can weed $\frac{2}{3}$ of a field in 12 days; how long will he take for the whole of it?

20. $\frac{3}{4}$ of a tank can be filled in $11\frac{1}{4}$ min.; how long will it take to fill the whole tank?

21. A man buys a table for £9 and sells it for 10 guineas. What fraction of the cost price is his profit?

22. After a boy has spent $\frac{2}{5}$ of his money, he has 6s. left; how much had he at first?

[23] If $\frac{4}{9}$ of my holiday costs £7, what will the rest of it cost at the same rate?

*24. The Princess Royal L.M.S. locomotive weighs 760 tons and can haul a train $3\frac{1}{8}$ times its own weight. Find the combined weight of the locomotive and train.

*25. A tank is $\frac{5}{8}$ full, and 75 gall. are required to fill it up. How much altogether can the tank hold?

26. How many jugs each holding $\frac{2}{5}$ gall. can be filled from a cask holding 16 gall., and how much then remains?

[27] How many pieces of tape $2\frac{3}{4}$ in. long can be cut from a length of 1 yd., and how much remains?

*28. How many articles costing $6\frac{3}{4}$d. each can be bought for £1, and how much remains?

[29] A man walks $4\frac{1}{2}$ mi. an hour; how many yards does he walk at this rate in 1 min.?

30. 3 boys share a sum of money. The oldest gets $\frac{2}{5}$ of it; and the youngest $\frac{1}{10}$ of it. If the oldest gets 21s., what do the others get?

*31. A, B, C, D give a party. A pays $\frac{1}{5}$ of the bill, and the rest is shared equally between B, C, D. What fraction of the bill does B pay?

*32. A man aged 27 marries a woman aged 24; he dies at the age of 81 and she dies at the age of 91. For what fraction of his life is the man married? For what fraction of her life is the woman a widow?

*33. A, B, and C buy a business; A pays $\frac{2}{5}$ of the cost, B pays $\frac{7}{15}$ of the cost, and C pays the rest, £966. What did the business cost?

*34. A man sells his car so that he loses $\frac{35}{100}$ of what he paid for it. Express the sale price as a fraction of the cost price.

*35. A man has to bicycle $\frac{3}{4}$ mi. to a station. If he bicycles at 12 mi. per hour, what fraction of the distance does he go in 3 minutes?

CHAPTER VI

DECIMALS: NUMERATION, ADDITION AND SUBTRACTION

Decimal and Common Fractions.   A *decimal* is merely a fraction whose denominator is a power of 10.

EXERCISE 41 (Oral)

Read off and write down as decimals:

	Thousands	Hundreds	Tens	Units	Tenths	Hundredths	Thousandths
1.				3	2		
2.					8		
3.				1	2	4	
4.				3	0	7	
5.						8	
6.						9	5
7.			4	0	2	6	
8.			9	1	0	0	3
9.							4
10.		1	0	3	6	0	7
11.				2	...	1	
12.				3	...	...	4
13.	1	...	5	...	...	6	
14.	7	2	...	...	3	...	8
15.	5	...	...	...		4	6

Make a table as above and show in it the following:—

16. 7·36.   17. 4·08.   18. 0·5.   19. 0·03.   20. 0·009.

21. 18·4.   22. 20·3.   23. 30·04.   24. 5·017.   25. 6·008.

26. 204·03.   27. 300·72.   28. 19·083.   29. 1000·8.   30. 1040·05.

31. 7 tenths.   32. 3 hundredths.   33. 8 thousandths.

34. $7 + \frac{3}{10} + \frac{9}{1000}$.   35. $204 + \frac{5}{100}$.   36. $80 + \frac{4}{10} + \frac{7}{1000}$.

Write down as decimals :

37. 5 tenths.   **38.** 9 hundredths.   **39.** 8 thousandths.

40. $\frac{7}{10}$; $\frac{2}{10}$; $\frac{5}{1000}$.

41. $\frac{3}{10}$; $\frac{8}{100}$; $\frac{6}{10,000}$.

42. $\frac{3}{10}+\frac{4}{100}$; $\frac{7}{10}+\frac{5}{1000}$.

43. $4+\frac{8}{10}$; $6+\frac{2}{100}$.

44. $5+\frac{1}{100}$; $9+\frac{4}{1000}$.

45. $30+\frac{1}{10}$; $700+\frac{9}{100}$.

46. $2+\frac{5}{10}+\frac{4}{100}+\frac{1}{1000}$.

47. $7+\frac{9}{10}+\frac{6}{1000}$.

48. $30+\frac{4}{100}+\frac{5}{10,000}$.

49. $600+3+\frac{4}{100}+\frac{8}{1000}$.

Write in full as in Nos. 40–49 :

50. 0·6; 0·08; 0·004.   **51.** 0·03; 0·1; 0·005.

52. 4·3; 5·07; 3·008.   **53.** 30·5; 40·06; 80·002.

54. 0·0804; 0·1007.   **55.** 200·04; 1·0101.

Metric System. The unit of length in the metric system is 1 metre (1 m.), which is a little more than a yard (about 39·4 inches). Fractions of the unit are denoted by the following prefixes :—

$\frac{1}{10}$ **deci** 0·1 ; $\frac{1}{100}$ **centi** 0·01 ; $\frac{1}{1000}$ **milli** 0·001.

$\frac{1}{10}$ metre = 1 **deci**metre (dm.).	1 m. = 10 dm.
$\frac{1}{100}$ metre = 1 **centi**metre (cm.).	1 dm. = 10 cm.
$\frac{1}{1000}$ metre = 1 **milli**metre (mm.).	1 cm. = 10 mm.

EXERCISE 42 (Oral)

Write down the following lengths in metres :—

	Metres, m.	Deci-metres, dm.	Centi-metres, cm.	Milli-metres, mm.
1.	3	5		
2.		7		
3.		4	6	
4.			8	
5.	2	...	5	
6.	3	...	6	8
7.	4	...	...	5
8.		7	...	2
9.	5	...	...	7
10.	8	2	...	4
11.	7	4	3	6
12.	6	1	...	3

13. Express in mm. the lengths in Nos. 9–12.

14. Express in cm. the lengths in Nos. 5–8.

15. Express in dm. the lengths in Nos. 3–7.

Make a table as on p. 53, and show in it the following lengths, and then express each length in metres :—

16. 2 m. 8 dm.; 3 m. 5 cm.   **17.** 4 dm. 5 cm.; 7 dm. 8 mm.
18. 3 m. 5 dm. 4 cm.   **19.** 6 dm. 7 cm. 5 mm.
20. 4 m. 8 cm. 6 mm.   **21.** 5 m. 2 dm. 9 mm.

Express in metres :

22. 5 dm.; 2 m. 8 dm.   **23.** 4 cm.; 3 m. 7 cm.
24. 6 mm.; 1 m. 2 mm.   **25.** 5 m. 4 dm. 6 cm.
26. 3 dm. 7 cm. 5 mm.   **27.** 8 m. 6 dm. 3 mm.
28. 1 m. 4 cm. 6 mm.   **29.** 10 m. 2 cm. 5 mm.
30. Express in mm. : 7 cm. 2 mm.; 8 dm. 3 mm.; 2 m. 4 cm.
31. Express in cm. : 4 cm. 2 mm.; 6 dm. 8 cm.; 3 dm. 4 mm.
32. Express in dm. : 3 dm. 4 cm.; 4 m. 6 cm.; 5 dm. 8 mm.

Express as compound quantities (m., dm., cm., mm.) :

33. 2·85 m.; 3·04 m.   **34.** 1·605 m.; 4·082 m.
35. 0·72 m.; 0·063 m.   **36.** 1·004 m.; 0·205 m.
37. 735 mm.; 420 mm.   **38.** 608 mm.; 1240 mm.
39. 6·3 cm.; 20·5 cm.   **40.** 106·4 cm.; 300·5 cm.
41. 7·8 dm.; 6·04 dm.   **42.** 25·3 dm.; 40·05 dm.

Just as small lengths are measured in the metric system in tenths of a metre, hundredths a metre, thousandths of a metre, so large lengths are measured in tens of metres, hundreds of metres and thousands of metres.

The following prefixes are used :—

10	**deka**	**D.**
100	**hecto**	**H.**
1000	**kilo**	**K or k.**

10 metres = 1 **dekametre** (Dm.).	10 m. = 1 Dm.
100 metres = 1 **hectometre** (Hm.).	10 Dm. = 1 Hm.
1000 metres = 1 **kilometre** (Km. or km.).	10 Hm. = 1 Km.

Notice *the use of the capital letter in* 1 Dm. (10 metres) *to distinguish it from* 1 dm. ($\frac{1}{10}$ metre).

The units most commonly used are kilometres, metres, centimetres, millimetres. Lengths are usually expressed in terms of one unit only, very rarely in terms of more than two units.

Since a metre is about 39 inches, it is easy to show that a kilometre is about ⅝ of a mile, that is "*about 10 minutes' walk*."

Example 1. Express 3 km. 2 Hm. 7 m. (i) in km., (ii) in m., (iii) as a compound quantity in km. and m.

The given length can be written in the form:

km.	Hm.	Dm.	m.
3	2	0	7

This shows that it can be expressed either as 3·207 km. or as 3207 m. or as 3 km. 207 m.

EXERCISE 43 (Oral)

Write down the following lengths (i) in km., (ii) in m. :—

	km.	Hm.	Dm.	m.	dm.	cm.	mm.
1.	2	4	7	5			
2.	3	1	6				
3.	1	5	...	2			
4.	6	...	...	8			
5.		7	3	4			
6.		8	...	2	4		
7.	1	...	4	...	6		
8.		3	...	4	5		
9.		6	2	...	7	8	
10.			5	7	3	4	
11.		2	...	3	...	5	
12.			5	...	6	...	8
13.	3	...	...	2	...	4	
14.					1	...	6
15.			4	...	...	...	5

16. Express as compound quantities in km. and m. the lengths in Nos. 1–4.

17. Express as compound quantities in m. and cm. the lengths in Nos. 9–11.

Make a table as above, and show in it the following lengths, and then express each length in km. :—

18. 2 km. 4 Hm. 3 Dm.
19. 3 km. 5 Dm. 7 m.
20. 1 km. 7 m. 2 dm.
21. 4 km. 5 m. 4 cm.
22. 6 Hm. 2 m. 5 dm.
23. 4 Dm. 3 m. 7 cm.
24. 8 m. 2 dm. 3 cm.
25. 2 m. 4 cm. 5 mm.

Express in metres:

26. 2 Dm. 5 m.; 6 Hm. 3 Dm.   **27.** 1 km. 5 Hm.; 2 km. 4 Dm.

28. 2 km. 4 Hm.; 7 Dm. 5 m.   **29.** 3 km. 7 m. 5 dm.

Express in kilometres:

30. 4 km. 3 Hm.; 2 km. 5 Dm.   **31.** 1 km. 8 m.; 7 Hm. 4 Dm.

32. 5 Hm. 2 m.; 6 Dm. 4 m.   **33.** 5 m. 7 dm.; 2 m. 5 cm.

34. 324 m.; 510 m.   **35.** 600 m.; 708 m.   **36.** 1428 m.; 3800 m.

37. 83 m.; 40 m.·   **38.** 6 m.; 9·3 m.   **39.** 64·5 m.; 0·75 m.

Express as compound quantities in km. and m.:

40. 3·84 km.; 6·2 km.   **41.** 8·07 km.; 1·003 km.

Multiplication and Division by Powers of 10

Multiplication.   8 tenths × 10 = 8 units, that is 0·8 × 10 = 8;

7 hundredths × 10 = 7 tenths, that is 0·07 × 10 = 0·7; and so on.

Thus to **multiply** a decimal by 10, we **move each figure** 1 place to the **left,** *treating the decimal point as fixed.*

Suppose the numbers are set out in columns:

	Hundreds	Tens	Units	Tenths	Hundredths	Thousandths	
0·87 =				8	7		
0·87 × 10 =			8	7			= 8·7
35·46 =		3	5	4	6		
35·46 × 10 =	3	5	4	6			= 354·6
1·604 =			1	6	0	4	
1·604 × 10 =		1	6	0	4		= 16·04
20·082 =		2	0	0	8	2	
20·082 × 10 =	2	0	0	8	2		= 200·82

Multiplying by 100 is the same as multiplying by 10 × 10:

$$18·624 × 100 = 186·24 × 10 = 1862·4;$$
$$18·6 \quad × 100 = 186 × 10 = 1860.$$

Thus to multiply a decimal by 100, we move each figure 2 places to the left, treating the decimal point as fixed.

Similarly for multiplication by 1000 :

$$7 \cdot 13 \times 1000 = 71 \cdot 3 \times 100 = 713 \times 10 = 7130.$$

Thus to multiply a decimal by 1000, we move each figure 3 places to the left, treating the decimal point as fixed.

Hence we have the following rule :—

To MULTIPLY a decimal by 10, 100, 1000, . . ., move each figure 1, 2, 3, . . . places to the LEFT, treating the decimal point as fixed.

Any empty place between the figures and the decimal point must be marked by a zero.

Division.   7 units $\div$ 10 = 7 **tenths,** that is $7 \div 10 = 0 \cdot 7$;
    8 **tenths** $\div$ 10 = 8 **hundredths,** that is $0 \cdot 8 \div 10 = 0 \cdot 08$;   and so on.

Suppose the numbers are set out in columns :

	Hundreds	Tens	UNITS	Tenths	Hundredths	Thousandths	
$7 \cdot 84 =$			7	8	4		
$7 \cdot 84 \div 10 =$				7	8	4	$= 0 \cdot 784$
$0 \cdot 49 =$				4	9		
$0 \cdot 49 \div 10 =$					4	9	$= 0 \cdot 049$
$20 \cdot 05 =$		2	0	0	5		
$20 \cdot 05 \div 10 =$			2	0	0	5	$= 2 \cdot 005$
$304 \cdot 8 =$	3	0	4	8			
$304 \cdot 8 \div 10 =$		3	0	4	8		$= 30 \cdot 48$

Thus to **divide** a decimal by 10, we **move each figure** 1 place to the **right,** treating the decimal point as fixed.

Dividing by 100 is the same as dividing by 10×10;

$$354 \cdot 7 \div 100 = 35 \cdot 47 \div 10 = 3 \cdot 547.$$

Thus to divide a decimal by 100, we move each figure 2 places to the right, treating the decimal point as fixed.

Similarly for division by 1000,

$$8 \cdot 639 \div 1000 = 0 \cdot 8639 \div 100 = 0 \cdot 08639 \div 10 = 0 \cdot 008639.$$

Hence we have the following rule:—

To DIVIDE a decimal by 10, 100, 1000, . . ., move each figure 1, 2, 3, . . . places to the RIGHT, treating the decimal point as fixed.

Any empty place between the figures and the decimal point must be marked by a zero.

Example 2.   Express as decimals: (i) $\frac{6217}{100}$; (ii) $\frac{5}{100}$; (iii) $\frac{840}{1000}$.

(i) $6217 \div 100$	(ii) $5 \div 100$	(iii) $840 \div 1000$
$= 62 \cdot 17$	$= 0 \cdot 05$	$= 0 \cdot 840 = 0 \cdot 84.$

Example 3.   Express as fractions having powers of 10 as denominators: (i) $0 \cdot 7$; (ii) $0 \cdot 83$; (iii) $0 \cdot 042$.

$$\text{(i) } 0 \cdot 7 = \tfrac{7}{10}; \qquad \text{(ii) } 0 \cdot 83 = \tfrac{8}{10} + \tfrac{3}{100} = \tfrac{83}{100};$$
$$\text{(iii) } 0 \cdot 042 = \tfrac{4}{100} + \tfrac{2}{1000} = \tfrac{42}{1000}.$$

Example 3 shows how any decimal can be written down at sight as a common fraction: the numerator is the number formed by the digits of the decimal disregarding *initial* zeros, the denominator is 1000 . . . where the number of zeros is the same as the number of figures after the decimal point. *Fractions thus obtained will often not be in their lowest terms.*

Thus $0 \cdot 0705 = \frac{705}{10000}$; this can be reduced to $\frac{141}{2000}$.

And $10 \cdot 206 = \frac{10206}{1000}$ or $10\frac{206}{1000}$, which reduces to $10\frac{103}{500}$.

Example 4.   Express $0 \cdot 0625$ as a common fraction in its lowest terms.

$$0 \cdot 0625 = \tfrac{625}{10000} = \tfrac{125}{2000} = \tfrac{25}{400} = \tfrac{1}{16}.$$

Example 5.   Express $4 \cdot 82$ kilometres in metres.

$$4 \cdot 82 \text{ km.} = (4 \cdot 82 \times 1000) \text{ m.} = 4820 \text{ m.}$$

Example 6.   Express 230 metres in kilometres.

$$230 \text{ m.} = (230 \div 1000) \text{ km.} = 0 \cdot 230 \text{ km.} = 0 \cdot 23 \text{ km.}$$

Note.   Examples 5, 6 may be worked by using columns:

	km.	Hm.	Dm.	m.	
Example 5	4	8	2	..	$= 4820$ m.
Example 6	..	2	3	0	$= 0 \cdot 23$ km.

EXERCISE 44 (mainly Oral)

Multiply each of the following numbers by 10, by 100, by 1000 :—

1. 4·1; 4·16.   **2.** 0·3; 0·387.   **3.** 50·2; 0·0502.

Divide each of the following numbers by 10, by 100, by 1000 :—

4. 60; 64·1.   **5.** 7·2; 7·03.   **6.** 0·91; 0·0805.

Write down the values of the following :—

7. 6·075 × 100.   **8.** 8·45 ÷ 10.   **9.** 7·6 × 100.
10. 0·97 × 10.   **11.** 5·21 × 1000.   **12.** 520 ÷ 100.
13. 0·03 × 10.   **14.** 70 ÷ 1000.   **15.** 60·01 × 10.
16. 0·603 ÷ 1000.   **17.** 30·07 × 100.   **18.** 320 ÷ 100000.

Write down as decimals :

19. $\frac{3}{10}$.   **20.** $\frac{45}{10}$.   **21.** $\frac{62}{100}$.   **22.** $\frac{538}{100}$.   **23.** $\frac{9}{100}$.
24. $\frac{83}{1000}$.   **25.** $\frac{70}{1000}$.   **26.** $\frac{4056}{1000}$.   **27.** $\frac{684}{10}$.   **28.** $\frac{6075}{100}$.
29. $\frac{3007}{1000}$.   **30.** $\frac{80}{100000}$.

Express as common fractions in their lowest terms :

31. 0·5.   **32.** 0·6.   **33.** 0·25.   **34.** 0·75.   **35.** 0·075.
36. 0·35.   **37.** 0·016.   **38.** 0·004.   **39.** 0·09.   **40.** 0·13.
41. 0·007.   **42.** 0·402.

Express in metres :

43. 6·4 km.   **44.** 0·08 km.   **45.** 485 cm.   **46.** 36 cm.
47. 9 cm.   **48.** 8 mm.   **49.** 180 dm.   **50.** 0·307 km.

Express in kilometres :

51. 365 m.   **52.** 72 m.   **53.** 9 m.   **54.** 80 m.
55. 27 cm.   **56.** 25 dm.   **57.** 470 m.   **58.** 750 mm.

Complete the following :—

59. 7·3 × ... = 730.   **60.** 0·085 × ... = 85.   **61.** 0·1 × ... = 100
62. 48 ÷ ... = 0·48.   **63.** 590 ÷ ... = 0·59.   **64.** 2·3 ÷ ... = 0·023.

[*For written work*]

Express as common fractions or mixed numbers, in their lowest
terms:

65. 0·375.   **66.** 0·125.   **67.** 0·32.   **68.** 0·065.

69. 1·0045.   **70.** 4·875.   **71.** 0·0625. **72.** 1·096.

73. 2·075.   **74.** 5·0085.   **75.** 3·0064. **76.** 1·0125.

77. 0·425.   **78.** 1·0256.   **79.** 3·0275. **80.** 2·608.

Addition and Subtraction

Example 7. Add:

	m.	dm.	cm.	mm.		metres.
	2	7	3	5	=	2·735
	4	0	1	8	=	4·018
		4	7	2	=	0·472
			6	5	=	0·065
Sum	7	2	9	0	=	7·290

∴ the sum is 7 m. 2 dm. 9 cm. or 7·29 m.

In all addition sums, start by adding upwards; then *check by adding
downwards*.

Example 8. Subtract the second quantity from the first:

	m.	dm.	cm.	mm.		metres.
	9	5	7	2	=	9·572
	2	8	3	...	=	2·830
Diff.	6	7	4	2	=	6·742

∴ the difference is 6 m. 7 dm. 4 cm. 2 mm. or 6·742 m.

Example 9. Subtract the second quantity from the first:

	m.	dm.	cm.	mm.		metres.
	6	3	...	...	=	6·*3*00
	1	5	3	7	=	1·537
Diff.	4	7	6	3	=	4·763

∴ the difference is 4 m. 7 dm. 6 cm. 3 mm. or 4·763 m.

After a little practice it will be found unnecessary to insert the zeros printed
in italics.

The answer may be *checked* by adding together the two lower lines.

EXERCISE 45

Add together, and *express each answer in terms of the highest unit named*:

1.	m.	dm.	cm.
	1	7	4
	2	5	3
	1	8	6

[2]	km.	Hm.	Dm.
	3	2	9
	1	0	7
	2	9	8

[3]	dm.	cm.	mm.
	5	0	6
		7	8
	1	4	5

[4]	2	4	5
	1	2	3
	3	1	2

5.	6	...	8
	7	5	...
	8	1	2

6.	2	3	4
	7	7	4
	6	9	2

Add together:

7.	4·62
	2·34

8.	2·83
	5·47

[9]	5·72
	1·38

10.	6·75
	4·3

[11]	14·37
	7·13

12.	3·091
	4·909

[13]	0·067
	0·958

14.	0·92
	0·099

[15]	37·18
	0·77
	21·09
	6·94

16.	4·087
	3·95
	0·07
	5·893

*17.	0·045
	1·709
	0·086
	9·14

*18.	53·07
	17·8
	3·56
	20·07

19. 0·872,   2·45,   3·008,   4·16,   1·75.
[20] 16·32, 20·04,   5·207,   0·918,   1·01.
*21. 0·0736, 0·6094, 1·0809, 0·0074, 0·9107.
*22. 0·0804, 0·00924, 0·1072, 0·02065, 0·3108.

Subtract the second quantity from the first, and *express each answer in terms of the highest unit named*:

23.	m.	dm.	cm.
	5	7	6
	1	8	4

[24]	dm.	cm.	mm.
	6	1	5
	1	7	8

[25]	km.	Hm.	Dm.
	4	0	5
	1	2	8

[26]	3	...	4
	1	6	8

27.	8	...	5
		6	7

28.	4	...	...
		3	4

Find the value of:

29. 5·8 − 1·3.

30. 3·4 − 1·8.

31. 4 − 1·2.

[32] 7·4 − 0·7.

[33] 2 − 0·6.

[34] 10 − 3·1.

35. 8 − 0·09.

[36] 1 − 0·1.

[37] 15 − 9·4.

Subtract the second number from the first:

38. 8·76	**39.** 0·837	**40.** 6·84	**[41]** 0·675
5·31	0·237	1·59	0·087

42. 7·6	**[43]** 7·63	**44.** 8·3	**45.** 1
2·38	0·683	1·074	0·586

[46] 4·08	**[47]** 1·23	**48.** 0·729	**[49]** 0·915
1·3	0·7	0·68	0·08

Find the value of:

50. $7·89 - 1·425$.   **[51]** $12·78 - 9·19$.   **52.** $3·07 - 0·895$.

[53] $5·01 - 0·724$.   ***54.** $0·1 - 0·0807$.   ***55.** $0·01 - 0·0002$.

56. $7·2 - 1·4 + 2·8 - 0·9$.   **[57]** $5 - 0·3 - 0·76 - 0·04$.

***58.** $10 - 0·05 - 0·06 + 0·01$.   ***59.** $0·1 - 0·08 - 0·007 + 1$.

***60.** $100 - 0·7 - 0·05 + 0·1$.   ***61.** $1·01 - 0·1 - 0·001 + 10$.

MISCELLANEOUS EXAMPLES

EXERCISE 46

[Give answers as decimals, not as common fractions]

1. In the diagram (not drawn to scale), ABC is a straight line. If the distance of A from B is 3·7 cm., and of B from C is 2·3 cm., find the distance of A from C.

[2] In the diagram (not drawn to scale), ABC is a straight line. If the distance of A from C is 5 cm., and of A from B is 2·75 cm., find the distance of B from C.

3. A fence is made of 10 hurdles each 1·65 m. long; find its length.

[4] A pile of 10 equal note-books is 12·5 cm. high; find the thickness of each notebook in mm.

5. A nail 2·3 cm. long is driven into a board 1·7 cm. thick; if the head of the nail is level with the top of the board, find what length of the nail projects outside the board in mm.

[6] 10 swings of a pendulum are timed to take 8·5 sec.; find the time of one swing.

7. A boy's temperature is 98·6 degrees at 4 p.m. If it rises 2·5 degrees in the next 5 hr., what is it at 9 p.m.?

8. The lengths of the sides of a triangle are 5·75 cm., 6·8 cm., 7·15 cm.; find the perimeter (i) in cm., (ii) in m.

[9] A tank 4·5 dm. deep contains water to a depth of 18·5 cm.; how far in cm. is the water-level below the top of the tank?

10. A pile of 100 sheets of paper is 2·4 cm. high; find the thickness of each sheet in millimetres.

11. Express (i) 1 cm. in kilometres; (ii) 25 mm. in metres.

*12. If 1 yd. =0·915 m., express 100 yd. in kilometres.

*13. A book is 5 cm. thick and each cover is 1·5 mm. thick; how thick is the book without its covers?

14. The rainfall in the 4 weeks of February was 0·45 in., 1·07 in., 0·6 in., 0·88 in.; find the total rainfall for the month.

15. A man walks 2·25 metres a second; find in kilometres the distance he walks in 100 seconds.

[16] A rectangle is 10·4 cm. long, 7·6 cm. wide; find its perimeter in decimetres.

*17. From a piece of tape 20 m. long, 100 pieces each 7·5 cm. long are cut off; how much remains?

[18] A frontage of 108 m. is divided into 10 equal sections; what is the width of 1 section, of 2 sections?

*19. If 1 metre is taken as 39·4 in. approximately, express 1 mm. in inches.

*20. The external diameter of a hollow metal pipe is 8·16 cm., and the metal is 1·7 cm. thick; find the internal diameter.

*21. The external dimensions of an open wooden box are 10·7 cm. by 8·2 cm. by 6 cm. high, and the wood is 8 mm. thick. Find in centimetres the internal dimensions of the box.

*22. How many hundredths are there in 0·025, and how many thousandths in 0·0105?

*23. If 1 cm. =0·394 in., find in inches the perimeter of a rectangle 1 m. long, 1 dm. wide.

*24. An unstretched spring is 48 cm. long, and the spring stretches 15 mm. for each ounce weight supported by it. Find in decimetres the length of the spring when it is supporting a body of weight 10 oz.

CHAPTER VII

DECIMALS: MULTIPLICATION AND DIVISION

Multiplication by Integers up to 12. Products of the following types can be written down at sight after a little practice :—

(i) $0·2 \times 3 = 2$ tenths $\times 3 = 6$ tenths $= 0·6$;

(ii) $0·7 \times 6 = 7$ tenths $\times 6 = 42$ tenths $= 4·2$;

(iii) $0·08 \times 9 = 8$ hundredths $\times 9 = 72$ hundredths $= 0·72$;

(iv) $0·005 \times 8 = 5$ thousandths $\times 8 = 40$ thousandths
$= 4$ hundredths $= 0·04$;

(v) $0·007 \times 600 = 0·007 \times 100 \times 6 = 0·7 \times 6 = 4·2$.

EXERCISE 47 (Oral)

Multiply :

1. 0·3 by 2, 4, 7.   **2.** 0·4 by 2, 3, 6.   **3.** 0·5 by 3, 4, 8.

4. 0·7 by 5, 9, 12.   **5.** 0·8 by 4, 5, 11.   **6.** 0·9 by 6, 11, 12.

7. 0·02 by 3, 4, 5.   **8.** 0·06 by 2, 8, 12.   **9.** 0·07 by 5, 11, 12.

10. 0·005 by 6, 7, 12.   **11.** 0·009 by 4, 10, 11.   **12.** 0·001 by 8, 11, 100.

13. 0·2 by 30, 400.   **14.** 0·6 by 70, 9000.   **15.** 0·8 by 50, 6000.

16. 0·03 by 70, 800.   **17.** 0·05 by 40, 300.   **18.** 0·007 by 60, 700.

Example 1. Multiply 6·28 metres by 7.

The process may be explained by comparing it with the multiplication of a compound quantity.

The reasoning used in the method on the right is exactly the same as that used in the method on the left.

Dm.	m.	dm.	cm.	metres.
	6	2	8	6·28
			7	7
4	3	9	6	43·96

$$\therefore 6·28 \text{ m.} \times 7 = 43·96 \text{ m.}$$

The working should always be arranged so that the units digit of the multiplier is under the right-hand digit of the multiplicand.

Example 2. Multiply 0·00845 by 6.

Put the 6 under the right-hand digit 5 of the multiplicand. Proceed as before; the decimal point comes under the decimal point in the multiplicand.

$$\begin{array}{r} 0·00845 \\ 6 \\ \hline 0·05070 \end{array}$$

$$0·00845 \times 6 = 0·0507.$$

Rough Check: $0·008 \times 6 = 0·048$; $\therefore 0·0507$ is a *reasonable* answer.

Notice that the answer is given as 0·0507, not 0·05070.

Example 3.   Multiply 63·57 by 12.

Put the 2 in 12 under the right-hand digit 7 of the multiplicand.
In multiplying, use the "12 times" table.

$$\begin{array}{r} 63{\cdot}57 \\ 12 \\ \hline 762{\cdot}84 \end{array}$$

$$\therefore\ 63{\cdot}57 \times 12 = 762{\cdot}84.$$

Rough Check: $60 \times 12 = 720$; $\therefore\ 762{\cdot}84$ is a *reasonable* answer.

Example 4.   Multiply 0·843 by 1200.

$$0{\cdot}843 \times 12 = 10{\cdot}116.$$

$$\therefore\ 0{\cdot}843 \times 1200 = 10{\cdot}116 \times 100 = 1011{\cdot}6.$$

$$\begin{array}{r} 0{\cdot}843 \\ 12 \\ \hline 10{\cdot}116 \end{array}$$

Rough Check:

$0{\cdot}8 \times 1200 = 9{\cdot}6 \times 100 = 960$ (about 1000). $\therefore\ 1011{\cdot}6$ is a *reasonable* answer.

EXERCISE 48

Multiply :

1. 3·74 by 2, 3, 7.   [2] 0·942 by 3, 8, 9.   **3.** 4·86 by 5, 7, 10.

[4] 23·8 by 3, 5, 10.   **5.** 0·0675 by 2, 4, 8.   [6] 63·5 by 4, 6, 7.

7. 0·0864 by 4, 5, 9.   **8.** 0·0075 by 6, 8, 10.

[9] 3·47 by 10, 11, 12.   **10.** 0·00125 by 8, 9, 12.

11. 0·0175 by 4, 11, 12.   [12] 0·325 by 6, 8, 12.

13. 2·83 by 400, 50.   [14] 65·7 by 700, 2000.

15. 0·0308 by 5000.   [16] 0·8025 by 60000.

[17] 11·99 by 110.   **18.** 0·00625 by 120.

Multiplication by any number

Method I.   *Counting the Decimal Places*

Multiply as in ordinary multiplication, *taking no notice of the decimal points. Then mark off in the product as many decimal places as there are* **in the multiplier and multiplicand together.**

Example 5.   Multiply 52·836 by 74·9.

Rough Estimate: $50 \times 70 = 3500.$

This method is based on the following principle :—

$$52{\cdot}836 = \tfrac{52836}{1000}, \ \ 74{\cdot}9 = \tfrac{749}{10}$$

$$\therefore\ 52{\cdot}836 \times 74{\cdot}9 = \tfrac{52836 \times 749}{1000 \times 10}$$

$$= \tfrac{39574164}{10000}$$

$$= 3957{\cdot}4164.$$

$$\begin{array}{r} 52836 \\ 749 \\ \hline 369852 \\ 211344 \\ 475524 \\ \hline 39574164 \end{array}$$

C

Example 6	Example 7

2410×0.00001832

1832
2410
―――――
3664
7328
18320
―――――
4415120

$(0 + 8)$ decimal places
product $= 0.04415120$
$ = 0.0441512$

187.5×0.0368

1875
368
―――――
5625
11250
15000
―――――
690000

$(1 + 4)$ decimal places
product $= 6.90000$
$ = 6.9$

Method II. *Automatic placing of decimal point in each partial product.*

Place the units digit of the multiplier under the right-hand digit of the multiplicand.

Example 8	Example 9

52.836×74.9

decimal points
$\downarrow$
52.836
74.9
――――――――
3698.52
211.344
47.5524
――――――――
Product 3957.4164

0.728×0.0325

0.728
0.0325
――――――
$.02184$
1456
3640
――――――
$.0236600$

Product $= 0.02366$

Check the position of the decimal point by counting the number of decimal places.

Method III. *Standard Form*

A number is said to be in standard form if there is exactly one digit (not zero) to the left of the decimal point, so that the number lies between 1 and 10.

Any number, not already in standard form, can be expressed as a number in the standard form multiplied or divided by a power of 10: for example, $7386.4 = 7.3864 \times 10^3$; $0.06972 = 6.972 \div 10^2$.

EXERCISE 49 (Oral)

Write down the missing numbers in index form:

1. $134 = 1.34 \times \ldots$ **2.** $280 = 2.8 \times \ldots$ **3.** $4716 = 4.716 \times \ldots$

4. $0.87 = 8.7 \div \ldots$ **5.** $0.0064 = 6.4 \div \ldots$ **6.** $0.0907 = 9.07 \div \ldots$

7. $63.24 = 6.324 \times \ldots$ **8.** $900.7 = 9.007 \times \ldots$ **9.** $0.00092 = 9.2 \div \ldots$

Write down the missing numbers:

10. $17 \times 0.4 = \ldots \times 4.$ **11.** $36 \times 0.07 = \ldots \times 7.$

12. $123 \times 0.45 = \ldots \times 4.5.$ **13.** $0.18 \times 0.91 = \ldots \times 9.1.$

14. $0.024 \times 35 = \ldots \times 3.5.$ **15.** $0.83 \times 0.061 = \ldots \times 6.1.$

16. $0.82 \times 1360 = \ldots \times 1.36.$ **17.** $347 \times 0.021 = \ldots \times 2.1.$

18. $0.43 \times 0.43 = \ldots \times 4.3.$

Transform the following products so that the multiplier is in the standard form:—

19. $17.36 \times 20.87.$ **20.** $0.863 \times 0.0724.$ **21.** $84.7 \times 0.0069.$

22. $5628 \times 112.3.$ **23.** $720.6 \times 0.902.$ **24.** $0.0617 \times 382.4.$

Example 10. Multiply 52.836 by 74.9.

Rough Estimate : $50 \times 70 = 3500.$
$52.836 \times 74.9 = 528.36 \times 7.49$
$\qquad\qquad\qquad = 3957.4164.$

$$
\begin{array}{r}
528.36 \\
7.49 \\
\hline
3698.52 \\
211.344 \\
47.5524 \\
\hline
3957.4164
\end{array}
$$

Example 11	**Example 12**
2410×0.00001832	187.5×0.0368

Rough Estimate : 2000×0.00002 *Rough Estimate :* 200×0.04
$\qquad\qquad = 2 \times 0.02 = 0.04.$ $= 2 \times 4 = 8.$
Product $= 2.41 \times 0.01832.$ Product $= 1.875 \times 3.68.$

$$
\begin{array}{r}
0.01832 \\
2.41 \\
\hline
0.03664 \\
7328 \\
1832 \\
\end{array}
\qquad
\begin{array}{r}
1.875 \\
3.68 \\
\hline
5.625 \\
1.1250 \\
.15000 \\
\hline
6.90000
\end{array}
$$

Product 0.0441512 $\therefore$ product $= 6.9.$

EXERCISE 50 [*Nos. 1–26 are intended for Oral work*]

Write down the values of:

1. $0 \cdot 2 \times 0 \cdot 3$.   **2.** $0 \cdot 7 \times 0 \cdot 4$.   **3.** $8 \times 0 \cdot 6$.   **4.** $6 \times 0 \cdot 5$.

5. $0 \cdot 9 \times 0 \cdot 1$.   **6.** $0 \cdot 03 \times 0 \cdot 6$.   **7.** $0 \cdot 02 \times 0 \cdot 1$.   **8.** $0 \cdot 15 \times 0 \cdot 4$.

9. $(0 \cdot 3)^2$.   **10.** $(0 \cdot 1)^2$.   **11.** $(0 \cdot 05)^2$.   **12.** $(0 \cdot 008)^2$.

13. $(0 \cdot 01)^3$.   **14.** $(0 \cdot 2)^3$.   **15.** $1 \cdot 2 \times 0 \cdot 7$.   **16.** $400 \times 0 \cdot 5$.

17. $1 \cdot 1 \times 0 \cdot 11$.   **18.** $210 \times 0 \cdot 01$.   **19.** $15 \times 0 \cdot 04$.   **20.** $1 \cdot 2 \times 0 \cdot 012$.

21. $0 \cdot 1 \times 0 \cdot 2 \times 0 \cdot 3$.   **22.** $0 \cdot 7 \times 20 \times 0 \cdot 03$.   **23.** $0 \cdot 01 \times 0 \cdot 1 \times 0 \cdot 1$.

24. $(0 \cdot 2)^2 \times 0 \cdot 4$.   **25.** $(1 \cdot 1)^2 \times 0 \cdot 05$.   **26.** $(0 \cdot 003)^2 \times 100$.

Find the values of:

27. $2 \cdot 14 \times 3 \cdot 2$.   **28.** $10 \cdot 3 \times 4 \cdot 1$.   [29] $243 \times 1 \cdot 5$.

30. $3120 \times 7 \cdot 9$.   [31] $4 \cdot 35 \times 1 \cdot 6$.   **32.** $62 \cdot 5 \times 2 \cdot 4$.

33. $3 \cdot 62 \times 0 \cdot 13$.   [34] $0 \cdot 218 \times 0 \cdot 27$.   **35.** $0 \cdot 0617 \times 0 \cdot 56$.

36. $4 \cdot 73 \times 140$.   **37.** $0 \cdot 0804 \times 1900$.   [38] $230 \times 0 \cdot 028$.

[39] $3625 \times 0 \cdot 056$.   **40.** $101 \times 0 \cdot 101$.   [41] $0 \cdot 102 \times 0 \cdot 031$.

[42] $980 \times 0 \cdot 79$.   **43.** $1900 \times 0 \cdot 909$.   [44] $2 \cdot 034 \times 14 \cdot 6$.

[45] $37 \cdot 06 \times 0 \cdot 384$.   **46.** $4 \cdot 375 \times 0 \cdot 512$.   [47] $98 \cdot 27 \times 36 \cdot 5$.

*48. $0 \cdot 00709 \times 20 \cdot 08$.   *49. $51 \cdot 9 \times 3 \cdot 714$.   *50. $0 \cdot 0809 \times 0 \cdot 908$.

*51. $1 \cdot 23 \times 0 \cdot 14 \times 150$.   *52. $0 \cdot 018 \times 5 \cdot 4 \times 1300$.

*53. $130 \times 22 \cdot 5 \times 0 \cdot 0464$.   *54. $1 \cdot 01 \times 0 \cdot 11 \times 0 \cdot 1001$.

*55. $207 \cdot 049 \times 38 \cdot 012$.   *56. $0 \cdot 078245 \times 400 \cdot 36$.

Short Division

Example 13. Divide $94 \cdot 72$ by 4.

$$4)\overline{94 \cdot 72}$$
$$\overline{23 \cdot 68}$$

Example 14. Divide $0 \cdot 375$ by 4.

$$4)\overline{0 \cdot 37500}$$
$$\overline{0 \cdot 09375}$$

EXERCISE 51 (Oral)

Express as decimals:

1. $4 \cdot 6 \div 2$.   **2.** $5 \cdot 8 \div 2$.   **3.** $7 \cdot 8 \div 3$.   **4.** $9 \cdot 1 \div 7$.

5. $0 \cdot 84 \div 4$.   **6.** $0 \cdot 72 \div 6$.   **7.** $0 \cdot 63 \div 9$.   **8.** $0 \cdot 32 \div 8$.

9. $1 \cdot 38 \div 3$.   **10.** $2 \cdot 4 \div 8$.   **11.** $8 \cdot 4 \div 12$.   **12.** $7 \cdot 7 \div 11$.

13. $0 \cdot 045 \div 5$.   **14.** $0 \cdot 056 \div 7$.   **15.** $0 \cdot 99 \div 11$.   **16.** $0 \cdot 96 \div 12$.

17. $0 \cdot 5 \div 2$.   **18.** $0 \cdot 6 \div 4$.   **19.** $0 \cdot 3 \div 5$.   **20.** $0 \cdot 4 \div 8$.

21. $1 \div 2$.   **22.** $2 \div 4$.   **23.** $6 \div 8$.   **24.** $3 \div 5$.

25. $14 \div 4$.   **26.** $21 \div 4$.   **27.** $21 \div 5$.   **28.** $15 \div 4$.

29. $20 \div 8$.   **30.** $10 \div 8$.   **31.** $1 \div 8$.   **32.** $3 \div 8$.

33. $0 \cdot 01 \div 4$.   **34.** $0 \cdot 015 \div 6$.   **35.** $0 \cdot 03 \div 4$.   **36.** $0 \cdot 5 \div 8$.

EXERCISE 52

Express as decimals :

  1. $7·08 \div 2$.   **2.** $34·11 \div 3$.   **[3]** $0·5072 \div 4$.   **[4]** $11·52 \div 6$.

  5. $13·44 \div 7$.   **[6]** $5·724 \div 9$.   **7.** $5·616 \div 8$.   **[8]** $0·3795 \div 11$.

  [9] $11·28 \div 12$. **[10]** $0·6464 \div 8$. **11.** $2·222 \div 11$.   **12.** $3·627 \div 9$.

  [13] $9·13 \div 2$.   **[14]** $101·4 \div 4$.   **15.** $0·0136 \div 5$.   **16.** $107 \div 4$.

  17. $0·0027 \div 6$. **18.** $39 \div 12$.   **[19]** $75 \div 8$.   **[20]** $20·5 \div 8$.

  21. $111 \div 6$.   **[22]** $0·1011 \div 5$. **[23]** $0·06363 \div 7$. **24.** $0·12012 \div 12$.

Common Fractions and Decimals. A fraction represents the result of dividing the number in the numerator by that in the denominator. For example, $3 \div 4$ is written $\frac{3}{4}$. But if we divide 3 by 4, using decimals, we obtain $0·75$; $\therefore$ $\frac{3}{4} = 0·75$.

$$4\overline{)3·00} \\ \overline{0·75}$$

Example 15. Express $\frac{5}{8}$ as a decimal.

Divide 5 by 8; $\therefore$ $\frac{5}{8} = 0·625$.

$$8\overline{)5·000} \\ \overline{0·625}$$

Short division should be used to find the quotient of one number divided by another whenever the divisor can be converted into a whole number, not greater than 12, by multiplying or dividing by any power of 10. Write the division sum as a fraction with one decimal point under the other and draw a line down the page to mark the new positions of the decimal points. Fill up any blank spaces in the numerator between the figures and the decimal points with zeros.

Example 16. Find the value of $9 \div 0·006$.

$$\frac{9}{0·006} = \frac{9000}{6};$$

$$6\overline{)9000} \\ \overline{1500}$$

$\therefore 9 \div 0·006 = 1500$.

Example 17. Find the value of $0·000805 \div 0·007$.

$$\frac{0·000805}{0·007} = \frac{0·805}{7};$$

$$7\overline{)0·805} \\ \overline{0·115}$$

$\therefore 0·000805 \div 0·007 = 0·115$.

Example 18. Find the value of $56·4 \div 1200$.

$$\frac{56·4}{1200} = \frac{0·564}{12};$$

$$12\overline{)0·564} \\ \overline{0·047}$$

$\therefore 56·4 \div 1200 = 0·047$.

EXERCISE 53

Express as decimals:

1. $\frac{1}{2}$, $\frac{1}{4}$, $\frac{3}{4}$. **2.** $\frac{1}{5}$, $\frac{2}{5}$, $\frac{3}{5}$, $\frac{4}{5}$. **3.** $\frac{1}{8}$, $\frac{3}{8}$, $\frac{7}{8}$.

[4] $\frac{17}{5}$, $\frac{9}{2}$, $\frac{11}{8}$. **5.** $\frac{21}{4}$, $\frac{27}{8}$, $\frac{33}{5}$. *6. $\frac{23}{4}$, $\frac{24}{5}$, $\frac{21}{8}$.

Express as common fractions in their lowest terms:

7. 0·375; 0·0625. **8.** 0·048; 0·104. **9.** 0·925; 0·0128.

Complete the following:—

10. $\frac{1·4}{0·3} = \frac{...}{3}$. [11] $\frac{4·5}{0·06} = \frac{...}{6}$. **12.** $\frac{0·009}{0·12} = \frac{...}{12}$.

[13] $\frac{0·33}{20} = \frac{...}{2}$. **14.** $\frac{3}{500} = \frac{...}{5}$. [15] $\frac{71}{4000} = \frac{...}{4}$.

Transform the following fractions so that the denominator becomes a whole number not greater than 12:—

16. $\frac{17}{80}$. [17] $\frac{3}{400}$. **18.** $\frac{12}{7000}$. [19] $\frac{9}{0·8}$.

20. $\frac{1·6}{0·09}$. *21. $\frac{1}{0·11}$. [22] $\frac{0·13}{200}$. [23] $\frac{0·04}{9000}$.

Express as decimals (or whole numbers):

24. 6·4 ÷ 20. **25.** 0·48 ÷ 30. **26.** 0·06 ÷ 0·3. [27] 0·003 ÷ 0·1

28. 0·24 ÷ 0·6. [29] 8 ÷ 0·2. **30.** 1 ÷ 0·05. [31] 0·74 ÷ 40.

[32] 3·15 ÷ 0·02. **33.** 3·1 ÷ 500. [34] 0·204 ÷ 0·006.

35. 0·9 ÷ 120. **36.** 21·01 ÷ 110. [37] 7·4 ÷ 0·08.

*38. 0·0801 ÷ 0·9. [39] 0·204 ÷ 1·2. [40] $\frac{67}{20}$.

41. $\frac{11·1}{30}$. [42] $\frac{1·34}{0·8}$. *43. $\frac{0·121}{0·11}$.

44. Write down as decimals, *without any working on paper*,
$\frac{1}{8}$, $\frac{1}{4}$, $\frac{3}{8}$, $\frac{1}{2}$, $\frac{5}{8}$, $\frac{3}{4}$, $\frac{7}{8}$.

45. Write down as common fractions, *without any working on paper*, 0·5, 0·375, 0·75, 0·125, 0·25, 0·625, 0·875.

Approximations

Example 19. Express $\frac{5}{6}$ as a decimal.

However many zeros are added to the dividend, the process of division never ends, and we obtain a succession of 3's in the quotient.

$$6\overline{)5·0000...}$$
$$\overline{0·8333...}$$

The number 0·8333... is called a *recurring decimal* and is written for short 0·8̇3̇, which is read "nought point eight, three recurring," a dot being placed over the figure which recurs.

Example 20. Divide 0·253 by 7.

$$7 | \overline{0·253,000,000,000,000,000,0...}$$
$$0·036,142,857,142,857,1...$$

The process of division never ends, and the group of figures, 142857, continually recurs in the quotient, which is written

$$0·036\dot{1}4285\dot{7},$$

a dot being placed above the first digit and above the last digit of the group which recurs.

In every division sum, the quotient either terminates or recurs.

In practical work, recurring decimals are never used. It is impossible to measure the length of a line *exactly* or to find the *exact* weight of an object. If the length of a line is stated to be 2·37 inches, it is meant only that its length is nearer to 2·37 in. than to 2·36 in. or 2·38 in., and we speak of the length as given in inches *correct to* 2 *places of decimals.* A more precise measurement may show that the length is 2·368 inches correct to 3 places of decimals. This agrees with the first statement because 2·368 is closer to 2·37 than to 2·36. In practical measurements, all answers are *approximate,* the important thing is that they should be *reliable as far as they go.*

The symbol $\simeq$ is used to mean "is approximately equal to." Thus from Example 19, $\frac{5}{6} \simeq 0·8$; $\frac{5}{6} \simeq 0·83$; $\frac{5}{6} \simeq 0·833$; these statements are correct as far as they go, namely to 1 place, 2 places, 3 places of decimals.

Example 21. Express 13·72504 correct to (i) the nearest whole number, (ii) 1 place of decimals, (iii) 2 places, (iv) 3 places, (v) 4 places.

(i) 13·7... is nearer to 14 than to 13,

∴ 13·72504 $\simeq$ 14 (to nearest whole number).

(ii) 13·72... is nearer to 13·7 than to 13·8,

∴ 13·72504 $\simeq$ 13·7 (to 1 place of decimals).

(iii) 13·72504 is just nearer to 13·73 than to 13·72, because 13·72500 is exactly half-way between them;

∴ 13·72504 $\simeq$ 13·73 (to 2 places of decimals).

(iv) Similarly, 13·72504 $\simeq$ 13·725 (to 3 places of decimals).

(v)   13·72504 $\simeq$ 13·7250 (to 4 places of decimals).

This example illustrates the fact that the working must be carried to *one* more place of decimals than is required in the result, and that if the extra digit obtained is 5 or more, then 1 must be added to the previous digit.

EXERCISE 54

Express the following numbers correct to (i) 1 place of decimals, (ii) 2 places of decimals:—

1. 3·548; 6·274; 1·906.   **2.** 8·379; 4·847; 0·666.

3. 2·963; 7·498; 9·092.   **4.** 6·798; 3·982; 7·096.

Express the following numbers correct to (i) the nearest whole number, (ii) 3 places of decimals:—

5. 6·80749; 5·48685.   **[6]** 18·62971; 24·70963.

7. 9·71255; 37·30968.   ***8.** 45·51547; 99·69971.

Express the following fractions (i) as recurring decimals, (ii) as decimals correct to 2 places of decimals:—

9. $\frac{1}{3}$, $\frac{2}{3}$, $\frac{1}{6}$.   **10.** $\frac{1}{9}$, $\frac{2}{9}$, $\frac{7}{9}$.   **[11]** $\frac{1}{11}$, $\frac{3}{11}$, $\frac{8}{11}$.

***12.** $\frac{1}{7}$, $\frac{2}{7}$, $\frac{3}{7}$.   **13.** $\frac{5}{9}$, $\frac{4}{11}$, $\frac{6}{7}$.   **[14]** $\frac{8}{9}$, $\frac{7}{11}$, $\frac{5}{7}$.

Express as decimals correct to 2 places of decimals:

15. $\frac{17}{6}$.   **[16]** $\frac{30}{7}$.   **17.** $\frac{50}{11}$.   **[18]** $\frac{43}{12}$.

19. 3·4 ÷ 7.   **[20]** 0·79 ÷ 6.   **[21]** 5·05 ÷ 9.   ***22.** 10·1 ÷ 11.

Express as decimals correct to 3 places of decimals:

23. 50 ÷ 9.   **[24]** 0·65 ÷ 12.   **25.** 0·08 ÷ 11.   **[26]** 0·48 ÷ 70.

27. 1 ÷ 60.   **28.** 77 ÷ 900.   ***29.** 13 ÷ 70.   ***30.** 203 ÷ 1100.

Significant figures may be defined as those which must be retained for any position of the decimal point.

For example, 4·03 m. = 403 cm. = 4030 mm. = 0·00403 km.

In each of these forms, the zero between the 4 and 3 remains and is "significant," but the zero at the end in 4030 mm. and the zeros at the beginning in 0·00403 km. are merely due to the change in position of the decimal point caused by the change in the unit of length and are therefore *not* "significant."

Example 22. Express, correct to 3 significant figures,

(i) 2·0762; (ii) 0·0020762.

(i) Each figure in 2·0762 is significant. Taking the first 3 figures, we obtain 2·07, but 2·0762 is nearer 2·08 than 2·07;

∴ the value is 2·08, correct to 3 significant figures.

(ii) The zeros at the beginning in 0·0020762 are not significant. Taking the first 3 significant figures, we obtain 0·00207, but 0·0020762 is nearer 0·00208 than 0·00207;

∴ the value is 0·00208, correct to 3 significant figures.

Example 23. The length of a bench is measured as 3·6 m., correct to the nearest cm. To how many significant figures is the length known?

It is given that the length differs from 3·6 m., or 360 cm., by less than 0·5 cm., and therefore lies between 360·5 cm. and 359·5 cm. Hence the length can be expressed as 360 cm., or 3·60 m., correct to *three* significant figures, and may be written (3·60 ± 0·005) m.

Note. The phrase "correct to 3 significant figures" is often abbreviated to "correct to 3 figures."

EXERCISE 55 (Oral)

Write down the values of the following, correct to the number of significant figures given in brackets :—

1. 1·8634 (3).
2. 27·485 (3).
3. 0·7476 (2).
4. 4732 (3).
5. 6448 (3).
6. 5447 (2).
7. 938 (1).
8. 2714 (1).
9. 40·636 (3).
10. 0·70562 (3).
11. 0·0804 (2).
12. 0·1032 (2).
13. 0·6972 (2).
14. 60·045 (3).
15. 100·472 (3).

Write down the following quantities to as many significant figures as the data justify :—

16. A length 2·4 dm., correct to the nearest mm.

17. A length 0·37 km., correct to the nearest m.

18. (i) (6·27 ± 0·01) m.; (ii) (6·27 ± 0·05) m.

State how many of the zeros you think are significant in Nos. 19, 20 :

19. £1 = 20s.; 1 hr. = 3600 sec.

20. A salesman's salary is £100 a year and in addition he earns from commissions about £350 a year.

21. The population of a town is stated to be 207009; express it correct to (i) 5, (ii) 4, (iii) 2 significant figures, also to 1 significant figure.

Express as decimals correct to 2 significant figures :

22. $\frac{1}{3}$; $\frac{1}{300}$.
23. $\frac{5}{9}$; $\frac{5}{90}$.
24. $\frac{2}{7}$; $\frac{2}{7000}$.
25. $\frac{0·05}{1·2}$.

A method of showing that a number such as 43000 is correct to 3 significant figures is to write it in the form $4·30 \times 10^4$. Use this method to represent the following :—

26. 600, if correct to 2 significant figures.

27. 93,000,000, if correct to 4 significant figures.

28. 5,600,000, if correct to 5 significant figures.

Division by Factors. If only an approximate value of the quotient is required, the difficulty of calculating the remainder does not occur, and therefore the process of repeated short division may be used with advantage if the divisor can be expressed in simple factors.

Example 24.   Evaluate $0.23789 \div 0.063$, correct to 2 places of decimals.

Since 2 places are required in the answer, keep 3 places in the working.

$$\frac{0.237|89}{0.063|} = \frac{237.89}{63}.$$

$$63\begin{cases}7\\9\end{cases}\begin{array}{l}237.89\\ \hline 33.984...\\ \hline 3.776...\end{array}$$

Quotient $= 3.78$, correct to 2 places.

Example 25.   Express $\frac{109}{420}$ as a decimal correct to 3 places.

Since 3 places are required in the answer, keep 4 places in the working.

$$\frac{10|9}{42|0} = \frac{10.9}{42}.$$

$$42\begin{cases}6\\7\end{cases}\begin{array}{l}10.9\\ \hline 1.8166...\\ \hline 0.2595...\end{array}$$

Since there are figures in the final quotient beyond 0.2595, the quotient is nearer to 0.260 than to 0.259.

Quotient $= 0.260$, correct to 3 places.

EXERCISE 56

Find the values of :

1. $29.4 \div 14$. 2. $43.2 \div 160$. [3] $0.108 \div 15$.
4. $0.0315 \div 1.8$. [5] $0.08 \div 2.5$. [6] $0.252 \div 210$.
7. $0.012 \div 0.32$. 8. $135 \div 0.036$. 9. $3.15 \div 4200$.
[10] $2.31 \div 0.066$. *11. $2331 \div 12600$. [12] $11.97 \div 0.84$.

Evaluate correct to 2 places of decimals:

13. $0.275 \div 0.42$. [14] $12.35 \div 7.7$. [15] $191 \div 360$.
16. $0.1 \div 0.063$. [17] $0.064 \div 0.35$. *18. $9.5072 \div 1.32$.

Express as decimals correct to 3 places of decimals :

19. $\frac{43}{144}$. [20] $\frac{53}{99}$. 21. $\frac{64}{125}$. *22. $\frac{406}{3150}$.

Division by any Number
Method I.   Standard Form

The division sum is written as a fraction which is then transformed so that the denominator contains exactly one digit (not zero) to the left of the decimal point.   To do this, write the fraction so that one decimal point is under the other, and draw a vertical line behind the first digit (not zero) of the denominator. *The position of the decimal point in the quotient should always be found by obtaining an approximate answer by short division*; a final rough check by multiplication is also desirable.

Example 26. Divide 0·8463 by 0·031.

$$\frac{0\cdot84|63}{0\cdot03|1} = \frac{84\cdot63}{3\cdot1}$$

$$3\underline{|84}$$
$$28 \ \textit{Rough estimate.}$$

$$\therefore \ 0\cdot8463 \div 0\cdot031 = 27\cdot3.$$

Rough Check: $0\cdot031 \times 27\cdot3 \eqsim 0\cdot03 \times 30 = 0\cdot9$; $0\cdot8463 \eqsim 0\cdot8$.

$$\begin{array}{r} 27\cdot3 \\ 3\cdot1\overline{)84\cdot63} \\ 62 \\ \hline 226 \\ 217 \\ \hline 93 \\ 93 \\ \hline \end{array}$$

Example 27. Divide 0·13962 by 35·8.

$$\frac{|0\cdot13962}{3|5\cdot8} = \frac{0\cdot013962}{3\cdot58}$$

$$4\underline{|0\cdot014}$$
$$0\cdot003 \ \textit{Rough estimate.}$$

$$\therefore \ 0\cdot13962 \div 35\cdot8 = 0\cdot0039.$$

$$\begin{array}{r} 0\cdot0039 \\ 3\cdot58\overline{)0\cdot013962} \\ 1074 \\ \hline 3222 \\ 3222 \\ \hline \end{array}$$

Rough Check: $35\cdot8 \times 0\cdot0039 \eqsim 40 \times 0\cdot004 = 0\cdot16$; $0\cdot13962 \eqsim 0\cdot14$.

Example 28. Evaluate $0\cdot00724 \div 0\cdot0892$, correct to 3 places of decimals.

$$\frac{0\cdot00|724}{0\cdot08|92} = \frac{0\cdot724}{8\cdot92}$$

$$9\underline{|0\cdot72}$$
$$0\cdot08 \ \textit{Rough estimate.}$$

Work the quotient to *four* decimal places.

$$\begin{array}{r} 0\cdot0811 \\ 8\cdot92\overline{)0\cdot7240} \\ 7136 \\ \hline 1040 \\ 892 \\ \hline 1480 \\ \end{array}$$

$$0\cdot00724 \div 0\cdot0892 = 0\cdot081, \text{ correct to 3 places.}$$

Rough Check: $0\cdot0892 \times 0\cdot081 \eqsim 0\cdot09 \times 0\cdot08 = 0\cdot0072$; $0\cdot00724 \eqsim 0\cdot007$.

Note on Remainders. The 1 in 1480 is under the 4 in 0·7240, and this was in the *fifth* place of decimals in the original dividend 0·00724. Therefore in the actual remainder the 1 in 1480 must also be in the fifth place of decimals.

$$\therefore \ \text{remainder} = 0\cdot0000148.$$

Method II. Divisor a whole number

Write the division sum as a fraction so that one decimal point is under the other, and draw a vertical line behind the last digit of the denominator.

Example 29.   Divide 0·8463 by 0·031.

$$\frac{0\cdot846|3}{0\cdot031|} = \frac{846\cdot3}{31}$$

Put the 2 in the quotient above the 2 in the first
product 62.

$$\therefore \ 0\cdot8463 \div 0\cdot031 = 27\cdot3.$$

Rough Check: $0\cdot031 \times 27\cdot3 \eqsim 0\cdot03 \times 30 = 0\cdot9$; $0\cdot8463 \eqsim 0\cdot8$.

```
        27·3
   31)846·3
       62
      ───
      226
      217
      ──
       93
       93
       ──
```

Example 30.   Divide 0·13962 by 35·8.

$$\frac{0\cdot1|3962}{35\cdot8|} = \frac{1\cdot3962}{358}$$

Put the 3 in the quotient above the 4 in the first product
1074.   The decimal point in the quotient comes in the same
column as the decimal point in the dividend; zeros must be
inserted in the blank spaces between the first figure of the
quotient and the decimal point.

$$0\cdot13962 \div 35\cdot8 = 0\cdot0039.$$

```
      0·0039
 358)1·3962
     1·074
     ────
     3222
     3222
     ────
```

Rough Check: $35\cdot8 \times 0\cdot0039 \eqsim 40 \times 0\cdot004 = 0\cdot16$; $0\cdot13962 \eqsim 0\cdot14$.

Example 31.   Evaluate $0\cdot00724 \div 0\cdot0892$ correct to 3 places of
decimals.

$$\frac{0\cdot0072|4}{0\cdot0892|} = \frac{72\cdot4}{892}$$

Work the quotient to *four* decimal places.

$$\therefore \ 0\cdot00724 \div 0\cdot0892 = 0\cdot081, \text{ correct to 3 places.}$$

```
      0·0811
 892)72·40
     71 36
     ────
      1 040
        892
       ────
       1480
```

Rough Check:

$0\cdot0892 \times 0\cdot081 \eqsim 0\cdot09 \times 0\cdot08 = 0\cdot0072$; $0\cdot00724 \eqsim 0\cdot007$.

For a note on the calculation of the *actual* remainder, if this is required,
see p. 75.

Oral Work.   Make rough estimates of the quotients in
Exercise 57, Nos. 1–15.

EXERCISE 57

[Check the answers by approximate multiplication]

Find the values of:

1. $22\cdot1 \div 1\cdot3$.   **2.** $0\cdot377 \div 2\cdot9$.   **[3]** $0\cdot0368 \div 2\cdot3$.

4. $803\cdot6 \div 5\cdot6$.   **[5]** $2\cdot958 \div 8\cdot7$.   **6.** $0\cdot1269 \div 9\cdot4$.

7. $0\cdot0783 \div 58$; $0\cdot0783 \div 0\cdot58$; $0\cdot0783 \div 0\cdot058$.

[8] $5\cdot75 \div 92$; $5\cdot75 \div 920$; $5\cdot75 \div 0\cdot92$.

[9] $7\cdot36 \div 115$, $0\cdot736 \div 115$; $0\cdot0736 \div 1\cdot15$.

10. $7 \cdot 14 \div 0 \cdot 017$.   11. $30 \cdot 1 \div 0 \cdot 0086$.   [12] $2 \cdot 0532 \div 0 \cdot 029$.

13. $19 \cdot 924 \div 3400$.   [14] $0 \cdot 36 \div 0 \cdot 064$.   [15] $6 \cdot 426 \div 0 \cdot 315$.

16. $0 \cdot 00217 \div 12 \cdot 4$.   17. $0 \cdot 6401 \div 173$.   [18] $0 \cdot 08748 \div 10 \cdot 8$.

[19] $0 \cdot 0374 \div 0 \cdot 748$.   20. $38 \cdot 75 \div 0 \cdot 0125$.   [21] $0 \cdot 14168 \div 0 \cdot 253$.

22. $0 \cdot 762531 \div 23 \cdot 1$.   [23] $0 \cdot 15573 \div 358$.   [24] $223 \cdot 44 \div 7350$.

25. $0 \cdot 7777 \div 35 \cdot 35$.   [26] $3 \cdot 425 \div 0 \cdot 002192$.

27. $157 \cdot 505 \div 0 \cdot 03706$.   *28. $416 \cdot 6477 \div 13 \cdot 81$.

*29. $15 \cdot 079932 \div 0 \cdot 427$.   *30. $7636 \cdot 356 \div 10101$.

*31. $0 \cdot 9833408 \div 30 \cdot 7294$.   *32. $47 \cdot 142933 \div 8270 \cdot 69$.

Evaluate correct to 3 places of decimals :

33. $4 \cdot 13 \div 7 \cdot 04$.   [34] $0 \cdot 091 \div 0 \cdot 728$.   35. $10 \div 492$.

[36] $0 \cdot 7821 \div 9 \cdot 316$.   [37] $0 \cdot 67 \div 5 \cdot 08$.   38. $1 \cdot 48 \div 10 \cdot 07$.

*39. $50 \cdot 07 \div 83 \cdot 5$.   *40. $54 \cdot 18 \div 86 \cdot 52$.   *41. $824 \cdot 6 \div 73 \cdot 6$.

Evaluate correct to 4 places of decimals :

42. $0 \cdot 5073 \div 0 \cdot 816$.   [43] $416 \cdot 5 \div 903$.   44. $0 \cdot 06264 \div 5 \cdot 37$.

[45] $7 \cdot 128 \div 10 \cdot 47$.   *46. $0 \cdot 4824 \div 2 \cdot 466$.   *47. $5 \cdot 872 \div 291 \cdot 4$.

Find the quotient to 2 places of decimals, and the corresponding remainder, in the following :—

48. $6 \cdot 32 \div 9 \cdot 12$; $6 \cdot 32 \div 91 \cdot 2$; $6 \cdot 32 \div 0 \cdot 912$.

[49] $0 \cdot 734 \div 0 \cdot 591$; $0 \cdot 734 \div 5 \cdot 91$; $73 \cdot 4 \div 59 \cdot 1$.

*50. $37 \cdot 3 \div 8 \cdot 47$; $3 \cdot 73 \div 8 \cdot 47$; $0 \cdot 373 \div 0 \cdot 0847$.

51. $18 \cdot 36 \div 13 \cdot 7$.   *52. $0 \cdot 05 \div 0 \cdot 0097$.   *53. $0 \cdot 483 \div 0 \cdot 729$.

Decimalisation of Money.   Note the following facts :—

1 florin $= 2$s. $= £(0 \cdot 1)$; $\therefore$ 1s. $= £(0 \cdot 05)$ and 6d. $= £(0 \cdot 025)$.

Thus   9s. $= £(0 \cdot 05 \times 9) = £(0 \cdot 45)$;

and   9s. 6d. $= £(0 \cdot 45 + 0 \cdot 025) = £(0 \cdot 475)$.

Example 32.   Express $4 \frac{1}{2}$d. as a decimal of 1s.

$4 \frac{1}{2}$d. $= 4 \cdot 5$d. $= (4 \cdot 5 \div 12)$s. $12 | 4 \cdot 5$

$\qquad = 0 \cdot 375$s. $\overline{0 \cdot 375}$

Example 33.   Express $£0 \cdot 725$ in s. d.

$£0 \cdot 725 = (0 \cdot 725 \times 20)$s. $= 14 \cdot 5$s. $= 14$s. 6d.

Or as follows :—

$£0 \cdot 7 = 14$s., $£0 \cdot 025 = 6$d. ; $\therefore$ $£0 \cdot 725 = 14$s. 6d.

EXERCISE 58 (Oral)

Express as decimals in pence :

1. $\frac{1}{2}$d.; $\frac{1}{4}$d.; $\frac{3}{4}$d.   **2.** $3\frac{1}{4}$d.; $10\frac{1}{2}$d.; $6\frac{3}{4}$d.

Express as decimals in shillings :

3. 6d.; 3d.; 9d.   **4.** $1\frac{1}{2}$d.; $7\frac{1}{2}$d.; $2\frac{1}{4}$d.

Express as decimals in £ :

5. 6s.; 10s.; 5s.   **6.** 14s.; 18s.; 24s.   **7.** 3s.; 7s.; 15s.

8. 13s.; 17s.; 21s.   **9.** £3 10s.; £7 15s.   **10.** £2 6s.; £5 11s.

11. £1 3s.; £2 9s.   **12.** 6s. 6d.; 12s. 6d.   **13.** 7s. 6d.; 11s. 6d.

14. 8s. 6d.; 14s. 6d.

Express in shillings, or shillings and pence :

15. £0·1; £0·3; £0·7.   **16.** £0·05; £0·25; £0·45.

17. £0·025; £0·075.   **18.** £0·425; £0·875.

Example 34. Express £3 13s. 9d. as a decimal of £1.

First reduce 9d. to shillings by dividing by 12; then bring down 13s.

$$\frac{12 | 9·00d.}{0·75s.}$$

9d. = 0·75s., ∴ 13s. 9d. = 13·75s.

Next reduce 13·75s. to £ by dividing by 20;

$$\frac{20 | 13·75s.}{0·6875£}$$

13s. 9d. = £0·6875, ∴ £3 13s. 9d. = £3·6875.

The working should be arranged in the abbreviated form shown; the figures in bold type are not part of the original quotients, but are brought down from the data.

$$\frac{12 |\; 9·00d.}{20 | \mathbf{13}·75s.}$$
$$\mathbf{3}·6875£$$

Example 35. Express £3 13s. 9d. as a decimal of £5.

From Example 34, £3 13s. 9d. = £3·6875;

$$\therefore \frac{£3\ 13s.\ 9d.}{£5} = \frac{3·6875}{5} = 0·7375;$$

∴ £3 13s. 9d. = 0·7375 of £5.

Example 36. Express £2 7s. $5\frac{3}{4}$d. as a decimal of £1, correct to 3 places.

$5\frac{3}{4}$d. = 5·75d.   Proceed as in Example 34.

∴ £2 7s. $5\frac{3}{4}$d. = £2·374, correct to 3 places.

$$\frac{12 | 5·75 \quad d.}{20 | \mathbf{7}·4791…s.}$$
$$\mathbf{2}·3739…£$$

Note. Unless the pence and farthings are equivalent to a number of farthings which is divisible by 3, the sum of money cannot be expressed as a *terminating* decimal of £1.

Example 37. Reduce £4·729 to £ s. d., to the nearest penny.

Leave the £4 as it is, and reduce £0·729 to shillings by multiplying by 20, giving 14·580s. Leave the 14s. as it is, and reduce 0·580s. to pence.

$$\begin{array}{r} £4·729 \\ 20 \\ \hline 14·580s. \\ 12 \\ \hline 6·96d. \end{array}$$

∴ £4·729 = £4 14s. 7d. to nearest penny.

Example 38. Find the value of 0·816 of £4, to the nearest penny.

0·816 of £4 = £(0·816 × 4) = £3·264.
Proceed as in Example 37.

$$\begin{array}{r} £3·264 \\ 20 \\ \hline 5·280s. \\ 12 \\ \hline 3·36d. \end{array}$$

∴ 0·816 of £4 = £3 5s. 3d., to nearest penny.

EXERCISE 59

Express as a decimal of £1 :

1. 3s. 9d.   **2.** 6s. 3d.   **3.** 18s. 6d.   **[4]** 1s. 9d.
[5] 5s. 4½d.   **6.** 15s. 1½d.   **7.** 3s. 5¼d.   **[8]** 7s. 6¾d.
[9] 10½d.   **10.** 2¼d.   **11.** £2 7s. 3¾d.   **[12]** £8 17s. 8¼d.

Express as a decimal of £1, correct to 3 places :

13. 4s. 5d.   **[14]** 16s. 7d.   **15.** 3s. 6½d.   **16.** 11s. 5¾d.
17. £1 4s. 11d.   **[18]** £3 16s. 4d.   **19.** £5 11s. 8½d.   **[20]** £7 4s. 7¼d.

Express as a decimal of £1, correct to 4 places :

21. 12s. 7d.   **[22]** 7s. 4¼d.   **[23]** £2 3s. 9½d.   **[24]** £3 10s. 2¾d.

Find the value, correct to the nearest penny, of :

25. £0·63.   **[26]** £0·85.   **27.** £0·738.   **[28]** £0·914.
29. £0·042.   **[30]** £0·807.   **[31]** £1·629.   **32.** £5·718.
[33] £0·0834.   **34.** £1·0095.   **[35]** £2·7036.   **36.** £8·4917.
[37] £2·7094.   **[38]** £0·3208.   **39.** £6·4009.   **[40]** £5·6618.

Express the first sum as a decimal of the second, correct to 3 places :

[41] 18s. 7d.; £2.   **42.** 9s. 5d.; £5.   **43.** 13s. 8½d.; £4.
[44] £1 6s. 10d.; £4.   **[45]** £3 16s. 8d.; £10.   **46.** £1 17s. 6½d.; £5.

Find the value, correct to the nearest penny, of :

47. 0·263 of £2.   **48.** 0·817 of £5.   **[49]** 0·6038 of £4.
*50. 0·7148 of £2 10s.   ***51.** 0·307 of £1 10s.   ***52.** 0·916 of £7 10s.

Decimalisation of Money by the Three-place Method. The following method for decimalising money at sight, correct to 3 places of decimals of £1, should be omitted unless it is learnt easily :—

$$£0·05 = 1s.; \quad £0·025 = 6d. = 24 \text{ farthings};$$
$$\therefore \ 1 \text{ farthing} = £0·001 + \tfrac{1}{24} \text{ of } £0·001.$$

Hence $2\tfrac{3}{4}$d. $= 11$ farthings $= £0·011 + \tfrac{11}{24}$ of $£0·001$
$= £0·011$, to 3 places, because $\tfrac{11}{24}$ is less than $\tfrac{1}{2}$.

But $3\tfrac{1}{4}$d. $= 13$ farthings $= £0·013 + \tfrac{13}{24}$ of $£0·001$
$= £0·014$, to 3 places, because $\tfrac{13}{24}$ is greater than $\tfrac{1}{2}$.

And $9\tfrac{1}{4}$d. $= 37$ farthings $= £0·037 + \tfrac{37}{24}$ of $£0·001$
$= £0·039$, to 3 places, because $\tfrac{37}{24}$ is greater than $1\tfrac{1}{2}$.

We therefore have the following *rule* :—

To express pence as a decimal of £1, correct to 3 places, use the fact that 1 farthing $\backsimeq$ £0·001, and for amounts between 3d. and 9d. add £0·001, and for amounts between 9d. and 1s. add £0·002.

Example 39. Express 7s. $5\tfrac{1}{2}$d. as a decimal of £1, correct to 3 places.

$$7s. = £0·35; \quad 5\tfrac{1}{2}d. = 22 \text{ farthings} = £(0·022 + 0·001);$$
$$\therefore \ 7s. \ 5\tfrac{1}{2}d. = £0·373, \text{ to 3 places.}$$

Example 40. Express £4·898 in £ s. d., to the nearest farthing.

£0·85 $= 17$s.; £0·048 $\backsimeq$ 46 farthings $= 11\tfrac{1}{2}$d., because this sum lies between 9d. and 1s.

$$\therefore \ £4·898 = £4 \ 17s. \ 11\tfrac{1}{2}d., \text{ to nearest farthing.}$$

EXERCISE 60

[*If additional practice is required, Exercise 59 should be used*]

Write down as decimals of £1, to 3 places :

1. 5s. 2d.	**[2]** 11s. 4d.	**3.** 12s. 8d.	**4.** 9s. 10d.
5. 1s. $1\tfrac{3}{4}$d.	**[6]** 3s. $9\tfrac{1}{2}$d.	**7.** 8s. $7\tfrac{1}{4}$d.	**[8]** 15s. $11\tfrac{1}{4}$d.
[9] 6s. $6\tfrac{1}{2}$d.	**[10]** 12s. $1\tfrac{1}{4}$d.	**11.** 13s. $10\tfrac{1}{2}$d.	**12.** 9s. $5\tfrac{3}{4}$d.
[13] 18s. $9\tfrac{1}{4}$d.	**14.** 14s. $8\tfrac{3}{4}$d.	**[15]** 7s. $11\tfrac{1}{2}$d.	**16.** 16s. $3\tfrac{1}{4}$d.

Write down in £ s. d., to the nearest farthing:

17. £0·257.   **[18]** £0·411.   **19.** £2·659.   **20.** £1·729.
21. £3·884.   **[22]** £5·362.   **23.** £4·585.   **[24]** £6·843.
25. £1·96.   **[26]** £2·491.   **27.** £3·63.   **[28]** £5·374.
29. £2·687.   **[30]** £3·265.   **[31]** £1·481.   **32.** £2·569.

Decimalisation of other Compound Quantities

Example 41. Express 8 cwt. 3 qr. 18 lb. as a decimal of 1 ton, correct to 4 places of decimals.

First reduce 18 lb. to qr. by dividing by 28; work this quotient to 4 places of decimals; then bring down 3 qr.

Reduce 3·6428 qr. to cwt. by dividing by 4; then bring down 8 cwt. Reduce cwt. to tons by dividing by 20 and work this quotient to 5 places.

$$28 \begin{cases} 4|18 \qquad \text{lb.} \\ 7 \overline{|\ 4·5} \end{cases}$$

$$4 \underline{|\ 3·6428 \ldots \text{qr.}}$$

$$20 \underline{|\ 8·9107 \ldots \text{cwt.}}$$

$$0·44553 \qquad \text{ton}$$

∴ 8 cwt. 3 qr. 18 lb. = 0·4455 ton, correct to 4 places.

Note. The figures in bold type are not part of the original quotients, but are brought down from the data.

Example 42. Reduce 2·7328 mi. to mi., ch., yd., to the nearest yard.

Leave the 2 mi. as it is and reduce 0·7328 mi. to ch. by multiplying by 80, giving 58·624 ch.
Leave the 58 ch. as it is and reduce 0·624 ch. to yd. by multiplying by 22, = 2 × 11.

∴ 2·7328 mi. = 2 mi. 58 ch. 14 yd., to the nearest yard.

$$
\begin{array}{r}
2·7328 \text{ mi.} \\
80 \\
\hline
58·6240 \text{ ch.} \\
2 \\
\hline
1·248 \\
11 \\
\hline
13·728 \quad \text{yd.}
\end{array}
$$

EXERCISE 61

[*Give the answers to Nos. 1–15 correct to 3 places of decimals*]

Express as a decimal of 1 ton:

1. 9 cwt.   **2.** 17 cwt. 2 qr.   **[3]** 14 cwt. 3 qr. 21 lb.
[4] 16 cwt. 2 qr. 10 lb.   **5.** 2 qr. 15 lb. 12 oz.   ***6.** 8 cwt. 3 st. 7 lb.

Express as a decimal of 1 mile:

[7] 5 fur. 6 ch.   ***8.** 6 fur. 8 ch. 11 yd.   **9.** 1240 yd.

6

Express the first quantity as a decimal of the second:

10. 2 ft. 5 in.; 1 yd.   [11] 37 min. 20 sec.; 1 hr.
12. 3 qt. 1 pt.; 1 gall.   *13. 7 lb. 10 oz.; 1 st.
[14] 3000 oz.; 1 cwt.   15. 4 ch. 18 yd. 2 ft. 3 in.; 1 ch.

Express in tons, cwt., qr., lb., to the nearest lb.:
16. 2·7328 tons.   [17] 1·3729 tons.   18. 3·1074 tons.

Express as compound quantities, correct to the nearest unit of the
    lowest given denomination:

19. 0·862 mi. (ch., yd., ft.).   [20] 2·374 mi. (mi., fur., yd.).
21. 7·826 hr. (hr., min., sec.).   [22] 4·316 gall. (gall., qt., pt.).
[23] 5·463 ch. (ch., yd., ft.).   24. 3·758 qr. (qr., lb., oz.).

Express the first quantity as a decimal of the second, correct to 3
    places:

25. 13 cwt. 3 qr.; 2 tons.   [26] 2 ft. 10 in.; 5 yd.
27. 6 fur. 3 ch.; 4 mi.   [28] 3000 yd.; 10 mi.
[29] 2000 lb.; 5 tons.   30. 41½ hr.; 5 days.

Express as compound quantities, correct to the nearest unit of the
    lowest given denomination, the values of:

31. 0·273 of 2 mi. (ch., yd., ft.). *32. 0·814 of 2½ hr. (hr., min., sec.).
[33] 0·9172 of 5 gall. (gall., qt., pt.).
*34. 0·6186 of 7½ tons (tons, cwt., qr.).

Averages. If a man spends £600 a year, we may say that his
average monthly expenditure is £(600 ÷ 12), that is £50. This does
not mean that actually he spends £50 each month, but that his total
expenditure for the year is the same as it would have been if he had
spent £50 a month.

Similarly, if a motorist travels 100 miles in 2½ hours, we may
say that his *average speed* for the journey is (100 ÷ 2½) miles per
hour, that is 40 miles per hour, or is ⅔ mile per minute. This does
not mean that he travels ⅔ mile each minute, or even that he travels
40 miles in each hour. It merely means that the journey takes
him the same time as if he had travelled 40 miles each hour or
⅔ mile each minute.

Example 43. A cricketer scores 17, 43, 15, 21, 18 runs respectively in 5 innings, being out each time. Find his average score.

He scores (17 + 43 + 15 + 21 + 18) runs in 5 innings,

$$\therefore \text{ his average} = \frac{17 + 43 + 15 + 21 + 18}{5} \text{ runs} = \frac{114}{5} \text{ runs};$$

∴ his average score is 22·8 runs.

Note. For the sake of comparison, cricket averages are usually given to 1 or 2 places of decimals, although it is impossible to score a decimal of a run. A man who scored 136 runs in 6 completed innings would have an average of $1\frac{36}{6}$ runs or 22·67 runs, to 2 places of decimals; this is a slightly lower average than the average of the cricketer in Example 43.

Thus one use of averages is to make comparisons.

The method of Example 43 may be expressed by the *rule*:

$$\text{Average} = \frac{\textbf{Total of Quantities}}{\textbf{Number of Quantities}}$$

EXERCISE 62

Find the average of:

1. 3; 8; 9; 21; 24.   [2] 1·2; 4·6; 2·8; 3·7; 2·4.

3. 2s. 6d.; 1s. 10d.; 3s. 5d. [4] 1 ft. 8 in.; 2 ft. 5 in.; 9 in.; 10 in.

5. 6·3 cm.; 6·2 cm.; 6·5 cm.; 6·7 cm.; 6·4 cm.

*6. 4·86 m.; 5·09 m.; 5·12 m.; 4·71 m.; 4·94 m.; 5·04 m.

Find correct to 2 places of decimals the average of:

7. 293; 708; 49; 318; 112; 186; 94.

*8. 41·36; 52·09; 117·41; 88·75; 60·09; 72·38.

9. A motorist took $1\frac{3}{4}$ hr. for a journey of 56 mi.; find his average speed in miles per hour.

10. A man earns £7 for 9 days work; find the average amount earned per day to the nearest penny.

[11] A clock gains $1\frac{1}{2}$ min. every 2 days; find the average gain per hour in seconds correct to 1 place of decimals.

[12] The number of hours of sunshine for successive days in a certain week was 8·5, 7·6, 2·4, 9·3, 9·6, 8·7, 3·6; find the daily average of hours of sunshine correct to 2 places of decimals.

[13] A car travels 30 mi. in 1 hr.; find its average speed in feet per second.

14. A batsman scored 1237 runs in 43 completed innings; find his average correct to 1 place of decimals.

[15] A bowler took 136 wickets for 2854 runs; find the average number of runs per wicket correct to 1 place of decimals.

16. A dealer buys 1 ton of tea for £170; find the average price per lb. correct to $\frac{1}{10}$d.

17. A man earns £400 a year; find his average daily earnings to the nearest penny, taking 1 year = 365 days.

*18. A man buys 10 tons of coal at 48s. per ton and 14 tons at 45s. per ton; find the average price per ton for the whole amount.

19. A man drives at 30 m.p.h. for 2 hr. and then at 40 m.p.h. for half an hour; find his average speed for the whole journey.

*20. A man buys 1000 articles at 3d. each; he sells 700 of them at $4\frac{1}{2}$d. each, and the rest at $2\frac{1}{2}$d. each. Find his average profit per article sold.

MISCELLANEOUS EXAMPLES

EXERCISE 63

1. Write down correct to 2 places of decimals:
(i) 2·719; (ii) 5·403; (iii) 8·597; (iv) 4·096.

2. Add: 0·3 × 0·2 to 4 × 0·06.

3. Express as common fractions, in their lowest terms:
(i) 0·65; (ii) 0·375; (iii) 0·208; (iv) 0·012.

4. Express £2·675 in £ s. d.

5. Express as decimals: (i) $\frac{7}{160}$; (ii) $\frac{481}{2^3 \times 5^5}$.

[6] Evaluate: (i) 0·605 × 0·24; (ii) 8·89 ÷ 0·14.

7. Reduce £3 7s. 9d. to the decimal of £1.

[8] Express $4\frac{1}{2}$ in. as the decimal of 1 yd.

9. The perimeter of a triangle is 18 cm., and the lengths of two of its sides are 5·47 cm., 6·68 cm.; find the third side.

[10] The rainfall in 4 successive weeks was 1·24 in., 0·83 in., 0·55 in., 2·18 in.; find the average rainfall per week.

*11. Find to the nearest penny the value of 0·1083 of £7 10s.

12. Reduce 7 cwt. 1 qr. 14 lb. to the decimal of 1 ton.

[13] Express 2·625 tons in tons, cwt., lb.

14. Find the cost in francs of 5 m. 40 cm. of ribbon at 1·75 francs per metre.

[15] Express £2 19s. 4½d. as a decimal of £5.

*16. Express 7128 in. as a decimal of 1 mi.

17. Express ¾ of 15s. 4d. as a decimal of £1.

*18. Find correct to 2 places of decimals the value of $\frac{7}{22} + \frac{13}{76}$. [Decimalise each fraction separately.]

19. Given that 1 yd. $\simeq$ 0·9144 m., express in metres, to the nearest decimetre, the height of the Chrysler Building in New York, 1032 ft.

*20. Simplify 2·54 × 2·7 ÷ 0·45.

21. A boy bicycles 11·5 km. in 40 min.; find his average speed in kilometres per hour.

*22. Simplify 3·559248 ÷ 0·504.

*23. The diameter of the revolving plate of a gramophone is 9 in. By how much, to the nearest $\frac{1}{100}$ in., does a French record 0·23 m. in diameter overlap the plate? [1 metre $\simeq$ 39·37 inches.]

*24. Arrange in ascending order of magnitude $\frac{22}{7}, \frac{333}{106}, \frac{355}{113}$.

Simplify the following expressions by multiplying numerator and denominator by a convenient power of 10, and reducing the fractions to their lowest terms :—

25. $\dfrac{0·75}{0·125 \times 0·3}$.   [26] $\dfrac{0·05 \times 0·15}{0·03 \times 0·25}$.   [27] $\dfrac{0·5 \times 0·75}{0·625}$.

28. $\dfrac{0·25 \times 3·5}{0·14 \times 0·05}$.   *29. $\dfrac{0·045 \times 2·75}{0·99 \times 0·125}$.   *30. $\dfrac{3·15 \times 2·8}{0·36 \times 4·9}$.

*31. 15 million farthings weigh 42 tons; find the weight of one farthing in ounces correct to 2 places of decimals.

32. Use the identity, $a^2 - b^2 = (a+b)(a-b)$, to evaluate $(8·42)^2 - (8·38)^2$.

33. Express 2 m. 35 cm. in yards, feet, inches, correct to the nearest inch. [1 metre $\simeq$ 39·37 inches.]

*34. How many strips of tape each 3·2 in. long can be cut from a length of 9 yd., and how much remains?

[35] 1 cu. ft. of water weighs 62·3 lb.; find in ounces the weight of 1 cu. in. of water, correct to $\frac{1}{100}$ oz.

36. Nice is 922 km. from Paris. Express the distance in miles to the nearest mile. [1 mile = 1·6093 kilometres.]

*37. The charge for borrowing £85 for a year is £4·45. What is the charge, to the nearest penny, for borrowing £100 for a year at the same rate?

*38. A man leaves his house at 9.15 a.m. and reaches a town, 46 mi. away, at 10.50 a.m. Find his average speed in miles per hour, correct to 1 place of decimals.

CHAPTER VIII

METRIC SYSTEM

Weight. The unit of weight in the metric system is 1 *gram* (gm.).

1 gram is the weight of 1 cubic centimetre of water,

under certain conditions of temperature and pressure.

All metric tables are constructed on the same principle (p. 53).

10 grams = 1 **dekagram** (Dg.).	$\frac{1}{10}$ gram = 1 **decigram** (dg.).
100 grams = 1 **hectogram** (Hg.).	$\frac{1}{100}$ gram = 1 **centigram** (cg.).
1000 grams = 1 **kilogram** (Kg.).	$\frac{1}{1000}$ gram = 1 **milligram** (mg.).

1000 kilograms = 1 metric ton or tonne.

The units most commonly used are kilograms, grams and milligrams. Weights are usually expressed in terms of one unit only, very rarely in terms of more than 2 units. A kilogram, often called for short a kilo, is approximately $2\frac{1}{5}$ lb.

Areas and Volumes. The tables are derived from the table for lengths :

100 (= 10^2) sq. mm. = 1 sq. cm.	1 sq. dekametre = 1 are (a.).
100 sq. cm. = 1 sq. dm.	100 ares = 1 hectare (Ha.).
100 sq. dm. = 1 sq. m.	
and so on.	1 hectare $\simeq 2\frac{1}{2}$ acres.

1000 (= 10^3) cu. mm. = 1 cu. cm.	1 cu. cm. of water weighs 1 gm.
1000 cu. cm. = 1 cu. dm.	1 cu. dm. of water weighs 1 Kg.
1000 cu. dm. = 1 cu. m.	
and so on.	

1 cubic centimetre is usually written 1 c.c.

Capacity. The unit of capacity is 1 **litre** (l.).

1 litre =1 cubic decimetre =1000 cu. cm.

10 litres =1 dekalitre (Dl.), $\frac{1}{10}$ litre =1 decilitre (dl.),
and so on.   and so on.

  1 litre of water (1000 c.c.) weighs 1 kilogram.
  1 litre ≏ 1¾ pints ≏ $\frac{9}{10}$ quart.

Money.   France :   100 centimes (c.) =1 franc (fr.).
         America :   100 cents (c.)   =1 dollar ($).

Constants. The relations between British and metric units
should be illustrated practically. A list of constants is given on
pp. vii–viii; the most important are as follows :—

   1 inch =2·540 cm..   1 cm. =0·3937 in.
   1 yard =0·9144 m.   1 m. =1·094 yd.
   1 mile =1·609 km.   1 km. =0·6214 mi.
   1 lb. =0·4536 kg.   1 kg. =2·205 lb.

     1 gall. =277·3 cu. in. =4·546 litres.
     1 litre =61·03 cu. in. =1·76 pints.

EXERCISE 64 (Oral)

1. Place on a sheet of squared paper a ruler graduated in cm.,
and read off the length of (i) 5 in. in cm.; (ii) 10 cm. in inches.
Hence express approximately 1 in. in cm., and 1 cm. in inches.

2. An English family went to live in France. How much butter
must be ordered each week if they need 5 lb. per week? How
much milk each day if they need 5 pints daily. Give answers in
round figures.

3. Name two objects in the room about 1 m. apart. Estimate
the breadth of the room (i) in yards; (ii) in metres.

4. 1 m. ≏ 39·37 in. Express in inches (i) 1 dm., (ii) 1 cm.;
and express 1 m. in yards, to 2 places of decimals.

Use the approximation, 8 km. ≏ 5 mi., for Nos. 5, 6 :

5. Havre is 200 km. from Paris; how many miles is this?

6. Bedford is 50 mi. from London; how many km. is this?

7. Draw on a piece of squared paper ruled in tenths of an inch a square of side 5 cm. How many small squares does it contain? Hence express approximately 1 sq. cm. in sq. in.

8. Point out some surface in the room about 1 sq. m. in area. Estimate the area of the door in sq. m.

9. Express 35 cm. (i) in dm., (ii) in m.; and express 24 dm. in m.

10. Express 150 sq. cm. (i) in sq. dm., (ii) in sq. m.; and express 480 sq. dm. in sq. m.

11. Point out objects in the room whose sizes are about (i) 1 c.c.; (ii) 1 cu. dm.; (iii) 1 cu. m.

12. Express in cu. dm., 750 c.c., 45 c.c., 8 c.c., 1250 c.c.

13. Express in c.c., 1·5 cu. dm., 0·75 cu. dm., 0·08 cu. dm.

14. How many c.c. are there in 1 litre, 12 litres, 0·4 litre, 0·06 litre?

15. How many litres are there in 2·5 cu. dm., 280 c.c., 35 c.c.?

16. What is the weight of (i) 10 c.c. of water; (ii) 2 cu. dm. of water; (iii) 3 litres of water?

17. How many c.c. of water weigh (i) 1 kg.; (ii) 50 gm.?

18. Point out an object that weighs about 1 kg.

19. 5 kg. ≃ 11 lb.; a boy weighs 110 lb., what is this in kg.? A man weighs 70 kg., what is this in lb.? in stones?

20. 1 litre ≃ 1¾ pt.; express approximately in pints (i) 4 litres, (ii) 2 cu. dm., (iii) 500 c.c.

21. Express (i) 10 fr. 50 c. in francs; (ii) 12 dollars 5 cents in dollars.

22. Any volume of copper is about 9 times as heavy as the same volume of water, or for short copper is about 9 times as heavy as water. Find approximately the weight of 10 cu. dm. of copper (i) in kg.; (ii) in lb. [See No. 19.]

23. Mercury is about 13·6 times as heavy as water. Find approximately the weight of 1 litre of mercury in kg.

24. Brass is about 8 times as heavy as water. Find approximately the volume in c.c. of a lump of brass which weighs 1 kg.

EXERCISE 65

1. Express in grams:

(i) 12 gm. 8 cg.; (ii) 15 mg.; *(iii) 4 Dg. 5 cg.

2. Express in kilograms:

(i) 3 Hg. 5 Dg.; (ii) 48 gm.; *(iii) 6 Dg. 5 dg.

Add and give the answers in grams:

3. 5 gm. 7 dg.; 8 gm. 9 cg.; 5 dg. 4 cg.

[**4**] 3 dg. 8 mg.; 7 cg. 5 mg.; 2 gm. 7 mg.

5. 1 Kg. 148 gm.; 2 Kg. 62 gm.; 2 Hg. 4 Dg.

Subtract the second quantity from the first and give the answers in Kg.:

6. 7 Kg. 375 gm.; 2 Kg. 180 gm.   [**7**] 2 Kg. 3 Dg.; 850 gm.

8. 5 Hg.; 75 gm.   ***9.** 8 Dg.; 24 gm. 6 dg.

***10.** Add 35 Dg., 37 Hg., 105 gm.; answer in Kg.

11. Subtract 15 mm. from 1 dm.; answer in metres.

[**12**] Subtract 2570 gm. from 3 Kg.; answer in Kg.

13. Express in francs the sum of 10 fr. 25 c., 7 fr. 65 c., 12 fr. 5 c., 9 fr. 75 c.; and subtract the sum from 50 fr.

Find the values of:

14. 6 gm. 7 dg. 3 cg. + 5 gm. 8 cg. 6 mg. + 2 gm. 14 mg. (in gm.).

***15.** 4 l. 7 cl. + 6 l. 5 cl. + 2 Dl. 3 l. + 2 dl. 8 cl. (in l.).

***16.** 6 Kg. 4 Dg. 5 gm. 7 dg. − 3 Hg. 8 gm. 9 dg. 5 cg. (in Kg.).

17. Subtract 275 sq. cm. from 1 sq. m. (answer in sq. m.).

18. Subtract 50 c.c. from 1 cu. dm. (answer in cu. dm.).

[**19**] Three parcels weigh 2 Kg. 150 gm., 1 Kg. 75 gm., 3 Kg. 875 gm., respectively. Find their total weight in Kg.

[**20**] A bottle contains 1 litre of milk; how many c.c. remain when 350 c.c. have been poured out?

21. A flask weighs 37·53 gm. when empty and 118·28 gm. when full of water. Find (i) the weight of the water; (ii) the capacity of the flask.

[**22**] From a sheet of cardboard 1 dm. square, a rectangular portion 8 cm. by 5 cm. is removed. Find in sq. dm. the area of what remains.

23. The capacities of three bottles are 250 c.c., 375 c.c., 525 c.c., respectively. Find their total capacity in litres.

24. The external diameter of a hollow metal pipe is 8·1 cm., and the internal diameter is 6·9 cm. Find the thickness of the metal.

25. The internal measurements of a rectangular tin are 8 cm. by 6 cm. by 5 cm.; express its capacity in litres, and find the weight in Kg. of the water it will hold.

*26. An empty flask weighs 32·5 gm.; find the total weight if 0·18 litre of water is poured into it.

*27. A litre of petrol weighs 0·7 Kg. Find in Kg. the total weight if 2 litres of petrol are put into a tin which weighs 270 gm. when empty.

Multiplication and Division

Example 1. Find in sq. m. the area of a rectangle of length 4 m. 75 cm. and breadth 3 m. 40 cm.

The length is 4·75 m.,
  The breadth is 3·4 m.,
∴ the area = 4·75 × 3·4 sq. m.
       = 16·15 sq. m.

$$\begin{array}{r} 4{\cdot}75 \\ 3{\cdot}4 \\ \hline 14{\cdot}25 \\ 1{\cdot}900 \\ \hline 16{\cdot}15 \\ \hline \end{array}$$

Note. 16·15 sq. m. = 16 sq. m. 1500 sq. cm.

Formal "practice" is reserved for Chapter X, but simple examples may with advantage be worked by practice methods at this stage; see Example 2.

Example 2. Given that 1 yd. ≏ 0·9144 m., express 3 yd. 2 ft. 5 in. in m., cm., to the nearest cm.

	m.	
	0·9144	1 yd.
	3	
	2·7432	3 yd.
1 ft. = ⅓ of 1 yd.	0·3048	1 ft.
	0·3048	1 ft.
4 in. = ⅓ of 1 ft.	0·1016	4 in.
1 in. = ¼ of 4 in.	0·0254	1 in.
Add	3·4798	3 yd. 2 ft. 5 in.

∴ 3 yd. 2 ft. 5 in. ≏ 3·4798 m. = 3 m. 48 cm. to nearest cm.

EXERCISE 66

1. Find in cm. the height of a pile of 9 notebooks if each is 1 cm. 7 mm. thick.

2. 76 fr. 50 c. is shared equally between 9 boys; how much does each receive?

[3] If 1 c.c. of copper weighs 8·8 gm., find the weight of 7·5 c.c. of copper.

4. Find the area of a rectangle 5·6 cm. long, 3·75 cm. wide.

5. A pile of 150 sheets of paper is 5·4 cm. high; find in mm. the thickness of one sheet.

[6] How many yards, to the nearest yard, does a man walk in 40 steps, each 0·85 m. long? [1 m. ≃ 1·09 yd.]

7. If 1 c.c. of petrol weighs 0·78 gm., find the weight of 1½ litres of petrol.

[8] A wooden cuboid, 5 cm. by 4 cm. by 3 cm., weighs 36·3 gm.; find the weight of 1 c.c. of the wood.

9. A man walks 6 km. in 50 min.; find his speed in km. per hour.

*10. How many pieces of tape, each 7 cm. long, can be cut from a length of 1 metre, and how much remains?

11. Express 7¼ in. in cm., mm., to nearest mm. [1 in. ≃ 2·54 cm.]

*12. Express ⅛ cu. m. in pints, to nearest pt. [1 l. = 1·761 pt.]

13. Express 2 lb. 12 oz. in kg., to nearest gm. [1 lb. ≃ 0·4536 kg.]

[14] Express 2 m. 15 cm. in ft., in., to nearest in. [1 m. ≃ 39·37 in.]

15. Taking 1 yd. = 0·9144 m., express in m., cm., to nearest cm. (i) 2 yd. 1 ft. 8 in.; (ii) 4 ft. 10½ in.

[16] The area of a rectangle is 2 sq. dm.; its breadth is 9·5 cm.; find its length to the nearest mm.

17. A rectangular tin which holds 1 litre is 12 cm. long, 6·5 cm. wide, internal measurements. Find its internal height to the nearest mm.

*18. How many cigars at 8 fr. 50 c. each can be bought with 100 fr., and how much money remains?

*19. A shell from a 40-cm. gun measures 1·5 m. from tip to base and weighs 956 kg. Express these three measurements in British units, correct to $\frac{1}{10}$ in. and the nearest lb. [1 m. ≃ 39·37 in.; 1 kg. ≃ 2·205 lb.]

*20. How many jars each holding 1·75 Kg. of jam can be filled from a vessel containing 100 Kg. of jam, and how much remains?

MISCELLANEOUS EXAMPLES

EXERCISE 67

1. A rectangular field is 386 m. long, 274 m. wide; express its perimeter in km.

2. Express in mg. the difference between 0·86 dg. and 0·24 gm.

[3] Find in gm. the weight of 35 cl. of water.

4. A racing car travels 350 m. in 10 sec.; express this speed in km. per hour.

[5] The weights of three articles are 27 gm. 45 cg., 108 gm. 65 cg., 8 Dg., respectively. Find their total weight in Kg.

6. Water is coming out of a tap at the rate of 75 c.c. per sec.; how many litres come out in $2\frac{1}{2}$ min.? How many pints per minute? [1 litre ≃ 1·76 pt.]

7. A wooden box without a lid is 2·5 dm. long, 1·5 dm. wide, 6·5 cm. high, external measurements. The wood is 7·5 mm. thick; find the internal measurements.

[8] How many cu. cm. blocks can be cut from a cuboid, 0·6 m. long, 0·25 m. wide, 1·4 dm. high?

9. Aluminium is $2\frac{1}{2}$ times as heavy as water; find in kg. the weight of 0·6 cu. dm. of aluminium.

*10. Taking 1 ton = 1016 Kg., express 6 cwt. 3 qr. in Kg. to the nearest Kg.

11. Find in grams the weight of half a litre of oil which is 0·9 times as heavy as water. How many oz. to nearest oz.? (See No. 16.)

[12] How many kilolitres of water can a tank 15 m. long, 8 m. wide, 4·5 m. deep, hold?

[13] A photograph 14 cm. high, 8·5 cm. wide is mounted on a card so that there is a margin 25 mm. wide all round. Find the perimeter of the card in dm.

14. Express 11 oz. in gm. to the nearest gm. [1 lb. ≃ 0·4536 Kg.]

15. A pan is 4 dm. long, 35 cm. wide, 7·5 mm. deep, internal measurements. Find its capacity in litres.

[16] Express 7 Hg. 8 Dg. in lb., oz., to the nearest oz.

[1 kg. ≃ 2·205 lb.]

*17. The diameter of a cigarette, 7 cm. long, is 7·5 mm. How many cigarettes can be packed in a box which measures internally 7 cm. by 15 cm. by 3 cm.?

*18. Given 1 mi. = 1·609 km., express 1240 yd. in km., to the nearest Dm.

*19. A flask weighs 64·27 gm. when empty and 150·35 gm. when full of water.   Find its weight when it is half full of water.

*20. The water in a bottle $\frac{3}{5}$ full weighs 52·8 gm.;   what would be the weight of the water if the bottle was $\frac{5}{8}$ full?

CHAPTER IX

GRAPHS

The object in representing facts graphically is to convey information *rapidly*.   Thus the table in Example 2, p. 94, gives the number of deaths per week from road accidents in Great Britain for a certain period.   It is quicker to see how this number went up and down by glancing at the graph than by reading through the table.

Example 1 (for Oral work).   A motor-car is fitted with a gauge which shows the number of gallons of petrol in the tank. When full, the tank holds 5 gall.   A motorist starts out at 10 a.m. and notes the readings on the gauge at hourly intervals.   The result is shown in the diagram given above:

PETROL GAUGE READINGS

Use a ruler to interpret the facts shown in the diagram, and answer the following :—

(i) What is the length in inches of the line which represents (*a*) 2 gall., (*b*) 5 gall.?

(ii) How much petrol is represented by an upright line of length (*a*) 1 in. (*b*) $\frac{1}{4}$ in., (*c*) 1·5 in.?

(iii) How much petrol did he start with?   How much had he at 1 p.m. and at 4 p.m.?

(iv) During what time is it probable that the car was not running?

(v) About what time did he fill up the tank?

(vi) The car averages 24 mi. to the gallon;   estimate the distances travelled in successive hours.

(vii) What meaning, if any, can you give to an upright inserted midway between the last two uprights?

(viii) Can you insert with fair accuracy an upright for 10.30 a.m., for 1.30 p.m., for 2.30 p.m.?

Use of Squared Paper. It was necessary to use a ruler to interpret the facts given by the petrol-gauge graph because it was drawn on *plain* paper; it saves time and trouble to use squared paper.

Example 2. The number of deaths per week from road accidents in Great Britain for the midsummer of 1934 was as follows :—

Week ending	June 30.	July 7.	July 14.	July 21.	July 28.	Aug. 4.	Aug. 11.
Deaths	142	180	143	143	157	148	160

Represent these facts by a graph.

First draw a line across the squared paper and mark on it points to represent the given weekly periods.

Next draw a line up the paper and graduate it to show the number of deaths. *Since in no week the number is less than* 140 *or greater than* 180, *it is unnecessary to show any graduation outside these limits.*

These two lines are called the **axes of reference,** and the graduations show the chosen **scales.**

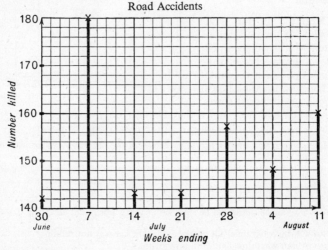

Road Accidents

Use the diagram to answer the following :—

    (i) In how many weeks were there more than 150 deaths?

    (ii) In how many weeks were there less than 145 deaths?

    (iii) Would an upright midway between the last two uprights have any meaning?

(iv) Are the lengths of the uprights shown in the graph proportional to the numbers of deaths?

(v) Between which two consecutive weeks was the fall in the number of deaths greatest?   Between which was the rise greatest?

The object in representing facts graphically is to convey information *rapidly*. *To make a graph easy to understand*, the following instructions must always be carried out :—

(i) Write above the graph a title or a brief explanatory heading.

(ii) The quantity whose values are selected must be measured along the axis across the page ; the quantity whose values are observed or calculated, along the axis up the page.

(iii) Write along each axis what that axis represents, and the unit unless this is shown on the graduated scale.

(iv) Choose as large a scale as the paper will allow, but it must be a scale which makes plotting and reading easy.

(v) Graduate each axis so as to show clearly the scale for that axis.

(vi) If two graphs are drawn on the same axes, label each clearly.

EXERCISE 68 (Oral)

State which quantity should be measured along the axis drawn *across* the page for the following graphs :—

1. Postage on parcels of various weights.

2. Number of passengers on the Underground at different times of day.

3. A boy's age and height.

4. The H.P. of a motor-car and the tax on it.

5. A travel graph : distance from home and time of day.

6. Record times for races of various lengths.

7. A man's age and his weight.

8. Stretch of a spiral spring produced by various loads.

9. A mark reducer : original marks and scaled marks.

10. A graph to convert miles to kilometres.

What scales would you choose and what would be the smallest and largest graduations to represent the following ranges of values, for the given lengths of axes?

11. Length 10 in. : from 7 to 53.

12. Length 10 in. : from 135 to 1050.

13. Length 10 in. : from 5·6 to 23·8.

14. Length 6 in. : from 45 to 100.

15. Length 8 in. : from 100 to 250.

16. Length 5 in. : from 0 to 1.

17. Length 5 in. : from 65 yd. to 295 yd.

18. Length 6 in. : from 2·75 lb. to 3·25 lb.

19. Length 7 in. : from 0·28 m. to 0·54 m.

20. Length 6 in. : from £500,000 to £800,000.

EXERCISE 69

Represent on squared paper the following statistics. State in each case whether any meaning can be attached to intermediate uprights, and if so, whether intermediate uprights can be inserted with fair accuracy without further data.

Give each diagram a title and write along each axis what that axis represents, and show how it is graduated.

1. The average diameter of oak trees of different ages :

Age in years .	10	20	30	50	70	100	150
Diameter in inches	5	10	14	23	32	41	54

Estimate (i) the diameter for an age of 40 years;
(ii) the age at which the diameter is 38 in.

[2] The average daily receipts of a certain grocer :

Day . .	Mon.	Tues.	Wed.	Thur.	Fri.	Sat.
Receipts in £	13	11	14	6	12	18

Which day was probably "early closing"?

3. The average weight of boys of different ages :

Age in years	11	12	13	14	15	16	17	18
Weight in lb.	79	85	92	...	114	129	142	146

What is the average weight at age 14?

4. The marks obtained out of 200 by a boy in successive fortnights of a term :

Number of fortnight	1	2	3	4	5
Marks obtained .	125	110	104	162	140

*5. Cars sold by a company in successive quarters of 1933, 1934:

Quarter	1st	2nd	3rd	4th	1st	2nd	3rd	4th
Number sold	420	560	620	510	440	630	740	580

What seems to be (i) the best month, (ii) the worst month for selling cars?

Locus Graphs. In representing a set of statistics by a graph it is not necessary to draw the whole of the uprights; the usual custom is to mark *only the top point of each upright*, and to leave the rest to the imagination.

Example 3 (for Oral work). The given diagram shows the temperature at stated times of a boy with a feverish cold. If his temperature had been taken more frequently, there would be more points marked on the graph; but there are sufficient to give a good idea of how his temperature changes.

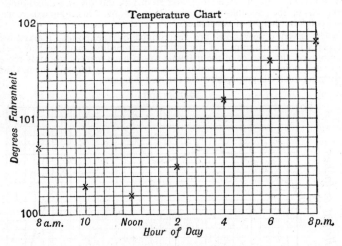

Make a copy of this diagram and draw a smooth curve through the marked points. This curve probably represents with fair accuracy the locus of the top points of the uprights which correspond to the boy's temperature at intermediate times; we therefore call it a locus-graph. It shows at a glance the boy's temperature (approximately) at any time between 8 a.m. and 8 p.m.

D

Use your figure to answer the following questions:—

    (i) What is approximately his temperature at 9 a.m., 5 p.m.?
    (ii) At what time is his temperature 101°, 101·7°?
    (iii) At what times is his temperature 100·4°?

The top points of successive uprights are often joined by straight lines in order to guide the eye rapidly from one point to the next; in such cases the intermediate points on the lines do not usually represent intermediate values. The road-accidents graph in Example 2, p. 94, appeared in a newspaper where it was shown with the top points joined by straight lines in order to make the rise and fall in the number of deaths more vivid, but in this case intermediate points on the lines have no meaning.

Example 4. The height of the barometer in inches is recorded at hourly intervals on a certain day as follows :—

Time	9 a.m.	10 a.m.	11 a.m.	12	1 p.m.	2 p.m.	3 p.m.
Inches	29·55	29·70	29·77	29·70	29·90	29·72	29·15

We select the times at which the height is observed, the time-axis is therefore taken *across* the page; unit, 1 in. represents 2 hr., the first graduation is 9 a.m.

All readings lie between 29 in. and 30 in.; ∴ the lowest graduation on the axis up the page may be taken as 29 in.; scale, 1 in. along axis represents 0·5 in., height of barometer.

The given observations are represented by the points, marked by crosses in the diagram. If an automatic recording machine had been employed, the pointer of the machine would have marked not only these isolated points but also a continuous curve passing through them, thus forming the locus graph shown in the next diagram.

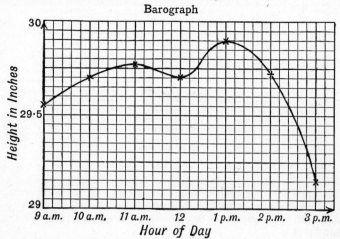

Barograph

Use the printed diagram to answer the following:—

(i) What is the height of the barometer at 9.36 a.m., 12.24 p.m., 1.24 p.m., 2.48 p.m.?

(ii) At what times is the height of the barometer 29·65 in., 29·80 in., 29·45 in.?

(iii) Between what times was the barometer rising?

(iv) Between what times was the barometer above 29·65 in.?

(v) How much did the barometer fall between 1.30 p.m. and 2.30 p.m.?

(vi) How much did the barometer rise between 9.30 a.m. and 10.30 a.m.?

(vii) What inferences can you draw from noticing that a special part of the graph *slopes downwards* and that one part slopes downwards more steeply than another part?

EXERCISE 70

1. The following table gives the distances in which a train can be stopped for various velocities :—

Velocity in m.p.h.	30	40	45	50	60
Distance in yards	100	176	223	276	400

Find from a graph (i) how much farther a train runs after the brakes are put hard on when the speed is 35 m.p.h., 55 m.p.h.; (ii) how fast a train is travelling if it can be stopped in 200 yd.

*2. If £100 is allowed to accumulate at 4% per annum compound interest, the amount is as follows :—

Number of years	0	5	10	20	30	35
Amount in £ .	100	122	148	219	324	395

Find from a graph the amount after (i) 15 years, (ii) 25 years, (iii) 33 years.

After what time will £100 amount to £350?

At 4% simple interest, the amounts of £100 after 10, 20, 30 years are £140, £180, £220, respectively; draw the corresponding simple interest graph on the same figure. After what time does the amount of £100 at compound interest exceed that at simple interest, at 4% per annum, by £50?

3. Expectation of life of an Englishman at different ages :

Age in years . .	30	40	50	60	70	80
Expectation in years	33·2	26·5	19·9	13·6	8·6	5·2

Find from a graph (i) how much longer an Englishman may expect to live at the age of 34, 53, 66; (ii) at what age the expectation of life is 22, 16, 11 years.

[4] The annual premium for a Life Assurance of £1000 varies with the age of the insurer when he makes the first payment:

Age . .	25	30	35	40	45
Premium in £	14¼	16½	19¼	23	27¾

Find from a graph (i) the premiums for starting at the age of 32, 38; (ii) the age at which a man started who had to pay a premium of £25 15s.

*5. The number of hours in the longest day in a year depends on the latitude:

Lat. in degrees .	25	35	45	50	55	60
Number of hours	13·6	14·4	15·4	16·1	17·1	18·5

Find from a graph (i) the number of hours in the longest day in latitudes 30°, 52°; (ii) the latitude in which the longest day is 15 hr., 18 hr.

6. The time of a complete oscillation of a pendulum depends on its length; the following results hold in London:—

Length in feet .	1	2	3	4	5	6
Time in seconds	1·11	1·57	1·92	2·21	2·48	2·71

Find from a graph (i) the time for lengths 2 ft. 6 in., 4 ft. 9 in.; (ii) the length to give a time, 2 sec.

The pendulum of a clock should make complete oscillations every 2 sec. if the clock is keeping time. How should the length be corrected if a complete oscillation takes 2·1 sec.? What alteration in length is required to reduce the time of a complete oscillation from 1·3 sec. to 1·2 sec.?

[7] The heights of a shell fired from a howitzer at various times after projection are as follows:—

Time in seconds . . .	5	10	20	30	35	40	50	60
Height in hundreds of feet	15	28	45	52	52	49	35	10

Find from a graph (i) the height after 15 sec., (ii) the times when the height is 4300 ft., (iii) the length of the time for which the height is more than 3000 ft.

[8] The British amateur running records are as follows :—

Distance in yards	150	200	440	600	880	1000
Time in seconds	14·6	19·4	47·0	70·8	112·2	132·4

(i) What would be the probable record for 500 yd., 750 yd.?

(ii) The American record for 300 m. (1 m. = 1·09 yd.) is 33·2 sec.; how does this compare with British records?

(iii) How far should it be possible for an amateur to run in 1 min., 2 min.?

9–12. Describe in general terms the following rough graphs, Nos. 9–12, and explain any peculiar features :—

9.

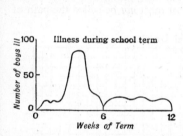

Illness during school term

10.

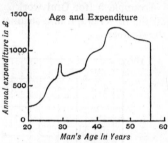

Age and Expenditure

[11]

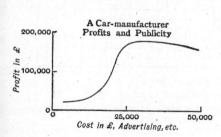

A Car-manufacturer Profits and Publicity

*12.

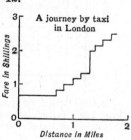

A journey by taxi in London

*13. The curves A, B, C show the number of people killed of ages from 0 to 70 in 1932 in road accidents. The three curves refer to motorists, pedestrians, and pedal cyclists. Which is curve A? Which is curve B? Give short reasons for your answer, and state in general terms the notable facts established by these graphs.

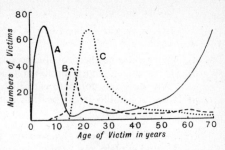

STRAIGHT LINE GRAPHS

Example 5 (for Oral work). The diagram shows some points on the travel graph of a steamer; it must *not* be called the path of the steamer.

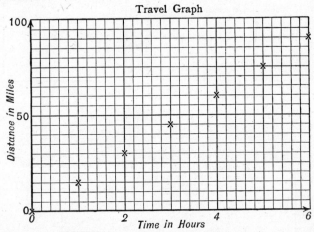

Travel Graph

(i) How far did the steamer travel in 2 hr., 4 hr., 6 hr.?

(ii) Use a ruler to see whether the marked points lie on a *straight* line. What does this mean? What is the speed of the steamer?

(iii) *Make a copy of the diagram* and draw on it travel graphs for speeds of 50 m.p.h., 25 m.p.h., 5 m.p.h.

(iv) Draw on your copy the travel graph of a man who goes at 10 m.p.h. for 1 hr., then at 20 m.p.h. for 3 hr., then at 15 m.p.h. for 2 hr.

(v) What is the meaning of the statement that one part of a travel graph is steeper than another part?

In this travel graph, the point where the axes of reference intersect represents zero time and zero distance and is called the **origin**; the fact that the distance the steamer goes is directly proportional to the time taken means that the graph must be a *straight line through the origin*, and this is true of the graph of any two quantities so related that one is directly proportional to the other.

Example 6. Draw a graph for converting kilograms to lb., given that 1 kg. $\backsimeq$ 2·2 lb. Use the graph to express 2·6 kg. in lb., and 8 lb. in kg., approximately.

Take 1 in. on the axis across the page to represent 2 kg., and 1 in. on the axis up the page to represent 5 lb., and call the origin O.

Ready-reckoner Graph

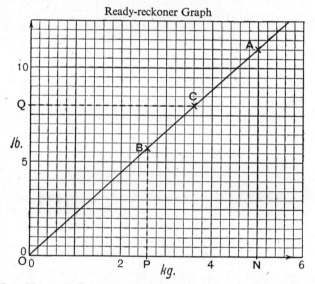

Since 5 kg. $\backsimeq$ 11 lb., we can obtain a point on the graph by marking off the distance ON along the kg. axis which represents 5 kg., and then moving upwards the distance NA which represents 11 lb.; then A is a point on the graph, and the required graph is the straight line which joins A to the origin O.

To express 2·6 kg. in lb., mark off the distance OP along the kg. axis which represents 2·6 kg.; by measurement we see that the distance PB from P up to the graph represents 5·7 lb.; ∴ 2·6 kg. $\backsimeq$ 5·7 lb.

To express 8 lb. in kg., mark off the distance OQ along the lb. axis which represents 8 lb.; by measurement we see that the distance QC from Q across to the graph represents 3·6 kg.; ∴ 8 lb. $\backsimeq$ 3·6 kg.

EXERCISE 71

[All answers should be based on readings from the graphs]

1. Interpret the given travel graph, stating the different speeds in miles per hour. What is the average speed for the whole journey? How can you tell without any calculation which part of the graph corresponds to the greatest speed?

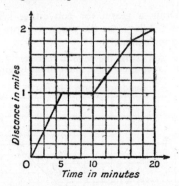

2. A spiral spring is suspended from one end, and its length is measured when different weights are attached to the other end:

Weight in gm.	10	15	30	50	75
Length in cm.	22	24	30	38	48

Draw a graph to show the relation between the length and the load, and use it to find:

  (i) the length if the load is 20 gm., 40 gm., 65 gm.;
  (ii) the load if the length is 23 cm., 28 cm., 42 cm.;
  (iii) the natural length, *i.e.* the length when there is no load.

Is the graph a straight line? If so, what does this mean? The corresponding graph for another spiral spring is a steeper straight line; what does this mean?

[3] Draw the travel graph of a man, travelling due north, who starts at 11 a.m. and walks at 4 m.p.h. for half an hour, then bicycles at 12 m.p.h. for $1\frac{3}{4}$ hr., then stops for $\frac{3}{4}$ hr., then motors at 32 m.p.h. for $1\frac{1}{4}$ hr. How far has he gone at 2.30 p.m.? What is the time when he has travelled 10 mi., 28 mi.? Find his total average speed.

[4] Draw a graph for converting miles to kilometres, for distances up to 5 mi., given that 1 mi. ≃ 1·6 km. Use the graph to express 2·3 mi. in km., and 6·2 km. in miles.

5. The diagram shows the travel graphs OCG, OQS of two men, X and Y respectively, who start from the same house at 10 a.m. and proceed on the same road.

(i) Describe the journey represented by OCG in detail, giving the various speeds. Can you tell at a glance when the man is moving fastest, when he is resting? How far does he go altogether? When does he start to come home?

(ii) Repeat (i) for the graph OQS.

(iii) When does X overtake Y?

(iv) When and where do X and Y pass one another?

(v) How far is X ahead of Y when he turns back?

(vi) How far does X go while Y is resting?

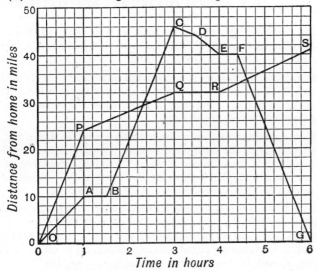

6. Draw a graph for converting degrees Centigrade to degrees Fahrenheit, given that 0° Centigrade, 100° Centigrade are equivalent to 32° Fahrenheit, 212° Fahrenheit respectively. Use the graph to express in degrees Fahrenheit, 35° Centigrade, 70° Centigrade, and to express in degrees Centigrade, 140° Fahrenheit, 185° Fahrenheit.

[7] Draw a graph for converting speeds in miles per hour to speeds in feet per second up to 60 m.p.h., given that 30 m.p.h. is the same speed as 44 ft. per second. Use the graph to express in feet per second, 22 m.p.h., 46 m.p.h., and to express in miles per hour, 20 ft. per second, 75 ft. per second.

*8. Marks in an examination run from 32 to 74. Draw a graph for scaling them to run from 0 to 100. What is the scaled mark if the original mark is 43? What is the original mark if the scaled mark is 83? If A obtains 20 more marks than B in the examination, how many more marks does A get than B after the scaling?

9. A motorist leaves home at 9 a.m.; the mileage recorded by his cyclometer, originally set at zero, is as follows :—

Time .	9.10	9.20	9.25	9.30	9.40	9.50	10.0	10.10	10.20
Mileage	2	5	9	12	16	19	24	31	37

Find from a graph (i) the readings at 9.36, 9.54, 10.15 a.m.; (ii) the distance travelled between 9.35 a.m. and 10.5 a.m.; (iii) the time when the distance travelled is 14 mi., 21 mi., 33 mi.

10. A cyclist starts from A at noon and rides steadily at 12 m.p.h. towards B, 60 mi. away. At 2 p.m. a motorist leaves B for A and travels at 36 m.p.h. Find from a graph when the two meet and their distance from A at this time.

[11] A pedestrian sets off to walk along a road at 4 m.p.h.; a cyclist starts from the same place an hour later and rides along the same road to a town 18 mi. away at 10 m.p.h., waits there for half an hour and then returns at the same speed. When and where does he meet the pedestrian on his return journey?

*12. A few years ago income tax was levied as follows : no tax on the first £150 of a man's income, on the next £250 the tax was 2s. 6d. in the £, and on income beyond this was 5s. in the £. Draw a graph to show the tax payable on any income up to £600. What was the income of a man whose tax was (i) £15, (ii) £50?

Draw *rough graphs* to illustrate Nos. 13–16.

13. A travel graph : a boy walks for 5 min., runs for 2 min., stands still for 3 min., and then returns to his starting-point in a car.

14. The inland postage for letters of various weights : charge up to 2 oz., $1\frac{1}{2}$d.; for each additional 2 oz., or part of it, $\frac{1}{2}$d. more.

[15] The time a person takes to run a hundred yards at different ages.

*16. The bank-balance of a man whose salary is paid only three times a year, namely at the end of March, of July, of December. Explain any special features the graph possesses.

17. Three men A, B, C travel from X to Y by the same road. A walks the distance in 5 hr. B cycles, starting $1\frac{1}{2}$ hr. after A and arriving 1 hr. before him. C motors, starting $\frac{3}{4}$ hr. after B and arriving $\frac{1}{2}$ hr. before him. Show by a graph that B and C pass A at the same place.

*18. X, Y are two places 32 mi. apart. A leaves Y at 1.10 p.m. and drives at a rate which would bring him to X at 2.30 p.m. for a meeting. On the way he meets B, who left X at 1 p.m. and has driven at 30 m.p.h. They talk for 10 min. and A hears that the meeting is at 2.15 p.m. At what rate must A drive for the rest of the journey to be in time. Solve graphically.

*19. To travel from one house to another I can either motor from door to door at an average speed of 20 m.p.h., or I can go by train at an average speed of 45 m.p.h.; but, if I travel by train, it is necessary to allow 20 min. at each end for the journeys between the houses and stations. Find graphically the shortest distance for which it is quicker to go by train, assuming that the distance between the stations is the same as that between the houses.

*20. A cyclist starts at 10 a.m. to ride to a place 8 mi. away, riding at 12 m.p.h. till he has a puncture. He waits 10 minutes trying to repair it and then walks on at 4 m.p.h. He arrives at his destination at 11.15 a.m. How far had he ridden when the puncture occurred?

THREE-MINUTE AND FOUR-MINUTE ORAL PRACTICE

ORAL PRACTICE 1–8 (Ch. I–III)

[Nothing must be written down except the answer]

Oral Practice 1 (3 min.)

1. Add: 67
108
84
19

2. Subtract: 5000
1806

3. 309×11.

4. $4004 \div 7$.

5. Express 2 lb. 8 oz. in oz.

6. 1 ft. 8 in. + 9 in.

7. 9 cwt. × 5, in tons, cwt.   **8.** Express $2^4 \times 2^4 \times 2^4$ as a power of 2.

9. Cost of 1 sq. yd. at 4d. per sq. ft.

10. 3 marbles weigh 2 oz., what do 1 dozen weigh?

Oral Practice 2 (3 min.)

1. Add: 219
703
418
615

2. 872×5.   **3.** $7536 \div 8$.

4. Express 90 in. in ft., in.

5. Express 1 mi. 540 yd. in yd.

6. 8 yd. × 3, in ch., yd.

7. 2 tons 16 cwt. ÷ 8.   **8.** How many cu. inches in a 5-inch cube?

9. 3 men can mow a field in 12 days, how long will 9 men take?

10. Write in index form the cube of 3^2.

Oral Practice 3 (3 min.)

1. Add: 518
678
405
99

2. 809×12.

3. $100001 \div 11$.

4. Express 3 gall. in pints.   **5.** $(30 \times 40 \times 50) \div 10$.

6. 2 cwt. – 50 lb., in cwt., lb.

7. 4 lb. 4 oz. × 8, in qr., lb.

8. Find in ft. the perimeter of a rectangle, 10 in. by 8 in.

9. Cost of half a lb. of tobacco at 9d. an oz.?

10. Express in powers of prime factors, $6^3 \times 10^2$.

Oral Practice 4 (3 min.)

1. Add: 69
   73
   8
   55
   47
   82
   ___

2. Subtract: 62147
            18368
            _____

3. Simplify $2^4 \times 2^6 \div 2^8$.
4. Express 50 oz. in lb., oz.
5. 5 ft. $-$ 1 ft. 8 in.
6. 5 fur. $\times$ 7, in mi., fur.
7. 2 hr. 30 min. $\div$ 10.
8. Cost of 15 envelopes, if 5 envelopes cost 4d.?

9. Write in index form the square root of $2^6 \times 3^4$.
10. The area of a field 40 yd. wide is 4840 sq. yd.; what is its length?

Oral Practice 5 (4 min.)

1. Add: 37
        703
        64
        8
        215
        96
        ___

2. 4038×9.
3. $100908 \div 12$.
4. Express 3000 yd. in mi., yd.
5. Express half an acre in sq. yd.
6. 3 qt. 1 pt. $\times$ 6, in gall., qt.
7. 7 yd. 2 ft. 10 in. $\div$ 11.
8. Cost of a carpet 3 yd. long, 8 ft. wide at 2s. per sq. ft.?

9. Write in index form the L.C.M. of 2×3^4, $2^2 \times 5^2$, $3^2 \times 5$, $2 \times 3^3 \times 5$.
10. A journey takes 10 hours at 24 miles per hour; how long does it take at 40 miles an hour?

Oral Practice 6 (4 min.)

1. Add: 48736
        3098
        72815
        _____

2. Subtract: 807062
           382574
           _____

3. 419×11.
4. Express 10 ac. in sq. yd.
5. 1 yd. $-$ 2 ft. 5 in.

6. 7 cwt. 3 qr. $\times$ 5, in tons, cwt., qr.
7. 2 mi. 3 fur. 6 ch. $\div$ 7.
8. Write in index form the square of 5^3.
9. 2 qt. of water weigh 5 lb.; what is the weight of 2 gall. of water?
10. A tank 6 ft. long, 2 ft. wide, holds 48 cu. ft.; what is its depth?

Oral Practice 7 (4 min.)

1. Add: 804
219
76
57
365

2. Subtract:
£   s.   d.
11   7   6
8 15 10

3. $20086 \div 11$.

4. Express 275 lb. in cwt., lb.

5. Express 4 ch. 15 yd. in yd.

6. 3 lb. 6 oz. $\times 7$, in lb., oz.

7. $(3^4 \times 3^4) \div (3^2 \times 3^6)$.

8. Cost of 12 articles at $7\frac{3}{4}$d. each.

9. How many times is 5 in. contained in 1 yd., and how much is over?

10. A car travels 8 miles in 12 minutes; what is its speed in miles per hour?

Oral Practice 8 (4 min.)

1. Add: 28
74
39
6
51
87

2. Subtract: 613072
218394

3. Subtract: £   s.   d.
20   0   0
7   8 $9\frac{1}{4}$

4. Express 1000 yd. in fur., yd.

5. Express 3 gall. 2 qt. in pints.

6. £3 11s. 8d. $\times 9$.   **7.** 7 qr. 9 lb. 5 oz. $\div 3$.

8. Find the missing digit if *83 is divisible by 11.

9. Find the total area of the four walls of a room, 12 ft. long, 8 ft. wide, 7 ft. high.

10. 8 men can mow a field in 9 days, how long will 6 men take?

ORAL PRACTICE 9–16 (Ch. IV–VIII)

[Nothing must be written down except the answer]

Oral Practice 9 (3 min.)

1. $\frac{3}{8}$ of £1, in s. d.   **2.** $\frac{1}{3} + \frac{1}{6}$.   **3.** Add: 1·03
3·07

4. $0·06 \times 70$.   **5.** $0·258 \div 3$.

6. Express $1\frac{1}{4}$ as a decimal.   **7.** £0·45, in s.

8. Share 59 fr. 50 c. equally among 7 boys.

9. What must be added to $\frac{1}{12}$ to make $\frac{1}{4}$?

10. After travelling 8 mi., I have done $\frac{2}{5}$ of my journey. How long is my journey?

Oral Practice 10 (3 min.)

1. $\frac{3}{4}$ of 3 lb., in lb. oz.   2. $\frac{20}{30} - \frac{1}{6}$.   3. Subtract : 10
                                                                                            0·09

4. 0·2 × 0·3.   5. 0·378 ÷ 70.
6. Express 2 m. 5 cm. in m.   7. $\frac{1}{7}$ as a decimal to 2 places.
8. What fraction is $4\frac{1}{2}$d. of 6d.?
9. Cost of 12 m. at 8 fr. 50 c. per metre?
10. $\frac{1}{2}$ acre is worth £40; what is $\frac{3}{4}$ acre worth?

Oral Practice 11 (3 min.)

1. $\frac{2}{3}$ of 2 yd., in yd. ft.   2. $7 ÷ \frac{1}{3}$.   3. Add : 0·82
                                                                                       2·08
                                                                                       1·1

4. 0·009 × 200.   5. 0·2 ÷ 25.
6. Express 0·05 as a fraction.   7. 0·625s. in pence.
8. Complete $\frac{2}{7} = \frac{6}{...} = \frac{...}{35} = \frac{1}{...}$.
9. Area of mat, 1·2 m. long, 0·9 m. wide?
10. Taking 1 yd. = 0·915 m., express 100 yd. in km.

Oral Practice 12 (3 min.)

1. $\frac{2}{3}$ of £2, in £ s. d.   2. $\frac{5}{12} ÷ \frac{3}{4}$.   3. Add : 0·37
                                                                                         1·64
                                                                                         5·09

4. 0·45 × 0·4.   5. 0·108 ÷ 12.
6. $\frac{3}{11}$ as a decimal to 2 places.   7. 0·85 ton, in cwt.
8. What must be added to $\frac{2}{3}$ to make $1\frac{1}{6}$?
9. Taking 1 litre = $1\frac{3}{4}$ pints, express 4 l. in qt., pt.
10. After spending $\frac{5}{8}$ of my money, I have 2s. left; what have I
    spent?

Oral Practice 13 (4 min.)

1. $\frac{3}{4}$ of 2 yd., in yd., ft., in.   2. $\frac{27}{28} - \frac{3}{14}$.   3. 10 − 0·08 − 0·02.
4. 0·625 × 0·8.   5. 0·09 ÷ 0·4.   6. £0·375, in s. d.
7. Express 0·08 as a fraction.
8. The perimeter of a rectangle is 1 ft. 9 in.; its length is $7\frac{1}{2}$ in.
   What is its breadth?
9. Taking 1 m. = 1·0936 yd., express $\frac{1}{2}$ km. in yards.
10. 1 c.c. of petrol weighs 0·85 gm.; what is the weight of 2 litres
    in kg.?

Oral Practice 14 (4 min.)

1. 9 in. × $1\frac{1}{2}$, in ft., in.   **2.** $\frac{1}{4} + \frac{1}{6} + \frac{1}{2}$.

3. Add : 0·35 and then subtract 0·8 from the sum.
$$1\cdot 65$$

4. 0·2 × 0·4 × 0·6.   **5.** 0·297 ÷ 1·1.   **6.** Express 13s. as a decimal of £1.

7. Subtract 5 sq. dm. from 1 sq. m. ; answer in sq. dm.

8. By what must $\frac{1}{2}$ be multiplied to make $1\frac{1}{4}$?

9. A pile of 200 sheets is 3·5 cm. high; what is the thickness of 1 sheet? Answer in mm.

10. Taking 1 pt. = 0·568 litre, express 1 qt. in c.c.

Oral Practice 15 (4 min.)

1. $\frac{5}{12}$ of £2, in s. d.   **2.** $1\frac{1}{2} \times 1\frac{1}{3}$.   **3.** Add : 0·109
$$0\cdot 83$$
$$0\cdot 776$$

4. 0·1 × 0·02 ÷ 0·5.   **5.** $\frac{3}{13}$ as a decimal to 2 places.

6. Express 3 kg. 45 gm. in kg.

7. Volume of a rectangular block, 4·5 cm. by 2 cm. by 1·5 cm.?

8. Zinc is 7 times as heavy as water; what is the weight of 1·5 cu. dm. of zinc in kg.

9. 12 articles are sold for 5s. 9d.; how much is this per article?

10. $\frac{2}{5}$ of a barrel contains 10 gall.; how much will the barrel hold?

Oral Practice 16 (4 min.)

1. $\frac{1}{4}$ of 1 guinea in s. d.   **2.** $1 - \frac{1}{2} - \frac{1}{4} - \frac{1}{8}$.   **3.** Subtract : 0·104
$$0\cdot 095$$

4. $(0\cdot 03)^3$.   **5.** 15 dm. + 52 cm., in m.

6. $\frac{107}{110}$ as a decimal to 2 places.

7. By what must 0·004 be multiplied to make 2?

8. How many articles at $2\frac{1}{2}$d. each can be bought for 1s., and how much money is over?

9. If copper is 9 times as heavy as water, how many c.c. of copper weigh 450 gm.?

10. A photograph is mounted on a card 10 in. high, 8 in. wide, so that there is a margin $\frac{1}{2}$ in. wide all the way round. What is the area of the photograph?

TESTS IN COMPUTATION

TESTS 1–8 (Ch. IV–VIII)

Test 1

1. (i) $3\frac{1}{4} - 2\frac{2}{3} + 4\frac{1}{6}$; (ii) $3\frac{1}{3} \div 2\frac{1}{3}$.

2. (i) $4\cdot52 \times 0\cdot065$; (ii) $46\cdot71 \div 0\cdot027$.

3. Express 15s. 9d. as a decimal of £1.

4. Express $0\cdot7264$ ton in cwt., lb., to nearest lb.

5. What fraction is 2 ft. 8 in. of 4 ft. 8 in.?

6. If 1 lb. $=0\cdot4536$ kg., express 2 lb. 6 oz. in kg., to nearest gm.

Test 2

1. (i) $\frac{10}{3} - 1\frac{3}{5} + 1\frac{1}{10}$; (ii) $2\frac{1}{2} \times 1\frac{3}{5} \div \frac{2}{3}$.

2. (i) $90\cdot05 \times 0\cdot608$; (ii) $0\cdot01189 \div 0\cdot58$.

3. Express 8 cwt. 3 qr. as a decimal of 1 ton.

4. Find in £ s. d., to the nearest penny, the value of £$3\cdot6094$.

5. $\frac{2}{3}(\frac{1}{6} + \frac{3}{4} \div 2\frac{1}{4}) + (3\frac{1}{4} - \frac{1}{6}) \div 1\frac{1}{4}$.

6. How many times is 1 m. 25 cm. contained in 3 km.?

Test 3

1. (i) $3 - 1\frac{1}{4} + 2\frac{1}{6}$; (ii) $(\frac{1}{3} - \frac{1}{4}) \div (\frac{1}{2} - \frac{1}{3})$.

2. (i) $0\cdot0462 \times 5\cdot65$; (ii) $9\cdot331 \div 430$.

3. Express 12s. $4\frac{1}{2}$d. as a decimal of £1.

4. Express $0\cdot849$ yd. in ft., in., to the nearest inch.

5. Express as decimals: (i) $\frac{7}{20} + \frac{3}{8}$; (ii) $\frac{59}{8 \times 5^4}$.

6. Given that 1 in. $=2\cdot540$ cm., express in metres, to 3 places of decimals, 2 ft. 7 in.

Test 4

1. (i) $3\frac{2}{5} + 1\frac{1}{10} - \frac{7}{4}$; (ii) $4\frac{1}{2} - (1\frac{1}{6} + 2\frac{1}{3}) \div 2$.

2. (i) $0\cdot0805 \times 0\cdot64$; (ii) $1\cdot25028 \div 0\cdot0207$.

3. Express 13s. $10\frac{3}{4}$d. as a decimal of £1, to 4 places.

8

4. Express 3·2794 cwt. in cwt., lb., oz., to the nearest oz.

5. What must be added to the sum of 5 Hg. 7 Dg.; 6 Dg. 8 gm.; 487 dg. to make 1 Kg. Answer in Kg.

6. How many pieces of tape each 8·5 cm. long can be cut from a length of 4 m., and how much remains?

Test 5

1. (i) $4\frac{11}{28} - 1\frac{15}{42} - 1\frac{3}{14}$; (ii) $1 - \frac{2}{3}(\frac{1}{2} + \frac{2}{5})$.

2. (i) $0·475 \times 0·0604$; (ii) $6·426 \div 0·315$.

3. Express 3 fur. 7 ch. 11 yd. as a fraction of $2\frac{1}{2}$ mi.

4. Find correct to 3 places of decimals the value of $\frac{117}{139} + \frac{19}{41}$.

5. If 1 gall. =4·546 litres, find the capacity in c.c. of 3 pt., to the nearest c.c.

6. From a sheet of tin 1 m. square, a rectangular portion 35 cm. by 8 cm. is removed. Find in sq. m. the area of what remains.

Test 6

1. (i) $6\frac{1}{72} - 1\frac{5}{36} - 2\frac{2}{27}$; (ii) $(3\frac{1}{4} - 1\frac{1}{2}) \div (2\frac{5}{8} - \frac{1}{2})$.

2. (i) $0·0607 \times 90·8$; (ii) $0·001972 \div 13·6$.

3. Express 1 qr. 17 lb. 8 oz. as a fraction of 1 cwt.

4. Evaluate $0·375$ of £3 $+\frac{5}{8}$ of £2 10s. $+$ £5·675.

5. Given 1 mi. =1·609 km., express 1 km. in miles, to 3 places of decimals.

6. A wooden cuboid 7 cm. by 6 cm. by 5 cm. weighs 0·1281 kg.; find in gm. the weight of 1 c.c. of the wood.

Test 7

1. (i) $2\frac{17}{104} - 1\frac{29}{52} + 2\frac{10}{39}$; (ii) $4\frac{2}{5} \times \frac{1}{2} - 6\frac{1}{5} \div 3$.

2. (i) $0·5075 \times 0·02008$; (ii) $2·01 \div 0·00375$.

3. Express 17 yd. 2 ft. 5 in. as a decimal of $1\frac{2}{3}$ ch., to 4 places.

4. Find to the nearest penny the value of £4 17s. 5d. $\times 2·37$.

5. Simplify $(1\frac{3}{4} \times 10\frac{2}{3} - 10\frac{2}{5}) \div (1\frac{9}{16} - 3\frac{1}{4} \div 2\frac{1}{6})$.

6. Given 1 kg. =2·205 lb., express 67·9 gm. in oz., to 2 places of decimals.

Test 8

1. (i) $\dfrac{1}{1\frac{1}{3}} + \dfrac{1}{2\frac{1}{2}} - \dfrac{1}{1\frac{1}{9}}$; (ii) $1\frac{1}{4} + \frac{3}{20}(4\frac{1}{3} - 2\frac{1}{2}) \times 5$.

2. (i) $(0\cdot02)^2 \times (0\cdot3)^3$; (ii) $337\cdot02 \div 0\cdot246$.

3. Express 3724 sq. yd. as a decimal of 1 ac., to 3 places.

4. How many lengths, each 1 m. 55 cm., can be marked off along a fence of length 0·25 km., and how much remains over?

5. Simplify $\left(\dfrac{14}{0\cdot35} + \dfrac{9}{0\cdot36} \right) \div \left(\dfrac{14}{0\cdot35} - \dfrac{9}{0\cdot36} \right)$.

6. Given 1 yd. = 0·9144 m., express 1 m. in yards, to 2 places of decimals.

REVISION PAPERS

PAPERS 1–8 (Elementary work)

Paper 1

1. What number multiplied by 17 gives 5253?

2. How many years are there from the beginning of A.D. 849 to the end of A.D. 1934?

3. I buy 3 articles for $2\frac{1}{2}$d., $3\frac{1}{4}$d., $4\frac{3}{4}$d. respectively; what change do I receive from one shilling?

4. (i) Divide £78 12s. by 16.
   (ii) Multiply £108 9s. 5d. by 120.

5. A charabanc takes 45 passengers; how many passengers can be carried by 18 charabancs?

6. If £1 is divided equally between some boys, each gets 1s. 4d.; how many boys are there?

Paper 2

1. (i) Add: 1278; 809; 5914; 7048; 35; 6143.
   (ii) Subtract 8946 from one hundred thousand.

2. The product of three numbers is 4301; two of them are 11 and 17, find the third number.

3. In 1933 there were 139 wet days in Winchester; how many more days were dry than wet?

4. A rectangular field is 436 yards long, 378 yards wide. Find the length in chains of the fence which encloses it.

5. Find the cost of 19 chairs at 16s. 4d. each.

6. A roller makes 118 revolutions in travelling 1298 feet. Find its circumference.

Paper 3

1. What is the excess of the sum of 785 and 439 over the difference between 901 and 208?

2. How many 3d. articles can be bought for £2 11s. 9d.?

3. Oranges are sold at 8 for sixpence. What is the price of 4 dozen, of 1 gross (12 dozen)?

4. To-day is Friday. What day of the week will it be in 900 days time? What day of the week was it 900 days ago?

5. A wheel is 16 ft. in circumference. How many revolutions does it make in travelling 4 furlongs?

6. An advertisement claims that a car runs 35 miles on 1 gallon of petrol, but actually it only does 28 miles to the gallon. How much more petrol is required for 1960 miles than would be needed if the claim were correct?

Paper 4

1. What must be taken from the sum of 9073 and 6284 to leave 10008?

2. Multiply 7084 by 3102. Divide the product by 121.

3. A man buys 150 shirts for £96 and sells them at 18s. 9d. each. Find the profit.

4. How many 1½d. stamps can be bought for £4 17s. 3d.?

5. How many pieces of string, each 20 in. long, can be cut from a length of 75 yd.?

6. A school contains 585 pupils. If there are 29 more girls than boys, find the number of boys.

Paper 5

1. (i) Write down the odd multiples of 19 which are less than 120.
   (ii) Find the quotient and remainder when 84184 is divided by 231.

2. Write down the cost of 1 dozen articles (i) at 5½d. each, (ii) at 7¾d. each, and the cost of 240 articles at 11¾d. each.

3. A grocer buys 45 cases each containing 56 lb. of tea and makes the tea up into 7-lb. packets. How many packets will there be, if there is no wastage?

4. How many tickets at 1s. 8d. each can be bought for £3 15s.?

5. A man walks 175 yd., taking strides of 30 in. each. How many fewer steps would he take if he increased his stride by 5 in.?

6. In a trial lasting one minute, a car travels at the rate of 9 yd. a second for 18 seconds, then 17 yd. a second for 26 seconds, and 23 yd. a second for the rest of the time. How far did it go in the minute?

Paper 6

1. The populations of the seven parishes into which a town is divided are 7219, 5863, 6015, 3186, 9074, 8117, 4928 respectively. How much is the total population short of 45,000?

2. Multiply £2 14s. 10d. by 43.

3. I buy 18 tons of coal and burn 12 cwt. of coal a week. How long will the coal last?

4. A hurdle is 8 ft. long. How many are required to enclose a rectangular piece of ground 136 yd. long, 112 yd. wide?

5. How many cigars at 1s. 9d. each can be bought for £2, and how much money remains?

6. 38 cars are parked side by side with 2 ft. between each and the next. If the breadth of each car is 5 ft., find in yards the total breadth of the row of cars, from one end of the row to the other end.

Paper 7

1. Add: 507163; 294308; 707195; 8259; 30574.

2. (i) Subtract £8 13s. 6½d. from £14 8s. 5¼d.
(ii) Divide £37 3s. 9d. by 21.

3. A man is paid 2s. 7½d. an hour ordinary time and 3s. 10d. an hour overtime. What does he get altogether for 10 hours work of which 2 hours is reckoned overtime?

4. The rungs of a 21-rung ladder are 15 in. apart, and the top and bottom rungs are 1 ft. from the ends. Find the length of the ladder in feet.

5. A man buys 6000 articles at 2¾d. each and sells them at 3½d. each. What profit does he make?

6. A 12-acre field is cut up into allotments each of area 950 sq. yd. How many allotments are there and what area is left over? (1 acre = 4840 sq. yards.)

Paper 8

1. What must be added to the difference between 15004 and 9007 to make ten thousand?

2. A man's pace is 30 in. How many paces does he take in walking 1 mile?

3. The total amount required to pay 4 bills is £241 3s. 1d.; three of the bills are £18 12s. 9d., £74 17s. 8d., £94 9s. 10d.; how much is the fourth bill?

4. A man starts with a salary of £250 a year and receives an increase of £18 a year after each year. What is his salary for (i) his 5th year, (ii) his 20th year?

5. If a lorry runs 15 mi. on a gallon of petrol, and if the petrol costs 1s. 2d. a gall., find the cost of the petrol for a journey of 330 mi.

6. A man buys a consignment of brushes for £7 17s. 6d. and makes a profit of £5 12s. 6d. by selling them at 4½d. each. How many brushes did he buy?

PAPERS 9–16 (Ch. I–III)

Paper 9

1. Find in prime factors the L.C.M. of 270 and 504.

2. (i) By how many yards is 4 mi. short of 8000 yd.?
   (ii) How many chairs 21 in. wide can be put in a row 14 ft. long?

3. If 5 lb. of tea cost 8s. 4d., find the cost of 3 lb. Find also the cost of 1 ton.

4. The area of a rectangular field, 385 yd. long, is 14 ac. Find its breadth.

5. A cheap return ticket is issued for the price of a single ticket and a quarter. What is the cost of a cheap return ticket for a journey for which the single ticket costs £1 7s. 8d.?

6. The diagram represents the cross-section of a girder 5 ft. long; the corners are right-angled and the dimensions are shown in inches. Find (i) the area of the cross-section in sq. in., (ii) the volume of the girder in cu. ft., cu. in.

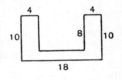

Paper 10

1. Find by prime factors the square root of 2304.

2. (i) Express 12475 oz. in cwt., lb., oz.
   (ii) How many times is 6 cwt. 3 qr. contained in 14 tons 17 cwt.?

3. Lace costs 10d. per foot, find the cost of a piece 11 ft. 6 in. long.

4. A car uses 15 gall. of petrol for a journey of 360 mi. How much does it use for 312 mi. at the same rate and how much does this amount of petrol cost at 1s. 5d. per gall.?

5. Find the area of a gravel path 8 ft. wide which runs all round a rectangular lawn 54 ft. long, 40 ft. wide.

6. How many rectangular blocks measuring 3 in. by 4 in. by 5 in. can be packed in a box measuring 4 ft. by 5 ft. by 6 ft. internally? Find also their weight in cwt. if the blocks weigh 28 lb. per cu. ft.

Paper 11

1. (i) Add: 6 fur. 7 ch. 18 yd.; 5 fur. 6 ch. 14 yd.;
       7 fur. 3 ch. 8 yd.; 4 fur. 4 ch. 16 yd.
    (ii) Divide 77 tons 12 cwt. 2 qr. by 45.

2. A man's income is £985 a year. How much does he save in a year in which he spends £591 more than he saves?

3. Find the cost of a carpet 5 yd. long, 4 yd. wide, at 2s. 6d. per sq. ft.

4. (i) 8 peaches cost 3s.; find the cost of 10 peaches.
    (ii) A man walks 110 yd. a minute; how long will he take to
       walk 15 mi.?

5. A truck is loaded with 624 boxes each weighing 35 lb.; find the weight of the load in tons, cwt.

6. The diagram represents the cross-section of a girder; the corners are right-angled and the dimensions are shown in inches. Find (i) the area of the cross-section in sq. in., (ii) the volume of a 4-ft. length of the girder in cu. ft., cu. in.

Paper 12

1. Find the cube root of 46656.

2. (i) Reduce 5 tons 7 cwt. 36 lb. to lb.
    (ii) Reduce 9280 yd. to mi., ch., yd.

3. Three whole tickets for a certain journey cost £1 14s. 6d.; find the cost of 6 tickets, one of which is half-price, for the same journey.

4. If the price of ribbon is lowered by $1\frac{3}{4}$d. a yard, find the decrease in price per mile.

5. A room 20 ft. long, 16 ft. wide, is carpeted so as to leave a border 2 ft. wide all round the edge. Find the cost of the carpet at 7s. 6d. per sq. yd. Find also the cost of covering the margin at $10\frac{1}{2}$d. per sq. ft.

6. A block of wood measuring 1 ft. 4 in. by 1 ft. 3 in. by 1 ft. 6 in. is cut down into the form of a cube of edge 1 ft. 2 in.; how many cu. in. of wood are cut away?

Paper 13

1. Express 10584 in prime factors. What is the least number by which it must be multiplied to give (i) a perfect square, (ii) a perfect cube?

2. (i) Subtract 6 ch. 17 yd. 2 ft. from 1 fur. 15 yd.
(ii) Divide 1028 tons 14 cwt. 1 qr. by 47.

3. A train travels 36 mi. in 45 min.; how far will it go in an hour and a quarter at the same rate?

4. Find the difference between the weight of 215 boxes each 1 lb. 14 oz. and the weight of 197 boxes each 2 lb. 3 oz.

5. A rectangular tin box with a lid is 7 in. long, 3 in. wide, 2 in. high. Find the area of tin sheeting used to make the box.

6. A metal block is 4 ft. long, 3 ft. wide, 16 in. high. If the metal weighs 490 lb. per cu. ft., find the weight of the block in tons, cwt.

Paper 14

1. Express $12 \times 16 \times 21 \times 28$ as the product of powers of prime numbers. Find its square root.

2. (i) How many times is £1 5s. 8d. contained in £29 10s. 4d.
(ii) Multiply 13 yd. 2 ft. 10 in. by 47. (Answer in ch., yd., etc.)

3. A machine, kept working continuously, crushes 45 tons of ore a day; how many lb. of ore per minute is this?

4. I have enough money to take a three weeks' holiday if I spend 25 shillings a day. How long a holiday can I take if I spend 35 shillings a day?

5. The cover of a safety matchbox is 7 cm. long, 4 cm. wide, 2 cm. high, and its ends are open. Find the area of the exterior surface of the cover.

6. The volume of a rectangular block is 1680 cu. in. (i) Find its height if it is 15 in. long, 7 in. wide. (ii) Find the area of the base if it is 1 ft. high.

Paper 15

1. Find the H.C.F. of 1512 and 6468.

2. (i) Express 70,000 sq. in. in sq. yd., sq. ft., sq. in.
(ii) What is the smallest amount that must be added to £100 to obtain an exact multiple of £1 17s. 3d.?

3. 24 men can repair a road in 15 days. How long will it take 20 men to do so if all work at the same rate?

4. A man buys articles at 3s. 8d. per dozen and sells them at 5¾d. each. Find the profit on the sale of 100 dozen. Find also the profit if he buys 50 dozen but is only able to sell 45 dozen of them.

5. Find the area of the ground plan of the house represented by the diagram; the corners are right-angled and the dimensions are shown in yards.

6. A rectangular tank, 12 ft. by 10 ft., and 7 ft. deep, contains water to a depth of 5 ft. How many blocks of cement, 4 in. by 4 in. by 3 in., can be put into the tank before the water overflows?

Paper 16

1. Lines are drawn so as to divide a rectangle 31 ft. 6 in. long, 25 ft. 8 in. wide into equal squares. Find the least possible number of squares.

2. (i) How many days are there in the years 1931 to 1940, inclusive?
   (ii) Find the cost of 17 tons of coal at £2 8s. 4d. per ton.

3. How many rails 32 ft. long are required for a double-track railway (*i.e.* with up-lines and down-lines) between two places 12 mi. apart?

4. On a map, 2 in. represents 1 mile. What area on the map represents 20 sq. mi. How many acres are represented by an area of half a square inch on the map?

5. A rectangular lawn 45 yd. long, 22 yd. wide, is surrounded by a path 4 ft. 6 in. wide. Find the area of the path in sq. yards. If a wall 5 ft. high runs along the outer edge of the path, find the area of the interior surface of the wall.

6. A closed box is 2 ft. long, 1 ft. 3 in. wide, 11 in. high, and is made of wood half an inch thick. Find the volume of the wood in cu. inches.

PAPERS 17-24 (Ch. I–VIII)

Paper 17

1. In 1932, the B.B.C. received £1,179,031 from licences and £237,834 from publications. The expenditure was £657,935, and in addition £50,000 was contributed to the Treasury. What balance remained?

2. (i) Simplify $3\frac{1}{2} - 1\frac{1}{2}$ of $1\frac{3}{4} + 2\frac{1}{4}$.

(ii) Express 8s. 9d. as a fraction of £1.

3. (i) Express $0 \cdot 0325$ as a vulgar fraction.

(ii) Evaluate $0 \cdot 0755 \times 1 \cdot 84$.

4. A man motors 80 mi. in 2 hr. 40 min.; find his average speed in miles per hour.

5. Taking 1 yd. $= 0 \cdot 9144$ m., express 1 ft. 5 in. in cm., correct to one place of decimals.

6. A beam of timber is 20 ft. long, 8 in. wide, 9 in. deep; the timber weighs 48 lb. per cu. ft. Find the weight of the beam in lb., and express it as a decimal of a ton, to 3 places.

Paper 18

1. (i) Simplify $2\frac{1}{5} + 3\frac{1}{3} - 1\frac{19}{20}$.

(ii) After a boy has spent $\frac{3}{5}$ of his money, he has 7s. left; how much had he at first?

2. (i) Express $\frac{134}{1250}$ as a decimal. (ii) Evaluate $0 \cdot 18513 \div 30 \cdot 6$.

3. (i) Express £4·8875 in £ s. d.

(ii) A field is 66 yd. long, 52 yd. wide; express its area as a decimal of 1 ac., to 3 places of decimals.

4. Find the cost of 5 m. 40 cm. of ribbon at 1 fr. 75 c. per metre.

5. If 1 rupee $=$ 1s. $4\frac{1}{4}$d., find the number of rupees that can be bought for £13 10s. 10d.

6. The diagram represents the cross-section of an iron bar 2 ft. long. The corners are right-angled and the dimensions are shown in inches. Find (i) the area of the cross-section, (ii) the weight of the bar if the iron weighs 0·32 lb. per cu. in.

Paper 19

1. *Write down* a rough estimate of the value of (i) £140·8 ÷ 7; (ii) £4 19s. × 201.

2. (i) Simplify $(\frac{2}{3} - \frac{3}{7})(\frac{5}{6} - \frac{4}{9})(\frac{3}{5}$ of $1\frac{1}{6})$.

    (ii) Express 3s. 9d. as a fraction of 8s. 3d.

3. (i) Express in metres the sum of 6 dm. 5 cm. 8 mm.; 9 dm. 8 cm. 4 mm.; 3 dm. 7 cm. 5 mm.; 206 mm.; 46 cm.

    (ii) Evaluate 0·6093 × 17·82.

4. (i) A car uses $7\frac{1}{2}$ gall. of petrol for 180 mi. How much does it use for 160 mi. at the same rate?

    (ii) A chair weighs 21 lb.; how many can be taken by a lorry that is not allowed to carry more than 30 cwt.?

5. Divide £750 between A, B, C so that A gets £30 more than B, and B gets £15 more than C.

6. Find a man's income in 1934 if he spent 11s. 8d. per day and saved £10 9s. 2d. per month.

Paper 20

1. Find in prime factors the L.C.M. of 66, 84, 112, 165, 189.

2. (i) Simplify $3\frac{17}{20} \times \frac{39}{83} \times 1\frac{3}{22} \div (6\frac{1}{3} + 4\frac{1}{15})$.

    (ii) How many $\frac{3}{4}$-lb. packets can be made up from 60 lb. of tea?

3. (i) Simplify 4·807 − 2·093 − 1·836 + 5·325.

    (ii) Divide 0·1428 by 25·5.

4. A man takes $3\frac{1}{2}$ hr. to bicycle a certain distance at $12\frac{1}{2}$ mi. per hour; how long will the same journey take in a car which goes 40 mi. per hour faster than the bicycle?

5. A workman is paid 1s. 5d. per hour. He works 9 hr. on 5 days a week and 6 hr. on Saturday. How much does he earn per week? If he works 7 hr. overtime he increases his weekly earnings to £4 6s. 3d.; at what rate per hour is he paid for overtime?

6. The diagram represents the cross-section of a girder, 2·4 m. long; the corners are right-angled and the dimensions are shown in cm. Find (i) the area of the cross-section, (ii) the volume in cu. dm.

Paper 21

1. Find the H.C.F. of 882; 396; 1404.

2. (i) Simplify $\frac{1}{4}(1\frac{1}{3}+1\frac{1}{2})-1\frac{2}{5}(\frac{1}{8}-\frac{1}{12})$.

(ii) Express 11 lb. 6 oz. as a fraction of 1 qr. 3 lb. 8 oz.

3. (i) Express 0·726 yd. in ft., in., to the nearest inch.

(ii) Evaluate $(0·16)^2 \times (0·05)^3$.

4. Taking 1 in.=2·540 cm., express 1 m. in inches, correct to 1 place of decimals.

5. Find the total cost of the following: 18 compasses at 7s. 3d. per dozen; 8 dozen pencils at 8s. 3d. per gross; 5 dozen rulers at $3\frac{3}{4}$d. each; 2 dozen drawing-boards at 2s. $3\frac{1}{2}$d. each; $2\frac{1}{4}$ dozen protractors at 4s. 6d. per dozen.

6. A rectangular tin with a lid is 6 in. long, $2\frac{1}{2}$ in. wide, 2 in. high. Find the area of tin used (i) allowing for no overlap, (ii) if the lid overlaps $\frac{1}{4}$ in. on all sides.

Paper 22

1. (i) Simplify $\frac{4}{9}$ of $1\frac{11}{83} \times 2\frac{1}{4} \div (\frac{1}{4}-\frac{1}{52})$.

(ii) A boy sleeps $10\frac{1}{2}$ hr. every day; for what fraction of each day is he awake.

2. (i) Express £3·729 in £ s. d., to the nearest penny.

(ii) Divide 20·75694 by 0·6855.

3. If £1 will purchase 81 francs, express £2 17s. 6d. in francs.

4. A train is timed to do a journey of 54 mi. in 1 hr. 48 min. If it starts 12 min. late, at what extra speed in miles per hour must it travel to arrive punctually?

5. When travelling by train, a man is allowed 60 lb. of luggage free; and he has to pay 16s. 3d. excess when his luggage weighs 2 cwt. 3 qr. 12 lb.; at what rate per lb. is the excess luggage charged?

6. The diagram represents the cross-section of a solid, $\frac{3}{8}$ in. thick. The corners are right-angled and the dimensions are shown in inches. Find (i) the area of the cross-section, (ii) the weight of the solid if the material weighs 4·6 oz. per cu. in.

Paper 23

1. (i) Simplify $(1\frac{1}{2} + 3\frac{3}{4})(3\frac{2}{3} - 2\frac{1}{5}) \div (2\frac{1}{4} - \frac{7}{8})$.

    (ii) A field of area $14\frac{1}{4}$ ac. is divided into allotments each of area $\frac{3}{4}$ ac. How many allotments are there?

2. (i) Evaluate $0·16 \times 0·015 \times 0·0625$.

    (ii) Express 13s. 10d. as a decimal of £1, correct to 3 places.

3. The escalator at the Holborn tube station is 156 ft. long and makes the ascent in 65 sec. Find the speed in miles per hour.

4. A headmaster is paid a fixed salary of £800 a year and a capitation fee of £3 10s. on each boy in the school after the first 50. There are 382 boys; how much does he receive altogether?

5. A box without a lid is 1 ft. long, $8\frac{1}{2}$ in. wide, 7 in. high, external measurements, and is made of wood $\frac{1}{4}$ in. thick. Find the volume of the wood used for making the box.

6. Two men, A and B, measure the length of a fence with their walking-sticks. A's stick is $37\frac{1}{2}$ in. long and he finds that the fence is between 52 and 53 times as long; B's stick is $34\frac{3}{4}$ in. and he finds that the fence is between 57 and 58 times as long. Find in yd., in., the limits between which the length of the fence lies.

Paper 24

1. The number of bunches of bananas imported in 1930 into the United Kingdom was as follows: British West India 5,923,877; Honduras 984,801; Colombia 3,352,002; Costa Rica 2,189,103; other countries 2,539,781. Find the total number imported. If the average weight of a bunch is 34 lb., find the total weight, to the nearest million lb.

2. (i) Simplify $4\frac{1}{2} \times 8\frac{3}{4} \times 2\frac{4}{5} \div (4\frac{1}{8} + 2\frac{1}{2} - 5\frac{7}{9})$.

    (ii) How many pieces of tape $3\frac{1}{4}$ in. long can be cut from a length of 5 yd., and how much remains?

3. (i) Divide $803·76$ by $63·04$.

    (ii) Express 1 ft. 7 in. as a decimal of 1 yd., correct to 3 places.

4. If $1\frac{1}{4}$ tons of coal cost £3 15s., find the cost of $2\frac{3}{4}$ tons.

5. I spend 9 days of a 6 weeks' holiday in Italy at 80 lire a day, and the rest in France at 100 francs a day when the exchange is 64 lire to the £ and 88 francs to the £. Fares amount to £12. Find the total cost of the holiday.

6. The diagram represents a metal sheet 1·2 cm. thick. The corners are right-angled and the dimensions are shown in cm. Find (i) the area of the upper surface of the sheet, (ii) the weight of the sheet to the nearest gm., if 1 c.c. of the metal weighs 7·5 gm.

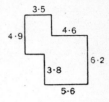

PART II

CHAPTER X

FRACTIONAL PARTS AND PRACTICE

The method for expressing one quantity as a fraction of another quantity of the same kind was explained in Chapter IV, see p. 34; the following exercise is intended merely for revision :—

EXERCISE 72 (Oral)

Simplify :

1. $\frac{1}{4}$ of 1s.
2. $\frac{1}{5}$ of £1.
3. $\frac{1}{10}$ of £1.
4. $\frac{1}{3}$ of 1 ft.
5. $\frac{1}{5}$ of 1 ton.
6. $\frac{1}{6}$ of 1 yd.
7. $\frac{1}{8}$ of 1s.
8. $\frac{1}{5}$ of 1 hr.
9. $\frac{1}{8}$ of 1 cwt.
10. $\frac{1}{8}$ of 1 gall.
11. $\frac{1}{4}$ of 1 ch.
12. $\frac{1}{8}$ of 1 mi.
13. $\frac{1}{8}$ of £1.
14. $\frac{1}{12}$ of 2s. 6d.
15. $\frac{1}{3}$ of £1.
16. $\frac{1}{16}$ of £1.

Express the first quantity as a fraction of the second :

17. 4d.; 1s.
18. 5s.; £1.
19. 3d.; 1s.
20. 9 in.; 1 yd.
21. 14 lb.; 1 cwt.
22. $1\frac{1}{2}$d.; 1s.
23. $1\frac{1}{2}$d.; 6d.
24. $1\frac{1}{2}$ in.; 1 ft.
25. 2s. 6d.; £1.
26. 6s. 8d.; £1.
27. 440 yd.; 1 mi.
28. 3s. 4d.; £1.

Example 1. Find the value of $\frac{3}{7}$ of £8 5s. 8d.

Divide £8 5s. 8d. into 7 equal shares and then find the value of 3 of these shares :

$$\frac{1}{7} \text{ of £8 5s. 8d.} = £1 \text{ 3s. 8d.}$$
$$\therefore \frac{3}{7} \text{ of £8 5s. 8d.} = (£1 \text{ 3s. 8d.}) \times 3 = £3 \text{ 11s.}$$

EXERCISE 73

Find the value of :

1. $\frac{2}{3}$ of 1s.
2. $\frac{3}{5}$ of £1.
3. $\frac{2}{3}$ of £1.
4. $\frac{3}{8}$ of £1.
5. $\frac{1}{5}$ of £2.
[6] $\frac{3}{4}$ of 10s.
7. $\frac{4}{5}$ of 2s. 6d.
[8] $\frac{2}{3}$ of 10s.

9. $\frac{3}{4}$ of 1 lb.   [**10**] $\frac{2}{5}$ of 1 ton.   **11.** $\frac{3}{4}$ of 1 yd.   [**12**] $\frac{5}{8}$ of 1 mi.

13. $\frac{7}{10}$ of 1 hr.   [**14**] $\frac{3}{20}$ of 15 gall. **15.** $\frac{5}{12}$ of £1.   [**16**] $\frac{3}{16}$ of £1.

17. $\frac{1}{3}$ of £2 10s. 6d.   [**18**] $\frac{1}{7}$ of £3 8s. 10d.

[**19**] $\frac{2}{3}$ of £5 5s.   **20.** $\frac{4}{9}$ of £5 11s. 9d.

[**21**] $\frac{3}{4}$ of 5 yd. 2 ft. 8 in.   **22.** $\frac{3}{5}$ of 7 tons 3 cwt. 3 qr.

*****23.** $\frac{5}{11}$ of £4 2s. 6d.   *****24.** $\frac{19}{55}$ of £8 8s. $5\frac{1}{4}$d.

*****25.** Subtract $\frac{2}{15}$ of 5s. 10d. from $\frac{5}{12}$ of 2s. 8d.

Simple Practice

Example 2. Find the cost of 55 note-books at $7\frac{1}{2}$d. each.

		£	s.	d.
	Cost at 1s. each	2	15	0
6d. $= \frac{1}{2}$ of 1s.,	Cost at 6d. each	1	7	6
$1\frac{1}{2}$d. $= \frac{1}{4}$ of 6d.,	Cost at $1\frac{1}{2}$d. each		6	$10\frac{1}{2}$
	Cost at $7\frac{1}{2}$d. each	1	14	$4\frac{1}{2}$

∴ the cost is £1 14s. $4\frac{1}{2}$d.

Note. A line is drawn below £2 15s. to prevent its being added in to the total cost.

Example 3. Find the cost of 37 tons of coal at £2 7s. 6d. per ton.

		£	s.	d.
	Cost at £1 per ton	37	0	0
	Cost at £2 per ton	74	0	0
5s. $= \frac{1}{4}$ of £1,	Cost at 5s. per ton	9	5	0
2s. 6d. $= \frac{1}{2}$ of 5s.,	Cost at 2s. 6d. per ton	4	12	6
	Cost at £2 7s. 6d. per ton	87	17	6

∴ the cost is £87 17s. 6d.

The explanations on the left of the lines drawn down the page in Examples 2, 3 need not be written down, and those to the right of it may be shortened. This also applies to Examples 6–12.

In these examples, the compound quantity is broken up into a set of *aliquot parts* of the principal unit, that is fractions having 1 as numerators.

Example 4. If the unit is 1s., show how to break up 10d. into the sum of aliquot parts or aliquot parts of aliquot parts.

10d. may be taken as the sum of

$\begin{cases} 6\text{d.} = \frac{1}{2} \text{ of 1s.} & \text{(leaves 4d.)} \\ 3\text{d.} = \frac{1}{2} \text{ of 6d.} & \text{(leaves 1d.)} \\ 1\text{d.} = \frac{1}{3} \text{ of 3d.} \end{cases}$ *or* more shortly
$\begin{cases} 6\text{d.} = \frac{1}{2} \text{ of 1s.} \\ 4d. = \frac{1}{3} \text{ of 1s.} \end{cases}$

Example 5. If the unit is £1, show how to break up 6s. 3d. into the sum of aliquot parts or aliquot parts of aliquot parts.

6s. 3d. may be taken as the sum of

$$\begin{cases} 5\text{s.} = \frac{1}{4} \text{ of £1} \quad \text{(leaves 1s. 3d.)} \\ 1\text{s.} = \frac{1}{5} \text{ of 5s.} \quad \text{(leaves 3d.)} \\ 3\text{d.} = \frac{1}{4} \text{ of 1s.} \end{cases}$$

or more shortly

$$\begin{cases} 5\text{s.} \quad = \frac{1}{4} \text{ of £1.} \\ 1\text{s. 3d.} = \frac{1}{4} \text{ of 5s.} \end{cases}$$

EXERCISE 74 (Oral)

Break up into the sum of aliquot parts or aliquot parts of aliquot parts of the given unit:

Nos. 1–5, unit 1s.

1. 9d.   **2.** 5d.   **3.** $7\frac{1}{2}$d.   **4.** $4\frac{1}{2}$d.   **5.** $7\frac{3}{4}$d.

Nos. 6–21, unit £1.

6. 11s.   **7.** 11s. 6d.   **8.** 11s. 9d.   **9.** 11s. 10d.
10. 12s. 6d.   **11.** 16s.   **12.** 16s. 4d.   **13.** 17s. 9d.
14. 6s. 6d.   **15.** 6s. 4d.   **16.** 4s. 8d.   **17.** 5s. 4d.
18. 8s. 4d.   **19.** 4s. $7\frac{1}{2}$d.   **20.** 12s. $4\frac{1}{2}$d.   **21.** 2s. $8\frac{1}{2}$d.

Nos. 22–25, unit 1 ton.

22. 14 cwt.   **23.** 6 cwt. 1 qr.   **24.** 17 cwt. 2 qr.   **25.** 5 cwt. 3 qr.

Nos. 26–29, unit 1 yd.

26. 1 ft. 4 in.   **27.** 1 ft. 9 in.   **28.** $10\frac{1}{2}$ in.   **29.** $7\frac{3}{4}$ in.

Nos. 30–33, unit 1 cwt.

30. 2 qr. 16 lb.   **31.** 3 qr. 11 lb.   **32.** 1 qr. 5 lb.   **33.** 3 qr. 22 lb.

EXERCISE 75

Find by Practice the cost of the following articles :—

1. 26 at 9d. each.   [**2**] 27 at 5d. each.
3. 68 at $4\frac{1}{2}$d. each.   [**4**] 94 at $7\frac{1}{2}$d. each.
5. 85 at 1s. 8d. each.   [**6**] 31 at 2s. 7d. each.
[**7**] 43 at £2 5s. each.   **8.** 67 at £1 15s. each.
[**9**] 72 at £1 12s. each.   **10.** 49 at £2 6s. each.
11. 65 at £5 4s. 8d. each.   [**12**] 86 at £3 12s. 6d. each.
[**13**] 92 at £4 6s. 8d. each.   **14.** 74 at £2 13s. 4d. each.
[**15**] 87 at £7 3s. 9d. each.   **16.** 66 at £5 6s. 3d. each.

Find by Practice the weight of the following :—

17. 35 books, each 9 oz. (in lb., oz.).

[18] 47 boxes, each 21 lb. (in qr., lb.).

19. 29 boxes, each 18 lb. (in qr., lb.).

[20] 38 jars, each 2 lb. 5 oz. (in lb., oz.).

21. 58 loads, each 1 ton 12 cwt.   **[22]** 76 loads, each 3 tons 9 cwt.

Work by Practice methods :

[23] 1 ft. 9 in. × 85 (in yd., ft., in.).

24. 2 yd. 2 ft. 8 in. × 74 (in yd., ft., in.).

[25] 2 hr. 25 min. × 52 (in hr., min.).

26. 3 cwt. 70 lb. × 39 (in cwt., lb.).

Example 6.   Find the cost of $31\frac{1}{2}$ lb. at 17s. $10\frac{1}{2}$d. per lb.

		£	s.	d.
	Cost at £1 per lb.	31	10	0
10s. = $\frac{1}{2}$ of £1,	„ 10s. „	15	15	0
5s. = $\frac{1}{2}$ of 10s.,	„ 5s. „	7	17	6
2s. 6d. = $\frac{1}{2}$ of 5s.,	„ 2s. 6d. „	3	18	9
3d. = $\frac{1}{10}$ of 2s. 6d.,	„ 3d. „		7	$10\frac{1}{2}$
$1\frac{1}{2}$d. = $\frac{1}{2}$ of 3d.,	„ $1\frac{1}{2}$d. „		3	$11\frac{1}{4}$
	Cost at 17s. $10\frac{1}{2}$d. per lb.	28	3	$0\frac{3}{4}$

Note.   Draw a line below £31 10s. to show that it must not be added into the answer.

Example 7.   Multiply £73 17s. $2\frac{1}{4}$d. by 157.

		£	s.	d.
157 times £1		157	0	0
„ „ £70		10990	0	0
„ „ £3		471	0	0
10s. = $\frac{1}{2}$ of £1,	„ „ 10s.	78	10	0
5s. = $\frac{1}{2}$ of 10s.,	„ „ 5s.	39	5	0
2s. = $\frac{1}{5}$ of 10s.,	„ „ 2s.	15	14	0
2d. = $\frac{1}{12}$ of 2s.,	„ „ 2d.	1	6	2
$\frac{1}{4}$d. = $\frac{1}{8}$ of 2d.,	„ „ $\frac{1}{4}$d.		3	$3\frac{1}{4}$
157 times £73 17s. $2\frac{1}{4}$d.		11595	18	$5\frac{1}{4}$

It is sometimes shorter to use a *subtraction method.*

Example 8.   Find the cost of 185 yards at 11d. per yard.

		£	s.	d.
	Cost at 1s. per yd.	9	5	0
1d. = $\frac{1}{12}$ of 1s.,	„ 1d. „		15	5
Subtract.	Cost at 11d. per yd.	8	9	7

Example 9. Find the weight of 74 loads, each weighing 2 tons 18 cwt.

		ton	cwt.
Weight at 1 ton per load		74	0
,, 3 tons ,,		222	0
2 cwt. = $\frac{1}{10}$ of 1 ton,	,, 2 cwt. ,,	7	8
Subtract. Weight at 2 tons 18 cwt. per load		214	12

EXERCISE 76

Find by Practice the cost of the following articles :—

1. 48 at £2 16s. each.   [2] 75 at £1 13s. each.
3. 86 at £3 12s. 9d. each.   [4] 37 at £2 6s. 2d. each.
5. 184 at 16s. 4½d. each.   [6] 272 at 8s. 4¾d. each.
7. 57 at £4 9s. 3d. each.   [8] 74 at £1 17s. 9¼d. each.
9. 3700 at 8s. 7¾d. each.   [10] 1550 at £1 13s. 2½d. each.

Find by Practice the total weight of the following :—

11. 83 loads, each 5 cwt. 1 qr. 14 lb.
[12] 136 loads, each 1 ton 12 cwt. 2 qr.
13. 190 loads, each 2 tons 16 cwt. 1 qr.
[14] 854 loads, each 3 cwt. 1 qr. 20 lb.

Find by Practice the total length of the following :—

*15. 345 rods, each 2 yd. 2 ft. 5 in. long; answer in ch., yd., etc.
*16. 218 rolls of wire, each 2 ch. 13 yd. 1 ft. long; answer in ch., yd., ft.

Find by Practice methods :

17. The cost of 265 tons of coke at 41s. 9d. per ton.
[18] The cost of 70,000 mats at 2s. 7¼d. each.
*19. The cost of 58¾ dozen articles at 4s. 6d. per dozen.

Use subtraction methods to find :

20. The cost of 87 yd. at 5½d. per yard.
[21] The cost of 168 yd. at 2s. 11¾d. per yard.
22. The weight of 63 boxes, each weighing 5 lb. 7 oz. (in lb., oz.).
*23. The weight of 275 boxes, each weighing 1 qr. 24 lb. (in cwt., qr., lb.).
*24. The cost of 1384 yd. at 1s. 10½d. per yard.

Compound Practice. The next example shows the process which is used when two compound quantities are involved.

Example 10. Find the cost of 5 tons 12 cwt. 2 qr. at £4 3s. 4d. per ton.

		£	s.	d.
Cost of 1 ton		4	3	4
„ 5 tons		20	16	8
„ 10 cwt.		2	1	8
„ 2 cwt.			8	4
„ 2 qr.			2	1
Cost of 5 tons 12 cwt. 2 qr.		23	8	9

10 cwt. = $\frac{1}{2}$ of 1 ton,
2 cwt. = $\frac{1}{5}$ of 10 cwt.,
2 qr. = $\frac{1}{4}$ of 2 cwt.,

In money sums, *vulgar fractions should not be used in the pence column*, unless only $\frac{1}{4}$d., $\frac{1}{2}$d., $\frac{3}{4}$d. occur. If the answer is required correct to the nearest penny, two places of decimals should be retained in the pence column in the working.

Example 11. Find, correct to the nearest penny, the cost of 3 tons 7 cwt. 3 qr. at £2 11s. 5d. per ton.

		£	s.	d.
Cost of 1 ton		2	11	5
„ 3 tons		7	14	3
„ 5 cwt.			12	10·25
„ 2 cwt.			5	1·7
„ 2 qr.			1	3·42
„ 1 qr.				7·71
Cost of 3 tons 7 cwt. 3 qr.		8	14	2·08

5 cwt. = $\frac{1}{4}$ of 1 ton,
2 cwt. = $\frac{1}{10}$ of 1 ton,
2 qr. = $\frac{1}{4}$ of 2 cwt.,
1 qr. = $\frac{1}{2}$ of 2 qr.,

∴ the cost is £8 14s. 2d. correct to the nearest penny.

Example 12. Find, correct to the nearest penny, the cost of 129 tons 11 cwt. 1 qr. at £2 6s. 2d. per ton.

	£	s.	d.		£
Cost of 1 ton	2	6	2	*or*	2·30833....
„ 10 tons	23	1	8	*use*	23·08333....
„ 120 tons	277	0	0	*decimals*	276·99996
„ 9 tons	20	15	6		20·77497
„ 10 cwt.	1	3	1		1·15416
„ 1 cwt.		2	3·7		0·11541
„ 1 qr.			6·92		0·02885
Total cost	299	1	5·62		299·07335

∴ the cost is £299 1s. 6d. correct to the nearest penny.

EXERCISE 77

Find by Practice the cost of:

1. 3 tons 6 cwt. at £2 10s. per ton.
2. 5 lb. 11 oz. at £1 14s. per lb.
[3] 2 tons 3 cwt. 2 qr. at £4 6s. 8d. per ton.
4. 5 cwt. 2 qr. 21 lb. at £4 10s. per cwt.
[5] 7 yd. 1 ft. 8 in. at £2 7s. 3d. per yard.
6. 5 gall. 3 qt. 1 pt. at £1 11s. 4d. per gallon.
7. 2 tons 12 cwt. 2 qr. 8 lb. at 2s. 4d. per cwt.
[8] 3 ch. 15 yd. 2 ft. at £48 2s. 6d. per chain.
*9. 24 ac. 3 r. 19 p. at £38 per acre.

Find, correct to the nearest penny, the cost of:

10. 6 cwt. 3 qr. 7 lb. at £1 4s. 6d. per cwt.
[11] 5 cwt. 2 qr. 21 lb. at 8s. 2$\frac{1}{2}$d. per cwt.
12. 4 tons 4 cwt. 1 qr. at £3 18s. per ton.
[13] 2 qr. 20 lb. 12 oz. at £2 7s. 9d. per quarter.
14. 7 yd. 2 ft. 5 in. at 15s. 4d. per yard.
*15. 8 ac. 3 r. 26 p. at £3 18s. 6d. per acre.
*16. 4 tons 1 cwt. 3 qr. 17 lb. at £52 8s. 6d. per ton.
*17. 15 tons 14 cwt. 60 lb. at £4 13s. 6d. per ton.

Find by Practice the dividend on:

18. £360 at 2s. 3d. in the £.   [19] £248 15s. at 1s. 8d. in the £.

Find by Practice the tax payable on:

[20] £854 at 5s. 9d. in the £.   21. £174 at 13s. 8$\frac{1}{2}$d. in the £.

Find, correct to the nearest penny, the cost of:

*22. 108 tons 13 cwt. 1 qr. at £2 3s. 2d. per ton.
*23. 173 tons 11 cwt. 2 qr. at £3 14s. 8d. per ton.
*24. 127 tons 6 cwt. 3 qr. 10 lb. at £2 7s. 8d. per ton.

MISCELLANEOUS EXAMPLES

EXERCISE 78

1. Find the cost of 150 handkerchiefs at 1s. 4d. each.
[2] Find the cost of 2$\frac{3}{4}$ yd. of material at 4s. 10d. per yard.
3. The duty on tobacco is 13s. 4d. per lb.; find the duty on 4 lb. 12 oz.

4. Find the income tax on £420 at 4s. 6d. in the £.

[5] Find the cost of 3 yd. 2 ft. of carpet at 8s. 10½d. per yard.

6. Find the cost of 360 coats at 18s. 11d. each.

*7. Use the fact that 1s. per lb. is equivalent to £112 per ton to find the cost per ton which is equivalent to 10½d. per lb.

8. Multiply 13s. 8d. by 2⅝ by a practice method. $(\frac{5}{8} = \frac{1}{2} + \frac{1}{8}.)$

[9] Find to the nearest penny the cost of 650 bulbs at 18s. per 1000.

*10. Evaluate by a practice method 0·65 of £3 11s. 8d.

*11. An agent receives a commission of £8 15s. on every £100 worth of orders he obtains. What is his commission on orders amounting to £136?

12. Find the cost of 92 yd. at 2s. 11¾d. per yard.

[13] What dividend is due on £180 at 3s. 10d. in the £?

14. A servant earns 18s. 6d. a week, but 9d. a week is deducted for health insurance. How much money does he receive for 52 weeks?

15. Taking 1 yd. = 0·9144 m., express 1 ft. 5¼ in. in cm., to the nearest mm.

*16. A car travels 46 mi. an hour; how far, to the nearest $\frac{1}{100}$ mi., does it go in 28 min. 40 sec.?

[17] Find in cwt., lb., oz. the weight of 840 boxes, each of which weighs 1 lb. 11 oz.

[18] Find the total cost of 1500 1½d. stamps and 1500 envelopes at 25s. per thousand.

19: £100 a year is equivalent approximately to 5s. 5¾d. a day. Use this fact to find, to the nearest penny, what daily expenditure is equivalent to £165 a year.

20. A bankrupt's liabilities (*i.e.* what he owes) amount to £435, and he is only able to pay 8s. 6d. for every £ he owes. Find the amount of his assets (*i.e.* what he possesses).

*21. How much is produced by a poor-rate of 3s. 2½d. in the £ on a rateable value of £12,850?

*22. The duty on cigars is 17s. 11d. per lb. and on cigarettes is 14s. 5d. per lb. Find the total duty on 75 lb. of cigars and 135 lb. of cigarettes.

23. A man who insures his life at the age of 40 pays annually £3 18s. 10d. for each £100 insurance. What is his annual payment on an insurance for £750?

*24. A tradesman bought 150 eggs at 3s. 2d. a score and 180 eggs at 2s. 1½d. a dozen. He sold them all at 5 for 1s. What was his profit?

*25. A car travels 6 mi. 1150 yd. in 8 min.; how far, to the nearest 10 yd., does it go in 11 min. 25 sec. at the same rate?

CHAPTER XI

RATE, RATIO AND PROPORTION

Rate and Ratio. If a man walks 7 miles in 2 hours, we say that he walks at the *rate* of $\frac{7}{2}$ miles per hour, $3\frac{1}{2}$ m.p.h. If a man earns 16s. for 3 hours' work, we say that his *rate* of pay is $\frac{16}{3}$s. per hour, 5s. 4d. per hour. In these examples, the word **rate** is used to state how a quantity is altering with the time; it is, however, also used in other ways: If I buy 3 lb. of tea for 5s., I pay at the *rate* of 1s. 8d. per lb.; if a laundry charges 2s. for washing 12 towels, the *rate* of charge is 2d. per towel.

In these examples the word rate is used in connection with two quantities of *different kinds*, it may of course also be used if the quantities are of the same kind: if the price of an article, usually sold for 12s., is reduced in a sale by 3s., the reduction is at the *rate* of "3d. in the shilling."

The sizes of two quantities of the *same kind* may be compared in two ways. The ages of two children might be compared by saying one is 9 months older than the other; the temperature of a sick person might be stated as 2 degrees above normal; in each case the comparison is made in the form of a *difference*. On the other hand, the scale of the model of a ship would be described as $\frac{1}{100}$, if 1 foot length of the model represents 100 feet length of the ship; it would be valueless to say that the model is 198 ft. shorter than the ship. Here the comparison is made in the form of a *ratio*; that is, the fraction which the first quantity is of the second.

Suppose a school contains 150 boys and 200 girls, then the number of boys is $\frac{3}{4}$ of the number of girls, and we say that the *ratio* of the number of boys to the number of girls is 3 to 4, written 3 : 4; and this ratio can be represented by the fraction $\frac{3}{4}$.

Ratios should be expressed as simply as possible; just as the fraction $\frac{8}{36}$ is reduced to $\frac{2}{9}$, so the ratio 8 : 36 is equivalent to 2 : 9

Thus a ratio is unaltered if the two numbers (or quantities) of the ratio are both multiplied, or both divided, by the same number. For example,

the ratio $\frac{5}{8} : \frac{3}{4}$ equals the ratio $\frac{5}{8} \times 12 : \frac{3}{4} \times 12$, that is $10 : 9$.

If the prices of two cars A, B are £450, £600 respectively,

$$\frac{\text{price of A}}{\text{price of B}} = \frac{£450}{£600} = \frac{3}{4} \quad \text{and} \quad \frac{\text{price of B}}{\text{price of A}} = \frac{£600}{£450} = \frac{4}{3};$$

and we write

price of A : price of B $= 3 : 4$ and price of B : price of A $= 4 : 3$.

Conversely, the statement that the ratio of the price of A to the price of B is $3 : 4$ means that the price of A is $\frac{3}{4}$ of the price of B, and that the price of B is $\frac{4}{3}$ of the price of A.

EXERCISE 79 (Oral)

Write the following rates in a simple form :—

1. 60 miles in 5 hours.
2. 18s. for 3 hours' work.
3. 4 lb. of coffee for 6s.
4. 15s. for 12 tickets.
5. 2s. 6d. for washing 6 shirts.
6. £30 rent for 4 months.
7. 5 cu. ft. of wood weigh 210 lb.
8. 8 wickets for 92 runs.
9. 12 teachers for 180 pupils.
10. Income £1000, tax £200.
11. House rent £60, tax £18.
12. Ordinary price 9s., reduction 3s.

Express each of the following ratios as simply as possible in the form $a : b$, and state what fraction the first quantity, or number, is of the second :—

13. A length of 8 in. to a length of 12 in.
14. A weight of 5 lb. to a weight of 10 lb.
15. A cost of 9d. per lb. to a cost of 1s. per lb.
16. 12 cm. to 4 cm.
17. 15 ft. to 10 ft.
18. 14 lb. to 18 lb.
19. 16 sq. in. to 36 sq. in.
20. 20 lb. to 5 lb.
21. 15s. to £2.
22. 18 to 36.
23. 32 to 24.
24. 5 to 25.
25. 36 : 6.
26. 30 : 90.
27. 0·4 : 1.
28. 7s. 6d. : £1.
29. 2 ft. 6 in. : 1 yd.
30. 4 cm. : 25 mm.
31. 50 m. : 1 km.
32. 5 gm. : 5 kg.
33. 3 pt. : 3 qt.
34. $\frac{1}{8} : \frac{1}{2}$.
35. $\frac{1}{4} : \frac{3}{4}$.
36. $1\frac{1}{2} : 2$.
37. 3 sq. ft. : 1 sq. yd.
38. 9 oz. : $1\frac{1}{2}$ lb.
39. $1\frac{1}{4}$ hr. : 45 min.

40. A speed of $7\frac{1}{2}$ mi. per hour to a speed of $12\frac{1}{2}$ mi. per hour.

41. Wages at 1s. 3d. per hour to wages at 12s. for 8 hr.

42. A price of 2s. 3d. per lb. to a price of $2\frac{1}{4}$d. per oz.

Taxation. The cost of the various national services, such as defence, the upkeep of the Army, Navy and Air Force, general administration carried out by the Civil Service, national debt interest, etc., is met by taxation, levied in accordance with the regulations contained in the Budget which is laid before the House of Commons each April by the Chancellor of the Exchequer.

Revenue is collected in many different forms, such as duties on commodities (customs and excise), special taxes (entertainment tax, motor tax, etc.), stamps on legal documents, death duties, etc., but the largest source is income tax and surtax.

The regulations for income tax change from year to year, but the general principle is that every person whose income exceeds £100 if unmarried, or £150 if married, pays a certain fraction of his income as tax, this fraction being small for small incomes and increasing as the income increases. For example, it might happen that a man whose income is £300 pays £15 tax, that is $\frac{1}{20}$ of his income, while a man whose income is £1000 pays £150 tax, that is $\frac{3}{20}$ of his income, and a man with an income of £4000 pays £1000 tax, that is $\frac{1}{4}$ of his income.

Income tax is usually quoted in a form such as "4s. in the £"; this would mean that on the part of a man's income to which this rate refers, the tax is 4s. for each £ of income.

Those who live in towns enjoy certain advantages such as street-lighting, efficient drainage and sanitation, public parks, free libraries, etc. The cost of these municipal services and other charges such as poor relief, etc., is met by the **Rates,** that is a tax levied on the house-holders in the town; there is a similar tax in rural districts.

The principle on which this tax is levied is that a man who lives in a house of " annual value " £60 a year ought to pay twice as much as a man whose house has an annual value of only £30 a year. The annual value is not necessarily the same as the annual rent, but is fixed by periodical assessments under Act of Parliament in which allowance is made for cost of maintenance and other charges and is called the *rateable value* or *assessed value*. The tax varies with the locality, from as little as 6s. in the £ up to as much as 25s. in the £, or even more, for every £1 in the rateable value. For example, if a house, whose rent may be £60 a year, is assessed at £50 a year and if a rate of 14s. in the £ is levied, the tax for that year would be (14 × 50)s., that is £35.

Bankruptcy. If a business is being conducted at a loss, a time will come when the *capital*, that is the money which has been put into the business, has all been spent and the owner of the business is no longer able to pay his debts.

If a *creditor*, that is a person to whom money is owed, is unable to get the money due to him, he can take legal proceedings and eventually, if the debt remains unpaid, the owner of the business will be "adjudicated a bankrupt." When this happens, all the owner's property, called his *assets*, is taken over by an official, called the *Receiver*, whose duty it is to pay the creditors as much of the amount due to them as is available.

Certain preferential claims must first be paid in full, if possible, such as rent, taxes and servants' wages; the remainder of the assets is then shared among the "unsecured creditors." Suppose, for example, the value of the remaining assets is £1000, and the *liabilities*, that is the total amount still owing, are £4000, each unsecured creditor will be paid at the rate of £1 for each £4 due to him, that is will receive $\frac{1}{4}$ of what he is owed, and the bankrupt is then said to pay at the rate of "5s. in the £."

Example 1. A man buys a house for £1650 and receives £132 rent a year for it. Find the ratio of the annual rent to the purchase price.

$$\frac{\text{annual rent}}{\text{purchase price}} = \frac{£132}{£1650} = \frac{11 \times 12}{11 \times 150} = \frac{2}{25};$$

∴ annual rent : purchase price = 2 : 25.

Example 2. The rateable value of a town is £265,400. Find the money obtained from a rate of 11s. 6d. in the £.

The ratio of the money obtained to the rateable value = $11\frac{1}{2}$: 20 = 23 : 40;

∴ the money obtained = $\frac{23}{40}$ of £265,400

$$= £(6635 \times 23) = £152,605.$$

Note. This result can be obtained by using a practice method:
   a rate of 10s. in the £ produces £132,700 ($\frac{1}{2}$ of £265,400);
   a rate of 1s. in the £ produces £13,270;
   a rate of 6d. in the £ produces £6,635;   then add.

Example 3. A bankrupt's assets are £432, and he can pay at 13s. 6d. in the £. Find his liabilities.

The ratio of his liabilities to his assets = 20 : $13\frac{1}{2}$ = 40 : 27;

∴ his liabilities = $\frac{40}{27}$ of £432 = £(16 × 40) = £640.

EXERCISE 80

Express the ratio of the first quantity to the second as simply as possible (i) as a fraction; (ii) in the form *a* : *b* (Nos. 1-8).

1. 960 mi.; 1320 mi.   **[2]** £1200; £640.   **3.** 2s. 4d.; 17s. 6d.

[4] 42 lb.; $\frac{1}{4}$ ton.   **5.** $2\frac{1}{4}$ hr.; 35 min.   **[6]** $11\frac{1}{4}$d.; 1s. $1\frac{1}{2}$d.

*7. 2¾d. per oz.; 5s. 6d. per lb.

8. 35 ft. per sec.; 500 yd. per min.

[9] Find the ratio of the length of the Ganges (1500 miles) to that of the Amazon (4000 miles).

[10] The tax on an income of £840 is £126. Find the ratio of the tax to the income.

11. A school contains 360 girls and 240 boys. Find the ratio of (i) the number of girls to the number of boys; (ii) the number of boys to the number of pupils.

12. A man earns £750 a year and spends £630 a year. Find the ratio of (i) his income to his expenditure; (ii) his savings to his income.

[13] Two cars cost £210, £375 respectively when new. After 6 months the market value of each has fallen £45. Find the ratio of their values (i) when new; (ii) after 6 months.

14. The sides of two squares are 6 in., 8 in. long. Find the ratio of (i) their perimeters; (ii) their areas.

15. Pressed pork is quoted at 6d. per ¼ lb. and roast pork at 3s. 6d. per lb. Find the ratio of their prices.

[16] A man sleeps 7½ hr. every day. Find the ratio of the time he is awake to the time he is asleep.

[17] A commercial traveller's commission is £25 4s., if he sells goods to the value of £189. Find the ratio of the commission to the sales.

18. A hotel charges at the rate of 10s. a day in winter and 5 guineas a week in summer. Find the ratio of summer to winter charges.

*19. In a town, the rates are 11s. 3d. in the £. Find the ratio of the rate paid to the rateable value.

20. An alloy consists of 27½ oz. of copper and 2¾ oz. of tin. Find the ratio by weight of copper to the alloy.

*21. A car travels 140 mi. in 3½ hr., and a train travels 30 mi. in 50 min. Find the ratio of the speed of the car to that of the train.

22. The average speeds of a train and a car are 45 m.p.h. and 36 m.p.h.; find the ratio of the time taken by the train to that taken by the car for equal distances. Find also the ratio of the speed of the train to that of the car.

[23] What money is produced by a rate of 8d. in the £ on a rateable value of £156,600?

*24. Find the rateable value of a town if £2400 is obtained from a rate of $2\frac{1}{2}$d. in the £.

*25. The rateable value of Winchester in 1934 was £226,140; the services administered by the City Council required a rate of 7s. 6d. in the £, those administered by the County Council required a rate of 5s. 10d. in the £. Find the cost of each of these services. The Grant received from the Exchequer was equivalent to a rate of 2s. 10d. in the £; how much was this Grant?

26. Find the tax on an income of £400, if no tax is paid on the first £150, and if tax is paid at 2s. in the £ on the remainder.

[27] Find the tax on an income of £900, if no tax is paid on the first £150, and if tax is paid at 2s. 6d. in the £ on the next £175, and at 5s. in the £ on the remainder.

28. A bankrupt paid 2s. 3d. in the £. His liabilities were £7840; what were his assets?

29. A bankrupt paid 1s. 4d. in the £. His assets were £435; what were his liabilities?

*30. A bankrupt's assets are £1628 and his liabilities are £12,762. Find what he can pay in the £, correct to the nearest penny.

———————

If we wish to find which of two given ratios is the greater, it is usually best to express each in the form $m : 1$, where m is calculated to as many places of decimals as is necessary.

Example 4. Each year, A earns £350 and saves £40, B earns £400 and saves £50. For which person is the ratio of savings to income the greater?

The ratio of savings to income is

$$\text{for A, } \frac{40}{350} = \frac{8}{70} \simeq 0{\cdot}114; \quad \text{for B, } \frac{50}{400} = \frac{1}{8} = 0{\cdot}125.$$

$\therefore$ the ratio for B of savings to income is the greater.

Example 5. Express the ratio of £2 13s. 6d. to £5 13s. 6d., in the form $m : 1$, giving m correct to 2 places of decimals.

$$\frac{\text{£2 13s. 6d.}}{\text{£5 13s. 6d.}} = \frac{107 \text{ sixpences}}{227 \text{ sixpences}} = \frac{107}{227} \simeq 0{\cdot}471;$$

$$\therefore \text{ the ratio} \simeq 0{\cdot}47 : 1.$$

Scales of maps are often given as ratios in such forms as 1 : 10,000, 1 : 250,000, etc. The scale 1 : 10,000 means that 1 inch on the map represents 10,000 inches on the ground, or more generally that 1 : 10,000 is the ratio of the distance between any two points on the map to the actual distance between the two places they represent; and the fraction $\frac{1}{10,000}$ is called the *representative fraction*, or more shortly the R.F. of the map.

Example 6. The scale of a map is 4 inches to 1 mile. Express this ratio in the form 1 : n.

$$\frac{4 \text{ inches}}{1 \text{ mile}} = \frac{4 \text{ in.}}{1760 \times 36 \text{ in.}} = \frac{1}{1760 \times 9} = \frac{1}{15840};$$

∴ the scale of the map is 1 : 15840.

Example 7. The scale of a plan is 1 : 120. Find the dimensions of a room which measures 2 in. by $1\frac{1}{2}$ in. on the plan.

1 in. on the plan represents 120 in., =10 ft., on the ground.

∴ 2 in. represents 20 ft. and $1\frac{1}{2}$ in. represents 15 ft.;

∴ the room is 20 ft. by 15 ft.

Example 8. The scale of a map is 2 in. to the mile. Find in acres the area of an estate represented by an area 5·4 sq. in. on the map.

A square, side 2 in., represents 1 sq. mi.,

that is, 4 sq. in. represent 640 ac.

∴ 5·4 sq. in. represent $\frac{640 \times 5\cdot4}{4}$ ac.,

that is (16 × 54) ac. or 864 ac.

EXERCISE 81

Express the following ratios in the form m : 1 :—

1. 6 : 4. **[2]** $1\frac{1}{2} : 2\frac{1}{2}$. **3.** 8 cwt. to 1 ton.

[4] $4\frac{1}{2}$ in. to 1 yd. **[5]** £8 12s. to £5. **6.** 1 m. to 5 mm.

Find m for the following pairs of equal ratios :—

[7] 36 : 24 = m : 1. **8.** 2s. : 2s. 6d. = m : 1.

*9. $\frac{10}{15} = \frac{m}{6}$. ***10.** $\frac{5}{25} = \frac{3}{m}$. **11.** $\frac{3}{4} = \frac{m}{100}$.

Which is the greater of the following pairs of ratios?

12. 2 : 3; 3 : 2.   **13.** 1 : 4; 1 : 5.   **[14]** 20 : 16; 16 : 12.

[15] 3 : 5; 3^2 : 5^2.   **16.** 5 : 2; 5^2 : 2^2.   *17. $\frac{1}{2} : \frac{1}{3}$; $\frac{1}{4} : \frac{1}{9}$.

Express the following ratios in the form m : 1, giving m correct to 2 places of decimals :—

[18] £1 6s. : £3 10s.   **19.** 1 mi. : 1000 yd.

*20. 3 cwt. 50 lb. : 5 cwt.   *21. £4 17s. 8d. : £5 5s.

22. Express the ratio of the length of the Mont Cenis tunnel ($7\frac{3}{4}$ mi.) to that of the Simplon tunnel ($12\frac{1}{2}$ mi.) in the form n : 100.

23. The scale of a plan is 4 in. to 10 ch.   Find its R.F.

[24] The scale of a map is 10 cm. to 1 km.   Find its R.F.

25. The scale of a map is 1 : 100,000.   Find in km. the length of a road which is represented by a line 4·7 cm. long on the map.

[26] The scale of a map is 1 : 40,000.   Find in inches, correct to $\frac{1}{100}$ in., the length on the map of a road $\frac{1}{4}$ mi. long.

27. A ground plan of a house is made on the scale 1 in. to 15 ft. Find the R.F. of the plan.   Find the length and breadth on the plan of a room 18 ft. by 12 ft.   What area on the ground is represented by 1 sq. in. on the plan?

*28. On a map, scale 1 in. to the mile, an island has an area of $3\frac{1}{2}$ sq. in.   Find its actual area in acres.

29. A train runs at 30 mi. an hour up a gradient of 1 in 110 (*i.e.* it rises 1 ft. vertically for each 110 ft. travelled).   How many feet does it rise in 1 min.?

*30. The rates on an assessment of £84 are £39 18s. a year.   How much in the £ is the annual rate?

Increase and Decrease in a given Ratio.   If the annual rent of a house is raised from £60 to £80, the ratio of the new rent to the old rent = 80 : 60 = 4 : 3, and we say that the rent has been *increased in the ratio* 4 : 3.   In other words, the new rent is $\frac{4}{3}$ times the old rent.

If the annual rent of a house is lowered from £60 to £48, the ratio of the new rent to the old rent = 48 : 60 = 4 : 5, and we say that the rent has been *decreased in the ratio* 4 : 5. In other words, the new rent is $\frac{4}{5}$ times the old rent.

The fraction $\frac{4}{5}$ by which the old rent £60 must be multiplied to give the new rent £48 is called a *multiplying factor*.

$$\frac{\text{New Quantity}}{\text{Old Quantity}} = \text{Multiplying Factor.}$$

The multiplying factor is *less* than 1 if the new quantity is *less* than the old quantity; it is *greater* than 1 if the new quantity is *greater* than the old quantity.

Example 9.   Increase 12s. 3d. in the ratio 10 : 7.

$$\text{Increased value} = 12\tfrac{1}{4}\text{s.} \times \frac{10}{7} = \frac{49}{4} \times \frac{10}{7}\text{s.}$$
$$= \frac{35}{2}\text{s.} = 17\text{s. 6d.}$$

Example 10.   Decrease 2 hours in the ratio 5 : 6.

$$\text{Decreased time} = 2\text{ hr.} \times \frac{5}{6} = \frac{2 \times 5}{6}\text{ hr.}$$
$$= \frac{5}{3}\text{ hr.} = 1\text{ hr. 40 min.}$$

Example 11.   In what ratio must £75 be increased to become £100 ?

The ratio, £100 : £75 = 100 : 75 = 4 : 3 ;

∴ if £75 is increased in the ratio 4 : 3, it becomes £100.

Check: £$(75 \times \frac{4}{3})$ = £(25×4) = £100.

Example 12.   Find the multiplying factor which alters 90 tons into 63 tons.

The ratio, 63 tons : 90 tons = 63 : 90 = 7 : 10 ;

∴ 90 tons $\times \frac{7}{10}$ = 63 tons ;

∴ the required multiplying factor is $\frac{7}{10}$.

EXERCISE 82 (*class discussion*)

1. Increase 144 in the ratio 7 : 4.

[2] Decrease 105 in the ratio 3 : 5.

[3] Increase 15s. in the ratio 6 : 5.

4. Decrease 30s. in the ratio 5 : 6.

5. Decrease 2$\frac{1}{2}$ yd. in the ratio 7 : 10.

[6] Increase 1 lb. 4 oz. in the ratio 4 : 1.

10

7. In a sale, prices are reduced in the ratio $3:5$. Find the sale prices of articles whose ordinary prices are (i) £1; (ii) $7\frac{1}{2}$d.

8. A photograph $3\frac{3}{4}$ in. by $2\frac{1}{4}$ in. is enlarged in the ratio $8:3$. Find the dimensions of the enlargement.

[9] A man reduces his weight in the ratio $5:7$. What does his weight become if originally it was 16 st.?

10. In what ratio must 24 be increased to become 32?

11. In what ratio must 100 be decreased to become 80?

12. In what ratio must £1 be increased to become £1 10s.?

[13] In what ratio must $1\frac{1}{4}$ lb. be decreased to become 1 lb.?

14. What multiplying factor alters 72 into 96?

[15] What multiplying factor alters 60 into 48?

[16] What multiplying factor increases £100 to £120?

17. What multiplying factor reduces 2s. 6d. to 1s. 6d.?

18. What multiplying factor increases 10s. by 2s. 6d.?

[19] What multiplying factor diminishes 1 ft. by 3 in.?

20. If the price of petrol rises from 1s. 6d. to 1s. 8d. per gallon, find the ratio in which the price increases.

[21] In what ratio is the speed of a train reduced when it falls from 54 m.p.h. to 45 m.p.h.

22. Two sums of money are in the ratio $4:5$; the smaller is 6s., what is the larger?

[23] Two distances are in the ratio $12:7$; the larger is 21 mi., what is the smaller?

*24. The ratio of the wholesale to the retail price of a commodity is $9:20$. What is the retail price per lb. if the wholesale price is 7s. 6d. per lb.?

25. What multiplying factor makes a number half as large again?

26. What multiplying factor diminishes a number by $\frac{3}{10}$ of itself?

[27] In what ratio is a number increased if it is increased by $\frac{1}{10}$ of itself?

*28. A number is diminished by $\frac{2}{5}$ of itself. In what ratio has it been decreased?

29. A rectangular rubber sheet 2 in. by 3 in. is stretched so as to measure 3 in. by $4\frac{1}{2}$ in., remaining rectangular. In what ratio has (i) its length, (ii) its breadth, (iii) its area increased?

*30. A man works 8 hr. a day; in what ratio have his earnings changed if his pay is altered from 1s. 6d. per hour to 15s. a day?

*31. In what ratio has the average speed changed, if the time for a certain journey is reduced from 2 hr. to 1 hr. 40 min.?

[32] When the price of electricity is reduced from 6d. to 5d. per unit, I increase my annual consumption from 300 units to 400 units. In what ratio does my bill for electricity alter?

*33. The price of a table is reduced from £24 to £16 10s. Find the reduced price of a set of chairs originally costing £56, if reduced in the same ratio.

34. A photograph measuring $7\frac{1}{2}$ in. by 5 in. is enlarged so that the larger side becomes 18 in.; what does the shorter side become? In what ratio is the area increased?

*35. The number of germs in a solution increases in the ratio 6 : 5 every 2 hr. At 4 p.m., 1500 are counted in a drop placed under a microscope. How many will there be in the drop at 8 p.m.? How many would there have been at 2 p.m.?

Direct Variation. Suppose a train is running at a constant speed of 48 m.p.h.;

in 5 min. it travels 4 mi.,   in 10 min. it travels 8 mi.,
in 15 min. it travels 12 mi.; and so on.

Thus the ratio of any two distances is equal to the ratio of the corresponding times taken:

8 mi. : 12 mi. = 2 : 3 and
10 min. : 15 min. = 2 : 3;

and we say that *the distance varies directly as the time.*

In 1 min. it travels $\frac{4}{5}$ mi., in x min. it travels $\frac{4}{5}x$ mi.

If we say that it travels y mi. in x min.,

$$y = \frac{4}{5}x$$

or $\qquad y \div x = \frac{4}{5},$

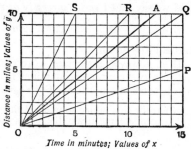

and we say that *y varies directly as x.*

The corresponding travel graph is represented by OA in the diagram; it is **a straight line through the origin.**

Oral Work. Interpret the travel graphs OP, OQ, OR, OS; state (i) what speed each represents; (ii) the value of $y \div x$ for each graph.

Inverse Variation. If a journey of some given length, say 120 mi., has to be made, the greater the speed the smaller is the time taken.

> At 10 m.p.h. the time is 12 hr.
>
> at 20 m.p.h. the time is 6 hr.,
>
> at 30 m.p.h. the time is 4 hr.; and so on.

Thus the ratio of any two times is equal to the *reciprocal* of the ratio of the corresponding speeds:

$$6 \text{ hr.} : 4 \text{ hr.} = 3 : 2 \quad \text{and} \quad 20 \text{ m.p.h.} : 30 \text{ m.p.h.} = 2 : 3;$$

and we say that *the time varies inversely as the speed.*

> At 1 m.p.h. the time is 120 hr.,
>
> at v m.p.h. the time is $\dfrac{120}{v}$ hr.;

and if we say that the time is t hr. when the speed is v m.p.h.

$$t = \frac{120}{v} \quad \text{or} \quad t \div \frac{1}{v} = 120,$$

and we say that t *varies inversely as* v.

If we plot values of t against values of $\dfrac{1}{v}$, we obtain **a straight line through the origin.**

It is, however, important to recognise the fact that the relation between two connected quantities is often not one either of direct or of inverse proportion. For example:

(i) If the side in one square is 3 times as long as the side of another square, the area of the first is 9 times, *not* 3 times, the area of the second.

(ii) A shopkeeper who sells buns at 1d. each would be willing to sell 12 dozen for less than 12s.

(iii) It probably costs more to feed 2 boys for 300 days than to feed 200 boys for 3 days.

Example 13. If 4 lb. of almonds cost 9s., find the cost of 7 lb. at the same rate.

If the number of lb. is increased in the ratio $7:4$, the cost is also increased in the ratio $7:4$; but 4 lb. cost 9s.,

$$\therefore \text{ 7 lb. cost 9s.} \times \tfrac{7}{4}, \quad \text{that is } \tfrac{63}{4}\text{s. or 15s. 9d.}$$

Example 14. 6 men take 12 hr. to weed a certain field; how long would 9 men take to do so, if all work at the same rate?

If the number of men is increased in the ratio $9:6$, the time is decreased in the ratio $6:9$; but 6 men take 12 hours,

$$\therefore \text{ 9 men take 12 hours} \times \tfrac{6}{9}, \quad \text{that is } \tfrac{12\times6}{9} \text{ hours or 8 hours.}$$

Oral Work. State the multiplying factors required for obtaining the answers to Exercise 83, Nos. 1–10, and simplify them.

EXERCISE 83

[Assume that the rates given in this exercise are uniform]

1. 14 lb. of icing sugar cost 4s.; find the cost of 21 lb.

[2] 20 tablets of soap cost 9s.; find the cost of 25 tablets.

3. 50 lb. of ground rice cost 7s. 6d.; find the cost of 35 lb.

4. 12 men can mow a field in 10 days; how long will 15 men take?

[5] A journey takes 6 hr. if I travel at 30 mi. an hour; how long will it take at 45 mi. an hour?

6. Five equal pipes fill a swimming-bath in 40 min.; how long does it take if only 4 of the pipes are used?

7. $1\frac{1}{2}$ tons of coal cost £3 12s.; find the cost of $2\frac{1}{2}$ tons.

[8] A boy bicycles $31\frac{1}{2}$ mi. in 3 hr.; how long will he take to go 35 mi. at the same rate?

[9] 65 lb. of potatoes cost 2s. $8\frac{1}{2}$d.; find the cost of 135 lb.

10. A hotel charges at the rate of 4 guineas a week; find the charge for 10 days.

[11] The rates on a rental of £75 are £32 10s.; find the rates on a rental of £42.

12. Railway fares were increased from 1d. a mile to $1\frac{3}{4}$d. a mile. What is the new fare for a journey which used to cost 8s. 4d.?

*13. A garrison has enough food for 24 days. How long will it last if each person's daily ration is reduced in the ratio 2 : 3.

14. A train takes 50 min. for a journey if it runs at 48 mi. per hour. At what rate must it run to reduce the time to 40 min.?

15. A man earns 52 shillings for a working week of 48 hr. If he is absent for 6 hr., how much should he receive?

*16. The lengths of the rims of 2 wheels of a carriage are 13 ft. 6 in., 10 ft. 6 in. In a certain journey, the larger makes 315 revolutions; how many revolutions does the smaller make?

17. What is the price of 1 cental (100 lb.) of wheat, if 480 lb. of wheat cost 33 shillings?

[18] Telegraph wire weighs 440 lb. per mile. Find the length of a line for which 13 cwt. 84 lb. is used.

[19] The railway fare for 3 adults and 3 children (half-price) was £2 8s.; what was the cost of the tickets for the 3 adults?

20. On a map whose scale is 5 in. to the mile the distance between two cross-roads is 4 in.; what would be the distance on a map whose scale is 2 in. to the mile?

*21. At 1s. 1d. per hour the weekly wage of a number of workmen is £143 10s. 10d. What would be the increase in the wages bill if the rate of pay had been 1s. 2d. per hour?

22. A candle 8 in. long after burning for 40 min. is $7\frac{1}{4}$ in. long. After how many more minutes is its length reduced to $1\frac{1}{4}$ in.?

*23. A cog-wheel which has 24 cogs fits into another which has 45 cogs. If the former turns 5 times in 4 sec., how many times does the latter turn in 12 sec.?

*24. A speedometer is adjusted to read correctly if the outer edge of the rim of the wheel is 88 in. If owing to over-size tyres being fitted the outer edge is increased to 91 in., find, to the nearest $\frac{1}{10}$ mi., the true length of a journey recorded as 60 mi.

*25. A town has enough rations for 10,000 people for 35 days. But after 5 days, 2500 refugees are admitted. If all are now put on half-rations, how much longer will the food last?

Compound Units. It is often convenient to invent special units for particular problems. For example, the amount of work required to regulate the traffic in a town each day might be described as 120 policeman-hours; this would mean that if 20 policemen were used, each would be on traffic duty for 6 hours a day; if 24 were used, each would be on traffic duty for 5 hours a day, and so on.

In Example 14, p. 149, the amount of work required to weed the field could be described as (12×6) man-hours.

Example 15. A puts 10 cows for 9 days and B puts 12 cows for 5 days into a field owned by X. Find the ratio of the amount A pays X to the amount B pays X, if there is a fixed charge per cow per day.

If the charge per cow per day is called 1 cow-day, A pays (10×9) cow-days and B pays (12×5) cow-days;

∴ amount A pays : amount B pays $= 90 : 60 = 3 : 2$.

Example 16. If 12 men earn £81 in 10 days, how much will 14 men earn in 8 days, if the daily wage is the same for each man.

If the money earned by 1 man in 1 day is called 1 man-day,

(12×10) man-days equal £81,

∴ (14×8) man-days equal $£\left(81 \times \frac{14 \times 8}{12 \times 10}\right), = £\frac{756}{10}$;

∴ 14 men in 8 days earn £75 12s.

EXERCISE 84

[Assume that the rates given in this exercise are uniform]

1. If 12 boys earn £9 in 6 days, how much will 8 boys earn in 9 days?

2. If 6 men mow 6 ac. of grass in 6 days, how many acres would 10 men mow in 9 days?

[3] If the wages of 4 men for 30 days amount to £39, how many men can be employed for 40 days at a cost of £260?

4. The gas for 10 gas-fires for 18 days cost £7. What is the cost of gas for 12 gas-fires for 5 days?

5. 16 men can make 800 boxes in 9 days; how long will 15 men take to make 1000 boxes?

[6] A man earns £7 10s. in 8 days, working 9 hr. a day; how much should he be paid for 20 days, working 6 hr. a day?

[7] A mowing machine will cut 10 ac. in 6 hr. if it is driven at 4 mi. an hour; how long will it take to cut 15 ac. if driven at 3 mi. an hour?

8. The cost of carriage of 36 tons for 28 mi. is £15. Find the cost of carriage of 42 tons for 54 mi. at a fixed rate per ton per mile.

9. A carpet 10 ft. long, 9 ft. wide costs £8. Find the cost of a carpet of the same quality 15 ft. long, 4 ft. wide.

[10] 25 men working 8 hr. a day remake a road in 63 days; how long would 45 men take, working 7 hr. a day?

11. 20 men can do a piece of work in 18 days; how long will 15 men take to do half as much again?

12. 36 teachers each working for 30 periods a week are required for a certain school; how many teachers would be needed if each teacher took 27 periods a week?

[13] 19 men working $7\frac{1}{2}$ hr. a day can do a piece of work in 21 days; how many hours a day must 45 men work to do it in 7 days?

14. A man pays £5 for keeping 10 horses in a field for 8 weeks; how much will he have to pay for keeping 12 horses in the field for 6 weeks?

*15. If a 6d. loaf weighs 40 oz. when wheat costs 36s. a quarter, what should a $7\frac{1}{2}$d. loaf weigh when wheat costs 32s. a quarter?

*16. If b men earn £c in d days, how much will x men earn in y days, at the same rate?

*17. If b men can mow c acres in d days, how long will x men take to mow y acres, at the same rate?

*18. A certain sum of money was just sufficient to maintain 12 men for 39 days when the index figure was 136. For how many days will the same sum maintain 17 men when the index figure is 156. [Assume that the cost of living is proportional to the index figure.]

*19. A train, travelling at the rate of 37 miles in 50 min., takes 6 hr. for a journey. How long will it take if it travels at the rate of 60 miles in $1\frac{1}{4}$ hr.?

20. A moneylender charges £3 for lending £36 for 8 months; what will he charge for lending £40 for 9 months?

*21. A contractor employs 15 men each working 8 hr. a day to do a piece of work in 27 days. At the end of 10 days, work has to be suspended for 5 days, and to finish the work in time he engages more men and all work at $8\frac{1}{2}$ hr. a day. How many more men does he engage?

Proportional Parts. The statement that the weights of 3 boys A, B, C are **proportional** to the numbers 9, 11, 12, means that

the ratio, A's weight : B's weight $=9:11$,

and the ratio, B's weight : C's weight $=11:12$;

also the ratio, A's weight : C's weight $=9:12=3:4$.

This is written concisely in the form,

A's weight : B's weight : C's weight $=9:11:12$.

Example 17. A rod 1 yard long is broken into three pieces whose lengths are in the ratios $4:2:3$. Find the length of each portion.

If the rod is divided into $(4+2+3)$ equal parts, the first piece contains 4 of these parts and is therefore $\frac{4}{9}$ of the whole rod.

$\therefore$ the length of the first piece $=\frac{4}{9}$ of 1 yd. $=16$ in.;

Similarly the length of the second piece $=\frac{2}{9}$ of 1 yd. $=8$ in.;

and the length of the third piece $=\frac{3}{9}$ of 1 yd. $=12$ in.

Check: 16 in. $+8$ in. $+12$ in. $=36$ in. $=1$ yd.

Example 18. Find four whole numbers proportional to 7s. 6d., 5s. 3d., 11s. 3d., 9s.

7s. 6d. $=30$ threepences; 5s. 3d. $=21$ threepences; 11s. 3d. $=45$ threepences; 9s. $=36$ threepences;

$\therefore$ 7s. 6d. : 5s. 3d. : 11s 3d. : 9s. $=30:21:45:36=10:7:15:12$.

Note. The result could have been obtained more shortly by expressing each sum in ninepences, or less simply by expressing each sum in pence.

Example 19. If $a:b=4:7$ and if $b:c=5:3$, find three whole numbers proportional to a, b, c.

$$a:b=4:7=20:35; \quad b:c=5:3=35:21;$$
$$\therefore a:b:c=20:35:21.$$

$\therefore$ a, b, c are proportional to the whole numbers 20, 35, 21.

Example 20. Divide £108 between A, B, C so that B has 5 times as much as C, and A has half as much again as B.

If C's share is taken as 1 unit, B's share is 5 units, and therefore A's share is $(5+\frac{1}{2}$ of 5) units, $=7\frac{1}{2}$ units.

$\therefore$ A's share : B's share : C's share $=7\frac{1}{2}:5:1=15:10:2$.

$\therefore$ A's share $=\frac{15}{15+10+2}$ of £108 $=\frac{15}{27}$ of £108 $=$£60;

B's share $=\frac{10}{27}$ of £108 $=$£40; C's share $=\frac{2}{27}$ of £108 $=$£8.

Check: £60 $+$ £40 $+$ £8 $=$ £108.

EXERCISE 85

[*Nos. 1–12 are intended for oral work or class-discussion*]

1. Divide £60 in the ratio (i) 2 : 3; (ii) 5 : 7; (iii) 4 : 1.

[2] Divide 2 ft. in the ratio (i) 3 : 5; (ii) 1 : 5; (iii) 9 : 7.

3. Divide £24 into three shares in the ratios 1 : 2 : 3.

[4] Divide 8s. into three shares in the ratios 5 : 2 : 9.

5. Divide 5 lb. into three parts in the ratios 7 : 4 : 9.

[6] Divide 1 ch. into three parts in the ratios $\frac{1}{2} : \frac{1}{4} : \frac{1}{6}$.

*7. Divide 5 tons into three parts in the ratios $\frac{1}{2} : \frac{1}{3} : 1\frac{1}{4}$.

8. Divide £7 into four parts in the ratios 2 : 4 : 5 : 9.

*9. Divide 7s. 6d. into four parts in the ratios $\frac{1}{2} : \frac{1}{3} : \frac{1}{4} : \frac{1}{6}$.

Find as simply as possible three whole numbers proportional to :

10. £2; £1 10s.; £3.   **[11]** $2\frac{1}{2}$ yd.; 5 ft.; 8 ft. 4 in.

12. $1\frac{1}{4}$ lb.; 2 lb.; 12 oz.   ***13.** 13s. 4d.; 19s. 4d.; 6s. 8d.

14. Share 1 guinea between 3 boys in the ratios 9 : 4 : 1.

[15] 20 tons of coal are shared between three families in the ratios 2 : 5 : 9; how much does each receive?

16. The sides of a triangle are in the ratios 1 : 1·5 : 2, and its perimeter is 1 yd. Find the length of each side.

17. The profits, £750, of a business are divided between 3 men so that their shares are proportional to 3, 4, 8. Find each share.

[18] 60 marks are distributed between three questions so that the amounts are proportional to 5, 4, 6. Find the marks for each question.

*19. A legacy of £450 is divided among 3 sons in the ratios $1\frac{1}{2} : 2\frac{1}{4} : 3$. How much does each receive?

20. A, B, C provide £250, £500, £750 respectively to buy a business, and their shares of the profits are proportional to the capital they provide. If the profits are £245, what does each receive?

*21. Divide 44 shillings into an equal number of shillings, florins, half-crowns.

Find the three smallest whole numbers proportional to *a*, *b*, *c* in Nos. 22–25:

22. $a:b=5:6$; $b:c=9:4$.   **[23]** $a:b=12:5$; $a:c=8:3$.

*24. $a=5b$; $b=3c$.   *25. $a=1\frac{1}{2}b$; $b=\frac{2}{3}c$.

26. Divide £1 15s. into two parts such that one is half as much again as the other.

[27] Divide £3 into two parts such that one is $\frac{2}{3}$ of the other.

28. Divide £66 between A, B, C so that A has twice as much as B, and B has half as much again as C.

*29. A load of 95 lb. is distributed between A, B, C, so that A carries $\frac{1}{3}$ of what B carries, and B carries 4 times as much as C. How much does B carry?

*30. A bankrupt owes B £2144, C £2130, D £771, E £315. His assets (what he possesses) are £1200. How much does B receive?

*31. A takes 10 days to build a fence which B can build in 8 days. If £4 10s. is paid for the job and if both work together, how much should A receive?

32. Three ingredients costing 3d., 4d., 1d. per lb. are mixed so that their weights are proportional to 2, 3, 7 respectively. Find the cost of 30 lb. of the mixture.

*33. A, B, C divide 2 gross of eggs so that B has 5 eggs for every 3 A has, and C has 8 eggs for every 7 B has, How many will each have?

*34. A can dig a trench in 10 days which would take B 12 days and C 15 days to dig. If £4 10s. is paid for the job, and if all work together, how much should each receive?

*35. Profits amounting to £2415 are divided between A, B, C, so that for every £4 A gets, B gets £5, and for every £9 B gets, C gets £16. Find the shares.

36. A puts £900 into a business for 1 year, and B puts into it £400 for 9 months. The profits shared between A and B are £180; how much should each receive?

[37] A man borrows £200 for 8 months from B and borrows £500 for 4 months from C, at equal rates of interest, and pays altogether £15 interest. How is the interest shared between B and C?

38. A man borrows £300 for 10 months from B, £500 for 9 months from C, and £700 for 3 months from D, and pays altogether £72 interest. How is this shared between B, C, and D?

*39. Three firms A, B, C undertake a piece of work for which £160 is paid. In carrying out the work, A provides 10 men for 15 days, B 8 men for 20 days, C 15 men for 6 days. If all the men are paid at the same rate, find the amount each firm receives.

*40. One employer has 40 workmen and another 75 workmen, and their weekly wage-bills are in the ratio 3 : 5. Find the ratio of the average wages per man paid by the two employers.

*41. Divide £330 among 4 persons A, B, C, D so that A may have twice as much as B, B twice as much as C, and A and C together as much as B and D together.

*42. Two partners A, B started with capitals of £6000, £4000 respectively. The profits at the end of each year are divided in proportion to their capitals invested in the business at the beginning of the year. A withdrew his profits at the end of each year, while B left his in the business. The profits for the first 3 years were £1400, £1584, £1639 15s. respectively. What was B's capital at the end of 3 years?

Use of Ratio in Problems

Example 21. If $\frac{3}{7}$ of a number is 42, what is the number?

If the number is divided into 7 equal parts, 3 of these parts make up 42. Therefore the ratio of the number to 42 equals 7 : 3.

∴ the number $= 42 \times \frac{7}{3} = 98$.

Algebraically, if the number is x, $\frac{3}{7}x = 42$;   ∴ $x = 42 \times \frac{7}{3}$.

Example 22. A boy, after spending $\frac{2}{9}$ of his money, has 4s. 8d. left. How much had he at first?

After spending $\frac{2}{9}$ of his money, $\frac{7}{9}$ of his money remains;

∴ the ratio of what he had at first to what remains equals 9 : 7.

∴ he had at first (4s. 8d.) $\times \frac{9}{7} = 8$d. $\times 9 = 6$s.

Example 23. A picture-dealer deducts 2s. in the £ for cash from the price on the ticket. If the cash price of a picture is £2 5s., find the price on the ticket.

For each 20s. marked on the ticket, the cash price is 18s.;

∴ the ratio of the marked price to the cash price $= 20 : 18 = 10 : 9$;

∴ the marked price $= £2\frac{1}{4} \times \frac{10}{9} = £2$ 10s.

EXERCISE 86

1. If $\frac{2}{5}$ of a number is 30, find the number.

2. When a man spends $\frac{5}{9}$ of his income, he saves £360 a year; find his income.

[3] When $\frac{5}{12}$ of a field has been ploughed, 42 ac. still remain to be done; find the area of the field.

4. If 2d. in the shilling is deducted for cash from the marked price of a chair, the cash price is 30s.; find the marked price.

[5] After paying tax at the rate of 2s. 6d. in the £1, a man has £630 left; what had he at first?

6. To each shilling a boy saves, his father adds sixpence; how much has the boy saved when he possesses 19s. 6d.

[7] The duty on a certain commodity is 3s. 4d. in the £. A consignment costs 4 guineas including duty; what is its value free of duty?

[8] After selling 85 copies of a book for every 100 copies printed, a publisher finds that 450 copies are left unsold. How many copies were printed?

9. A shopkeeper makes a profit of 4s. in the £ on the cost price of his goods. What does he pay for an article which he sells for 30 shillings?

[10] By selling my car for £84, I lose at the rate of 6s. in the £ on the price I paid for it. What did I pay for it?

11. A retailer makes a profit of 7s. 6d. in the £ on the cost price of his goods. What is his profit on an article he sells for £5 10s.?

*12. A watch was 2 min. slow at 8 a.m., and 1 min. fast at 6 p.m. on the same day. Find when it was right if it gained time uniformly.

*13. In Réaumur's thermometer, freezing-point and boiling-point of water are marked 0, 80 respectively; in Fahrenheit's thermometer they are marked 32, 212. What is the Fahrenheit reading for 12 Réaumur?

14. Coal at 48s. a ton is mixed with coke at 36s. a ton in the ratio 5 : 3 by weight. Find how much money is saved by using 10 tons of the mixture instead of 11 tons of coal.

*15. In an excursion by rail, the ratio of the number of whole tickets to the number of half-tickets was 2 : 3. Find the number of people who travelled if the equivalent of 84 full tickets was required.

16. An empty bottle weighs 11 oz.; when full of water it weighs 36 oz. and when full of alcohol it weighs 31 oz. Find the ratio of the weights of equal volumes of alcohol and water. Find also the weight of 1 cu. ft. of alcohol, if 1 cu. ft. of water weighs 62·3 lb.

*17. A train X passes three stations A, B, C at 9 a.m., 9.40 a.m., 10.32 a.m. respectively. Another train Y passes A, B at 9.50 a.m., 10.15 a.m. respectively. If both trains travel uniformly, find the time at which Y will pass C. Find also the speed of Y if X is travelling at 24 m.p.h.

18. A man receives a dividend of 10,000 francs which he exchanges at 84 fr. to the £. Income tax is then deducted at 5s. in the £. What is his net receipt to the nearest penny?

*19. A, B, C had each full chests of tea containing respectively 60 lb., 100 lb., 120 lb.; the chests were emptied, and the contents were well mixed and then replaced in the chests. How many pounds of A's tea is probably now in C's chest?

*20. A bank fails and pays its depositors 2s. 3d. in the £; a man who had £2000 in this bank and £550 elsewhere has liabilities of £2500. He declares himself bankrupt; how much in the £ can he pay his creditors, to the nearest penny?

CHAPTER XII

PERCENTAGE

Percentage and Ratio. Suppose that in a consignment of eggs, 1 in every 20 is bad, then it follows that 5 in every 100 are bad, and we say that 5 *per cent.* of the eggs in the consignment are bad. The ratio of the number of bad eggs to the total number is 1 : 20 or 5 : 100; a percentage is simply a ratio in which the second number is 100, and may be represented by a fraction whose denominator is 100.

For example, 7 per cent., *written* 7%, may denote the ratio 7 : 100 or may be represented by the fraction $\frac{7}{100}$.

It should be noted that in some cases it is customary to take the second number of the ratio as 1000; birth-rates and death-rates are usually quoted in this form. For example, in 1930 in England

and Wales the birth-rate was 16·3 per *thousand* of the population and the death-rate was 11·4 per *thousand* of the population.   These rates are equivalent to the ratios 16·3 : 1000 and 11·4 : 1000 and could be expressed as 1·63% and 1·14% respectively.

Example 1.   Express in percentage form the statement: At a certain school, 3 boys in every 4 own bicycles.

$\frac{3}{4}$ of the total number of boys own bicycles;

∴ in every 100 boys, ($\frac{3}{4}$ of 100) boys own bicycles;

∴ in every 100 boys, 75 boys own bicycles.

The statement may therefore be written:

At a certain school, 75% of the boys own bicycles.

Example 2.   If 30% of the pupils in a school are boys, what percentage of the pupils are girls?

In every 100 pupils, there are 30 boys and therefore there are (100 − 30) girls, that is 70 girls;

∴ 70% of the pupils are girls.

Or we may say,

the ratio of the number of boys to the number of pupils is 30 : 100,

∴ the ratio of the number of girls to the number of pupils is 70 : 100,

∴ 70% of the pupils are girls.

EXERCISE 87 (Oral)

Express in percentage form the statements in Nos. 1–10:

1. 1 day in every 5 days is wet.

2. A boy obtains 7 marks out of 10.

3. 3 men in every 10 men possess motor vehicles.

4. 3 pupils in every 50 pupils are absent from school.

5. 7 people in every 25 die before the age of 50.

6. A tax is at the rate of 1s. in every £.

7. A boy gets 1 sum in every 3 sums wrong.

8. 1 orange in every 8 oranges in a box is bad.

9. The interest is £1 on every £40.

10. In 1930, the birth-rate in Scotland was 19·6 per thousand of the population.

Write down the answers to the following :—

11. If 5% of the pupils in a school are absent, what percentage are present?

12. If a man spends 70% of his income, what percentage does he save?

13. In a railway accident 85% of the passengers were unhurt, what percentage were injured?

14. If 16% of those who enter for a competition get prizes, what percentage get nothing? How many per thousand get nothing?

15. If 28% of the population are men and 30% are women, what percentage are children? How many per thousand are children?

16. A man spends 10% of his income on rent and 55% on household expenses; what percentage remains?

17. A boy eats 35% of a cake and gives away 25% of it; what percentage of the cake is left?

18. On a boat, 24% of the passengers travel 1st class, 32% travel 2nd class, and the rest 3rd class. What percentage travel 3rd class?

Percentages and Fractions. Percentages can be represented by fractions. For example, 40% denotes the ratio 40 : 100, and is therefore represented by $\frac{40}{100}$, that is $\frac{2}{5}$ or 0·4.

Conversely any fraction or decimal can be expressed as a percentage by transforming it so that its denominator is 100. For example, $\frac{3}{4} = \frac{75}{100}$; $\therefore \frac{3}{4}$ is equivalent to 75%.

The following table illustrates different ways used for representing fractions in every-day life :—

Fraction	Decimal	Per cent.	Per thousand	s. in the £
$\frac{3}{8}$	0·375	37·5	375	7s. 6d.

Example 3. Express (i) $\frac{2}{3}$, (ii) 0·225 as percentages.

$$\text{(i)} \quad \frac{2}{3} = \frac{\frac{2}{3} \times 100}{100} \quad or \quad \frac{2}{3} = \frac{2}{3} \text{ of } 100 \text{ per cent.}$$

$$= \frac{66\frac{2}{3}}{100} \qquad\qquad = \frac{200}{3} \text{ per cent.}$$

$$= 66\frac{2}{3}\% . \qquad\qquad = 66\frac{2}{3}\% .$$

$$\text{(ii)} \quad 0·225 = 0·225 \times 100 \text{ per cent.} = 22·5\% .$$

Example 4. Find the value of $62\frac{1}{2}\%$ of £4.

$$62\frac{1}{2}\% \text{ of } £4 = \frac{62\frac{1}{2}}{100} \text{ of } £4 = £(4 \times \tfrac{1\ 2\ 5}{2\ 0\ 0})$$

$$= £\frac{5}{2} = £2 \text{ 10s.}$$

Example 5. A boy obtains 52 marks out of 80 for a paper. What percentage is this?

The boy obtains $\frac{5\ 2}{8\ 0}$ of the total, that is $(\frac{5\ 2}{8\ 0} \times 100)$ per cent.;

∴ he obtains 65% of the total.

Example 6. Express £2 12s. 6d. as a percentage of £30.

$$\frac{£2 \text{ 12s. 6d.}}{£30} = \frac{2\frac{5}{8}}{30} = \frac{21}{8} \times \frac{1}{30} = \frac{7}{80};$$

but $\frac{7}{8\ 0}$ is equivalent to $\frac{7}{8\ 0} \times 100$ per cent. $= \frac{3\ 5}{4}$ per cent.;

∴ £2 12s. 6d. is $8\frac{3}{4}\%$ of £30.

Example 7. Find correct to the nearest penny the value of $6\frac{3}{4}\%$ of £7 16s. 9d.

$$16s. \text{ 9d.} = 16\cdot75s. = £0\cdot8375;$$

∴ the required value $= \frac{6\frac{3}{4}}{100}$ of £7·8375 $= £(0\cdot078375 \times 6\frac{3}{4})$.

	£
The value can now be found by ordinary multi-plication or by a practice method as follows:—	0·07837
Since the answer is required to the nearest penny, 6 times,	0·47022
we keep 5 places of decimals in the working. $\frac{1}{2}$ times,	0·03918
	$\frac{1}{4}$ times, 0·01959
∴ value $= £0\cdot529$, to 3 places, $= 10\cdot58s. = 10s.$ 6·96d. $6\frac{3}{4}$ times,	0·52899
$= 10s.$ 7d., to nearest penny.	

The practice method may also be worked as follows:—

	£	s.	d.
	7	16	9
10 %		15	8·1
5 %		7	10·05
1 %		1	6·81
$\frac{1}{2}\%$			9·40
$\frac{1}{4}\%$			4·70
$6\frac{3}{4}\%$		10	6·96

The working has been taken to 2 places of decimals in the pence column.

As before, the value is 10s. 7d., to nearest penny.

F

11

Insurance. The chance of a man's house being burnt down is small, but if it should happen, the consequences are very serious. The object of insurance is to enable a man to protect himself against small risks of heavy losses, by making comparatively small annual payments. It is the pooling or averaging out of a common risk.

For example, the owner of a house, by paying an insurance company 1s. 6d. per each £100 at which his house is valued, can insure it against loss by fire. Thus if the house is valued at £2000, the owner pays each year (1s. 6d. ×20), that is £1 10s., and in the event of a fire will be paid the sum of money at which the damage caused by the fire is assessed.

The sum paid each year to cover the risk is called the *premium*, the document issued by the company binding them to cover the risk is called the *policy*, and in the example given above we say that the insurance is at the rate of "1s. 6d. per cent.," an abbreviation for "1s. 6d. for each £100 of the insured value."

One feature of insurance is that those who insure must not make a profit out of disaster : it is illegal knowingly to insure property for more than it is worth (actually or potentially), and to insure against a risk in which the insurer has no financial interest. For example, a man is not allowed to insure the life of another person whose death would cause him no monetary loss. These laws are made in order to protect insurance companies against fraud and to avoid causing temptation to commit crimes.

Some forms of insurance are now compulsory : the owner of a car, when applying for a licence, is required to prove that he is insured against third-party risks so that anyone who is injured by his negligent driving is sure of receiving compensation. National Health Insurance is also compulsory for anyone employed at wages less than £8 a week, the payment of the premium being shared between the employer and the employee.

The other principal form of insurance is life insurance; this takes various forms : (i) a whole life policy, which in return for an annual premium secures a lump sum payment at death ; (ii) an endowment policy which, in return for an annual premium for some fixed number of years, secures a lump sum payment at a definite age, such as 55 or 60 or 65, or an annual payment (called a *deferred annuity*) starting at some definite age and continuing either as long as the insured person lives or for a fixed number of years.

Usually if the insured person dies before the age at which the policy *matures* (*i.e.* the date when payments begin to be due from the Company), the whole or some fraction of the amount paid in premiums is returned to the insured person's estate. All sensible people take out some form of life or endowment insurance, as soon as they can afford to do so.

Example 8. A merchant insures goods in his warehouse valued at £12,500 at the rate of 4s. per cent. What annual premium does he pay?

In *insurance*, the phrase, 4s. per cent., means 4s. per £100.

The premium for a policy of £100 is £$\frac{1}{5}$;

∴ the premium for a policy of £12,500 is £($\frac{1}{5}$ × 125), =£25.

Example 9. A man takes out a whole life insurance policy for £1000 on his 25th birthday, by paying a premium of £13 2s. a year. If he dies when he is $64\frac{1}{2}$ years old, how much more does the Company pay his estate than he has paid in premiums to the Company.

In the period, age 25 to age $64\frac{1}{2}$, 40 annual premiums are paid.

∴ amount paid in premiums = (£13 2s.) × 40 = £524;

∴ the difference = £1000 − £524 = £476.

Note. The Company is able to afford to do this because it has earned interest on the annual payments which the man has been making for 40 years.

Life insurance is beneficial, partly because it is a form of self-imposed saving, but chiefly because it enables a man to make provision for his dependents (his wife or children) in the event of his dying at an early age.

EXERCISE 88

[Nos. 1–30 are suitable for class-discussion]

Express the following percentages as fractions and as decimals :—

1. 25%; 50%; 75%.　　　　[2] 5%; 15%; 85%.

[3] 2%; 4%; 300%.　　　　**4.** $2\frac{1}{2}$%; $112\frac{1}{2}$%; $37\frac{1}{2}$%.

Express the following percentages as fractions and as ratios :—

[5] 150%; 200%; 275%.　　**6.** $33\frac{1}{3}$%; $6\frac{2}{3}$%; $9\frac{3}{8}$%.

Express the following as percentages :—

7. $\frac{1}{2}, \frac{1}{3}, \frac{1}{4}, \frac{1}{5}, \frac{7}{5}$.　　　　[8] $\frac{1}{20}, \frac{1}{25}, \frac{1}{30}, \frac{1}{40}, \frac{36}{25}$.

9. 0·35, 0·08, 1·4, 0·065.　　**10.** $1\frac{1}{2}$, 1·75, 4, $1\frac{1}{3}$, 2·3.

[11] $\frac{3}{4}, \frac{4}{5}, \frac{5}{6}, \frac{7}{8}$.　　　　[12] $\frac{8}{15}, \frac{3}{16}, \frac{17}{20}, \frac{11}{25}$.

13. The ratios, 1 : 2; 7 : 10.　　[14] The ratios, 3 : 8; 5 : 12.

Find the values of the following :—

15. 60% of 5s.　　　**16.** 180% of 25s.　　　[17] 75% of 1s.

18. $33\frac{1}{3}$% of 2s.　　***19.** 235% of £5.　　　**20.** $12\frac{1}{2}$% of £40.

[21] $166\frac{2}{3}$% of 1 yd.　　[22] 55% of 1 ton.　　[23] 34% of 2 m.

Express the first quantity in each pair as a percentage of the second quantity :

24. 2s.; 8s.　　　[25] 9s.; 12s.　　　**26.** 2d.; 6d.

[27] 4 ft.; 1 yd.　　[28] 3 cwt.; 1 ton.　　**29.** 20 oz.; 1 lb.

[30] 48 cm.; 1 m. **31.** 9 fur.; 1 mi. ***32.** 7½ in.; 2½ yd.

[33] £1 10s.; £60. **34.** £6; £4 10s. ***35.** 37s. 6d.; £7 10s.

36. A boy obtains 72% in an examination, full marks being 450. How many marks does he get?

[37] A salesman receives 7½ per cent. commission on his sales. What is his commission for selling a wireless set for £70?

38. A boy scores 45 marks out of 60. What percentage is this? How much per thousand is this?

[39] A man whose income is £576 a year spends £36 a year on rent. What percentage of his income is spent on rent?

[40] What is 8 per cent. of 2½ tons?

[41] The components of gunpowder are as follows: nitre 75%, charcoal 15%, sulphur 10%. How many cwt. of each are there in 1 ton of gunpowder?

42. The customs duty on a watch is 33⅓% of its value. What is the duty if the watch is worth £4?

***43.** The population of the world is almost 1800 million, of whom about 720 million are European. What percentage of the world's population is European?

Find, correct to the nearest penny, the value of:

44. 4% of £3 8s. 6d. [45] 7% of £21 11s. 4d.

[46] 3½% of £16 9s. 8d. [47] 5¼% of £43 14s. 5d.

48. 2¾% of £79 5s. 10d. ***49.** 6⅜% of £17 18s. 2d.

***50.** What premium is charged to insure property worth £2870 against fire, if the premium is ³⁄₁₆ per cent. of the value?

***51.** 1607 candidates entered for an examination, and it was stated that 73·55 per cent. passed. How many passed?

[*Remember that in all insurance rates "per cent." means "per £100 of insured value."*]

52. Find the premium for insuring warehouse goods, valued at £350, against fire at the rate of 2s. 6d. per cent.

[53] Find the premium for insuring the hull and machinery of a steamer, valued at £45,000, at the rate of 4 guineas per cent. Find the duty on the policy at the rate of 1d. per cent.

54. The window glass in a private house can be insured at the rate of 15s. per £100 of rent. Find the premium for insuring the glass in a house rented at £65 a year.

*55. The premium paid to insure the contents of a house against fire, at the rate of 1s. 4d. per cent., is £2 10s. Find the value for which the contents are insured.

[56] For National Health insurance a man pays 9d. a week and a woman 7d. a week. How much annual premium does each pay, taking 1 year = 52 weeks?

57. A man takes out a life insurance policy for £1000 on his 35th birthday; the premium is £1 15s. per cent. (*i.e.* per £100 of amount of policy). How much has he paid altogether in premiums when he is $60\frac{1}{2}$ years old?

*58. A man on his 60th birthday is able to buy for £1000 an annuity of £84 16s. a year, paid half-yearly, the first payment being made when he is $60\frac{1}{2}$ years old. How long must he live to receive back more than he has paid?

*59. In 1930, there were 15,760 accidental deaths in England and Wales, of which 6404 were due to motor vehicles. What percentage of the deaths were due to motor vehicles? Answer to 2 places of decimals. How many deaths per thousand of accidental deaths were due to motor vehicles?

*60. In 1926, 48·7 per cent. of the population of 53,200,000 of the Soviet Union could not read. How many was this, to the nearest hundred thousand?

Percentage Changes. The importance of a change in the size or value of a quantity is often estimated by calculating what percentage the increase or decrease is of the **original** value. For example, if a car costs £400 when new and if its value is £320 at the end of 1 year, the decrease in value is £80; this is 20 per cent. of the original value, £400, and we say that the car has depreciated in value by 20% after 1 year's use.

Note. If A and B are any two numbers, A is $\frac{A}{B} \times 100$ per cent. of B.

An *increase* of say 30 per cent. means that for each 100 units in the original value there is an increase of 30 units, making the new value 130 units.

∴ the ratio of the increase to the original value is 30 : 100;
∴ the increase is $\frac{30}{100}$ times the original value.

Also the ratio of the new value to the original value is 130 : 100;

∴ the new value is $\frac{130}{100}$ times the original value.

Similarly the ratio of the new value to the increase is 130 : 30;

∴ the new value is $\frac{130}{30}$ times the increase; and so on.

A *decrease* of say 20 per cent. means that for each 100 units in the original value there is a decrease of 20 units, making the new value 80 units.

∴ the ratio of the new value to the original value is 80 : 100;
∴ the new value is $\frac{80}{100}$ times the original value; and so on.

The ratios used as multipliers in the examples just given are called *multiplying factors*; *oral* practice of the form indicated in the next exercise is intended to secure facility in their use.

EXERCISE 89 (Oral)

By what must a number be multiplied to increase it by:

1. 17%. **2.** 83%. **3.** 70%. **4.** 20%. **5.** 139%.

By what must a number be multiplied to decrease it by:

6. 9%. **7.** 37%. **8.** 61%. **9.** 30%. **10.** 40%.

11. Increase 300 by 8%. **12.** Decrease 400 by 20%.

13. Decrease 80 by 10%. **14.** Increase 60 by 30%.

15. If the price of an article is increased by 9%, write down

    (i) the ratio of the new price to the old price;
    (ii) the ratio of the new price to the change in price;
    (iii) the factor by which the new price must be multiplied to give the old price.

16. If the price of an article is decreased by 7%, write down

    (i) the ratio of the new price to the old price;
    (ii) the ratio of the change in price to the new price;
    (iii) the factor by which the change in price must be multiplied to give the old price.

17. Repeat No. 15 for a decrease of 10% in price.

18. Repeat No. 16 for an increase of 20% in price.

19. If the number of pupils in a school increases by 30% in a certain period, write down the factor by which

(i) the number at the beginning must be multiplied to give the number at the end.

(ii) the change in numbers must be multiplied to give the number at the end.

20. Repeat No. 19 for a decrease of 20% for the period.

21. (i) A exceeds B by 13%, write down the ratio of A to B.

(ii) C is 19% less than D, write down the ratio of C to D.

Complete the following:—

22. If A exceeds B by 5%, $A = B \times ...$; $B = A \times ...$.

23. If C is 12% less than D, $C = D \times ...$; $D = C \times ...$.

24. If A exceeds B by 6%, $A - B = B \times ...$; $A - B = A \times ...$.

25. If C is 8% less than D, $D - C = C \times ...$; $D - C = D \times ...$.

26. If A exceeds B by 10%, $A = (A - B) \times ...$.

27. If C is 10% less than D, $C = (D - C) \times ...$.

28. If A is 70% of B, $A = B \times ...$; $B = A \times ...$.

29. If A exceeds B by x per cent., $B = A \times ...$.

30. If C is y per cent. less than D, $D = C \times ...$.

Example 10. A man, whose salary is £750 a year, receives an increase of 8 per cent. Find his new salary.

The ratio of the new salary to the old salary is 108 : 100;

$$\therefore \text{ the new annual salary} = £750 \times \tfrac{108}{100} = £810.$$

Or as follows: the increase $= \tfrac{8}{100}$ of £750 a year $= £60$ a year;

$$\therefore \text{ the new annual salary} = £750 + £60 = £810.$$

Example 11. If a man's salary is raised from £250 a year to £280 a year, find the increase per cent.

The increase is £30 a year; therefore the ratio of the increase to the first salary is 30 : 250, that is 3 : 25.

$$\therefore \text{ the increase per cent.} = \tfrac{3}{25} \times 100 \text{ per cent.} = 12\%.$$

Example 12. 117 is 36% of a certain number. Find the number.

The ratio of the number to 117 equals 100 : 36;

$$\therefore \text{ the number} = 117 \times \tfrac{100}{36} = 325.$$

Or algebraically, if x is the number, $\tfrac{36}{100}x = 117$;

$$\therefore x = 117 \times \tfrac{100}{36} = 325.$$

Example 13. A line, whose true length is known from calculation to be 7·5 cm., is found by drawing and measurement to be 7·2 cm. What is the error per cent.?

The error = 7·5 cm. − 7·2 cm. = 0·3 cm.; therefore the ratio of the error to the true length is 0·3 : 7·5, that is 3 : 75 or 1 : 25;

$$\therefore \text{ the error per cent.} = \tfrac{1}{25} \times 100 \text{ per cent.} = 4\%.$$

Note. A thorough discussion of relative error and error per cent. is reserved for Chapter XVI, see p. 229.

Example 14. After 5% of a bill has been deducted from it, £57 remains to be paid. How much was the bill?

After 5% of the bill has been deducted, 95% of the bill remains.

$$\therefore \text{ the ratio of the bill to £57 equals } 100 : 95;$$

$$\therefore \text{ the bill is £57} \times \tfrac{100}{95}, \text{ that is £60.}$$

Or the working may be finished as follows :—

95% of the bill is £57; $\therefore$ 100% of the bill is £57 $\times \tfrac{100}{95}$;
$\therefore$ the bill is £60.

EXERCISE 90

1. Increase 80 by 35%.   [**2**] Decrease 75 by 40%.

3. Decrease 216 by $37\tfrac{1}{2}\%$.   [**4**] Increase 416 by 125%.

Find the number or quantity of which :

5. 25% is 7.   [**6**] 76% is 57.   **7.** $37\tfrac{1}{2}\%$ is 84.

[**8**] 30% is 1s.   **9.** $7\tfrac{1}{2}\%$ is 12s. 6d.   *****10.** $16\tfrac{2}{3}\%$ is 4 oz.

11. What number when increased by 20% becomes 144?

[**12**] What number when decreased by 20% becomes 108?

[**13**] What sum of money when increased by 35% becomes £216?

14. What sum of money when decreased by 35% becomes £156?

15. A man, whose salary is £380 a year, receives an increase of 15%; find his new salary.

16. A car costs £175 when new; after 1 year, its value is £105. By how much per cent. has its value decreased?

[**17**] A man spends £440 a year, and this is 80% of his income. What is his income?

*****18.** A rectangular enclosure is 80 ft. long, 25 ft. wide. If the length of each side is increased by 20%, find the increase in the area in sq. ft.; find also the percentage increase in the area.

19. 55 per cent. of the pupils in a school are girls. What percentage of the pupils are boys? Find the number of pupils if there are 216 boys.

20. What are full marks for a paper if a boy who gets 112 marks obtains 70 per cent. of the total?

[**21**] A spends 88% of his income. Find his income if he saves £81 a year.

22. If 10% is deducted from a bill, £27 remains to be paid. How much is the bill?

*23. 15% of a sum of money is £27 15s.; find the value of $16\frac{1}{2}$% of the same sum.

[**24**] The number of pupils in a school increased by 15% during a year. Find the number at the beginning of the year if there were 322 at the end of the year.

25. My bank deposit has increased by 40% during the past year. It is now £504; what was it a year ago?

*26. A reel of cotton, which cost $1\frac{1}{2}$d. in 1914, cost 10d. in 1917. Find the increase per cent. in the price.

*27. Wireless licences increased from 3,412,000 in 1930 to 4,330,000 in 1931. Find the increase per cent., to the nearest whole number.

28. Calculation shows that the true length of a line is 3·2 in.; a result obtained from drawing and measurement is 3·4 in.; find the error per cent.

*29. Find the error per cent. in taking the area of a field which is 165 yd. long, 120 yd. wide, as 4 ac.

*30. 24% by weight of an explosive mixture is saltpetre. Find the weight of a sample in which the other ingredients weigh 9·12 gm.

31. In a sale the price of an armchair was lowered by 30% to 3 guineas. How much was it reduced?

[**32**] If the price of an article is raised by 8%, the increase in the price is 10 shillings. Find the new price.

*33. A man buys a house and lets it for £80 a year. Repairs cost him £8 a year. If his net annual receipts (that is, rent less cost of repairs) amount to 5% of what he paid for the house, find the price of the house.

*34. The weight of a liquid was 3·75 gm. before heating and 3·25 gm. after heating. Find the loss per cent. of its weight, correct to 2 figures.

Gain and Loss per Cent. If a dealer buys an article for £100 and sells it for £101, his profit is a small one for the transaction; but if he buys an article for £2 and sells it for £3, his profit is relatively large, although he gains £1 in both cases. In order to be in a position to perform the first transaction, he must first pay out £100 and his profit is only 1 per cent. of this amount; but in order to be in a position to perform the second transaction, he must first pay out only £2, and his profit (£1) is 50 per cent. of this amount. The fair way of comparing two sale-transactions is therefore to calculate the percentage that the profit (or loss) is of the **cost price,** because the cost price is what the dealer has had to invest in the goods he hopes to sell again.

Gain or loss per cent. is *never* calculated on the number of articles sold. If a dealer sells 100 articles at a profit of £20, it is impossible to calculate his gain per cent. unless the cost price of the articles can be found; if the 100 articles cost £200, he gains 10%; if they cost £50, he gains 40%; if they cost £2000, he gains 1%.

In calculating any percentage change, the increase or decrease is expressed as a percentage of the *first* value; buying comes before selling, thus gain or loss is expressed as a percentage of the buying price (*i.e.* the cost price), *not* of the selling price.

The pupil must therefore remember that the phrase, **gain or loss per cent.,** is always taken to mean the percentage that the gain or loss is of the **cost price.***

Example 15. An article costing 30s. is sold at a profit of 15%; find the selling price.

The profit $=\frac{15}{100}$ of the *cost* price $=\frac{15}{100}$ of 30s. $=4\frac{1}{2}$s.;

∴ the selling price $=$ 30s. $+$ 4s. 6d. $=$ 34s. 6d.

Example 16. An article costing £55 is sold for £50; find the loss per cent.

The loss $=$ £55 $-$ £50 $=$ £5; ∴ the loss is $\frac{5}{55}$ of the *cost* price;

∴ the loss per cent. $=(\frac{5}{55} \times 100)$ per cent. $=9\frac{1}{11}\%$.

Example 17. A dealer gained 40% by selling an article for 21s.; find the cost price.

If the cost price is 100s., the gain is 40s., ∴ the selling price is 140s.;

∴ cost price $=\frac{100}{140}$ of selling price

$=\frac{100}{140}$ of 21s. $=$ 15s.

---

* The commercial practice is different: a manufacturer finds it convenient to express his estimated profit as a percentage of his selling price.

Example 18. A man buys eggs at 1s. 9d. a score and sells them at 8 for a shilling. Find his gain per cent.

Choose any convenient number of eggs, and find the cost price and selling price of *this number*. Here, a convenient number is 80, because both the cost price and selling price of 80 eggs are a whole number of shillings.

80 eggs cost $1\frac{3}{4}$s. $\times 4 = 7$s.; 80 eggs are sold for 10s.;

∴ the cost price is 7s., the selling price is 10s., and the gain is 3s.

∴ the gain is $\frac{3}{7}$ of the cost price;

∴ the gain per cent. $= (\frac{3}{7} \times 100)$ per cent. $= 42\frac{6}{7}\%$.

Note. It saves time to write **C.P.** for cost price, **S.P.** for selling price.

EXERCISE 91 (Oral)

Write down the factor by which the C.P. must be multiplied to give the S.P. in the following :—

   1. Gain 10%.   **2.** Gain 50%.   **3.** Gain 30%.   **4.** Loss 10%.

   5. Loss 20%.   **6.** Loss 40%.   **7.** Gain 5%.   **8.** Loss 25%.

   9. Loss 8%.

Write down the S.P. in the following :—

  10. C.P. 20s.; gain 10%.   **11.** C.P. 20s.; loss 10%.

  12. C.P. £10; loss 20%.   **13.** C.P. £8; gain 50%.

  14. C.P. £60; gain 25%.   **15.** C.P. £40; loss 30%.

Write down the factor by which the S.P. must be multiplied to give the C.P. in the following :—

  16. Gain 20%.   **17.** Gain 80%.   **18.** Gain 5%.   **19.** Loss 10%.

  20. Loss 40%.   **21.** Loss 25%.   **22.** Gain 8%.   **23.** Loss 12%.

  24. Loss 6·5%.

Write down the C.P. in the following :—

  25. S.P. £12; gain 20%.   **26.** S.P. £15; gain 50%.

  27. S.P. £8; loss 20%.   **28.** S.P. £14; loss 30%.

  29. S.P. £7; gain 40%.   **30.** S.P. £12; loss 60%.

  31. S.P. £12; loss 40%.   **32.** S.P. £42; gain 5%.

Write down the gain or loss per cent. in the following :—

  33. C.P. £50; gain £6.   **34.** C.P. £200; loss £40.

  35. C.P. 1s.; loss 3d.   **36.** C.P. 1s. 8d.; gain 4d.

37. S.P. £10; gain £2.

38. S.P. £60; loss £20.

39. S.P. 1s.; loss 3d.

40. S.P. 1s.; gain 3d.

41. C.P. £50; S.P £58.

42. C.P. £400; S.P. £460.

43. C.P. £30; S.P. £42.

44. C.P. £90; S.P. £100.

45. C.P. 8d.; S.P. 1s.

46. C.P. 4½d.; S.P. 6d.

47. C.P. 2s. 6d.; S.P. 2s.

48. C.P. £1 5s.; S.P. 15s.

EXERCISE 92

Find the S.P. in the following:—

1. C.P. £15; gain 5%.

[2] C.P. 6s.; gain 33⅓%.

[3] C.P. £75; loss 8%.

4. C.P. 3s. 4d.; loss 17½%.

[5] C.P. 12s. 6d.; loss 13⅓%.

*6. C.P. £2 1s. 8d.; gain 4½%.

Find the gain or loss per cent. in the following:—

7. C.P. £45; gain £9.

[8] C.P. 6s. 8d.; loss 2s.

9. C.P. £1; S.P. 24s.

[10] C.P. 9d.; S.P. 11½d.

[11] C.P. £4 10s.; S.P. £4.

12. C.P. 16s. 3d.; S.P. 18s. 6d.

13. S.P. 15s.; gain 5s.

[14] S.P. 15s.; loss 5s.

*15. S.P. 1s. 9d.; loss 3½d.

*16. S.P. £10 15s.; gain 27s. 6d.

Find the C.P. in the following:—

17. S.P. £7; gain 5%.

[18] S.P. 12s.; loss 4%

19. S.P. 16s. 6d.; loss 12%.

20. S.P. £2; gain 6⅔%.

*21. S.P. £5 10s.; loss 31¼%.

*22. S.P. 8s. 6d.; gain 13⅓%.

23. A dealer buys a bicycle for £12 and sells it for £15; find his gain per cent.

24. I bought a house for £1200 and was forced to sell it for £1000; find my loss per cent.

[25] A man bought a chair for 35 shillings and sold it at a gain of 15 per cent. How much profit did he make?

26. I bought a car for £375 and sold it one month later at a loss of 12 per cent. How much did I lose?

[27] By selling a golf club for 30 shillings, a dealer makes a profit of 25%; find what the dealer paid for it.

28. If I sell my house for £840, I shall lose 20%; what did I pay for the house?

[29] Potatoes are bought at 7s. per cwt. and sold at 1d. per lb.; find the gain per cent.

[30] Steel screws costing 5s. per gross are retailed at $6\frac{1}{2}$d. per dozen; find the gain per cent.

31. A grocer buys 100 eggs for 7s. 6d.; 4 are broken and the rest are sold at 8 a shilling. Find his gain per cent.

[32] If I sell my wireless set for £9, I shall lose 64 per cent.; what did I pay for it?

33. By selling a picture for £6 a dealer makes a profit of 80 per cent.; what did he pay for it?

[34] A car is sold for £635 at a gain of 27 per cent. How much is the profit?

*35. A 100-lb. chest of tea is bought for £8 15s. Find the gain per cent. if the tea is sold at 2s. 3d. per lb.

*36. A grocer buys 1500 bananas at 8d. a dozen; he sells 900 of them at two for 3d. and the rest at three for 4d. Find his gain per cent.

37. A man buys eggs at 10 for a shilling and sells them at 8 for a shilling; find his gain per cent.

[38] Christmas cards are bought at 15s. per 100 and are sold at 2s. a dozen; find the gain per cent.

39. 1 cwt. of tea costs £7, at what price per lb. must it be sold to make a profit of 20%?

*40. Oranges are bought at the rate of 3 for 2d.; how many must be sold for 1s. to gain 80 per cent.?

*41. A tradesman offers an article for £1 6s. 8d., but is willing to deduct 25 per cent. of the bill for cash. If the tradesman paid 16s. 8d. for the article, find his gain per cent. on a cash sale.

*42. The following table shows a week's business for a tradesman whose total weekly expenses are £3.

C.P. of article	2s.	5s.	7s. 6d.	18s.
Number sold	33	40	16	10
Gain per cent.	25	18	60	35

Find the tradesman's net profit for the week.

MISCELLANEOUS EXAMPLES

EXERCISE 93

1. A man saves $\frac{3}{8}$ of his income. What percentage is this?

[2] What is $16\frac{2}{3}\%$ of 1 chain?

3. A man travels 8% of a journey by bus, 87% by train, and walks the rest of the way. For what % of his journey does he walk?

4. What is $14\frac{3}{4}\%$ of £5?

5. Soap, which had a pre-war price of 3d. per tablet, rose to 1s. 2d. per tablet in the war. Find the % increase to the nearest whole number.

[6] What percentage is 8s. of £3 6s. 8d.?

7. My insurance premium is 8 guineas a year for my car which is valued at £350; what percentage is the premium of the value?

8. If A exceeds B by 80 per cent., find the factor by which A must be multiplied to give B.

9. A man measures the length of a road as 1934 yd. It is really 1910 yd.; find his error per cent., to one place of decimals.

10. 150 marks are assigned to each of two papers; if a boy obtains 63 marks for the first, how many must he get for the second to secure 36% on the whole?

[11] If the National Debt is £7,700,000,000 and the national income is £850,000,000, what percentage, to 1 place of decimals, is the income of the debt?

*12. I can hire a boat at the rate of 5 guineas for 7 days, but have to pay a deposit of 15% of the hire in advance. How much is the deposit if I take the boat for 10 days, at the same rate of hire and deposit?

[13] If butter cost 1s. 4d. per lb. yesterday and has risen 25% to-day and will fall 25% to-morrow, what will be the price to-morrow?

14. The price of a hat is reduced from 21s. to 17s. 6d.; find the percentage reduction.

[15] If a carpet 12 ft. by 8 ft. is laid in a room, there is a margin 1 ft. wide all the way round. What percentage of the area of the floor is the area of the margin?

16. If the profit on a wireless set, sold at a gain of $32\frac{1}{2}\%$, is £6 10s., find the sale price.

[17] A coal merchant buys coal at 32s. per ton, and in addition pays 13s. per ton carriage. Find his gain per cent. if he sells it at 2s. 9d. per cwt.

*18. A man, measuring a rectangle 120 yd. by 80 yd., makes each side 15 per cent. too small. By how much per cent. will his estimate of the area be too small?

19. If wages are increased $12\frac{1}{2}\%$ all round, the weekly wage-bill paid by a firm becomes £198. What is the increase per week in the bill?

[20] 2 gall. of spirit containing 10% of water are mixed with 5 gall. of spirit containing 8% of water, and 1 gall. of water is added to the mixture. What is now the percentage of water?

*21. A London merchant bought wine in France at 30 francs per litre, the price including free delivery in London, and sold it at £2 5s. per gallon, the rate of exchange being 75 francs to the £. Find his gain per cent. [Take 1 gall.=4·5 litres.]

22. An agent receives $2\frac{1}{2}\%$ commission on orders under £10 and 5% on other orders. He obtains 12 orders of £8 each and 7 orders of £25 each. Find his average percentage commission, to 1 place of decimals, on the total.

*23. A man buys 100 gall. of milk for £8 16s. and then adds 10 gall. of water; 10% of the mixture gets spilt and he sells the rest at 3d. per pint. Find his gain per cent.

24. A legacy of £4500 is left to 3 persons so that, after duties totalling 20% have been paid, their shares are proportional to 1, $1\frac{1}{2}$, 2. Find the shares.

*25. A is 40% older than B; by how much per cent. is B younger than A?

26. Last month petrol was 1s. 8d. per gallon and I used 80 gall. This month the cost has increased by 15% and I shall use 15% less. What will be the percentage change in my expenditure on petrol?

27. B is 20% heavier than A, and C is 25% heavier than B; by how much per cent. is C heavier than A?

*28. A man buys goods catalogued at £350 subject to successive discounts of 25, 10, $2\frac{1}{2}$ per cent. This means that he is allowed to deduct 25% from the catalogued price, then 10% from this reduced price, and $2\frac{1}{2}\%$ from the last. What does he pay?

*29. In 1933 a firm paid £7000 in wages and £2100 for other expenses and made a profit of £1400. In 1934, it paid 75% more in wages and 45% more for other expenses. If the receipts increased by 60 per cent., find the increase per cent. of the profits.

*30. On a journey across London, a taxi averages 20 m.p.h. for 70% of the distance, 25 m.p.h. for 10% of it, and 8 m.p.h. for the remainder. Find the average speed for the whole journey.

*31. By what percentage must a motorist increase his average speed in order to reduce by 20% the time a particular journey takes?

*32. 20 lb. of bronze contained 87% of copper and 13% of tin by weight. With how much copper must it be melted to obtain bronze containing 10% of tin by weight?

*33. Two partners invest £2000 and £1200 respectively in a business and agree that 20% of the annual profit is to be divided equally between them, and the remainder in proportion to the capital invested. The profit for the first year is £260; how will this be shared between them?

CHAPTER XIII

FURTHER AREAS AND VOLUMES

Area of a Rectangle

EXERCISE 94 (Oral)

1. Into how many squares, each of side 1 in., can a square of side 1 ft. be divided? Express 1 sq. in. in sq. ft.

2. Into how many squares, each of side 1 mm., can a square of side 1 cm. be divided? Express 1 sq. mm. in sq. cm.

3. Use a piece of squared paper ruled in inches and tenths of an inch for the following :—

   (i) How many small squares are there in each square inch? What is the area of each small square?

   (ii) Draw on the squared paper a rectangle 0·9 in. long, 0·7 in. broad. How many small squares does it contain? What is the area of the rectangle?

   (iii) Repeat (ii) for a rectangle, 1·7 in. long, 1·3 in. broad.

4. (i) Into how many squares, each of side $\frac{1}{4}$ in., can a square of side 1 in. be divided? What is the area of a square of side $\frac{1}{4}$ in.?

   (ii) A rectangle is $\frac{7}{4}$ in. long, $\frac{5}{4}$ in. broad. Into how many squares, each of side $\frac{1}{4}$ in., can it be divided? What is the area of the rectangle?

These examples illustrate the fact that the number of units of area in a **rectangle** *is obtained by multiplying together the numbers of units in the length and in the breadth, a result which was given in Ch. II, see p. 15, for whole numbers.*

Express :

    5. 1 sq. yd. in sq. ft.; 1 sq. ft. in sq. yd.

    6. 1 sq. m. in sq. cm.; 1 sq. cm. in sq. m.

    7. 3 sq. yd. in sq. ft.   **8.** 10 sq. cm. in sq. dm.

    9. 50 sq. mm. in sq. cm.   **10.** 3 sq. m. in sq. cm.

    11. 32 ac. in sq. mi.   **12.** 400 sq. ch. in ac.

Find the areas of the following rectangles :—

    13. 4 in. by 3 in. in sq. ft.   **14.** $\frac{1}{2}$ ft. by $\frac{1}{4}$ ft. in sq. in.

    15. 1 dm. by 1 cm. in sq. cm.   **16.** 5 cm. by 2 cm. in sq. dm.

    17. 2 ft. by 6 in. in sq. yd.   **18.** 4 ch. by 5 ch. in ac.

Example 1. Find the area of a rectangle 2 ft. 4 in. long, 1 ft. 3 in. broad.

$$\text{Length} = 2\tfrac{1}{3} \text{ ft., breadth} = 1\tfrac{1}{4} \text{ ft.;}$$
$$\therefore \text{ area} = (2\tfrac{1}{3} \times 1\tfrac{1}{4}) \text{ sq. ft.} = (\tfrac{7}{3} \times \tfrac{5}{4}) \text{ sq. ft.}$$
$$= \tfrac{35}{12} \text{ sq. ft.} = 2\tfrac{11}{12} \text{ sq. ft.}$$

Example 2. How many tiles, each 9 in. by 8 in., are required for the floor of a room, 15 ft. 4 in. long, 13 ft. 6 in. wide?

$$15 \text{ ft. } 4 \text{ in.} = 184 \text{ in.,} \quad \therefore \text{ 15 ft. } 4 \text{ in.} \div 8 \text{ in.} = 23;$$
$$13 \text{ ft. } 6 \text{ in.} = 162 \text{ in.,} \quad \therefore \text{ 13 ft. } 6 \text{ in.} \div 9 \text{ in.} = 18.$$
$$\therefore \text{ the tiles can be arranged in 23 rows, 18 tiles in each row;}$$
$$\therefore \text{ number of tiles required} = 23 \times 18 = 414.$$

Note. In this arrangement, no tiles are broken; but if this possibility can be disregarded, we can work as follows :—

$$\text{Area of floor} = (15\tfrac{1}{3} \times 13\tfrac{1}{2}) \text{ sq. ft.;}$$
$$\text{area of 1 tile} = (\tfrac{3}{4} \times \tfrac{2}{3}) \text{ sq. ft.}$$
$$\therefore \text{ number of tiles} = (\tfrac{46}{3} \times \tfrac{27}{2}) \div (\tfrac{3}{4} \times \tfrac{2}{3})$$
$$= 23 \times 9 \times 2 = 414.$$

Example 3. How many handkerchiefs, each 14 in. square, can be cut from material 30 in. wide, 2 yd. long? What is the area of the material left over?

30 in. $\div$ 14 in. $= \frac{30}{14} = 2\frac{1}{7}$; 2 yd. $\div$ 14 in. $= \frac{72}{14} = 5\frac{1}{7}$;

$\therefore$ 2 rows of handkerchiefs, 5 in each row, can be cut out;

$\therefore$ 10 handkerchiefs can be cut out.

Area of remaining material $= \{(72 \times 30) - (14 \times 14 \times 10)\}$ sq. in.
$= (2160 - 1960)$ sq. in. $= 200$ sq. in.

Note that $\frac{72 \times 30}{14 \times 14}$ is just more than 11, although only 10 handkerchiefs can be obtained.

Example 4. Find to the nearest shilling the cost of a rug, 8 ft. 6 in. long, 4 ft. 8 in. wide, at 1s. 9d. per sq. ft.

Area of rug $= (8\frac{1}{2} \times 4\frac{2}{3})$ sq. ft., and 1 sq. ft. costs $1\frac{3}{4}$s.;

$\therefore$ cost of rug $= (8\frac{1}{2} \times 4\frac{2}{3} \times 1\frac{3}{4})$s. $= (\frac{17}{2} \times \frac{14}{3} \times \frac{7}{4})$s.
$= \frac{833}{12}$s. $= 69\frac{5}{12}$s.

But $69\frac{5}{12}$ is nearer to 69 than to 70,

$\therefore$ cost of rug $= £3$ 9s., to the nearest shilling.

EXERCISE 95

Find the perimeters and areas of the following rectangles, giving the perimeters as compound quantities and the areas in terms of the unit indicated in brackets :—

1. 2 ft. by 1 ft. 3 in. (sq. ft.).   **[2]** 1 ft. 6 in. by 8 in. (sq. ft.).

[3] 12 ft. by 8 ft. 9 in. (sq. ft.).   **4.** 6·4 cm. by 3·8 cm. (sq. cm.).

[5] 3·2 m. by 5 dm. (sq. m.).   **[6]** 2 ft. 6 in. square (sq. ft.).

*7. 12 ft. 2 in. by 10 ft. 6 in. (sq. ft.).

8. 5 yd. 1 ft. 6 in. by 3 yd. 1 ft. (sq. yd.).

Find the lengths of the following rectangles :—

9. Area 48 sq. ft., breadth 4 ft.

[10] Area 10 sq. ft., breadth 1 ft. 8 in.

11. Area 7 sq. yd., breadth 6 ft. 9 in.

*12. Area 18·9 sq. cm., breadth 3·5 cm.

Find in acres the area of a field :

[13] 24 ch. long, 15 ch. wide.   **14.** 165 yd. long, 55 yd. wide.

Find the cost of the following carpets :—

  15. 6 ft. by 2 ft. 9 in. at 3s. per sq. ft.

  [16] 7 ft. 6 in. by 3 ft. 6 in. at 2s. per sq. ft.

  *17. 16 ft, 8 in. by 12 ft. 9 in. at 2s. 8d. per sq. ft.

Find the cost per sq. ft., correct to the nearest penny, of the
    following :—

  18. An Indian carpet, 14 ft. by 12 ft., at 16 guineas.

  [19] A Shiraz rug, 4 ft. 6 in. by 2 ft. 6 in., at 32s. 6d.

  [20] A Turkey carpet, 15 ft. 9 in. by 12 ft. 3 in., at £28.

Find the areas of the following figures in which all the corners are
    right-angled and the dimensions are shown in inches :—

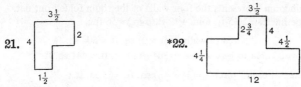

21.   *22.

  23. A rectangular 12-acre field is 150 yd. wide; find its length
and perimeter, to the nearest yd.

  [24] What is the area in acres of a road 88 ft. wide, $5\frac{1}{2}$ mi. long?

  25. Find the cost of concreting a courtyard 32 ft. long, $13\frac{1}{2}$ ft.
wide, at 1s. 9d. per sq. yd.

  26. A plot of ground 120 yd. long, 66 yd. wide is sold for £1080;
what is the price per acre?

  [27] How many tiles, each 1 ft. by 6 in., are needed for the floor
of a room 13 ft. 6 in. long, 12 ft. wide?

  28. How many planks, each 8 ft. long, 9 in. wide are required
for the floor of a room 16 ft. by 9 ft.?

  [29] How many paving stones, each 2 ft. 3 in. by 1 ft. 8 in., are
needed for a courtyard 60 yd. long, 40 yd. wide?

  30. How many dusters, 18 in. wide, $2\frac{1}{2}$ ft. long, can be made
from 50 sq. yd. of cloth?

  *31. The length and breadth of a sheet of paper are measured as
6·2 in., 4·8 in., correct to $\frac{1}{10}$ in. Within what limits, correct to
$\frac{1}{10}$ sq. in., does its area lie?

  *32. A rectangular sheet of cardboard, 25 cm. by 16 cm., weighs
18·3 gm.; an oval is cut out of it and is found to weigh 10·2 gm.
Find the area of the oval, to the nearest sq. cm.

*33. How many pieces of cardboard, each 5 in. square, can be cut from a sheet 4 ft. long, 3 ft. wide. What area remains over?

*34. How many dusters, each 16 in. square, can be cut from material 7 ft. long, 3 ft. wide. What area remains over?

Example 5. Find the cost of the paper for the walls of a room, 15 ft. 6 in. long, 12 ft. 6 in. wide, 9 ft. high, allowing 63 sq. ft. for doors, windows, etc., if the paper costs 3s. 6d. per piece, 12 yd. long, 21 in. wide.

	15 ft. 6 in.	12 ft. 6 in.			
height	Side wall	End wall	Side wall	End wall	9 ft.

<-------------perimeter------------->

The diagram represents the four walls of the room folded out flat.
The perimeter = 2(15 ft. 6 in. + 12 ft. 6 in.) = 56 ft.;

$$\therefore \text{ area of walls} = (56 \times 9) \text{ sq. ft.} = 504 \text{ sq. ft.};$$
$$\therefore \text{ area to be papered} = (504 - 63) \text{ sq. ft.} = 441 \text{ sq. ft.}$$

But area of each "piece" $= (36 \times \frac{2\frac{1}{2}}{12})$ sq. ft. $= 63$ sq. ft.;

$$\therefore \text{ number of pieces required} = 441 \div 63 = 7;$$
$$\therefore \text{ the paper costs } (3s. 6d.) \times 7, \text{ that is 24s. 6d.}$$

Note. Wall-paper is sold in rolls or pieces, usually 12 yd. long, 21 in. wide, that is of area 63 sq. ft., = 7 sq. yd.

A whole number of "pieces" must be bought; for example, if the area to be papered is 58 sq. yd., although $\frac{58}{7}$ pieces, $= 8\frac{2}{7}$ pieces, are sufficient, 9 pieces must be bought.

Example 6. Axminster carpet 27 in. wide is sold at 7s. 6d. per yard length. Find the cost of the carpet for a piece 16 ft. 4 in. long, 13 ft. 6 in. wide.

The carpet is sold in the form of a long rectangle, 27 in. wide; a strip 3 ft. long costs $7\frac{1}{2}$s.

$$\therefore (\frac{9}{4} \times 3) \text{ sq. ft. of carpet costs } 7\frac{1}{2}\text{s.}$$
$$\therefore 1 \text{ sq. ft. of carpet costs } (\frac{15}{2} \times \frac{4}{9} \times \frac{1}{3})\text{s.,} = \frac{10}{9}\text{s.}$$
$$\therefore (16\frac{1}{3} \times 13\frac{1}{2}) \text{ sq. ft. of carpet cost } £(\frac{10}{9} \times \frac{1}{20} \times \frac{49}{3} \times \frac{27}{2}).$$
$$\therefore \text{ the cost of the carpet} = £\frac{49}{4} = £12 \text{ 5s.}$$

Note. Since the carpet is sold in a roll 27 in. wide, one side of the made-up carpet must be a multiple of 27 in.; in this example, 13 ft. 6 in. $\div$ 27 in. $= 13\frac{1}{2}$ ft. $\div 2\frac{1}{4}$ ft. $= \frac{27}{2} \times \frac{4}{9} = 6$; and the carpet is made by joining together 6 strips, each 16 ft. 4 in. long.

EXERCISE 96

Find the total area of the four walls of a room :

1. 17 ft. long, 11 ft. broad, 8 ft. high.

[**2**] 14 ft. 9 in. long, 11 ft. 3 in. broad, 8 ft. 6 in. high.

3. 15 ft. 7 in. long, 13 ft. 9 in. wide, 9 ft. 3 in. high.

[**4**] 5 m. 75 cm. long, 4 m. 50 cm. wide, 3 m. 50 cm. high (in sq. m.).

5. Find the area of cardboard used for making a closed box, 5 in. by 4 in. by 3 in.

[**6**] Repeat No. 5 for a closed box, 4·5 cm. by 3·5 cm. by 3 cm.

7. Find the total area of the external surface of an *open* tank, 7 ft. long, 5 ft. wide, 3 ft. high, external measurements.

[**8**] Repeat No. 7 for an open tank, 4 ft. 6 in. long, 3 ft. 9 in. wide, 2 ft. 8 in. high.

9. Find the total area of the walls of a room 12 ft. high, if the breadth is 24 ft. and the floor area is 600 sq. ft.

10. A cistern 6 ft. long, 4 ft. wide, contains water to a depth of 1 ft. 3 in.; find the area of the wet surface.

Find the cost of the paper for the walls of the rooms, Nos. 11–14, if each "piece" of paper is 21 in. wide and 12 yd. long :

11. 17 ft. long, 11 ft. wide, 9 ft. high, at 3s. per piece, allowing 63 sq. ft. for doors, etc.

[**12**] 18 ft. long, 13 ft. 6 in. wide, 10 ft. high, at 6s. per piece, allowing 126 sq. ft. for doors, etc.

13. 9 ft. 3 in. long, 8 ft. 3 in. wide, 7 ft. 6 in. high, at 2s. 6d. per piece, allowing 50 sq. ft. for doors, etc., and assuming that a whole number of pieces must be bought.

[**14**] 15 ft. 9 in. long, 12 ft. 9 in. wide, 8 ft. high, at 4s. 6d. per piece, allowing 70 sq. ft. for doors, etc., and assuming that a whole number of pieces must be bought.

Find in shillings the cost per sq. ft. of the materials in Nos. 15, 16 :

15. 30 in. wide at 5s. per yard length.

[**16**] 56 in. wide at 8s. 9d. per yard length.

Find the cost of the carpets in Nos. 17–20 :

17. 16 ft. by 9 ft., if the carpet is 27 in. wide, at 6s. per yard.

[**18**] 15 ft. by 8 ft., if the carpet is 32 in. wide, at 8s. 6d. per yard.

*19. 19 ft. 6 in. by 15 ft. 9 in., if the carpet is 27 in. wide, at 8s. per yard.

*20. 18 ft. by 16 ft. 6 in., if the carpet is 22 in. wide, at 4s. 2d. per yard.

21. Find the cost of making a cistern $6\frac{1}{2}$ ft. long, 4 ft. broad, $3\frac{1}{2}$ ft. deep, without a lid, at 1s. 6d. per sq. ft.

[22] Find the area of a wall 7 ft. 6 in. high which encloses a courtyard 24 yd. long, 28 ft. wide.

*23. Planks 5 in. wide, 4 ft. high, are placed side by side to form a paling round a plot of ground 35 yd. long, $27\frac{1}{2}$ yd. wide. What length of planking is used, and what is its cost at 1s. 6d. per sq. ft.?

24. A room is 18 ft. long, 14 ft. broad, 10 ft. high. There is a door 8 ft. by 3 ft. and there are two windows, each 5 ft. 6 in. by 4 ft. Find the cost (i) of distempering the walls at $\frac{3}{4}$d. per sq. ft., (ii) of carpeting the floor at 6s. 6d. per sq. yd.

*25. An open tin box, 1 ft. 9 in. long, 9 in. wide, 8 in. high, is fitted with a tin lid which overlaps to a depth of 1 in. all round. What is the total area of tin sheeting used for the box and lid?

*26. A rectangular cigarette tin, fitted with a lid, is 6 in. long, $2\frac{1}{2}$ in. wide, 2 in. high, and the lid overlaps $\frac{1}{4}$ in. on all four sides. Find the total area of the tin used.

Example 7. A room 16 ft. long, 12 ft. wide, has a carpet in the middle, leaving a margin 18 in. wide all round which is covered with linoleum at 4s. 6d. per sq. yd. Find the cost of the linoleum.

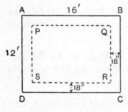

In the diagram, not drawn to scale, PQRS represents the carpet and ABCD the floor. The margin is $1\frac{1}{2}$ ft. wide;

$$\therefore \text{PQ} = \{16 - (1\frac{1}{2} \times 2)\} \text{ ft.} = 13 \text{ ft.};$$

$$\therefore \text{PS} = \{12 - (1\frac{1}{2} \times 2)\} \text{ ft.} = 9 \text{ ft.};$$

$\therefore$ area of carpet $= (13 \times 9)$ sq. ft., and area of floor $= (16 \times 12)$ sq. ft.;

$\therefore$ area of linoleum $= (192 - 117)$ sq. ft. $= 75$ sq. ft. $= \frac{25}{3}$ sq. yd.

$\therefore$ cost of linoleum $= (4\frac{1}{2} \times \frac{25}{3})$s. $= (\frac{9}{2} \times \frac{25}{3})$s. $= 37\frac{1}{2}$s.

$$= 37\text{s. } 6\text{d.}$$

Note. It is quicker to use the "subtraction" method than to divide up the border into rectangles.

EXERCISE 97

1. Find the area of a path running all round a lawn 60 ft. long, 40 ft. wide, if the path is (i) 5 ft. wide, (ii) 4 ft. 6 in. wide.

[2] Find the area of a frame round the edge of a picture 3 ft. wide, 2 ft. 6 in. high, if the frame is (i) 3 in. broad, (ii) $1\frac{1}{2}$ in. broad.

3. A sheet of tin measures 4 dm. 7 cm. by 3 dm. 6 cm. If a strip 2·5 cm. wide is cut off all round, find in sq. cm. the area of the part cut off.

[4] A photograph, 6 in. wide, 10 in. high, is mounted on a card so that there is a margin $1\frac{1}{2}$ in. wide at top and bottom and $\frac{3}{4}$ in. wide along the sides. Find the area of the part of the card which is not covered.

5. A room, 15 ft. long, 13 ft. wide, has a carpet in the middle of the floor, leaving a margin all round which is stained. What area is stained if the margin is (i) 1 ft. wide, (ii) 15 in. wide?

[6] A photograph 6 in. by $3\frac{1}{2}$ in. is mounted on card and framed. The frame is $\frac{3}{4}$ in. wide all round and measures 11 in. by 8 in. externally. Find the area of the visible part of the card.

7. Find by the subtraction method the shaded area in the diagram,

(i) if $a=2\frac{1}{2}$, $b=1\frac{1}{2}$, $c=2$, $d=1$;

[(ii)] if $a=6\frac{1}{4}$, $b=2\frac{1}{2}$, $c=4\frac{3}{4}$, $d=1\frac{1}{2}$;

the units being inches.

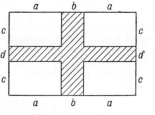

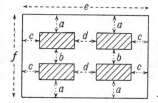

*8. The diagram represents a rectangular brick wall pierced with four equal rectangular windows. Find the area of the surface of brickwork, if $a=2\frac{3}{4}$, $b=1\frac{1}{2}$, $c=3\frac{1}{4}$, $d=2\frac{1}{2}$, $e=21$, $f=15$; the units being feet.

*9. A walled garden is 25 yd. long, 20 yd. wide, internal measurements. A gravel path $4\frac{1}{2}$ ft. wide runs round its edge inside the wall, and a paved path 5 ft. wide runs round the outside edge of the wall which is 6 in. thick. Find the area of each path.

10. A border 2 ft. wide is stained all round the edge of the floor of a room 20 ft. by 16 ft., and the rest is carpeted at 7s. 6d. per sq. yd. Find the cost of the carpet. Find also the cost of staining at $1\frac{1}{4}$d. per sq. ft.

11. Linoleum at 3s. per sq. yd. is put down in a room 20 ft. by 18 ft. so as to leave a margin 18 in. all round. Find the cost.

[12] A room is 15 ft. long, 12 ft. wide. Find the cost of staining a border 1 ft. 6 in. wide all round the edge of the floor at 1s. per sq. yd.

13. A carpet, 10 ft. 6 in. by 8 ft. 4 in., is laid in a room, 12 ft. 8 in. by 11 ft. 3 in., and the border is stained at 2d. per sq. ft. Find the cost of staining.

14. A border 20 in. wide all round the edge of the floor of a room, 16 ft. by 15 ft., is tiled. How many tiles are required if each tile is 5 in. by 4 in.?

*15. A border 2 ft. wide round the edge of the floor of a room, 22 ft. by 16 ft., is stained and the rest is carpeted. Find the ratio of the stained to the carpeted area. If the carpet costs 12s. 6d. per sq. yd. and the staining costs 2d. per sq. ft., find the total cost.

*16. A room 16 ft. 6 in. long, 16 ft. wide, is carpeted so as to leave a margin 1 ft. 9 in. wide all round, which is covered with linoleum. If the carpet is made up from a roll 30 in. wide at 10s. 6d. per yard length and if the linoleum costs 6s. per sq. yd., find the cost of (i) the carpet, (ii) the linoleum.

Volume of a Cuboid

EXERCISE 98 (for discussion)

1. How many cubes, edge $\frac{1}{2}$ in., are required for building up 1 cu. in.? What is the volume in cu. in. of a cube, edge $\frac{1}{2}$ in.?

2. How many cubes, edge $\frac{1}{2}$ in., are required for building up a cuboid, $2\frac{1}{2}$ in. by 2 in. by $1\frac{1}{2}$ in.? What is the volume in cu. in. of (i) each small cube, (ii) the cuboid? What is the value of $2\frac{1}{2} \times 2 \times 1\frac{1}{2}$?

3. How many cubes, edge 1 cm., are required for building up 1 cu. dm.? What is the volume in cu. dm. of a cube, edge 1 cm.?

4. How many cubes, edge 1 cm., are required for building up a cuboid $1\cdot5$ dm. by $1\cdot4$ dm. by $1\cdot2$ dm.? What is the volume in cu. dm. of (i) each small cube, (ii) the cuboid?

5. How many cubes, each of edge $\frac{1}{2}$ in., can be cut from a cuboid $3\frac{1}{2}$ in. by $2\frac{1}{2}$ in. by $1\frac{1}{2}$ in.? What is the volume of (i) each small cube, (ii) the cuboid? What is the value of $3\frac{1}{2} \times 2\frac{1}{2} \times 1\frac{1}{2}$?

These examples illustrate the fact that the number of units of volume in a cuboid is obtained by multiplying together the numbers of units in the length, breadth, and height of the cuboid, a result which was obtained in Ch. II, see p. 21, for whole numbers.

Express:

6. 1 cu. ft. in cu. in.; 1 cu. in. in cu. ft.

7. 1 cu. dm. (1 litre), in cu. cm.; 1 c.c. in litres.

8. 3 cu. yd. in cu. ft.   **9.** 100 c.c. in cu. dm.

10. 10 cu. mm. in c.c.   **11.** 12 cu. in. in cu. ft.

Find the volumes of the following cuboids:—

12. 5 in. by 4 in. by $\frac{1}{2}$ in.   **13.** 1 ft. by $3\frac{1}{2}$ in. by $1\frac{1}{2}$ in.

14. 1 dm. by 5 cm. by 2 cm.   **15.** 1 m. by 8 dm. by 7·5 cm.

Example 8. Find the number of bricks in a stack, 10 ft. 6 in. long, 6 ft. 9 in. wide, 5 ft. 6 in. high, if each brick is 9 in. by $4\frac{1}{2}$ in. by 3 in.

$$\text{Volume of stack} = (10\tfrac{1}{2} \times 6\tfrac{3}{4} \times 5\tfrac{1}{2}) \text{ cu. ft.};$$

$$\text{volume of 1 brick} = (\tfrac{3}{4} \times \tfrac{3}{8} \times \tfrac{1}{4}) \text{ cu. ft.};$$

$$\therefore \text{ number of bricks} = (\tfrac{21}{2} \times \tfrac{27}{4} \times \tfrac{11}{2}) \div (\tfrac{3}{4} \times \tfrac{3}{8} \times \tfrac{1}{4})$$

$$= \tfrac{21}{2} \times \tfrac{27}{4} \times \tfrac{11}{2} \times \tfrac{4}{3} \times \tfrac{8}{3} \times \tfrac{4}{1}$$

$$= 21 \times 3 \times 11 \times 8 = 5544.$$

Note. The data imply that it is *possible* to build up a stack of the stated size; the reader should verify that one way of doing so would be to have 22 layers, each containing 18 rows of bricks with 14 bricks in each row.

Example 9. A rectangular tank, with a horizontal base 6 ft. 9 in. long, 4 ft. 8 in. wide, internal measurements, contains 84 cu. ft. of water. Find the depth of the water.

$$\text{Depth} = \frac{\text{volume}}{\text{area of base}}.$$

Area of base $= (6\tfrac{3}{4} \times 4\tfrac{2}{3})$ sq. ft. $= (\tfrac{27}{4} \times \tfrac{14}{3})$ sq. ft.;

$$\therefore \text{ depth of water} = [84 \div (\tfrac{27}{4} \times \tfrac{14}{3})] \text{ ft.}$$

$$= (84 \times \tfrac{4}{27} \times \tfrac{3}{14}) \text{ ft.} = \tfrac{8}{3} \text{ ft.} = 2 \text{ ft. 8 in.}$$

Example 10.   Find the rise in the water-level caused by pumping 30,000 gallons of water into a swimming-bath, 80 ft. long, 45 ft. wide, given that 1 cu. ft. $=6\frac{1}{4}$ gall.

$$30,000 \text{ gall.} = (30,000 \div 6\tfrac{1}{4}) \text{ cu. ft.} = \tfrac{30000 \times 4}{25} \text{ cu. ft.}$$

But the area of the surface of the water is (80×45) sq. ft.,

$$\therefore \text{ rise in water-level} = \{\tfrac{30000 \times 4}{25} \div (80 \times 45)\} \text{ ft.}$$

$$= \tfrac{30000 \times 4}{25 \times 80 \times 45} \text{ ft.}$$

$$= \tfrac{4}{3} \text{ ft.} = 1 \text{ ft. } 4 \text{ in.}$$

EXERCISE 99

Find the volumes of the following rectangular blocks :—

1. 4 ft. 6 in. by 4 ft. by 2 ft. 9 in.   **2.** 45 cm. by 24 cm. by 5 mm.

[3] 6·5 in. by 2 in. by 1·5 in.   *4. 2 ft. 8 in. by 2 ft. 3 in. by 1 ft. 2 in.

5. Find the volume of air-space in a room 16 ft. long, 12 ft. wide, 8 ft. 6 in. high.

[6] How many cu. ft. of wood are there in a table-top, 13 ft. 6 in. long, 5 ft. 4 in. wide, $1\frac{1}{2}$ in. thick?

7. A lock in a canal is 40 yd. long, 7 yd. wide. When the sluices are opened, the depth of water in the lock decreases from 15 ft. to 11 ft. How many cu. ft. of water run out?

*8. How many rectangular blocks, each $2\frac{1}{2}$ in. by 2 in. by $1\frac{1}{2}$ in., can be packed in a box, 7 ft. 6 in. by 6 ft. 6 in. by 3 ft. 6 in., internal measurements? How many 4-inch cubes can be packed in this box, with faces parallel to the sides of the box, and how much space is left unoccupied?

9. How many bricks, each 25 cm. by 15 cm. by 8 cm., are required for a wall 32 m. long, 3 m. high, 40 cm. thick?

*10. Find the capacity in litres of a tank, 12 dm. by 8 dm. by 5 dm., internal measurements. How many cubes, edge 7 cm., can be packed in the tank, with faces parallel to the sides of the tank, and how much space is left unoccupied?

11. Find the capacity in litres of a tin 2·4 dm. long, 7·5 cm. wide, 12 cm. high.

12. A beam 9 ft. long, 6 in. wide, 4 in. deep, is made of wood which weighs 30 lb. per cu. ft.; find the weight of the beam.

[13] Find the weight in lb. of a wooden plank 12 ft. long, 8 in. wide, $2\frac{1}{2}$ in. thick, if the wood weighs 36 lb. per cu. ft.

[14] Find, to the nearest gm., the weight of a rectangular steel plate 7·2 cm. by 6·5 cm. by 8 mm., if the steel weighs 8 gm. per c.c.

15. Find the weight of petrol which a tin, 1·5 dm. long, 1·2 dm. wide, 4 dm. high, can hold, if 1 c.c. of petrol weighs 0·7 gm.

16. The volume of a rectangular block, $4\frac{1}{2}$ in. long, $2\frac{1}{2}$ in. wide, is 30 cu. in.; what is its height?

[17] The volume of the lid of a chest 5 ft. 4 in. long, 2 ft. 3 in. wide is $1\frac{1}{4}$ cu. ft.   Find in inches the thickness of the lid.

18. A tank 10 ft. 6 in. long, 8 ft. wide, contains 35 cu. ft. of water. Find in inches the depth of the water.

19. A rectangular tank $1\frac{1}{2}$ m. long, 88 cm. wide, contains water to a depth of 65 cm.   The water is transferred to an empty tank 2 m. long, 1 m. wide; find the depth of the water.

*20. A tank 6 ft. long, 5 ft. wide, 3 ft. high, contains water to a depth of 1 ft. 6 in.   A metal block, 4 ft. by 3 ft. by 1 ft. 3 in. is put into the tank and totally submerged.   Find in inches the amount the water-level rises.

*21. If the water in the tank in No. 20 is transferred to an empty tank 4 ft. 6 in. long, 3 ft. 4 in. wide, 5 ft. high, find the depth of the water-level below the top of the tank.

In Nos. 22–26, *assume that* 1 *cu. ft.* $=6\frac{1}{4}$ *gall.*

22. How many gallons of water will a tank 3 ft. long, 2 ft. wide, 1 ft. 4 in. deep hold?

[23] A railway trough is $1\frac{1}{2}$ ft. wide, 8 in. deep, and half a mile long.   How many gallons of water will it hold?

[24] A swimming-bath is 100 yd. long, 80 ft. wide.   How many gallons must be pumped into it to raise the water-level $1\frac{1}{2}$ in.?

25. A tank 5 ft. long, 2 ft. 8 in. wide, contains 150 gall. of water; find the depth of the water.

*26. Find in tons the weight of water which a tank 8 ft. long, 7 ft. wide, 6 ft. deep, will hold, given that 1 gall. of water weighs 10 lb.

In Nos. 27–31, *use the fact that* 1 *c.c. of water weighs* 1 *gm.*

27. Find in kg. the weight of $1\frac{1}{2}$ litres of water.

28. How many litres of water weigh 2·75 kg.?

[29] Find in kg. the weight of water which a cistern 1·5 m. long, 1·2 m. wide, 64 cm. high, will hold.

[30] The water in a tin weighs 2·88 kg.; if the tin is 2·4 dm. long, 1·5 dm. wide, find the depth of the water.

31. 560 kg. of water are drawn out of a tank 2·5 m. long, 1·4 m. wide. What distance does the water-level fall?

*32. A tank 16 ft. long, 7 ft. broad, contains 12½ tons of water. Find the depth of water if 1 cu. ft. of water weighs 1000 oz.

*33. A wooden beam, having a square cross-section, is 9 ft. long and weighs 3½ cwt. If the wood weighs 32 lb. per cu. ft., find the thickness of the beam.

*34. Find the value of a rectangular stack of coal, 20 yd. long, 8 ft. wide, 5½ ft. high, if the coal costs £1 18s. per ton, reckoning 44 cu. ft. to the ton.

35. How many loads are required to gravel a path 28 yd. long, 7½ ft. wide, to a depth of 4 in., if 17½ cu. ft. go to the load?

*36. An iron armour plate is 22 ft. long, 15 ft. wide, and weighs 25 tons. If 1 cu. ft. of iron weighs 3¾ cwt., find correct to $\frac{1}{10}$ in. the thickness of the plate.

Material for making a Box. The method was explained on p. 23.

Example 11. Find the weight of an empty open rectangular pan made of aluminium 0·5 cm. thick, if the base is 20 cm. long, 15 cm. wide, measured internally, and if the pan can hold 1½ litres of water, given that 1 c.c. of aluminium weighs 2·5 gm.

1 litre = 1000 c.c., ∴ internal volume of pan = 1500 c.c.

∴ internal height of pan = {1500 ÷ (20 × 15)} cm. = 5 cm.

Since the aluminium is 0·5 cm. thick,

external length = (20 + 1) cm. = 21 cm.,
external breadth = (15 + 1) cm. = 16 cm.,
(no lid), external height = (5 + 0·5) cm. = 5·5 cm.

Therefore, by the subtraction method,

volume of aluminium = (21 × 16 × 5·5 − 20 × 15 × 5) c.c.
= (1848 − 1500) c.c. = 348 c.c.

But 1 c.c. of aluminium weighs 2·5 gm.;

∴ weight of empty pan = (2·5 × 348) gm. = 870 gm.

EXERCISE 100

Find the volume of the wood required for making the *closed* boxes, Nos. 1–6:

1. External dimensions: 10 in. by 9 in. by 8 in.; wood $\frac{1}{2}$ in. thick.

[**2**] External dimensions: 4 in. by 3 in. by $2\frac{1}{2}$ in.; wood $\frac{1}{4}$ in. thick.

3. External dimensions: 14 cm. by 9·5 cm. by 6 cm.; wood 7·5 mm. thick.

[**4**] Internal dimensions: 4 in. by $3\frac{1}{2}$ in. by 2 in.; wood $\frac{1}{4}$ in. thick.

5. Internal dimensions: 2 ft. 5 in. by 1 ft. 3 in. by 1 ft. 1 in.; wood $\frac{1}{2}$ in. thick.

[**6**] Internal dimensions: 20 cm. by 12·5 cm. by 9·5 cm.; wood 1·25 cm. thick.

Find the volume of the wood required for making the *open* boxes, Nos. 7–10:

7. External dimensions: 11 in. long, 6 in. wide, 5 in. high; wood $\frac{1}{2}$ in. thick.

[**8**] External dimensions: 17·5 cm. long, 14 cm. wide, 10 cm. high; wood 7·5 mm. thick.

[**9**] Internal dimensions: 2 ft. 6 in. long, 1 ft. 7 in. wide, 9 in. high; wood $\frac{1}{2}$ in. thick.

10. Internal dimensions: 2·4 dm. long, 1·15 dm. wide, 9·5 cm. high; wood 5 mm. thick.

11. Find the weight of a closed box, made of wood $\frac{1}{2}$ in. thick, measuring internally 1 ft. by 8 in. by 5 in., if the wood weighs 48 lb. per cu. ft.

[**12**] An open rectangular tank is made of concrete, the sides and base being 1 ft. thick. Externally, the tank is 13 ft. long, 8 ft. broad, 5 ft. high. Find its weight in tons, if the concrete weighs 140 lb. per cu. ft.

13. The external dimensions of a closed rectangular cistern are 3 ft. 6 in. by 2 ft. 9 in. by 2 ft. 3 in., and the thickness of the material is $\frac{3}{4}$ in. How many gallons, to the nearest gallon, will the cistern hold? [1 cu. ft. $= 6\frac{1}{4}$ gall.]

14. A wooden door 81 in. high, 32 in. wide is 2 in. thick, except for 4 rectangular panels, each 30 in. by 10 in., which are only $\frac{1}{2}$ in. thick. Find the amount of wood in the door and the weight of the door if the wood weighs 48 lb. per cu. ft.

*15. The foundations of the outer walls of a rectangular building are of concrete to a depth of 3 ft. and a width of 15 in., and the external dimensions are 70 ft. by 38 ft. How many tons of concrete, to the nearest ton, were required, if 1 cu. ft. of concrete weighs 150 lb.?

16. The external dimensions of a closed chest, made of wood $1\frac{1}{2}$ in. thick, are 1 yd. by 2 ft. 6 in. by 2 ft. 3 in. Find the cost of lining the whole of the interior at 6d. per sq. ft.

Volume of Solid of uniform cross-section

The *abbreviated* statement

Volume = area of cross-section × length

is true for any shape of cross-section, provided only that it is uniform.

Example 12. A water-can of uniform cross-section holds $2\frac{1}{2}$ gallons. The area of its base is 54 sq. in., internal measurement; find its internal height, given 1 cu. ft. $= 6\frac{1}{4}$ gall.

$$2\frac{1}{2} \text{ gall.} = (2\frac{1}{2} \div 6\frac{1}{4}) \text{ cu. ft.} = (\tfrac{5}{2} \times \tfrac{4}{25}) \text{ cu. ft.} = \tfrac{2}{5} \text{ cu. ft.};$$

∴ volume of can $= \frac{2 \times 1728}{5}$ cu. in., and area of base = 54 sq. in.;

∴ internal height = volume ÷ (area of base)

$$= (\tfrac{2 \times 1728}{5} \div 54) \text{ in.} = \tfrac{2 \times 1728}{5 \times 54} \text{ in.}$$
$$= \tfrac{64}{5} \text{ in.} = 12 \cdot 8 \text{ in.}$$

Example 13. The dimensions of the cross-section of a steel girder are shown in inches in the given diagram. If the steel weighs 4·8 oz. per cu. in., find the weight of the girder per foot-run, to the nearest lb.

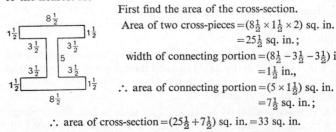

First find the area of the cross-section.

Area of two cross-pieces $= (8\frac{1}{2} \times 1\frac{1}{2} \times 2)$ sq. in.
$$= 25\frac{1}{2} \text{ sq. in.};$$

width of connecting portion $= (8\frac{1}{2} - 3\frac{1}{2} - 3\frac{1}{2})$ in.
$$= 1\frac{1}{2} \text{ in.},$$

∴ area of connecting portion $= (5 \times 1\frac{1}{2})$ sq. in.
$$= 7\frac{1}{2} \text{ sq. in.};$$

∴ area of cross-section $= (25\frac{1}{2} + 7\frac{1}{2})$ sq. in. = 33 sq. in.

∴ volume of portion of girder 1 ft. long (12 in. long),

= area of cross-section × length = (33×12) cu. in.

But 1 cu. in. of steel weighs 4·8 oz.,

∴ weight of girder per foot-run $= (4·8 \times 33 \times 12)$ oz.

$$= \tfrac{4·8 \times 33 \times 12}{16} \text{ lb.} = 118·8 \text{ lb.}$$

∴ weight per foot-run $= 119$ lb., to nearest lb.

Note. The area of the cross-section can also be found as follows: From a rectangle $8\frac{1}{2}$ in. wide, $(1\frac{1}{2}+5+1\frac{1}{2})$ in. high, subtract two rectangles, each $3\frac{1}{2}$ in. by 5 in.

EXERCISE 101

Find the volume of a rail of uniform cross-section, given:

1. Area of cross-section $= 4·5$ sq. in., length $= 1$ ft. 6 in.

[2] Area of cross-section $= 12·8$ sq. cm., length $= 1·25$ m.

Find the length of a girder of uniform cross-section, given:

[3] Volume $= 1500$ cu. in., area of cross-section $= 7·5$ sq. in.

4. Volume $= 4·4$ cu. dm., area of cross-section $= 12·5$ sq. cm.

Find the area of the cross-section, assuming it to be uniform, of a solid, given:

5. Volume $= 294$ cu. ft., length $= 28$ yd.

[6] Volume $= 92·8$ c.c., length $= 6·4$ m.

7. A vessel of uniform cross-section of area 8·4 sq. dm. contains 5·46 litres of water. What is the depth of the water?

8. What is the base area of a vessel of uniform cross-section of internal height 3·75 dm., if its capacity is $1\frac{1}{2}$ litres?

[9] The area of the cross-section of a steel rail is 15 sq. cm.; find the weight of the rail per metre run, if 1 c.c. of steel weighs 7·8 gm.

10. The dimensions of the L-shaped cross-section of a bar, 2 ft. long, are shown in inches in the diagram. Find (i) the volume of the bar, (ii) the weight if the material weighs 0·3 lb. per cu. in.

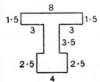

11. The dimensions of the cross-section of a girder 2·5 m. long are shown in cm. in the diagram. Find (i) the volume of the girder, (ii) the weight if the material weighs 7·8 gm. per c.c.

12. 1 in. of rain over an area of 150 sq. yd. is collected in a tank 10 ft. long, 8 ft. wide. What is the rise of water in the tank in inches?

[13] An empty rectangular tank is 5 ft. long, 4 ft. wide, 3 ft. deep. Rain water runs into it from roofs of total horizontal area 100 sq. yd. What depth of rainfall in inches will fill the tank?

[14] The average depth of a pond of area 3 ac. is 7 in. If 1 cu. ft. of water weighs $62\frac{1}{2}$ lb., find the weight of water in the pond, to the nearest 10 tons.

15. A log of wood 10 ft. long has a uniform cross-section of area 180 sq. in. Find its weight if the wood weighs 44 lb. per cu. ft.

16. A can of uniform cross-section contains 1 gall. of water. Find, to the nearest sq. in., the area of the cross-section if the water is 8 in. deep. [1 gall. $\simeq$ 277 cu. in.]

*17. A rectangular gutter is $4\frac{1}{2}$ in. wide, $2\frac{1}{2}$ in. deep. If water flows along it at 4 ft. per second, find the number of gallons which pass a given point in 8 min., if the gutter remains full. [1 cu. ft. $=6\frac{1}{4}$ gall.]

*18. A metal rail 7 yd. long of uniform cross-section weighs $6\frac{3}{4}$ cwt. If the metal weighs 4·5 oz. per cu. in., find the area of the cross-section of the rail.

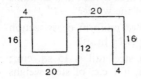

*19. The diagram shows the dimensions in feet of the ground plan of a trench of uniform width, 4 ft. If a man can excavate 25 cu. ft. per hour, how long will it take 12 men to dig the trench to a depth of $5\frac{1}{2}$ ft.?

*20. The cross-section of a pipe is 4 sq. in., and water is pouring out of it at the rate of 6 ft. per second. If the pipe remains full, find the number of gallons discharged by the pipe in 5 min. [1 cu. ft. $=6\frac{1}{4}$ gall.]

MISCELLANEOUS EXAMPLES

EXERCISE 102

1. The area of a rectangular board is 20 sq. ft. 81 sq. in.; the width is 3 ft. 11 in., find the length.

[2] Blankets measuring 56 in. by 78 in. cost 22s. 9d. per pair. Find the cost per sq. yd.

3. Find the weight of a rectangular block of wood, 2 ft. by 9 in. by $1\frac{1}{2}$ in., if 1 cu. ft. of the wood weighs 45 lb.

[4] A hall is 40 ft. 6 in. long, 15 ft. 6 in. high, and its width is $\frac{2}{3}$ of its length. Find the total area of the four walls.

[5] A border 21 in. wide all round the edge of the floor of a room, 21 ft. 6 in. by 20 ft., is stained at a cost of 2d. per sq. ft. Find the cost.

6. 2250 gall. of water are drawn out of a tank, 18 ft. long, 15 ft. wide; find how much the water-level falls. [1 cu. ft. $= 6\frac{1}{4}$ gall.]

7. A fertiliser costs 7s. 6d. for a 28-lb. bag. It is used at the rate of 2 oz. per sq. yd. Find the cost for a lawn, 42 yd. long, 80 ft. wide.

8. A swimming-bath 30 yd. long, 40 ft. wide, is being filled by a pipe which delivers 60 cu. ft. of water a minute. How long will it take for the water-level to rise 1 in.?

9. A metal sheet, 8 in. long, 6 in. wide, weighs 9 lb. 6 oz. If 1 cu. ft. of the metal weighs 450 lb., find the thickness of the sheet.

[10] A metal sheet, 2 ft. 2 in. long, 1 ft. 4 in. wide, $\frac{1}{8}$ in. thick, weighs 15 lb. Find the weight of 1 cu. ft. of the metal, to the nearest lb.

[11] The cross-section of a pipe is 42 sq. cm., and water is pouring out of it at the rate of 1·25 m. per second. If the pipe remains full, find the number of litres discharged per minute.

*12. A rectangular grass field, 260 yd. long, 180 yd. wide, is surrounded by a paved walk $2\frac{1}{2}$ yd. wide, and a roadway 15 yd. wide runs round outside the pavement. Find the area of (i) the pavement, (ii) the roadway.

*13. An open cardboard box, 1 ft. long, 8 in. wide, 5 in. high, is fitted with a cardboard lid which covers the top and one of the larger sides and both of the smaller sides. Find the total area of cardboard required for the box and lid.

14. A lawn, 30 yd. long, 40 ft. wide, is surrounded by a path 5 ft. wide. How many cu. ft. of gravel are required to cover the path to a depth of 3 in.?

*15. The external dimensions of a closed rectangular cistern are 5·5 dm. by 3·6 dm. by 2·5 dm., and the material is 5 mm. thick. How many litres will the cistern hold?

*16. Find in lb. the weight of a box, without a lid, 2 ft. 4 in. long, 2 ft. $1\frac{1}{2}$ in. wide, 1 ft. $4\frac{1}{2}$ in. high, external measurements, made of wood $\frac{3}{4}$ in. thick, if 1 cu. ft. of the wood weighs 48 lb.

17. A roll of wire 375 m. long weighs 2·88 kg. Find the area of the cross-section of the wire if the material weighs 9·6 gm. per c.c.

*18. A block of copper, 2 in. by $1\frac{3}{4}$ in. by 6 in. weighs $6\frac{3}{4}$ lb. It is drawn out into wire of cross-sectional area $\frac{1}{40}$ sq. in. Find the weight of a length of 35 ft. of the wire.

CHAPTER XIV

CIRCLES AND CYLINDERS

Circumference of a Circle

Example 1. A fine thread is wrapped 5 times round a circular cylinder (like a reel of cotton) of diameter 4 cm.; and the thread, when unwrapped, measures 62·9 cm. Find the value of the ratio of the circumference to the diameter.

5 times the circumference is 62·9 cm., ∴ circumference = 12·58 cm.;

$$\therefore \frac{\text{circumference}}{\text{diameter}} = \frac{12 \cdot 58 \text{ cm.}}{4 \text{ cm.}} = 3 \cdot 145.$$

Note. All measurements are approximate; so therefore also are the results. A better approximation would be obtained by wrapping the thread 20 times round the cylinder.

Example 2. A scratch is made at a point on the rim of a pulley which can rotate on an axle. The pulley is then rolled along a graduated ruler, starting with the scratch in contact with the 5-in. graduation, and after 3 complete revolutions it is found that the reading of the position of the scratch is 28·55 in.

The diameter of the pulley is 2·5 in., find the value of the ratio of the circumference to the diameter.

In 3 revolutions, the pulley moves (28·55 − 5) in., = 23·55 in.;

∴ circumference of pulley = (23·55 ÷ 3) in. = 7·85 in.;

$$\therefore \frac{\text{circumference}}{\text{diameter}} = \frac{7 \cdot 85 \text{ in.}}{2 \cdot 5 \text{ in.}} = 3 \cdot 14.$$

The approximate results in these Examples suggest that the ratio of the circumference of any circle to its diameter is about 3·14, and it can be proved that it is 3·14159265 . . . ; it is denoted by the

Greek letter π, and a convenient approximation for π is $\frac{22}{7}$, since $\frac{22}{7} = 3.1428 \ldots$ We therefore write

$$\frac{\text{circumference}}{\text{diameter}} = \pi \quad \text{or} \quad \text{circumference} = \text{diameter} \times \pi.$$

But if the radius of a circle is r units, its diameter is $2r$ units;

∴ **the circumference of a circle, radius r units, is $2\pi r$ units, where $\pi \simeq \frac{22}{7}$ or, to a closer approximation, $\pi \simeq 3.1416$.**

Approximate results should be expressed as decimals, not as vulgar fractions.

Example 3.   Find the circumference of a circle of radius 4 cm.

Circumference $= \text{radius} \times 2\pi$

$\qquad = (2\pi \times 4)$ cm. $\simeq (8 \times 3.14)$ cm.

$\qquad \simeq 25.1$ cm.

$$\begin{array}{r} 3.14 \\ 8 \\ \hline 25.12 \end{array}$$

Example 4.   Find the radius of a circle whose circumference is 10 in.

If the radius is r in., the circumference is $2\pi r$ in.;

∴ $2\pi r = 10$;   ∴ $r = \frac{10}{2\pi} = \frac{5}{\pi} \simeq 5 \div \frac{22}{7}$;

∴ $r \simeq \frac{35}{22} \simeq 1.59$;

∴ the radius is 1.59 in., approximately.

$$\begin{array}{r} 1.59 \\ 22\overline{)35.00} \\ 22 \\ \hline 130 \\ 110 \\ \hline 200 \\ 198 \end{array}$$

Note. Do not give the answer as $1\frac{13}{22}$ in. because vulgar fractions are generally used only for exact results.

Do not substitute for π its approximate numerical value before it is necessary to do so.

Example 5.   The diameter of the wheel of a car is $2\frac{1}{2}$ ft.   Find the number of revolutions made by the wheel per minute when the car is travelling at 40 mi. an hour.

In 60 min. the car travels $(40 \times 1760 \times 3)$ ft.,

∴ in 1 min. the car travels $\frac{40 \times 1760 \times 3}{60}$ ft.

Since the circumference of the wheel, diameter $2\frac{1}{2}$ ft., is $(\pi \times \frac{5}{2})$ ft.,

the car travels $\frac{5\pi}{2}$ ft. for each revolution of the wheel.

∴ the number of revolutions made in 1 min.

$$= \frac{40 \times 1760 \times 3}{60} \div \frac{5\pi}{2} = \frac{2 \times 1760 \times 2}{5\pi}$$

$$= \frac{8 \times 176}{\pi} \simeq \frac{8 \times 176 \times 7}{22}, \quad \text{that is } 448;$$

∴ the wheel makes 448 revs. per min., approximately.

EXERCISE 103

[Do not give any of the answers to more than 3 figures]

Find the lengths of the circumferences of the circles, Nos. 1–9 :

[Take $\pi = 3\frac{1}{7}$ in Nos. 1–3, and take $\pi = 3 \cdot 14$ in Nos. 4–9; $3\frac{1}{7}$ is a slightly closer approximation to π than $3 \cdot 14$.]

1. Radius, 14 in.   2. Diameter, 5·6 cm.   [3] Radius, 6·3 m.

4. Radius, 3 in.   [5] Radius, 4·5 in.   [6] Diameter, 20 in.

7. Diameter, 15 cm.   [8] Diameter, 25 yd.   [9] Radius, 70 yd.

Find the radii of the circles, Nos. 10–15 :

[Take $\pi = 3\frac{1}{7}$ in Nos. 10–12, and take $\pi = 3 \cdot 14$ in Nos. 13–15.]

[10] Circumference, 11 in.   11. Circumference, 8·8 cm.

12. Circumference, 1 ch.   [13] Circumference, 100 yd.

[14] Circumference, 6·4 dm.   15. Circumference, 8 in.

[16] The minute-hand of a clock is 8 in. long. What distance does the tip of this hand move in 1 hr.? [Take $\pi = 3 \cdot 14$.]

17. A $\frac{1}{4}$-mi. running-track is a circle. Find its radius in yards. [Take $\pi = \frac{22}{7}$.]

[For the remainder of this exercise, take π to be $3 \cdot 14$ or $\frac{22}{7}$, whichever is the more convenient. Give the answers as decimals, not vulgar fractions.]

18. The diameter of a semicircular protractor is 3·5 in.; find its perimeter.

[19] AB is a diameter of a circular pond of radius 100 yd. How much farther does a man go who walks from A to B round the edge than a man who rows straight across the pond?

*20. A boy finds the value of π experimentally by wrapping a piece of thread 5 times round a cylinder of diameter 5 in. He finds that the length of the thread when unwrapped is 78·65 in. What value for π should he obtain?

21. A bicycle wheel is 28 in. in diameter. How many revolutions does it make per mile?

22. A bicycle wheel, diameter 28 in., is making 25 revolutions in 10 sec. At what speed in miles per hour is the bicycle travelling?

*23. A dog-cart is being driven at 10 mi. an hour. If each wheel is 35 in. in diameter, find the number of revolutions made by each wheel per minute.

*24. A wheel of diameter 7 in. is rotating at 3000 revolutions per minute. Find the speed of a point on the rim in feet per second.

*25. A bucket is raised from the bottom of a well 55 ft. deep by a rope wound on an axle of diameter $1\frac{1}{2}$ ft. How many turns of the axle are required to bring the bucket up to the top? [Neglect the thickness of the rope.]

26. The radii of the inner and outer edges of a circular running-track are 70 yd. and 75 yd. What is the difference between the lengths of the two edges? Would it be the same if the two radii were 100 yd. and 105 yd.?

*27. The inner edge of a circular running-track is $\frac{1}{4}$ mi. long. If the track is 10 yd. wide, find the length of the outer edge of the track.

*28. A quadrant (*i.e.* quarter of a circle) of radius 8 in. is cut away from each corner of a rectangle 3 ft. long, $2\frac{1}{2}$ ft. wide. Find the perimeter of the remaining figure.

29. An arc AB of a circle, of radius 10 in., subtends an angle 144° at the centre O of the circle. Find the length of the arc AB. [arc $= \frac{144}{360}$ of circumference.]

*30. An arc AB of a circle subtends an angle 144° at the centre O of the circle. If the length of the arc AB is 4·4 cm., find the radius of the circle.

*31. A rectangular table-top has its corners rounded off into quarter-circles of 5 in. radii. By how much, to the tenth of an inch, is the perimeter of the table-top reduced?

*32. Four equal tins of circular section, radius $2\frac{1}{2}$ in., stand touching two by two. Find, to the nearest inch, the shortest length of string required for tying them together, allowing 3 in. for the knot.

*33. A piece of wire is in the form of an arc of a circle of radius 10 in., subtending an angle 150° at the centre of the circle. It is bent into the form of a complete circle; find the radius of this circle.

*34. A piece of wire 1 yd. long is bent into the form of a semi-circular arc and its diameter. Find the radius.

Area of a Circle

Example 6. A circle of radius 3 in. is drawn on a piece of squared paper, ruled in inches and tenths of an inch. It is found by counting that there are about 2828 small squares inside the circle. [In counting, disregard those small squares for which less than half the square lies inside the circle, and count as whole squares those for which more than half the square is inside the circle.] Use this result to calculate the ratio of the area of the circle to the area of the square on the radius.

The area of 100 small squares = 1 sq. in.;

∴ the area of 2828 small squares = 28·28 sq. in.

Since the radius is 3 in., area of square on radius = 9 sq. in.;

$$\therefore \quad \frac{\text{area of circle}}{\text{area of square on radius}} \simeq \frac{28 \cdot 28 \text{ sq. in.}}{9 \text{ sq. in.}} \simeq 3 \cdot 14.$$

The reader should repeat this experiment with another circle, say of radius 2 in.; he will then obtain approximately the same value for this ratio; and these results suggest that the value of this ratio is actually the number denoted by π. Thus

$$\frac{\text{area of circle}}{\text{area of square on radius}} = \pi \quad \text{or} \quad \text{area of circle} = (\text{square on radius}) \times \pi.$$

But if the radius of a circle is r units, the square on the radius contains r^2 units of area;

∴ the area of a circle, radius r units, is πr^2 units of area.

The reader should use this fact to show that the area of a circle of diameter d in. is $\frac{1}{4}\pi d^2$ sq. in.

If π is taken as $3\frac{1}{7}$ or as 3·14, results must not be given to more than 3 figures.

Example 7. Find the area of a circle whose diameter is 9 cm.

Since the diameter = 9 cm., the radius = 4·5 cm.;
∴ area of circle = $\pi(4\cdot5)^2$ sq. cm. $\simeq$ (3·14 × 20·25) sq. cm.
$\simeq$ 63·6 sq. cm.

$$\begin{array}{r} 20\cdot25 \\ 3\cdot14 \\ \hline 60\ 75 \\ 2\ 025 \\ 8100 \\ \hline 63\cdot5850 \end{array}$$

Example 8. Find the diameter of a circle whose area is 154 sq. in.

If the radius of the circle is r in., the area = πr^2 sq. in.;

$$\therefore \ \pi r^2 = 154; \quad \therefore \ r^2 = \frac{154}{\pi} \simeq 154 \div \tfrac{22}{7};$$

$$\therefore \ r^2 \simeq 49; \quad \therefore \ r \simeq 7.$$

∴ the diameter of the circle is 14 in., approximately.

The figure bounded by two concentric circles is called an **annulus**.
If the radii of the outer and inner circles are R in., r in.,

area between circles $= (\pi R^2 - \pi r^2)$ sq. in.
$$= \pi(R^2 - r^2) \text{ sq. in.,}$$

and it is sometimes easier to express this in factors :

area of annulus $= \pi(R + r)(R - r)$ sq. in.

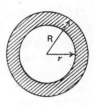

For example, if the radii are 8·6 in., 7·9 in.,
area of annulus $= \pi(8·6 + 7·9)(8·6 - 7·9)$ sq. in.
$$\simeq (\tfrac{22}{7} \times 16·5 \times 0·7) \text{ sq. in.}$$
$$\simeq (22 \times 16·5 \times 0·1) \text{ sq. in., that is } 36·3 \text{ sq. in.}$$

EXERCISE 104

[*Do not give any of the answers to more than* 3 *figures*]

Find the areas of the circles, Nos. 1–6 :

Take $\pi = 3\tfrac{1}{7}$ in Nos. 1–3, and take $\pi = 3·14$ in Nos. 4–6 :

1. Radius, 7 cm.   **[2]** Radius, 1 ft. 9 in.   **3.** Diameter, 2·8 in.

[4] Radius, 10 in.   **[5]** Diameter, 11 cm.   **6.** Diameter, 5 ft.

Find the radii of the circles whose areas are given in Nos. 7, 8,
taking $\pi = 3\tfrac{1}{7}$:

7. (i) 616 sq. in.;   (ii) 38·5 sq. cm.   **[8]** 15·4 ac.

*9. Find the diameter of a circle of area 5544 sq. yd.
[Take $\pi = 3\tfrac{1}{7}$.]

[*For the remainder of this exercise, take* π *to be* 3·14 *or* $\tfrac{22}{7}$,
whichever is the more convenient, except where otherwise stated.
Give the answers as decimals, not vulgar fractions.]

[10] Find the area of the top of a penny, diameter 1·3 in.

11. Find the area of a semicircle of diameter 3 ft. 6 in.

[12] A circle of diameter 3 in. is cut out of a sheet of paper 3 in.
square; what is the area of the remainder?

13. A circle of radius 4 in. is drawn on squared paper ruled in
inches and tenths of an inch, and the number of small squares
inside the circle is counted.   What should be the result?
[$\pi \simeq 3·1416$.]

*14. A donkey's head is tied by a rope 20 yd. long to a post in
a fenced field 50 yd. square.   What area of the ground can the
donkey cover if the post is (i) at a corner of the field, (ii) at the
middle point of one side of the field?

15. Find the circumference of a circle whose area is 3850 sq. yd.

16. 440 yd. of fencing are available for enclosing part of a field. Find the area of the enclosure (i) if square, (ii) if circular.

*17. How many plants can be put in a circular flower-bed whose circumference is 5 ft. 6 in., allowing 20 sq. in. for each plant?

18. Find the area of the ring between two concentric circles of radii 3 in. and 4 in.

19. From a metal sheet, 4 in. square, four quadrants of a circle, each of radius 2 in., are cut away at the corners. Sketch the shape of what remains, and find its area.

[20] A circular pond of diameter 28 ft. is surrounded by a path 7 ft. wide. Find the area of the path.

21. A circular metal plate of radius 10 in. weighs 5 lb.; find the weight of a plate of the same material and thickness of radius 1 ft. [There is no need to substitute for π.]

*22. Find the radius of a circle whose area is equal to the sum of the areas of two circles of radii 3 in., 4 in. respectively. [There is no need to substitute for π.]

*23. A rectangular lawn 15 yd. by 10 yd. is surrounded by flower-beds: a man can, without stepping off the lawn, water the ground up to a distance of 2 yd. from the edge. What is the total area of the flower-beds he can so water?

*24. OA, OB are two radii of a circle, centre O, radius 4 in.; if the angle between OA and OB is 144°, find the area of the part of the circle between OA and OB. [This area is called a *sector* of the circle of angle 144°. What fraction is the area of the sector of the area of the circle?]

*25. Find the area of a sector of a circle of radius 6 cm., if the angle of the sector is 108°. [Use the method indicated in No. 24.]

Area of Surface of a Circular Cylinder

A solid, whose cross-section is uniform and circular, such as a curtain rod or a pencil of circular section, is called a **circular cylinder,** and the radius of the cross-section is called the *radius of the cylinder*, and the straight line which passes through the centre of every cross-section is called the *axis of the cylinder*. The length of the axis is often called the *length* of the cylinder, as for a pencil, but this depends to some extent on the kind of cylindrical object. Thus for a jug of circular cross-section, the length of the axis is called the *height* of the cylinder, while for a circular disc, like a penny, the length of the axis is called the *thickness* of the cylinder, and for a garden roller the length of the axis is called the *width* of the cylinder. The name used is merely a matter of common sense.

A rectangular sheet of paper can be rolled up into the shape of a circular cylinder with open ends. Therefore

the area of the curved surface of a cylinder
=perimeter of base × height of cylinder.

If the radius of a cylinder is r units and if the height of the cylinder is h units, the perimeter of the base is $2\pi r$ units,

∴ area of curved surface of cylinder $=2\pi rh$ units of area.

In order to find the area of the *total* surface of a solid circular cylinder, it is necessary also to calculate the area of each end.

The area of each end is the area of a circle of radius r units, and is therefore πr^2 units of area.

$$\therefore \text{ total area of surface} = (2\pi rh + 2\pi r^2) \text{ units of area}$$
$$= 2\pi r(h+r) \text{ units of area.}$$

Example 9. Find the total area of the surface of a solid cylinder, base-radius 3 in., height 4 in.

$$\text{Perimeter of base} = (2\pi \times 3) \text{ in.} = 6\pi \text{ in.}$$
$$\therefore \text{ area of curved surface} = (6\pi \times 4) \text{ sq. in.} = 24\pi \text{ sq. in.};$$
$$\text{and area of base} = (\pi \times 3^2) \text{ sq. in.} = 9\pi \text{ sq. in.}$$
$$\therefore \text{ total area of surface} = (24\pi + 9\pi \times 2) \text{ sq. in.} = 42\pi \text{ sq. in.}$$
$$\backsimeq 42 \times \tfrac{22}{7} \text{ sq. in.}$$
$$\therefore \text{ total area of surface is 132 sq. in., approximately.}$$

Notice that in the above working the substitution for π is done as late as possible.

EXERCISE 105

[Nos. 1, 2 are intended for Oral work]

1. A rectangular sheet of paper 11 in. wide, 5 in. high, is rolled into the form of an open hollow cylinder, 5 in. high. What is the greatest possible diameter of the cylinder (take $\pi = \tfrac{22}{7}$)? What is the area of its curved surface? What is the area of the smallest piece of paper which will cover one end of it?

2. The radius of an open hollow cylinder is 3·5 cm. and the height of the cylinder is 6 cm. A cut is made straight down the surface so that the cylinder can be unwrapped to form a rectangle. Find the breadth, height, and area of the rectangle.

Find the areas of the curved surfaces of the cylinders, Nos. 3–6:

3. Radius 7 in., height 5 in.   [**4**] Length 1 dm., radius 3 cm.

5. Diameter 2·8 cm., width 8 cm.

[**6**] Diameter 1 yd., thickness ½ in.

Find the *total* areas of the surfaces of the solid cylinders, Nos. 7–10:

7. Radius 2 in., height 5 in.   [**8**] Radius 1 dm., thickness 5 mm.

[**9**] Diameter 1 ft., width 1 yd. **10.** Diameter 5 cm., length 12 cm.

Find the total area of the external surface of a cylinder closed at one end and open at the other end, with the given external measurements, Nos. 11, 12:

11. Radius 3 in., height 2 in. [**12**] Diameter 6 cm., height 1 dm.

Find the radius of each cylinder, Nos. 13, 14:

13. Area of curved surface 110 sq. in., height 5 in.

[**14**] Area of curved surface 79·2 sq. cm., height 3 cm.

Find the height of each cylinder, Nos. 15–17:

15. Area of curved surface 13·2 sq. cm., radius 6 cm.

[**16**] Total area of surface of solid cylinder 660 sq. in., radius 5 in.

*****17.** Total exterior area of surface of hollow cylinder closed at one end 198 sq. cm., exterior diameter 6 cm.

18. Find the area of thin tin. sheeting required for making a tin cylinder, radius 4 cm., height 6 cm., with a slip-on lid which overlaps 5 mm.

*****19.** The funnel of a ship is 12 ft. in external diameter and 60 ft. high. Find the number of pounds of paint required to cover it externally, if 1 lb. of paint covers 72 sq. ft.

*****20.** A garden roller is 2 ft. 6 in. in diameter and is 3 ft. 6 in. wide. What area does it cover in 40 revolutions?

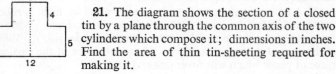

21. The diagram shows the section of a closed tin by a plane through the common axis of the two cylinders which compose it; dimensions in inches. Find the area of thin tin-sheeting required for making it.

22. A cylindrical tank, 7 ft. in diameter, contains water to a depth of 4 ft.   Find the total area of the wetted surface.

*23. The internal section of a tunnel is a rectangle 24 ft. wide, surmounted by a semicircle, and the greatest height is 20 ft.   Find the total area of the sides and roof of the tunnel, if it is 50 yd. long.

*24. A fence contains 36 cylindrical posts, each 4 in. in diameter and 2 ft. 10 in. high.   The sides and tops of the posts are painted. Find the total cost at 3d. per sq. ft.

Volume of Circular Cylinder.   The volume of any solid of uniform cross-section, see p. 190, is given by the rule,

area of cross-section × length.

If a circular cylinder is of radius r units and of height h units, the area of its cross-section is πr^2 units of area,

∴ **volume of cylinder = $\pi r^2 h$ units of volume.**

Also if a hollow tube is l in. long, and if its outer and inner radii are R in., r in.,

volume of material composing tube
$$= (\pi R^2 l - \pi r^2 l) \text{ cu. in.} = \pi l (R^2 - r^2) \text{ cu. in.}$$
$$= \pi l (R + r)(R - r) \text{ cu. in.}$$

Example 10.   Find the number of gallons of water in a cylindrical tank, 8 ft. in diameter, if the water is 3 ft. deep.   [1 cu. ft. $= 6\frac{1}{4}$ gall.]

Since the radius is 4 ft., and the depth of water is 3 ft.,

Volume of water $= (\pi \times 4^2 \times 3)$ cu. ft. $= (\pi \times 16 \times 3 \times \frac{25}{4})$ gall.

$= 300\pi$ gall. $\backsimeq (300 \times 3 \cdot 14)$ gall.

$\backsimeq 942$ gall.

Example 11.   A cylindrical tank, 3 ft. in diameter, contains 150 gall. of water.   Find the depth of the water.   [1 cu. ft. $= 6\frac{1}{4}$ gall.]

150 gall. occupy $(150 \div \frac{25}{4})$ cu. ft., that is 24 cu. ft.

Radius of base $= \frac{3}{2}$ ft.,   ∴ area of base $= \pi \times (\frac{3}{2})^2$ sq. ft.;

∴ depth of water = volume of water ÷ (area of base)

$$= (24 \div \frac{9\pi}{4}) \text{ ft.} = \frac{24 \times 4}{9\pi} \text{ ft.}$$

$$\backsimeq \frac{24 \times 4 \times 7}{9 \times 22} \text{ ft.}$$

$$\backsimeq \frac{112}{3 \times 11} \text{ ft.} \backsimeq 3 \cdot 39 \text{ ft.}$$

$$\begin{array}{r} 3\,|\,112 \\ \hline 11\,|\,37 \cdot 33 \\ \hline 3 \cdot 39 \end{array}$$

Example 12. Find the volume of metal in a hollow pipe, 2 ft. long, of internal diameter 10 in., made of metal $\frac{1}{2}$ in. thick.

Internal radius = 5 in.,   ∴ external radius = $(5 + \frac{1}{2})$ in. = $5\frac{1}{2}$ in.

The cross-section is the area between two concentric circles, radii $5\frac{1}{2}$ in. and 5 in.;

∴ area of cross-section = $\pi\{(5\frac{1}{2})^2 - 5^2\}$ sq. in., see p. 199,

$$= (\pi \times 10\frac{1}{2} \times \frac{1}{2}) \text{ sq. in.}$$

But the length of the pipe is 24 in.,

∴ volume of metal $\simeq (\frac{22}{7} \times \frac{21}{4} \times 24)$ cu. in., that is 396 cu. in.

EXERCISE 106

[Take 1 cu. ft. = $6\frac{1}{4}$ gall. ; do not give results to more than 3 figures]

Find the volumes of the circular cylinders, Nos. 1–4:

1. Radius $3\frac{1}{2}$ in., height 6 in.

[2] Diameter 2·1 cm., length 2 dm.

3. Diameter 1·4 m., thickness 1 cm.

[4] Radius, 0·35 in., length 2 ft.

Find the heights of the circular cylinders, Nos. 5, 6:

[5] Volume 66 cu. in., radius 2 in.

6. Volume 4 litres, radius 5 cm.

Find the diameters of the circular cylinders, Nos. 7, 8:

7. Volume 44 cu. in., height 3·5 in.

[8] Volume 385 cu. cm., height 1 dm.

9. A telegraph pole is 21 ft. high and 8 in. in diameter. Find its weight if the wood weighs 36 lb. per cu. ft.

[10] Find the weight of 10 m. of silver wire, diameter 4 mm., if 1 c.c. of silver weighs 10·5 gm.

11. A cylindrical tank is 4 ft. in diameter and $5\frac{1}{4}$ ft. high, internal measurements. How many gallons will it hold?

12. A cylindrical tank, 6 ft. in diameter, contains 550 gall. of water. Find the depth of the water.

*13. A circular lawn, diameter 40 m., is given a top-dressing 1 cm. thick. Find, to the nearest kg., the weight of the amount required, if 1 cu. m. of dressing weighs 2·7 kg.

Find the volume of metal in the hollow pipes, Nos. 14–16:

14. Internal radius 3 cm., metal 1 cm. thick, length 6 cm.

[15] External diameter 11 in., metal $\frac{1}{2}$ in. thick, length 1 ft.

*16. External diameter 6 in., metal $\frac{1}{4}$ in. thick, length 100 yd.

17. How many cylindrical glasses, diameter 3 in., height 5 in., can be filled from a cylindrical vessel, diameter 1 ft., height 2 ft. 6 in., full of milk. [There is no need to substitute for π.]

[18] A cylindrical jar, diameter 6 in., depth 8 in., is full of water. If this water is poured into an empty cylindrical jar of diameter 4 in., find the depth of the water. [There is no need to substitute for π.]

19. Find the weight per metre of wire of sectional area 0·13 sq. cm., if 1 cu. dm. of the material weighs 7·7 kg.

[20] A solid cylinder 5 in. in diameter, 6 in. long, is packed in a box which measures internally 5 in. by 5 in. by 6 in., and the empty space is filled with sawdust. Find the volume of sawdust required.

21. Find the volume of the closed tin whose dimensions are given in Ex. 105, No. 21.

*22. A groove of semicircular section, radius 3 in., is made across one face of a wooden cube of edge 1 ft., parallel to an edge. Find the volume of the solid which remains.

23. Water is pouring into a cylindrical tank of diameter 20 ft. at the rate of 4000 gall. per minute. Find, to the nearest inch, the rise of water-level per minute.

[24] Find the number of gallons discharged in an hour from a pipe 6 in. in diameter through which water is flowing at $3\frac{1}{2}$ ft. per second, if the pipe remains full.

*25. A bath holding $5\frac{1}{2}$ cu. ft. is filled in 5 min. by water from a pipe of diameter $1\frac{3}{4}$ in. At what speed in ft. per sec. is the water flowing in the pipe, if the pipe remains full?

*26. The curved surface of a cylinder is formed from a sheet of paper 6 in. square, and the ends of the cylinder are closed by circular caps. Find the greatest possible volume of the cylinder.

MISCELLANEOUS EXAMPLES

EXERCISE 107

[Do not give results to more than 3 figures]

1. The diameter of the clock-face on a town-hall is 9 ft. Find the area of the clock-face, to the nearest sq. ft.

2. The hour-hand of a clock is 4 in. long; find the distance the tip of this hand travels in 45 min.

[3] The circumference of a circle is 1 mile long. Find the area of the circle, to the nearest acre.

4. The wheel of a vehicle is 35 in. in diameter. Find the number of revolutions made by the wheel for each mile the vehicle travels.

5. ABCD is a rectangular plate, AB=6 in., BC=3 in.; two quadrants, centres A, B, each of radius 3 in. are cut away from the plate. Sketch the shape of what remains, and find its area.

[6] The perimeter of a semicircular window is 9 ft.; find (i) the diameter, (ii) the area of the window.

7. A uniform metal circular plate of radius 6 in. weighs 12 lb. Three circular holes, each of radius 2 in., are pierced in it; find the weight of the remainder.

8. The girth of a solid circular cylinder is 6 in., and its length is 11 in.; find its volume.

9. The wheel of a bicycle, 28 in. in diameter, is making two revolutions per second. At what speed in miles per hour is the bicycle travelling?

[10] The base of a metal plate, $\frac{1}{2}$ in. thick, is a rectangle 6 in. by 5 in., from which quadrants each of radius 2 in. have been removed at each of the four corners. Find the weight of the plate if the metal weighs 5 oz. per cu. in.

*11. Find the radius of a circle whose area is equal to the sum of the areas of three circles of radii 3 in., 4 in., 1 ft., respectively.

12. A cylindrical well, internal diameter $10\frac{1}{2}$ ft., contains 14,000 gall. of water. Find the depth of the water, to the nearest foot.

[13] An archway is formed by two vertical walls, 5 ft. high, 8 ft. apart, surmounted by a roof of semicircular section. The length of the archway is 20 ft.; find the area of its internal surface.

*14. The area of a sector of a circle of radius 7 cm. is 55 sq. cm.; find the angle of the sector.

[15] A path 2 yd. wide surrounds a circular pond of diameter 40 yd. How many cu. yd. of gravel are required to gravel the path to a depth of 3 in.?

16. A goat is tethered by a chain 10 yd. long to a ring which can slide along a low straight rail 15 yd. long, in the middle of a field. What is the area of ground the goat can cover?

*17. A bar 2 ft. long of square cross-section, side $\frac{3}{8}$ in., is recast so as to have a circular cross-section of diameter $\frac{1}{4}$ in. What does its length become, to the nearest inch?

18. A swimming-bath 22 yd. long, 10 yd. wide, $7\frac{1}{2}$ ft. deep is filled by water issuing from a pipe of diameter 6 in. at 4 ft. per second. How many minutes does it take to fill the bath?

*19. Water flows through a cylindrical pipe of diameter 10 in. at the rate of 10 ft. per second, the area of the cross-section of the stream in the pipe being $\frac{3}{4}$ of that of the pipe. Find the number of gallons discharged per minute.

*20. Four circular holes, each of diameter $3\frac{1}{2}$ in., are punched through a flat circular disc of diameter 25 in. Find what percentage of the disc has been removed. Find also the diameter of a circular disc of the same thickness whose volume is equal to the portion which remains.

*21. The diameter of a hollow cylindrical roller, closed at both ends, is 21 in., and its width is 3 ft., external measurements. If the sides and ends are $\frac{1}{2}$ in. thick, and if the material weighs 5 oz. per cu. in., find the weight of the roller in lb., to the nearest lb.

*22. The radius of a parallel of latitude of the Earth in latitude 60° is 2000 mi. What is the difference of longitude of two places 1000 mi. apart, each in latitude 60°?

CHAPTER XV

SIMPLE INTEREST AND DISCOUNT

If a man occupies a house which does not belong to him, he pays the owner money, called the *rent* of the house, for being allowed to make use of it. If you put money into the Post Office Savings Bank, you are lending money to the Government, and if you deposit £1 for 1 year, the Government will pay you 6d. for being allowed to make use of your money, and this payment is called *interest*. Just as the house for which a man pays rent remains the property of the landlord, so the £1 you have put in the bank remains your property; one year's rent of a house and one year's interest on money deposited in the bank are merely fair payments for being allowed to make use of what has been borrowed for the year.

Any money lent or borrowed is called the **Principal,** and the charge made for its use is called the **interest** and depends on how much has been borrowed and the length of time for which it is borrowed.

If the charge for borrowing £100 for 1 year is £4, we say that *interest is reckoned at the rate of* 4 *per cent. per annum*, or merely at 4 per cent., as the words *per annum* are implied if not actually stated.

Interest is usually paid at fixed intervals, yearly, half-yearly, or quarterly, just as rent is so paid; and in this case the principal is said to be lent at **simple interest.** If the simple interest for any given time is added to the principal, the sum is called the **amount** at simple interest for that time.

Thus if a man borrows £400 for 3 years at 5 per cent. per annum, *the simple interest* for 1 year is $\frac{5}{100}$ of £400, that is £20, and therefore for 3 years is £60; and the *amount* at simple interest for 3 years is £460.

Compound Interest

In transactions where the interest as it falls due is not paid to the lender but is added on to, *i.e.* compounded with, the principal, the money is said to be lent at **compound interest,** and the total sum owed after any given time is called the **amount** at compound interest for that time; the difference between the amount and the original principal is called the **compound interest.**

EXERCISE 108 (Oral)

Find the simple interest on, and the amount at simple interest of:

1. £100 for 1 yr. at 3%.
2. £100 for 1 yr. at $4\frac{1}{2}$%.
3. £100 for 3 yr. at 4%.
4. £100 for 4 yr. at 5%.
5. £100 for 2 yr. at $3\frac{1}{2}$%.
6. £100 for 6 yr. at $2\frac{1}{2}$%.
7. £100 for $\frac{1}{2}$ yr. at 8%.
8. £100 for 3 mo. at 6%.
9. £200 for 1 yr. at 4%.
10. £300 for 1 yr. at 7%.

11. £400 for 2 yr. at 3%.   **12.** £800 for 3 yr. at 4%.

13. £200 for 4 yr. at $2\frac{1}{2}$%.   **14.** £400 for 2 yr. at $3\frac{1}{2}$%.

[*Nos.* 15–18 *should be omitted, if not taken orally*]

Find the amount (i) at simple interest, (ii) at compound interest of, and the difference between the compound interest and simple interest on :

15. £800 for 2 yr. at 5 per cent. per annum.

16. £200 for 3 yr. at 10 per cent. per annum.

17. £1600 for 2 yr. at $2\frac{1}{2}$ per cent. per annum.

18. £12,500 for 3 yr. at 4 per cent. per annum.

Study the following table :—

Principal	Rate	Time in years	Interest	Amount
£300	4% p.a.	1	£12	£312
£300	4% p.a.	2	£24	£324
£300	4% p.a.	3	£36	£336

This illustrates the fact that

the simple interest is proportional to the time ;

and it is obvious that

the Amount is **not** *proportional to the time.*

Calculation of Simple Interest

Method I.   Direct Proportion

Example 1. Find the simple interest on £285 for $2\frac{1}{2}$ years at 3 per cent.   Find also the amount after $2\frac{1}{2}$ years.

The interest on £285 for 1 year is $\frac{3}{100}$ of £285,

∴ the interest on £285 for $2\frac{1}{2}$ years is ($\frac{3}{100}$ of £285) $\times 2\frac{1}{2}$.

∴ interest $= £(285 \times \frac{3}{100} \times \frac{5}{2}) = £\frac{171}{8} = £21\frac{3}{8} = £21$ 7s. 6d.

∴ the amount $= (£285 + £21$ 7s. 6d$) = £306$ 7s. 6d.

If the numbers involved have no simple factors, the interest is calculated more easily by using a practice method than by working with awkward fractions.

14

Example 2. Find to the nearest penny the simple interest on £239 4s. 5d. for $2\frac{3}{4}$ years at $4\frac{1}{2}\%$.

Rough Estimate : Interest on £200 for 3 yr. at 4% is £24.

Interest on £100 for $2\frac{3}{4}$ years at $4\frac{1}{2}\% = £(4\frac{1}{2} \times 2\frac{3}{4}) = £(\frac{9}{2} \times \frac{11}{4})$
$$= £\frac{99}{8} = £12\frac{3}{8}.$$

$\therefore$ required interest $= \dfrac{12\frac{3}{8}}{100}$ of £239 4s. 5d. $= 12\frac{3}{8}\%$ of £239 4s. 5d.

4s. 5d. $= 4\cdot4166...$s. $= £0\cdot2208$, to 4 places.

£
239·2208

10% is $\frac{1}{10}$ of 100%	23·92208	10%	£ 0·6036
2% is $\frac{1}{5}$ of 10%	4·78441	2%	
$\frac{1}{4}\%$ is $\frac{1}{8}$ of 2%	0·59805	$\frac{1}{4}\%$	s. 12·072
$\frac{1}{8}\%$ is $\frac{1}{2}$ of $\frac{1}{4}\%$	0·29902	$\frac{1}{8}\%$	d. 0·864
	29·60356	$12\frac{3}{8}\%$	

$\therefore$ the interest is £29 12s. 1d., to nearest penny.

Note. It is shorter, though less easy, to regard $12\frac{3}{8}$ as $(12\frac{1}{2} - \frac{1}{8})$; $12\frac{1}{2}\% = \frac{1}{8}$ of 100%; then *deduct* $\frac{1}{8}\%$, that is $\frac{1}{8}$ of 1%.

Method II.　Simple Interest Formula

The method of Example 1 on p. 209, which should first be worked, may be used to obtain a general formula :

To find the simple interest on £P for T years at R% per annum.

The interest on £P for 1 year is $\dfrac{R}{100}$ of £P, $= £\dfrac{P \times R}{100}$;

$\therefore$ the interest on £P for T years is $£\left(\dfrac{P \times R}{100}\right) \times T$, $= £\dfrac{P \times R \times T}{100}$.

Hence we have the following formula :—

If the simple interest on £P for T years at R% per annum is £I,

$$I = \frac{P \times R \times T}{100}$$

Example 3. Find the simple interest on £213 6s. 8d. for 15 months at 3% per annum.

Principal $= £213\frac{1}{3} = £\frac{640}{3}$;　time $= 15$ months $= \frac{5}{4}$ years;

$\therefore$ in the formula, $P = \frac{640}{3}$,　$T = \frac{5}{4}$,　$R = 3$;

$\therefore$ the interest £I is given by $I = \frac{640}{3} \times 3 \times \frac{5}{4} \times \frac{1}{100} = 8$;

$\therefore$ the simple interest is £8.

Note. In the formula, T is the number of years; we must therefore express 15 months as $\frac{5}{4}$ years.

If the principal contains an awkward fraction of a £, it is often shorter to use decimals. For ordinary rates of interest and lengths of time, the principal should be expressed in £, to 4 places of decimals, to make sure of obtaining the interest to the nearest penny.

Example 4. Find to the nearest penny the simple interest on £239 4s. 5d. for $2\frac{3}{4}$ years at $4\frac{1}{2}\%$.

$$4s.\ 5d. = 4\cdot4166...s. = £0\cdot2208,\ \text{to 4 places.}$$

∴ with the notation of the formula,

$$P = 239\cdot2208, \quad R = \tfrac{9}{2}, \quad T = \tfrac{11}{4};$$
$$\therefore\ I = 239\cdot2208 \times \tfrac{9}{2} \times \tfrac{11}{4} \times \tfrac{1}{100}$$
$$= \frac{2\cdot392208 \times 99}{8}$$
$$= 29\cdot60357.$$

$$\begin{array}{r} 239\cdot2208 \\ 2\cdot39221 \\ \hline 8)236\cdot82859 \\ \hline 29\cdot60357 \end{array}$$

∴ the interest is £29 12s. 1d., to nearest penny.

Note. To multiply by 99, multiply by $100 - 1$;
$2\cdot392208 \times 99 = 2\cdot392208 \times (100 - 1)$
$= 239\cdot2208 - 2\cdot392208.$

$$\begin{array}{rl} & £0\cdot6036 \\ s. & 12\cdot072 \\ d. & 0\cdot854 \end{array}$$

The working may also be completed by using a practice method as in Example 2 on p. 210.

In calculating the interest for a period between two given dates, assume that the year contains 365 days. Do not count the day when the money is deposited, but count the day when it is removed. For example, to find the number of days for the period May 28 to August 11,

(i) Subtract 28 from 31 (31 days in May)
(ii) Add the days of any complete months
(iii) Add the last date
∴ period = 75 days.

$$\begin{array}{r|r} \text{May} & 3 \\ \text{June} & 30 \\ \text{July} & 31 \\ \text{Aug.} & 11 \\ \hline & 75 \end{array}$$

Example 5. Find to the nearest penny the simple interest on £450 at 6% per annum from July 4 to August 16.

Number of days,

$$\begin{array}{r|r} \text{July} & 27 \\ \text{Aug.} & 16 \\ \hline & 43 \end{array}$$

∴ with the notation of the formula,

$$P = 450, \quad R = 6, \quad T = \tfrac{43}{365};$$
$$\therefore\ I = 450 \times 6 \times \tfrac{43}{365} \times \tfrac{1}{100} = \tfrac{54 \times 43}{730}$$
$$= \tfrac{2322}{730} \simeq 3\cdot1808.$$

$$\begin{array}{rl} & £0\cdot1808 \\ s. & 3\cdot616 \\ d. & 7\cdot392 \end{array}$$

∴ the interest is £3 3s. 7d., to nearest penny.

EXERCISE 109

Find the simple interest on, and the amount at simple interest of :

1. £350 for 3 yr. at 6%.   **[2]** £420 for 5 yr. at $2\frac{1}{2}$%.

[3] £184 for 2 yr. at 5%.   **4.** £845 for $3\frac{1}{2}$ yr. at 6%.

[5] £765 for $2\frac{1}{2}$ yr. at $5\frac{1}{3}$%.   **6.** £62 10s. for $2\frac{1}{4}$ yr. at $3\frac{1}{5}$%.

7. £375 for 2 yr. 8 mo. at $4\frac{1}{2}$%.   **[8]** £192 for 20 mo. at $2\frac{3}{4}$%.

Find to the nearest penny the simple interest on :

9. £48 for 2 yr. at 4%.   **[10]** £272 for $2\frac{1}{2}$ yr. at 3%.

[11] £528 for $1\frac{1}{2}$ yr. at $3\frac{1}{2}$%.   **12.** £416 for 16 mo. at $4\frac{1}{2}$%.

[13] £632 for 14 mo. at $5\frac{1}{4}$%.   **14.** £168 10s. for 3 yr. at 4%.

[15] £342 16s. for $2\frac{1}{2}$ yr. at $3\frac{1}{2}$%. **16.** £47 11s. 4d. for 4 yr. at $2\frac{1}{2}$%.

[17] £169 3s. 5d. for 2 yr. at $4\frac{1}{4}$%.

18. £604 13s. 10d. for $1\frac{1}{4}$ yr. at 6%.

19. £860 5s. 7d. for 3 yr. at $4\frac{1}{8}$%.

*20. £946 14s. 2d. for 100 days at $4\frac{1}{4}$%.

*21. £724 from April 5 to June 10 at $4\frac{1}{2}$%.

*22. £847 16s. 4d. from August 17 to November 4 at $5\frac{1}{2}$%.

Inverse Problems on Simple Interest

Example 6. At what rate per cent. per annum will £300 yield £60 interest in 5 years?

The interest on £300 for 5 years is £60.

∴ the interest on £300 for 1 year is £12.

∴ the interest on £100 for 1 year is £4.

∴ the rate is 4% p.a.

Note. p.a. is often used as an abbreviation for *per annum.*

Example 7. In what time will £400 amount to £472 at 6% p.a. simple interest?

The interest = £472 − £400 = £72.

The interest on £400 at 6% is £24 for 1 year.

∴ the interest on £400 at 6% is £72 for $\frac{72}{24}$ years, = 3 years.

Example 8. What sum of money will yield £54 interest in 3 years at 6% p.a.?

The interest on £100 for 3 years at 6% is £18.

£18 interest is yielded by £100.

∴ £54 interest is yielded by £$(100 × \frac{54}{18})$, = £300.

EXERCISE 110 (Oral)

In Nos. 1–4, find the rate per cent. p.a. if:

1. £600 yields £72 interest in 4 yr.

2. £400 amounts to £428 in 2 yr.

3. £700 yields £105 interest in $2\frac{1}{2}$ yr.

4. £250 amounts to £265 in $1\frac{1}{2}$ yr.

In Nos. 5–8, find in what time:

5. £300 will yield £60 interest at 5% p.a.

6. £800 will amount to £896 at 4% p.a.

7. £500 will yield £105 interest at $3\frac{1}{2}$% p.a.

8. £150 will amount to £186 at 6% p.a.

In Nos. 9–12, find what sum of money will yield:

9. £48 interest in 4 yr. at 3% p.a.

10. £70 interest in $2\frac{1}{2}$ yr. at 4% p.a.

11. £126 interest in $3\frac{1}{2}$ yr. at 6% p.a.

12. £72 interest in 9 yr. at $2\frac{1}{2}$% p.a.

13. Find the rate per cent. p.a. if the interest on £100 for x yr. is £y.

14. Find the rate per cent. p.a. if the interest on £P for T yr. is £I.

15. In what time will £100 yield £x interest at y per cent. p.a.?

16. In what time will £P yield £I interest at R per cent. p.a.?

17. What sum of money will yield £x interest in 1 yr. at y per cent. p.a.?

18. What sum of money will yield £I interest in T years at R per cent. p.a.?

Example 9. If the simple interest on £560 for 4 years is £78 8s., find the rate per cent. per annum.

With the notation of the formula, P = 560, T = 4, I = $78\frac{2}{5}$, and it is required to find the value of R.

$$\frac{P \times R \times T}{100} = I; \quad \therefore \ P \times R \times T = 100 \times I; \quad \therefore \ R = \frac{100 \times I}{P \times T};$$

$$\therefore \ R = 100 \times 78\frac{2}{5} \times \frac{1}{560} \times \frac{1}{4}$$

$$= 100 \times \frac{392}{5} \times \frac{1}{560} \times \frac{1}{4} = \frac{7}{2};$$

$$\therefore \ \text{the rate of interest is } 3\frac{1}{2}\% \text{ p.a.}$$

Example 10. In what time will £640 amount to £684 at $2\frac{1}{2}\%$ p.a. simple interest?

With the notation of the formula P = 640, I = 684 − 640 = 44, R = $2\frac{1}{2}$, and it is required to find the value of T.

$$P \times R \times T = 100 \times I; \quad \therefore T = \frac{100 \times I}{P \times R};$$

$$\therefore T = \frac{100 \times 44}{640 \times 2\frac{1}{2}} = \frac{100 \times 44 \times 2}{640 \times 5} = 2\frac{3}{4};$$

$$\therefore \text{ the time is } 2\frac{3}{4} \text{ years.}$$

Example 11. What sum of money will yield £81 interest in $2\frac{1}{2}$ years at $4\frac{1}{2}\%$ p.a. simple interest.

With the notation of the formula, I = 81, T = $2\frac{1}{2}$, R = $4\frac{1}{2}$, and it is required to find the value of P.

$$P \times R \times T = 100 \times I; \quad \therefore P = \frac{100 \times I}{R \times T};$$

$$\therefore P = \frac{100 \times 81}{4\frac{1}{2} \times 2\frac{1}{2}} = \frac{100 \times 81 \times 2 \times 2}{9 \times 5} = 720;$$

$$\therefore \text{ the principal is £720.}$$

EXERCISE 111

Find the unknown quantities in Nos. 1–16:

	Principal	Interest	Amount	Time	Rate % p.a.
1.	£120	£18	...	3 years	...
2.	£640	...	£696	$2\frac{1}{2}$ years	...
[3]	£240	...	£267	...	$4\frac{1}{2}$
4.	£960	£198	...	...	$5\frac{1}{2}$
5.	...	£48	...	$1\frac{1}{4}$ years	$5\frac{1}{3}$
[6]	...	£42	...	$1\frac{2}{3}$ years	$4\frac{1}{2}$
7.	£360	...	...	$2\frac{1}{2}$ years	$4\frac{1}{2}$
[8]	£10	...	...	5 months	$4\frac{1}{2}$
9.	£1560	£245 14s.	...	$3\frac{1}{2}$ years	...
[10]	£205	...	£207 1s.	146 days	...

	Principal	Interest	Amount	Time	Rate % p.a.
11.	£2000	£422 10s.	...	...	$3\frac{1}{4}$
[12]	...	£341 5s.	...	1 year	5
13.	£487 10s.	...	...	5 years	3
[14]	£840	...	£913 10s.	...	$3\frac{1}{2}$
15.	£835	£12 10s. 6d.	...	3 months	...
[16]	£280	...	£324 16s.	4 years	...

17. A man borrows £160 on the condition that he pays back £169 after 9 months.   At what rate % p.a. is interest charged?

18. After what time will £5 amount to 5 guineas at $2\frac{1}{2}\%$ p.a.?

19. The Post Office Bank pays interest at the rate of $2\frac{1}{2}\%$ p.a. How much have I in the Bank if my interest for 9 months is 5s. 3d.?

[20] A moneylender charges 3d. a month interest on a loan of 5s. Find the rate % p.a.

*21. If the interest on £25 for $3\frac{1}{2}$ yr. is £3 18s. 9d., find the interest on £100 for 3 months at the same rate.

[22] If the rate of interest is reduced from 5% p.a. to $3\frac{1}{2}\%$ p.a., find the decrease in a half-year's interest on £540.

23. A man lends £500 at 4% p.a., £800 at $3\frac{1}{4}\%$ p.a., and £700 at 6% p.a.   How much interest does he receive each year and what is the average rate per cent. per annum of the interest on the total sum of money lent?

24. Find correct to the nearest penny the interest on £500 at 5% from June 1 to June 29.

*25. A man borrowed £100 at $7\frac{1}{2}\%$ p.a. and when he repaid it the interest correct to the nearest penny was £2 9s. 4d.   For how many days did the loan run?

*26. If £160 amounts to £166 in 8 mo., find to what it will amount in 1 yr. at the same rate of interest.

*27. If the rate of interest on a loan is raised from 3% to $3\frac{1}{2}\%$, the annual interest is increased by £1 7s. 6d.   How much is the loan?

True Present Worth and Discount. For a given rate per cent. and given time, the amount is proportional to the principal.

For example, at 4% p.a. for $1\frac{1}{2}$ years we have:

Principal	Interest	Amount
£100	£ 6	£106
£200	£12	£212
£300	£18	£318

and so on.

Therefore, for a given rate per cent. and given time, if the amount is given the principal can be found by proportion.

Example 12. Find what sum will amount to £332 in 9 months at 5% p.a.

The interest on £100 for 9 months at 5% is £$(5 \times \frac{3}{4})$, and therefore the amount is £$(100 + \frac{15}{4})$, $= £\frac{415}{4}$.

The amount is £$\frac{415}{4}$ if the principal is £100;

∴ the amount is £332 if the principal is £$(100 \times \frac{4}{415} \times 332)$;

∴ the principal is £320.

Example 12 shows that £320 amounts in 9 months at 5% p.a. to £332; it follows that at this rate of interest, a man who is owed £320 now is in as good a position as a man who will be due to receive £332 in 9 months' time. For this reason, £320 is called the *true present worth* of £332 due in 9 months' time, reckoning simple interest at 5% p.a.

Further, if a man is due to pay £332 in 9 months' time, it would be fair to allow him to clear off the debt by paying £320 now, that is £12 less than the nominal amount of the debt or bill, and this reduction of £12 is called the *true discount*, allowed for an immediate payment; *it is the interest on the true present worth for the time which will elapse before the debt is due to be paid.*

Example 13. Find correct to the nearest penny the true present worth of a bill for £95 due in 7 months' time, allowing interest at $4\frac{1}{2}$% p.a. Find also the true discount.

Interest on £100 for 7 months at $4\frac{1}{2}$% p.a. $= £(\frac{9}{2} \times \frac{7}{12}) = £\frac{21}{8}$;

∴ in 7 months, £100 amounts to £$(100 + \frac{21}{8})$, $= £\frac{821}{8}$;

∴ the present worth of £$\frac{821}{8}$ is £100;

∴ the present worth of £95 is £$(100 \times \frac{8}{821} \times 95)$.

Hence, we find by reduction that

the present worth is £92 11s. 5d., to the nearest penny;

∴ the discount $= £95 - £92$ 11s. 5d. $= £2$ 8s. 7d.

EXERCISE 112

Find the principal which amounts at simple interest to :

1. £654 in 2 yr. at $4\frac{1}{2}\%$ p.a.   [2] £795 in $1\frac{1}{2}$ yr. at 4% p.a.

3. £522 in $2\frac{1}{2}$ yr. at $3\frac{1}{2}\%$ p.a.   [4] £378 in 16 mo. at $3\frac{3}{4}\%$ p.a.

5. £1065 in 21 mo. at $6\frac{1}{4}\%$ p.a.   [6] £602 in 20 mo. at $4\frac{1}{2}\%$ p.a.

Find the true present worth and the true discount, reckoning simple interest, of the following bills :—

7. £84 due in 2 yr., allowing $2\frac{1}{2}\%$ p.a.

[8] £249 due in 9 mo., allowing 5% p.a.

9. £176 due in 20 mo., allowing 6% p.a.

[10] £770 due in 8 mo., allowing 4% p.a.

Find correct to the nearest penny the true present worth and true discount, reckoning simple interest, of the following bills :—

11. £200 due in 3 mo., allowing 4% p.a.

[12] £75 due in 8 mo., allowing 6% p.a.

13. £350 due in 9 mo., allowing $4\frac{1}{2}\%$ p.a.

[14] £74 16s. 3d. due in 15 mo., allowing $5\frac{1}{2}\%$ p.a.

15. £437 10s. due in 8 mo., allowing $4\frac{3}{4}\%$ p.a.

Practical Discount. It is a custom of shopkeepers in certain cases to deduct a certain percentage from the marked prices of their goods for a cash payment. Thus many tailors allow a *discount* of 10% off the quoted price of a suit to those who pay cash on delivery. For example, the price of a suit is quoted as £14 by a tailor to a customer whom he does not expect will pay him for a year or so after the suit has been made, but he is willing to deduct 10% of £14, that is £1 8s., from the price if the customer pays at once. The cash price of the suit is therefore £12 12s., and the amount deducted, here £1 8s., is called the *cash discount*.

In shops, cash discounts are always calculated as fractions or percentages of the *marked prices*; a discount of 1d. in the shilling is equivalent to a deduction of $\frac{1}{12}$ of the marked price, that is $8\frac{1}{3}\%$ of the marked price.

When a retailer buys goods from a wholesale merchant, the prices in the trade catalogue issued by the wholesaler are usually subject to a *trade discount*, which is a percentage of the catalogued prices; this percentage varies from time to time according to the costs of raw materials, manufacture, taxation, and so on.

Example 14. A watch is marked £18, but a discount of 2s. 6d. in the £ is allowed for cash. What is the cash discount?

$$\text{The rate of discount} = \frac{2s.\ 6d.}{£1} = \frac{1}{8};$$

∴ the cash discount on £18 is $\frac{1}{8}$ of £18, that is £2 5s.

Example 15. In a wholesale catalogue, a wireless set is quoted at £65, but the retailer is allowed a discount of 30%. What price is paid by the retailer?

The discount $= \frac{8}{10}$ of £65 = £19 10s.;

∴ the retailer pays £65 − £19 10s., that is £45 10s.

Alternatively, as follows :—

Since a discount of 30% is allowed, the retailer pays 70% of the catalogued price;

∴ the retailer pays $\frac{7}{10}$ of £65, that is £45 10s.

EXERCISE 113

1. What percentage represents a discount of (i) 1s. in the £; (ii) 2d. in the s.?

2. Find the discount on a bill of £1, if the rate of discount is (i) 10%; (ii) $37\frac{1}{2}$%.

3. A tailor gives a discount of 2s. in the £ on a suit quoted at 15 guineas. What is the cash price?

[4] A manufacturer's catalogued price of a car is £240, but he allows the retailer 30% discount. What does the retailer pay for the car?

5. Find the cost of 15 gross of pencils at $1\frac{3}{4}$d. each, if a discount of (i) $2\frac{1}{2}$%, (ii) $\frac{1}{2}$d. in the s., is allowed.

[6] Find the cost of 1 cwt. of tea at 2s. 6d. per lb., if a discount of 10% is allowed.

7. A shopkeeper marks a piano 50 guineas, but accepts £50 8s. for a cash payment. Express the discount as a percentage.

8. A carpet is quoted at £24 in a wholesaler's catalogue, but the retailer only pays £20 for it. Express the trade discount allowed (i) as a percentage, (ii) at so much in the £.

[9] A shopkeeper gives a discount of 10% for cash. At what price is an article marked, if its cash price is 13s. 6d.?

10. A manufacturer allows the retailer a discount of 35% on the catalogued prices. What is the catalogued price of a rug for which the retailer pays £2 12s.?

11. A tradesman sends a customer a bill for £5 10s., of which 20% is gross profit. If the customer is allowed a discount of 1s. in the £, find the net profit.

*12. The wholesaler allows the retailer a trade discount of 25% on an article listed at £54. The retailer gives a cash discount of 5% on the listed price; what profit does the retailer make?

*13. The catalogue price of a carpet is £16, but the retailer is allowed a trade discount of 25%. At what price must the retailer sell it to gain 25% of what he pays for it?

*14. The catalogue price of a watch is £15, but the retailer is allowed a trade discount of 40%. If the retailer sells the watch for £15, find his gain per cent.

*15. The catalogue price of an article is 22s., but the retailer is allowed a trade discount of $33\frac{1}{3}$%. He charges 22s. for the article, but allows a discount of $12\frac{1}{2}$%; find his net profit and his gain per cent.

The next section may be omitted at a first reading.

Banker's Discount. If a merchant A buys goods from another merchant B, payment is often made by what is called a *Bill of Exchange*, which is a document drawn up by B, called the *Drawer* of the bill, stating the sum of money to be paid and the date on which payment is to be made. The document is then signed by A, who is called the *Acceptor* of the bill.

When the bill has been signed and stamped, it forms a legal promise on the part of A to pay the agreed sum at the stated date. But it may happen that B requires the money before the date on which it is due, and in this case he takes the document to a Bank or a *Bill-broker* who will not pay him the full face-value (or nominal value) of the bill, but a smaller amount depending on the length of time before the bill matures (*i.e.* is due for payment by A), provided of course that A is a reliable creditor. In actual practice, the bill-broker calculates the simple interest on the nominal value of the bill for the time which will elapse before the payment is due, and deducts this from the nominal value of the bill.

Since a bill of exchange does not mature legally till 3 days after the stated date, the bill-broker, when calculating the interest, adds 3 days to the length of time the bill has still to run nominally, these 3 days being called *days of grace*.

Example 16. Find how much a bill-broker gives for a bill of £400, drawn on June 1 for 2 months, which he discounts on July 6 at 5%.

Since 3 days' grace are allowed, the bill matures on August 4; therefore when it is discounted on July 6, there remain 29 days before payment will be made.

Interest on £400 for 29 days at 5% is £$(4 \times 5 \times \frac{29}{365})$;

∴ the discount $= £\frac{116}{73} = £1$ 11s. 9d., to nearest penny.

∴ the bill-broker gives (£400 − £1 11s. 9d.), = £398 8s. 3d.;

∴ the "discounted value" of the bill is £398 8s. 3d.

Note. The sum £1 11s. 9d., deducted by the bill-broker, is called *banker's* discount or *commercial* discount. It should be noted that it is slightly larger than the *true* discount, because it is calculated as a percentage of the face-value of the bill, whereas the true discount is the same percentage of the true present worth of the bill.

EXERCISE 114

Find correct to the nearest penny the discounted values of the following bills, allowing 3 days' grace :—

1. £100, drawn on June 1 for 1 mo. and discounted on June 6, at 5%.

[**2**] £1000, drawn on May 10 for 3 mo. and discounted on May 12, at 4%.

3. £2500, drawn on August 20 for 4 mo. and discounted on December 1, at 3%.

[**4**] £750, drawn on March 10 for 20 days and discounted on March 13, at $4\frac{1}{2}$%.

5. £1800, drawn on July 12 for 56 days and discounted on August 20, at $3\frac{1}{2}$%.

[**6**] £5500, drawn on July 1 for 1 mo. and discounted on July 1, at 4%.

Find correct to the nearest penny the discount on the following bills, allowing 3 days' grace :—

7. £300, drawn on May 15 for 3 mo. and discounted on July 20 at 5%.

[8] £1250, drawn on March 1 for 6 mo. and discounted on April 20, at 4%.

[9] £4500, drawn on March 20 for 14 days and discounted on April 1, at $3\frac{1}{2}$%.

10. £138, drawn on September 22 for 60 days and discounted on October 5, at $4\frac{1}{2}$%.

*11. A bill for £680, drawn on March 1 for 3 mo., is discounted on March 20 for £674 6s. 9d. Find the rate of discount, allowing 3 days' grace.

*12. A bill for £436, drawn on June 24 for 90 days, is discounted on July 13 for £431 2s. 9d. Find the rate of discount, allowing 3 days' grace.

*13. [*The third-tenth-tenth Rule.*] Prove that the interest on £P for n days at R per cent. per annum is $£\dfrac{P \times 2nR}{73000}$, and that this is approximately equal to

$$£(P \times 2nR) \times (1 + \tfrac{1}{3} + \tfrac{1}{30} + \tfrac{1}{300}) \div 10^5.$$

Use this rule to find correct to the nearest penny the simple interest on £175 for 37 days at 4% p.a.

Use the "third-tenth-tenth rule," see No. 13, to find to the nearest penny :

*14. The simple interest on £230 for 45 days at $3\frac{1}{2}$% p.a.

*15. The simple interest on £583 10s. for 24 days at $4\frac{1}{2}$% p.a.

*16. The banker's discount on a bill for £385 drawn on September 15 for 1 mo., if discounted on September 20 at 4%, allowing 3 days' grace.

*17. The banker's discount on a bill for £630 drawn on May 10 and nominally due on August 12, if discounted on May 14 at 3%, allowing 3 days' grace.

MISCELLANEOUS EXAMPLES

EXERCISE 115

1. Find the simple interest on £260 for 15 mo. at 7% p.a.

[2] Find the rate of interest if £150 amounts to £157 in 16 mo., at simple interest.

3. A man's annual interest on his Savings Bank deposit is 27s. 6d. If the rate of interest is $2\frac{1}{2}$% p.a., find the size of his deposit.

[4] At what rate % p.a. will the yearly interest on £625 be the same as the yearly interest on £550 at 8% p.a.?

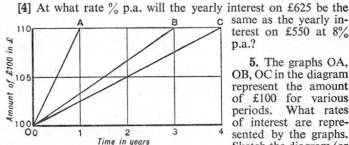

5. The graphs OA, OB, OC in the diagram represent the amount of £100 for various periods. What rates of interest are represented by the graphs. Sketch the diagram (or reproduce it on squared paper) and draw, on your sketch, graphs showing the amount at (i) 5%, (ii) 4%, (iii) 2%.

6. A discount of $17\frac{1}{2}$% is allowed on an article catalogued at £8 15s. What is its cash price?

7. What sum of money amounts to £627 in $2\frac{1}{2}$ yr. at 4% p.a. simple interest?

[8] A man borrows £10 at 1% per month simple interest and repays £2 after 4 mo. How much does he still owe?

[9] After what time will £7 amount to 7 guineas at 4% p.a. simple interest?

*10. A club of 264 members has to meet a bill of £100 in 7 months' time. Each member subscribes 7s. 6d. and the money accumulates at 5% p.a. simple interest. What balance remains when the bill has been paid?

11. A shopkeeper gives a discount of $12\frac{1}{2}$% on the marked price of a chair for cash. If the cash price is £2 9s., find the marked price.

[12] A man lends on mortgage £600 at $5\frac{1}{2}$% p.a. and £900 at $4\frac{1}{4}$% p.a. What is the average rate of interest on the total sum lent?

13. A man earns £2500 a year and invests each year 18 per cent. of it at 5% p.a. simple interest. How much interest does he receive in the first 3 yr. from the time he began to invest money in this way?

14. A man borrows £40 from a moneylender and discharges his debt at the end of 3 mo. by repaying £42 8s. At what rate per cent. p.a. is interest charged on the loan?

*15. In what time does a sum of money increase by $4\frac{1}{2}\%$, if invested at 6% p.a. simple interest?

[16] Find correct to the nearest penny the interest on a loan of £243 5s. at $5\frac{1}{2}\%$ p.a. which runs from April 5 to June 3.

*17. A sum of money amounts to £840 after 1 yr. and to £882 after 2 yr. at simple interest. Find the amount after 2 more years and the rate per cent. p.a. at which interest is paid.

*18. During the War the Government borrowed money at 5% p.a. simple interest. In 1927 it offered to call each £100 borrowed £142, and to pay $3\frac{1}{2}\%$ p.a. on that sum. What is the change in income of a man who had originally lent £5000?

*19. A man lends £1000, partly at $3\frac{1}{2}\%$ p.a. and the rest at 4% p.a. He receives each year £39 7s. 6d. in interest; how much did he lend at 4%?

20. The true discount on a bill for £780 due in 8 months' time is £30. At what rate per cent. p.a. is interest reckoned?

21. The catalogue price of a table is £5, but the retailer is allowed a trade discount of 35%. At what price does the retailer sell it if he makes a profit of 40%?

*22. If it would cost £300,000,000 to electrify the railways in Great Britain, and if this would result in saving $7\frac{1}{2}$ million tons of coal a year, find the price of the coal per ton, if the amount saved would pay interest at 4% on the capital outlay.

[23] A sum of money amounts at simple interest to £688 in 3 yr. at $2\frac{1}{2}\%$ p.a. To what would it amount in $2\frac{1}{2}$ yr. at $3\frac{1}{4}\%$ p.a. simple interest?

*24. At the beginning of the year I have £24 7s. 5d. in the Savings Bank. During the year I make deposits of £1 10s. on March 15, 18s. on July 4, £5 10s. on December 23, and withdraw £2 on September 21. Interest is allowed at the rate of $\frac{1}{2}$d. per £ per month on every complete pound on deposit for the whole month and is credited at the end of the year. How much have I got in the bank at the end of the year, including the interest credited?

CHAPTER XVI

APPROXIMATIONS

"The important thing about approximate answers is that they should be right *as far as they go.*"

As was pointed out in Chapter VII, see p. 71, any result deduced from approximate data can only be approximate and must not contain more figures than are justified by the degree of accuracy of the data. No practical measurements, such as those of length, area, weight, etc., can be exact, and the degree of accuracy of results so obtained should be stated: for example, it may be given that the length of a bench is 4·03 m., correct to the nearest cm., and this means that the true length is between 4·035 m. and 4·025 m.; this could also be indicated by writing the length as $(4·03 \pm 0·005)$ m.; another very important way of expressing the same fact is to say that the length is 4·03 m., correct to 3 significant figures.

Contracted Addition and Subtraction. In general, *two* more places of decimals should be retained in the working than are required in the answer; no account need then be taken of figures outside this range.

Example 1. Find, correct to 1 place of decimals, the sum of

186·34725, 8·91567, 100·5723, 47·83191.

Since the answer is required correct to 1 place of decimals, retain 3 places in the working.	186·347|25
	8·915|67
Draw a line down the page, marking off 3 places of decimals, and ignore all figures to the right of it.	100·572|3
	47·831|91
The sum is 343·7, correct to 1 place of decimals.	343·665|

Example 2. Find, to the nearest 100,000, the difference between 40,736,842 and 29,472,568.

	40736|842
To obtain the answer to the nearest 100,000, retain the thousands column in the working.	29472|568
	11264|***

The difference is 11,300,000, to the nearest 100,000.

Example 3. Find, correct to 3 places of decimals, the value of

$$\tfrac{1}{6} - \tfrac{1}{2}(\tfrac{1}{6})^2 + \tfrac{1}{3}(\tfrac{1}{6})^3 - \tfrac{1}{4}(\tfrac{1}{6})^4 + \ . \ . \ .$$

The values of $\tfrac{1}{6}$, $(\tfrac{1}{6})^2$, $(\tfrac{1}{6})^3$, . . . are found by successive division by 6. Since the final result is required to 3 places, 5 places are retained in the working, and the process is continued until the first 5 decimal places are all zeros. It saves times to arrange the positive and negative terms in separate columns.

	Plus	Minus
$\tfrac{1}{6} = 0 \cdot 16667$	0·16667	
$\tfrac{1}{2}(\tfrac{1}{6})^2 = 0 \cdot 02778 \div 2$		0·01389
$\tfrac{1}{3}(\tfrac{1}{6})^3 = 0 \cdot 00463 \div 3$	0·00154	
$\tfrac{1}{4}(\tfrac{1}{6})^4 = 0 \cdot 00077 \div 4$		0·00019
$\tfrac{1}{5}(\tfrac{1}{6})^5 = 0 \cdot 00013 \div 5$	0·00003	
	0·16824	0·01408
	0·01408	
	0·15416	

∴ the value is 0·154, correct to 3 places of decimals.

Note. To obtain the value, correct to 4 places of decimals, we should start by retaining 6 places in the working; but if this is done it will be found that the result is 0·154151, and this is a border-line case where it is possible that, with a closer approximation, the result may prove to be nearer 0·1541 than 0·1542. In such exceptional cases as this, it becomes necessary to retain 7 places of decimals in the working.

EXERCISE 116

Find, correct to the number of places of decimals indicated in brackets, the values of:

1. $7 \cdot 605812 + 0 \cdot 913645 + 1 \cdot 286712 + 5 \cdot 071658$ (2).

2. $18 \cdot 97904 + 6 \cdot 512783 + 12 \cdot 90712 + 0 \cdot 896705$ (2).

[3] $0 \cdot 7430727 + 2 \cdot 8165723 + 1 \cdot 6929457$ (3).

4. $18 \cdot 7246812 - 7 \cdot 8156073$ (2).

[5] $3 \cdot 960754 - 1 \cdot 0986254$ (3).

[6] $12 \cdot 6438162 - 8 \cdot 7174735$ (4).

7. $8 \cdot 07254 - 2 \cdot 89173 + 0 \cdot 90954 - 3 \cdot 50816$ (2).

[8] $7 \cdot 14916 + 2 \cdot 8375 - 6 \cdot 37488 + 1 \cdot 96723$ (2).

9. The population of the United Kingdom was made up as follows :—

	England	Wales	Scotland
1921	35,230,225	2,656,474	4,882,497
1931	37,354,917	2,593,014	4,842,554

Find (i) the total population for 1921 and for 1931, correct to 4 significant figures, (ii) the increase in the total population for the period 1921–1931, correct to 3 significant figures.

[10] Net receipts from income tax were made up as follows :—

	England and Wales	Scotland	Ireland
1929	£218,851,564	£17,282,382	£1,739,106
1930	£235,553,636	£18,041,937	£1,743,731

Find (i) the total receipts for 1929 and for 1930, correct to 4 significant figures, (ii) the increase in the total receipts, correct to 3 significant figures.

[11] Imperial Airways issued the following traffic figures for the 5 years, 1927 to 1931 :—

	1927	1928	1929	1930	1931
Letters	2,334,850	2,911,345	3,941,070	5,104,365	6,348,720
Passengers	26,469	34,502	29,338	30,993	34,162
Miles flown	867,675	1,032,842	1,345,217	1,295,848	1,721,962

Find, correct to 3 significant figures, the total of each item for the 5 years.

12. The value in £ of goods imported into and exported from Great Britain by air for the 5 years 1927 to 1931 was as follows :—

	1927	1928	1929	1930	1931
Imports	1,251,921	2,003,551	1,990,350	1,656,682	2,022,522
Exports	1,439,346	981,139	1,003,219	834,533	773,958

Find, correct to the nearest £10,000, the total value for the 5 years of (i) imports, (ii) exports, (iii) excess of imports over exports.

Find, correct to 4 significant figures, the values of :

13. $\frac{1}{4} + \frac{1}{4^2} + \frac{1}{4^3} + \frac{1}{4^4} + \ldots$ **[14]** $\frac{1}{7} + \frac{1}{7^2} + \frac{1}{7^3} + \frac{1}{7^4} + \ldots$

[15] $\frac{1}{3} - \frac{1}{3^2} + \frac{1}{3^3} - \frac{1}{3^4} + \ldots$ ***16.** $\frac{1}{2} + \frac{1}{2 \cdot 3} + \frac{1}{2 \cdot 3 \cdot 4} + \frac{1}{2 \cdot 3 \cdot 4 \cdot 5} + \ldots$

17. $\frac{1}{7} - \frac{1}{2}\left(\frac{1}{7}\right)^2 + \frac{1}{3}\left(\frac{1}{7}\right)^3 - \frac{1}{4}\left(\frac{1}{7}\right)^4 + \ldots$

*18. $4\left\{\left(\frac{1}{2} + \frac{1}{3}\right) - \frac{1}{3}\left(\frac{1}{2^3} + \frac{1}{3^3}\right) + \frac{1}{5}\left(\frac{1}{2^5} + \frac{1}{3^5}\right) - \ldots\right\}$

Contracted Multiplication

In general, *two more significant figures* should be retained in the working than are required in the product. The position of the decimal point should be obtained by a rough estimate, just as is necessary if a slide rule is used.

Example 4. Find, correct to 2 places of decimals, the value of
814·7325 × 0·00426308.

Rough Estimate: 800 × 0·004 = 3·2 (count the decimal places).

Since the product is about 3, and since 2 places of decimals are required, we must find the value of the product, correct to 3 *significant figures*, and must therefore retain 5 *significant figures in the working*.

$$
\begin{array}{r}
8147,325 \\
4263\ 08 \\
\hline
(a)\quad 32589 \\
(b)\quad 1629 \\
(c)\quad 488 \\
(d)\quad 24 \\
\hline
(e)\quad 34730 \\
\end{array}
$$

(a) First multiply by 4. Since only 5 figures are needed in the working, put a comma after the 7 in 8147325 and multiply 8147 by 4; this gives 5 figures, namely, 32588, but we carry 1 from 3 × 4 so that this becomes 32589.

(b) Cross off the digit 7 in the top line and multiply 814 by 2, but carry 1 from 7 × 2.

(c) Cross off the digit 4 in the top line and multiply 81 by 6, but carry 2 from 4 × 6.

(d) Cross off the digit 1 in the top line and multiply 8 by 3.

(e) The sum is 34730, but the rough estimate gave 3·2.

∴ the product is 3·47, correct to 2 places of decimals.

EXERCISE 117

Evaluate correct to 2 significant figures:

    1. 27·84 × 13·23.   **[2]** 1·695 × 0·3486.   **[3]** 8716 × 9248.

Evaluate correct to 3 significant figures:

    [4] 3·7214 × 2·5168.   **5.** 70916 × 41837.

Evaluate correct to 2 places of decimals:

    6. 0·39326 × 2·3174.   **7.** (2·1638)^2.

Evaluate correct to 3 significant figures:

    [8] 2·71564 × 3·18247.   **9.** 72·6358 × 64·7183.

Evaluate correct to the number of places of decimals indicated in brackets :

[10] $3 \cdot 62471 \times 0 \cdot 256372$ (2).   **11.** $0 \cdot 716244 \times 0 \cdot 638173$ (3).

[12] $271 \cdot 085 \times 0 \cdot 362185$ (2).   [13] $3 \cdot 14159 \times 176 \cdot 432$ (1).

Evaluate correct to 4 significant figures :

[14] $809 \cdot 43627 \times 35 \cdot 1284$.   **15.** $(0 \cdot 0571826)^2$.

16. The average postal receipts in 1931 were £133,469 per day. Find the total receipts for the year, correct to 4 figures.

17. The population of London in 1931 was 8,202,818, and the death-rate for the year was $11 \cdot 872$ per thousand. Find the number of deaths in London in 1931, correct to 3 figures.

Evaluate :

*18. $1 \cdot 7394 \times 2 \cdot 1243 \times 3 \cdot 8143$ correct to 2 decimal places.

*19. $36 \cdot 7134 \times 4 \cdot 8624 \times 2 \cdot 3154$ correct to 3 significant figures.

*20. $(2 \cdot 17246)^2 \times 38 \cdot 517$ correct to the nearest integer.

Contracted Division. In general, *two more significant figures* should be retained in the working than are required in the quotient.

Example 5. Find, correct to 1 place of decimals, the value of

$$0 \cdot 876243 \div 0 \cdot 0342174.$$

Rough Estimate : $\dfrac{0 \cdot 87}{0 \cdot 03} \Big| \dfrac{6243}{42174} \simeq \dfrac{87}{3} \simeq 30.$

```
                          25·60
        3·4̶2̶1̶7̶)87·624  │ (a)
               68 434   │
               19 190   │ (b)
               17 108   │
                2 082   │ (c)
                2 053   │
                   29   │ (d)
```

Since the quotient is about 30, and since it is required correct to 1 place of decimals, we must find the quotient, correct to 3 significant figures, and must therefore retain 5 significant figures in the working.

(a) Write down the divisor and dividend to 5 figures; the first digit in the quotient is 2.

(b) The first remainder is 19190; cross off the right-hand digit 7 of the divisor, and divide 19190 by 3421; the next digit in the quotient is 5; since $7 \times 5 = 35$, 3 must be carried in multiplying 3421 by 5; 5 times 1 is 5, and 3 makes 8, then continue as usual.

(c) Cross off the next digit 1 of the divisor, and divide 2082 by 342; the next digit in the quotient is 6; since $1 \times 6 = 6$, 1 must be carried in multiplying 342 by 6.

(d) Since 3 significant figures are required in the answer, the working ceases as soon as 4 figures have been obtained in the quotient.

The quotient is $25 \cdot 6$, correct to 1 place of decimals.

EXERCISE 118

Evaluate correct to 2 significant figures:

1. $81·17 \div 32·54$. **[2]** $4·273 \div 681·3$. **3.** $596·7 \div 0·08134$.

Evaluate correct to 3 significant figures:

[4] $17·364 \div 2·9175$. **5.** $66·324 \div 0·051728$.

Evaluate correct to 2 places of decimals:

6. $5·268 \div 8·147$. **[7]** $8·3647 \div 5·1923$.

Evaluate correct to 4 significant figures:

[8] $73·2698 \div 278·314$. **9.** $48379·46 \div 0·0726384$.

[10] $0·907364 \div 76·0824$. **[11]** $3596728 \div 513·8247$.

Evaluate correct to 3 places of decimals:

[12] $8·172945 \div 59·6304$. **13.** $0·372691 \div 0·624738$.

14. The area of Hampshire is 1458·3 sq. miles, and its population in 1931 was 472,022. Find the average per sq. mile, to the nearest whole number.

15. In 1931, exports by air from Great Britain amounted to £7,961,877 and imports by air to £14,041,065. Express the exports as a percentage of the imports, correct to 4 figures.

Evaluate correct to 2 significant figures:

*16. $\dfrac{32·736 \times 2·4683}{4·2973}$. ***17.** $\dfrac{19·6273 \times 0·481736}{57·2438}$.

Errors. If a length is stated to be 2·4 cm., correct to the nearest mm., then the true length is between 2·35 cm. and 2·45 cm.; therefore the error in taking the length as 2·4 cm. does not exceed 0·05 cm., and this is called the maximum *absolute error*.

Thus if a number is given correct to a stated number of figures, the maximum absolute error is represented by a 5 in the next place.

The standard of accuracy of a measurement is not, however, judged by *absolute* error. For example, an error of 1 in. in the size of a 15-in. collar is so big as to make the collar almost useless, but an error of 1 in. in marking out a 100-yd. running-track is of no importance, although the absolute error is 1 in. in each case. What matters in estimating the importance of an error is the *ratio* of the absolute error to the true value, and this is called the *relative error*. Thus, in the above example, the relative error in the size of the collar is $\frac{1}{15}$ and in the length of the track is $\frac{1}{3600}$; the second relative error is much smaller than the first, but it is easier to compare them if they are expressed as percentages:

$$\text{thus } \tfrac{1}{15} \simeq 7\% \quad \text{and} \quad \tfrac{1}{3600} \simeq 0.03\%.$$

If the relative error is expressed as a percentage, it is called the *percentage error* or the *error per cent*.

In calculating percentage errors, it is usually sufficient to work to one significant figure, because this indicates sufficiently clearly the degree of accuracy of measurement.

When the true value is unknown, as is often the case, the relative error is taken as the ratio of the maximum absolute error to the measured value, and if the relative error is less than $\frac{1}{10}$, the result to 1 significant figure will not in general be affected by doing so.

Example 6. The length of a line is 7·2 cm., correct to the nearest mm. Find (i) the maximum absolute error, (ii) the relative error and error per cent., to 1 significant figure.

(i) The true length lies between 7·15 cm. and 7·25 cm.;
∴ the maximum absolute error is 0·05 cm.

(ii) The relative error $\simeq \dfrac{0.05}{7.2} \simeq 0.007$;

∴ the error per cent. $\simeq 0.7\%$.

EXERCISE 119

Find to 1 significant figure the maximum absolute error, the relative error and error per cent. in Nos. 1–7:

1. A length of 4·5 cm., correct to the nearest mm.

[2] A weight of 0·328 kg., correct to the nearest gm.

3. A profit of 11s. 3d., correct to nearest penny.

4. A time of 10·4 sec., correct to nearest $\frac{1}{5}$ sec.

[5] A weight of 7 lb. 10 oz., correct to nearest oz.

6. A length is known to be 2480 yd., correct to 3 figures.

[7] A weight is known to be 1 ton, within 20 lb.

Find to 1 significant figure the error per cent. in Nos. 8–12:

8. Calculated length 5·32 cm., by measurement 5·4 cm.

[9] Calculated volume 86·62 c.c., by measurement 86·5 c.c.

10. π is taken as $3\frac{1}{7}$ instead of 3·14159 . . .

[11] $\sqrt{3}$ is taken as $1\frac{3}{4}$ instead of 1·7321 . . .

[12] 1 m. is taken as 39 in. instead of 3·2809 . . . ft.

13. A line is measured as 7·5 cm.; if the maximum error per cent. is 4%; between what limits (to 2 figures) does the true length lie?

14. A sum of money is given in £ correct to 3 places of decimals; show that the error is less than half a farthing.

*15. A speed is given as 118 ft. per sec. correct to the nearest ft. per sec. What is the maximum error in calculating the distance travelled in 20 min.?

*16. A merchant buys tea wholesale at the rate of 1s. $10\frac{3}{8}$d. per lb., correct to the nearest $\frac{1}{8}$d. What is the maximum error in calculating the wholesale price per cwt.?

Addition

It is important to remember that it is useless to give more significant figures in a result than are justified by the data, taking account of the uses that have been made of the data.

Example 7. Find the sum of the numbers,

$$8·633, \ 1·728, \ 2·413, \ 5·712,$$

if each is given correct to 4 significant figures.

$8·633 \pm 0·0005$
$1·728 \pm 0·0005$
$2·413 \pm 0·0005$
$5·712 \pm 0·0005$
$18·486 \pm 0·002$

∴ the sum lies between 18·488 and 18·484 and may be expressed as
either 18·5, correct to 3 figures,
or 18·486 ± 0·002.

Subtraction

Example 8.   Subtract 49·37 from 92·84 if each number is given correct to 4 significant figures.

Greatest difference	*Least difference*	
92·845	92·835	∴ the difference is 43·5, correct
49·365	49·375	to 3 significant figures, or may be
43·48	43·46	written 43·47 ± 0·01.

EXERCISE 120

In Nos. 1–12, each number is given correct to the number of significant figures shown in brackets.   Find the value of each expression (i) to as many significant figures as the data justify, (ii) in the form A ± x :

1. 237 + 834 + 179 + 408 (3).

[2] 10·36 + 47·44 + 26·07 + 27·91 + 11·86 (4).

3. 714·5 + 580·3 + 542·4 + 718·6 + 200·2 (4).

[4] 1·030 + 2·804 + 0·5172 + 0·7214 (4).

[5] 307 + 26·4 + 116 + 17·9 + 120 (3).

[6] 872 − 467 (3).   **7.** 4·618 − 1·096 (4).

8. 149 − 63·2 (3).   **[9]** 3·524 − 0·8172 (4).

10. 562 − 183 − 209 + 486 + 257 (3).

[11] 7·326 − 1·082 + 8·109 − 1·030 (4).

12. 31·56 − 8·072 − 3·147 − 11·20 + 4·108 (4).

State the limits between which the values of the expressions in Nos. 13–17 lie, and write the values in the form A ± x :

13. The perimeter of a triangle whose sides are measured as 6·2 cm., 5·7 cm., 4·3 cm., to the nearest mm.

14. The sum of 7s. 4d., 3s. 9d., 5s. 2d., 2s. 8d., 6s. 11d., if each amount is correct to the nearest penny.

[15] The difference of 5 lb. 7½ oz. and 3 lb. 12½ oz., if each weight is correct to the nearest ¼ oz.

[16] The sum of 1s. 6½d., 2s. 4¼d., 8¾d., 1s. 5½d., if each amount is correct to the nearest farthing.

17. The difference of 2½ mi. and 2¼ mi., if each length is correct to the nearest 20 yd.

*18. The value of π is $3\cdot14159265$ . . . ; express correct to 4 significant figures the value of $3\frac{1}{7} - \pi$.

19. A flask when empty weighs $63\cdot45$ gm. and when full of water weighs $201\cdot07$ gm., each weight being correct to the nearest centigram. Between what limits does the weight of the water lie? Find the volume of the flask to as many significant figures as the data justify.

20. The weight of 1 c.c. of copper is given as $(8\cdot8 \pm 0\cdot05)$ gm. Between what limits does the weight of 20 c.c. of copper lie?

[21] The weights of three blocks are given as $(5\cdot86 \pm 0\cdot04)$ gm., $(4\cdot76 \pm 0\cdot04)$ gm., $(3\cdot86 \pm 0\cdot02)$ gm. Find a similar expression for their total weight, and express it to as many significant figures as the data justify.

22. The volume of a block is given as $(17\cdot63 \pm 0\cdot06)$ c.c.; a portion of it is removed and the volume of the remainder is found to be $(12\cdot54 \pm 0\cdot05)$ c.c. Find a similar expression for the volume of the portion removed and express it to as many significant figures as the data justify.

*23. The length of a thread wound 10 times round a cylinder is measured independently by 7 boys as follows : $85\cdot6$ cm., $85\cdot7$ cm., $85\cdot5$ cm., $85\cdot8$ cm., $85\cdot5$ cm., $85\cdot9$ cm., $85\cdot8$ cm. What length should be taken for the circumference of the cylinder?

*24. On a certain road leading to Winchester the distances on the signposts are given correct to the nearest $\frac{1}{4}$ m. A motorist passes a signpost "Winchester $7\frac{1}{2}$ miles," and 6 min. later another "Winchester $3\frac{1}{2}$ miles." Between what limits, in miles per hour, does his average speed lie?

Multiplication. Suppose that the length and breadth of a rectangle are $6\cdot3$ cm., $5\cdot4$ cm., correct to the nearest mm., and that it is required to find the area to as great a degree of accuracy as the data justify.

The area according to the actual measurements is

$$(6\cdot3 \times 5\cdot4) \text{ sq. cm., that is } 34\cdot02 \text{ sq. cm.;}$$

But actually all we can say is that the area does not exceed $(6\cdot35 \times 5\cdot45)$ sq. cm., that is $34\cdot6075$ sq. cm., and is not less than $(6\cdot25 \times 5\cdot35)$ sq. cm., that is $33\cdot4375$ sq. cm.

Therefore the area is 30 sq. cm., correct to *one* significant figure, but cannot be given correct to *two* figures.

Since the area lies between $33\cdot4$ sq. cm. and $34\cdot6$ sq. cm. (nearly), the area may be given as $(34 \pm 0\cdot6)$ sq. cm. approximately.

Example 9. Find, as accurately as the data justify, the volume of a rectangular block 3·27 in. by 2·63 in. by 1·95 in., if the error in each measurement does not exceed 0·01 in.

The volume cannot exceed

$$(3·28 \times 2·64 \times 1·96) \text{ cu. in., that is } 16·972032 \text{ cu. in.}$$

and cannot be less than

$$(3·26 \times 2·62 \times 1·94) \text{ cu. in., that is } 16·569928 \text{ cu. in.}$$

Therefore the volume is 17 cu. in., correct to *two* significant figures.

Since the volume lies between 17·0 cu. in. and 16·5 cu. in., the volume may be given as $(16·75 \pm 0·25)$ cu. in.

Note. If the measurements had been given correct to 3 significant figures, the error in each measurement would not have exceeded 0·005 in.

Division. If the dividend and divisor are both approximate, the largest value of the quotient is obtained by taking the largest value of the dividend and the *smallest* value of the divisor; and the smallest value of the quotient is obtained by taking the smallest value of the dividend and the *largest* value of the divisor.

Example 10. The area of a rectangular field is 24,500 sq. yd. and its length is 185 yd., both measurements being correct to 3 significant figures. Find, as accurately as the data justify, the breadth of the field.

The actual area is between 24550 sq. yd. and 24450 sq. yd., and the actual length is between 185·5 yd. and 184·5 yd.

To obtain the greatest possible breadth, we take the *greatest* area and *least* length:

$$\text{greatest breadth} = \frac{24550}{184·5} \text{ yd.} \simeq 133·1 \text{ yd.}$$

Similarly, taking the *least* area and *greatest* length,

$$\text{least breadth} = \frac{24450}{185·5} \text{ yd.} \simeq 131·8 \text{ yd.}$$

Therefore, the breadth is 130 yd., correct to *two* significant figures.

Since the average of 133·1 and 131·8 is about 132·5, the breadth may be given as $(132·5 \pm 0·7)$ yd.

Note. The breadth obtained from the actual measurements is $\frac{24500}{185}$ yd., $\simeq 132·4$ yd. Thus the "measured" breadth represents closely the *mean* value indicated by $(132·5 \pm 0·7)$ yd.; the object of the working set out in the example is to find out how large an error there may be in taking the "measured" breadth as the actual breadth.

Reliability of Results. The examples given above illustrate the fact that if two numbers are each given correct to n significant figures, the value of their product and their quotient can generally be obtained correct to $(n-1)$ significant figures, and, if taken to n figures, the result is a close approximation to the mean value, that is the average of the greatest and least possible values. But border-line cases occur where $(n-1)$ figures are not reliable.

EXERCISE 121

In Nos. 1–8, each number is given correct to the number of significant figures shown in brackets. Find the value of each expression (i) to as many significant figures as the data justify, (ii) in the form $A \pm x$:

1. 5×4 (1).   **2.** 0.65×0.24 (2).   [3] 3.7×2.4 (2).

[4] 0.453×1.26 (3).   **5.** $0.84 \div 2.1$ (2).   [6] $4.7 \div 1.8$ (2).

[7] $0.623 \div 2.46$ (3).   [8] $151 \div 472$ (3).

In Nos. 9–17, give the answers correct to as many significant figures as the data justify. Write them also in the form $A \pm x$:

9. The length and breadth of a rectangle are measured as 5·6 cm., 4·8 cm., correct to the nearest mm. Find the area.

[10] The length and breadth of a rectangular field are measured as 264 ft., 182 ft., correct to the nearest ft. Find the area.

*11. The circumference of a circle of radius r in. is $2\pi r$ in., where π lies between 3·141 and 3·142. Find, to the nearest $\frac{1}{10}$ in., the circumference of a circle of actual radius 4·65 in.

12. The time of 15 swings of a pendulum is measured as 12·6 sec. to the nearest $\frac{1}{5}$ sec. Find the time of 1 swing.

13. The area of a rectangle is 34·6 sq. in. and its length is 7·25 in., both measurements being correct to 3 significant figures. Find the breadth.

[14] The volume of a rectangular block is 68·5 c.c., and the base area is 14·5 sq. cm., both measurements being correct to 3 significant figures. Find the height.

*15. The number of deaths in a large town for a certain period was 368, and it was stated that this was at the rate of 1·20 (to 3 figures) per thousand. Find the population of the town.

16. The weight of 7·5 c.c. of a metal is 52·5 gm., each quantity being correct to one place of decimals. Find the weight of 1 c.c. of the metal.

*17. In July 1932, there were 12,800,000 insured persons in Great Britain, of whom 23·2 per cent. were unemployed. If the data are correct to 3 significant figures, find the number of unemployed.

*18. In a table of cricket averages a batsman is stated to have an average of 31·68, correct to 2 places of decimals, for 32 completed innings. Show that this statement must be incorrect.

*19. It was stated in the Press that Sir Malcolm Campbell took 11·83 sec. for a measured mile and that his average speed was therefore 304·311 miles per hour. Find his average speed to as many figures as the data justify if the time was measured correct to (i) $\frac{1}{10}$ sec., (ii) $\frac{1}{100}$ sec., assuming that the distance was measured correctly.

MISCELLANEOUS EXAMPLES

EXERCISE 122

1. A distance is given as 3·84 mi. correct to 3 significant figures. Find the greatest possible error in yards.

2. To 5 significant figures, $\sqrt{2}=1·4142$, $\sqrt{3}=1·7321$. Find as accurately as the data justify the values of (i) $\sqrt{3}+\sqrt{2}$; (ii) $5\sqrt{3}-6\sqrt{2}$.

[3] Calculate $1-\frac{1}{2}+\frac{1}{3}-\frac{1}{4}+\frac{1}{5}-\frac{1}{6}+\frac{1}{7}-\frac{1}{8}+\frac{1}{9}-\frac{1}{10}$, correct to 6 places of decimals.

4. The greatest known ocean depth is 32090 ft. in the Pacific; express this in miles to 3 figures.

5. In an examination there were 1607 candidates of whom 73·55% (to 4 figures) passed. How many passed?

[6] Find to the nearest inch the difference between 5 mi. and 8 km. [1 m. = 39·37011 in.]

7. It is known that 1 c.c. of a liquid weighs 0·84 gm. correct to 2 figures. What is the greatest possible error in calculating the weight of 2 litres of the liquid?

[8] In 1932 the London rainfall was 25·39 in., and the total duration of the rain was 469 hr. Express the rate in inches per hour to 2 figures.

9. Given 1 yd. =91·44 cm., express 1 m. in feet to 3 significant figures.

[10] Given 1 gall. =4·546 litres, express 1 litre in pints to 3 significant figures.

11. In 1931 the population of Great Britain was 44,790,485 and the revenue was £770,963,000. Find the revenue per head in £ to 3 significant figures.

*12. To how many significant figures is it correct to take the product of 0·347 and 2·8818 as 1 ?

[13] 32·3125 c.c. of gold weigh 621·0834 gm.; find the weight of 1 c.c. of gold to 4 figures.

[14] At the election in 1931 the total electorate was 29,952,361, and 21,656,373 votes were recorded. What percentage of the electorate, to 3 figures, voted?

15. The Scouts of the British Empire increased from 756,883 in 1930 to 808,307 in 1931. Find the increase per cent., to 3 figures.

[16] If 40 mi. per hr. is equivalent to 34·74 knots, find the number of feet in a nautical mile, to the nearest 10 ft. [1 knot =1 nautical mile per hour.]

*17. The output of coal in 3 mo. was 57,065,000 tons and the average profit was 4·225d. per ton. Find the total to the nearest £10,000.

18. Find to 1 figure the error per cent. in taking 32 m. as equivalent to 35 yd. [1 m. =39·3701 in.]

19. In 1932 a motor-boat travelled a measured mile at an average speed of 124·91 mi. per hour. Find in seconds the time taken, to 3 figures.

*20. Out of 10,000 people born, 6652 live to be 35 yr. old, 4418 live to be 60, 2279 live to be 70. Find to 3 figures what percentage (i) of persons of age 35 may expect to survive to 60, (ii) of persons of age 60 may expect to die before 70.

*21. If 1 litre =1·7616 pt., express 1 lb. in grams to the nearest gram, given 1 gall. of water weighs 10 lb. and 1 litre of water weighs 1 kg.

[22] The record for the present Derby course (1 mi. 4 fur.) is 2 min. 34·4 sec.; express this speed in miles per hour to 3 figures.

*23. 5 cu. ft. of wood, weighing 46 lb. per cu. ft., and 102 lb. of metal, weighing 556 lb. per cu. ft., are used in making an article. Find to the nearest lb. the average weight per cu. ft. of the article.

*24. The rateable value of a district is £133,224. Find to the nearest farthing how much in the £ must be levied to raise £2500 ?

CHAPTER XVII

MISCELLANEOUS EXTENSIONS

Averages

Example 1. At the 8 performances of a play in a week the numbers present were 1473, 1641, 1709, 1688, 1483, 1429, 1846, 1955 respectively. Find the average number present per performance.

Since there were more than 1400 present at every performance we need only calculate the average attendance above 1400: the numbers exceed 1400 by

$$73, 241, 309, 288, 83, 29, 446, 555,$$

that is, by 2024 in all;

$$\therefore \text{ the average exceeds 1400 by } \tfrac{2024}{8}, \text{ that is 253,}$$
$$\therefore \text{ average} = 1400 + 253 = 1653.$$

Note. As a rough check, it should be noted that the average of any set of numbers must lie between the smallest and largest number in the set.

Example 2. A man walks from his house to a town 6 mi. away at 4 mi. per hour and bicycles back again at 12 mi. per hour. Find his average speed for the double journey.

He walks 6 mi. at 4 m.p.h. in $1\frac{1}{2}$ hr.;

he bicycles 6 mi. at 12 m.p.h. in $\frac{1}{2}$ hr.

$\therefore$ he travels altogether 12 mi. in 2 hr.;

$\therefore$ his average speed for the double journey is 6 m.p.h.

Note. The average speed is not the same as the average of 4 m.p.h. and 12 m.p.h., because he spends more time travelling at 4 m.p.h. than at 12 m.p.h.

Example 3. If 9 lb. of tea at 1s. 8d. per lb., 12 lb. of tea at 1s. 10d. per lb. and 15 lb. of tea at 2s. 4d. per lb. are mixed together, find the value per lb. of the mixture.

9 lb., 12 lb.. 15 lb. are proportional to 3, 4, 5.

3 lb. of tea at 1s. 8d. per lb. are worth 5s.;

4 lb. of tea at 1s. 10d. per lb. are worth 7s. 4d;

5 lb. of tea at 2s. 4d. per lb. are worth 11s. 8d.

$\therefore$ the value of $(3+4+5)$ lb. of the mixture is 24s.

that is, 12 lb. of the mixture are worth 24s.;

$\therefore$ 1 lb. of the mixture is worth 2s.

Note. The value of the mixture per lb. is not the average of 1s. 8d., 1s. 10d., 2s. 4d., because the amounts of the three qualities, which are mixed together, are not equal.

EXERCISE 123

Find the average of :

    1. 3, 5, 7, 9, 11, 13, 15.   **2.** 752, 763, 759, 754, 772.

    [3] 3·4, 8·1, 1·9, 0·4.   **[4]** $31\frac{1}{2}$, $32\frac{1}{4}$, $31\frac{2}{3}$, $33\frac{3}{4}$.

    5. 3s. 6d., 4s. 8d., 2s. 10d., 7s. 3d., 5s. 4d., 1s. 5d.

    *6. 2 t. 15 cwt. 1 qr., 1 t. 7 cwt. 2 qr., 4 t. 12 cwt. 3 qr.

Find the cost per lb. of the following mixtures :—

    [7] 6 lb. at 1s. 6d. per lb., 9 lb. at 2s. 4d. per lb.

    8. 12 lb. at 7d. per lb., 8 lb. at $8\frac{1}{4}$d. per lb., 10 lb. at 9d. per lb.

    *9. 35 lb. at 3s. 5d. per lb., 55 lb. at 4s. 2d. per lb.

    10. Find the average cost per book of 8 books, 5 of which cost 3s. each and the rest 5s. each.

What is the average cost per book of 800 books, 500 of which cost 3s. each and the rest 5s. each?

    11. In 1932, Larwood took 162 wickets for 2084 runs; find the average number of runs per wicket, to the nearest whole number.

    *12. A firm buys 824 tons of coal at £2 7s. 6d. per ton and 776 tons at £2 4s. per ton. Find, to the nearest halfpenny, by how much the average price per ton exceeds £2 4s.; hence find, to the nearest halfpenny, the average price per ton.

    13. A cyclist rides 35 mi. at 10 mi. per hour and a further 30 mi. at 12 mi. an hour. Find the total time his journey takes and his average speed for the journey.

    [14] A motorist drives for 2 hr. at 32 m.p.h. and for half an hour at 42 m.p.h.; find his average speed for the whole journey.

    15. A cricketer's average was 17 for 5 completed innings. He obtained 16, 3, 28, 12 runs in his first four innings; what was his score in his last innings?

    [16] The average age of 5 men is 46, and the average age of 4 of them is 43; what is the age of the fifth man?

    17. A firm's monthly sales from July to November were respectively £8775, £7869, £7907, £8564, £8753. Find the value of the sales in December if the monthly average for the half-year was £8472.

    *18. A team of eight entered for a shooting competition. The best marksman scored 85 points; if he had scored 92 points, the average score for the team would have been 84. How many points altogether did the team score?

19. The average annual profits of a company for its first four years were £350 a year. For the first two years the losses were £420 and £230 respectively, and for the third year the profits were £750. Find the profits for the fourth year.

20. If 30 lb. of tea costing 1s. 8d. per lb. are mixed with 50 lb. of tea costing 2s. per lb., find the cost price of the mixture per lb., and the price per lb. at which it must be sold to gain 20 per cent.

[21] If 35 tons of coal costing 41s. per ton are mixed with 55 tons of coal costing 50s. per ton, find the price per ton at which the mixture must be sold to gain $33\frac{1}{3}$ per cent.

***22.** A swimmer, who takes 30 strokes per minute, can swim 1 mi. in 38 min. 20 sec. What is the average distance he travels per stroke, to the nearest inch?

***23.** The average age of m boys is b years and of n girls is c years. Find the average age of all together.

***24.** The average age of x boys and y girls is p years. If the average age of the boys is r years, find the average age of the girls.

***25.** The average noon temperature for Monday, Tuesday, and Wednesday was 53°, and for Tuesday, Wednesday, and Thursday was 56°. If the noon temperature on Thursday was 60°, find the noon temperature on Monday.

Inverse Problems on Mixtures

Example 4. In what ratio must coffee at 1s. 5d. per lb. be mixed with coffee at 1s. 11d. per lb. to produce a mixture worth 1s. 7d. per lb.?

If the mixture is sold at 1s. 7d. per lb., each lb. of the cheaper coffee in the mixture is sold at a profit of 2d., and each lb. of the dearer coffee is sold at a loss of 4d.

Therefore, if the profits and losses balance, the mixture contains 2 lb. of the cheaper coffee for each 1 lb. of the dearer coffee.

Therefore if coffee at 1s. 5d. per lb. is mixed with coffee at 1s. 11d. per lb. in the ratio 2 : 1, the mixture is worth 1s. 7d. per lb.

The working may be set out as follows:—

   1 lb. at 1s. 5d. in a mixture at 1s. 7d. per lb. gives 2d. profit;
   1 lb. at 1s. 11d. in a mixture at 1s. 7d. per lb. gives 4d. loss.
   ∴ ratio of coffee at 1s. 5d. per lb. to coffee at 1s. 11d. per lb.
          equals 4 : 2,   that is 2 : 1.

Example 5. In what ratio must coal costing 44s. per ton be mixed with coal costing 60s. per ton, so that the mixture can be sold for 60s. per ton at a gain of 20 per cent.?

If the cost price is 100s., the profit is 20s., and therefore the selling price is 120s.;

∴ the cost price $=\frac{100}{120}$ of the selling price;

but the selling price of 1 ton $=60$s.,

∴ the cost price of 1 ton $=\frac{100}{120}$ of 60s. $=50$s.

Therefore the coal is mixed so that the cost price of 1 ton of the mixture is 50s.

1 ton at 44s. in a mixture at 50s. gives 6s. profit;

1 ton at 60s. in a mixture at 50s. gives 10s. loss.

∴ ratio of coal at 44s. per ton to coal at 60s. per ton

equals 10 : 6,   that is 5 : 3.

EXERCISE 124

In what ratio must the following commodities be mixed to produce a mixture of the stated value, Nos. 1–6 :—

1. Teas at 2s. per lb. and 2s. 8d. per lb.; mixture 2s. 2d. per lb.

[2] Chocolates at 3s. 4d. per lb. and 5s. per lb.; mixture 4s. per lb.

3. Sugars at 3d. per lb. and $3\frac{3}{4}$d. per lb.; mixture $3\frac{1}{2}$d. per lb.

[4] Cocoas at 9d. per lb. and 1s. $1\frac{1}{2}$d. per lb.; mixture 11d. per lb.

5. Coals at 28s. per ton and £2 per ton; mixture 35s. 6d. per ton.

[6] Currants at 3s. $3\frac{3}{4}$d. per 7 lb. and 3s. $9\frac{3}{4}$d. per 7 lb.; mixture 6d. per lb.

7. How many lb. of tea at 2s. 6d. per lb. must be mixed with 100 lb. at 1s. 4d. per lb. to make the mixture worth 1s. 8d. per lb.?

[8] A crate contains 36 dozen golf balls, some are sold at 15s. a dozen and the rest at 24s. a dozen.   The average price is 1s. 7d. per ball; how many are there of each kind?

*9. In what ratio by volume must a liquid weighing 0·6 gm. per c.c. be mixed with a liquid weighing 1·1 gm. per c.c. so that the mixture may weigh 0·75 gm. per c.c.?

10. In what ratio must tobacco costing 10d. per oz. be mixed with tobacco costing 1s. 4d. per oz. so that a profit of 25% is made by selling the mixture at 1s. 3d. per oz.

16

[11] In what ratio must tea costing 2s. 7½d. per lb. be mixed with tea costing 3s. 3d. per lb. so that a profit of 20% is made by selling the mixture at 3s. 6d. per lb.

12. In what ratio must coffee costing 1s. 7d. per lb. be mixed with chicory costing 4d. per lb. so that a profit of 50% is made by selling the mixture at 2s. per lb.?

[13] Oranges costing 5s. 8d. per 100 are mixed with oranges costing 7s. 2d. per 100 so that a profit of 12½% is made by selling them at 10 for 9d. In what ratio are they mixed?

14. In what ratio must coal costing 39s. 9d. per ton be mixed with coal costing 48s. 9d. per ton so that a profit of 30% is made by selling the mixture at 58s. 6d. per ton?

*15. A liquid consists of 85% pure spirit and the rest water. In what ratio must it be mixed with water so that the mixture contains 75% pure spirit?

*16. A liquid X contains 80% pure spirit, and a liquid Y contains 55% pure spirit. In what ratio must X and Y be mixed so that the mixture contains 70% pure spirit?

Rate of Working

Example 6. A can do a piece of work in 3 days, B can do it in 9 days, and C in 4½ days. How long will they take if all work together?

In 1 day, A can do $\frac{1}{3}$ of the work and B can do $\frac{1}{9}$ of the work.

Since C takes $\frac{9}{2}$ days to do it, he does $\frac{2}{9}$ of the work in 1 day.

$\therefore$ A, B, C together do $(\frac{1}{3} + \frac{1}{9} + \frac{2}{9})$ of the work in 1 day;

$\therefore$ A, B, C together do $\frac{2}{3}$ of the work in 1 day;

$\therefore$ A, B, C together do the whole work in $\frac{3}{2}$ days;

$\therefore$ they take $1\frac{1}{2}$ days.

Example 7. One tap fills a bath in 12 min. and another tap fills it in 15 min. The waste-pipe can empty the bath in 10 min. In what time will the bath be filled if both taps are turned on and if the waste-pipe has been left open accidentally?

In 1 min. the first tap fills $\frac{1}{12}$ of the bath, the second tap fills $\frac{1}{15}$ of the bath, and the waste-pipe empties $\frac{1}{10}$ of the bath. Therefore if both taps are turned on, with the waste-pipe open,

$$(\tfrac{1}{12} + \tfrac{1}{15} - \tfrac{1}{10}) \text{ of the bath is filled in 1 min.;}$$
$$\text{but } \tfrac{1}{12} + \tfrac{1}{15} - \tfrac{1}{10} = \tfrac{5+4-6}{60} = \tfrac{3}{60} = \tfrac{1}{20},$$
$$\therefore \tfrac{1}{20} \text{ of the bath is filled in 1 min.;}$$
$$\therefore \text{ the bath will be filled in 20 min.}$$

EXERCISE 125

1. A can do a piece of work in 30 days, and B can do it in 6 days. How long will A and B take, working together?

2. A bath can be filled by 1 tap in 10 min. and by another tap in 15 min. How long does it take to fill the bath if both taps are turned on?

3. A can do a piece of work in 12 days which A and B, working together, can do in 8 days. How long would B take, working alone?

[4] Two taps, running together, can fill a bath in 4 min., which is filled by one of the taps by itself in 7 min. How long would it take if the other tap is running by itself?

5. A cistern can be emptied by 3 pipes in 3 hr.; one alone would take 6 hr., another alone 9 hr.; how long would it take with the third pipe alone?

6. A tap fills a bath in 15 min. and the waste-pipe empties it in 12 min. If the bath is full and the tap is turned on, and the waste-pipe is open, how long will it be before the bath is empty?

[7] A sum of money is sufficient to pay A's wages for 21 days or B's wages for 28 days. For how long will it suffice to pay the wages of A and B together?

8. A, B, C, working together, take 30 min. to address a pile of envelopes. A and B together would take 40 min.; A and C together would take 45 min. How long would each take, working alone?

9. A and B can do a piece of work together in 15 days. They both start, but after 6 days B gets ill and A then takes 30 more days to finish it by himself. How long would each take, working alone?

[10] A cistern can be filled by 3 taps, A, B, C, when turned on separately in 24 min., 10 min., 27 min. respectively. If all are turned on together for $4\frac{1}{2}$ min. and if B, C are then turned off, how much longer is it before the cistern is full?

11. A can plough a field in 60 hr., B can do it in 48 hr. and C in 50 hr. How long will C take to finish it by himself if he starts when A and B have each done 12 hr. work?

*12. A, B can do a piece of work in 15 days and 18 days respectively, working separately. A, B work together for 3 days, then B leaves, and after another 3 days C joins, and the work is finished in 4 days more. How long would C take to do the whole thing by himself?

[13] A, B, C can do a piece of work in 11 days, 20 days, 55 days respectively, working alone. How soon can the work be done if A is assisted by B and C on alternate days?

*14. A has 270 envelopes to address. If B helps him, they do it in 1 hr. If B and C did them together, they would take 45 min. A starts alone, and after 2 hr. there are 50 left. How long would it take C to finish these alone?

15. £3 are paid for a task which A can do in 3 days, B in 4 days, and C in 6 days. If all work together, how much money should each receive?

*16. 5 guineas are paid for a task which A, B, C, working together, can do in 4 days, and A, B, working together, can do in 6 days, and A alone in 10 days. If all work together, how much money should each receive?

*17. £25 are paid for a task which A can do in 32 days, B in 20 days, B and C together in 12 days, and D in 24 days. If A, B, C, D work together, how much money should each receive?

*18. A sum of money is sufficient to pay the wages of A and B for 20 days, or the wages of B and C for 24 days, or the wages of A and C for 40 days. For how long will it suffice to pay B's wages?

Harder Fractions

Example 8. Simplify $\dfrac{3\frac{1}{4} - \frac{4}{5} \text{ of } \frac{5}{6}}{4\frac{1}{3} \div \frac{1}{5} - (\frac{3}{10} + 21\frac{1}{5})}$.

Numerator $= 3\frac{1}{4} - (\frac{4}{5} \times \frac{5}{6}) = 3\frac{1}{4} - \frac{2}{3} = 3\frac{3-8}{12} = 2\frac{7}{12}$;

denominator $= (\frac{13}{3} \times \frac{5}{1}) - (21\frac{3+2}{10}) = \frac{65}{3} - 21\frac{1}{2} = 21\frac{2}{3} - 21\frac{1}{2} = \frac{1}{6}$;

∴ fraction $= 2\frac{7}{12} \div \frac{1}{6} = \frac{31}{12} \times \frac{6}{1} = \frac{31}{2} = 15\frac{1}{2}$.

Example 9. Simplify $4 - \dfrac{5}{1 + \dfrac{1}{3 + \dfrac{1}{2 + \frac{1}{4}}}}$.

$\dfrac{1}{2 + \frac{1}{4}} = \dfrac{1 \times 4}{2\frac{1}{4} \times 4} = \frac{4}{9}$;

∴ expression $= 4 - \dfrac{5}{1 + \dfrac{1}{3 + \frac{4}{9}}} = 4 - \dfrac{5}{1 + \frac{9}{31}}$

$= 4 - \frac{5 \times 31}{40} = 4 - \frac{31}{8} = \frac{1}{8}$.

EXERCISE 126

Simplify:

1. $\dfrac{3\frac{3}{4}+2\frac{2}{3}}{3\frac{3}{4}-2\frac{2}{3}}$.

2. $\dfrac{2\frac{1}{4}-1\frac{4}{5}}{5\frac{3}{10}-2\frac{6}{7}}$.

[3] $\dfrac{\frac{1}{3}(\frac{1}{4}+\frac{1}{5})}{\frac{1}{5}(\frac{1}{5}-\frac{1}{6})}$.

4. $\dfrac{1\frac{1}{4}\times7}{12\frac{7}{12}-11\frac{1}{3}}$.

5. $\dfrac{3\frac{7}{12}+2\frac{4}{15}}{1\frac{5}{8}\div1\frac{2}{3}}$.

[6] $\dfrac{\frac{5}{7}\text{ of }\frac{2}{9}\times13\frac{1}{2}}{\frac{1}{9}\div2\frac{1}{3}+40}$.

7. $6\frac{11}{25}\times1\frac{3}{7}-2\frac{3}{5}\div\frac{3}{11}+2\frac{31}{40}\div2\frac{5}{16}$.

[8] $\dfrac{2\frac{1}{2}\times4\frac{7}{8}}{4\frac{1}{3}\times\frac{21}{64}-2\frac{1}{6}\div1\frac{7}{9}}$.

[9] $\dfrac{3\frac{1}{3}\times2\frac{1}{4}}{3\frac{1}{3}-2\frac{1}{4}}\div\dfrac{5\frac{1}{7}}{2\frac{3}{5}}$.

[10] $\dfrac{2\frac{3}{4}-1\frac{7}{8}}{1\frac{1}{3}+2\frac{1}{2}}\times7\frac{2}{3}$.

11. $\dfrac{6\frac{1}{2}}{9\frac{1}{3}}-\dfrac{4\frac{1}{2}}{7}+\dfrac{6\frac{1}{3}}{12\frac{4}{9}}$.

[12] $\dfrac{5(20\frac{1}{2}+12\frac{3}{4})-35}{27\times3\frac{1}{2}}$.

[13] $\dfrac{\frac{1}{2}\div1\frac{8}{13}-\frac{1}{3}\times\frac{11}{14}}{\frac{1}{2}\times\frac{16}{21}-\frac{1}{3}\div1\frac{1}{13}}$.

*14. $\dfrac{3\frac{1}{4}-\frac{2}{3}\text{ of }(\frac{5}{8}-\frac{1}{11})}{\frac{2}{9}+\frac{7}{12}+\frac{8}{33}}$.

*15. $\dfrac{2\frac{1}{8}\div(1\frac{2}{55}-\frac{19}{11})}{3\frac{1}{7}\times4\frac{2}{3}-12\frac{3}{8}}$.

*16. $\dfrac{\frac{18}{35}\text{ of }7\frac{7}{8}-2\frac{1}{3}-1\frac{1}{4}}{(2\frac{3}{5}-1\frac{3}{5})\div3\frac{5}{12}}$.

*17. $\dfrac{\frac{5}{7}\div3\frac{1}{13}-\frac{3}{8}\text{ of }\frac{7}{12}}{(1\frac{1}{2}-\frac{1}{5}+\frac{1}{8})\div(1\frac{5}{6}-\frac{2}{3})}$.

*18. $\left(\frac{1}{7}-\frac{1}{8}\text{ of }\frac{1\frac{1}{3}}{7}\right)\div\left\{(\frac{4}{7}-\frac{1}{8})\div\frac{15}{2\frac{1}{4}}\right\}$.

*19. $\dfrac{2}{3+\dfrac{4}{5-3\frac{2}{3}}}$.

*20. $\dfrac{1}{9-\dfrac{7}{\frac{1}{2}+\frac{1}{3}}}$.

*21. $\dfrac{2}{1+\dfrac{3}{5+\dfrac{2}{1+\frac{1}{4}}}}$.

Problems involving Fractions

Example 10. I spend $\frac{1}{4}$ of my money on lunch and $\frac{1}{6}$ of the remainder on tea. If 10s. is left, what had I at first?

After spending $\frac{1}{4}$ of my money, $\frac{3}{4}$ of my money remains.

After spending $\frac{1}{6}$ of this remainder, $\frac{5}{6}$ of this remainder is left, that is $\frac{5}{6}$ of $\frac{3}{4}$ of the original amount is left.

But $\frac{5}{6}$ of $\frac{3}{4}=\frac{5}{8}$, therefore $\frac{5}{8}$ of the original amount is 10s.;

$\therefore \frac{1}{8}$ of the original amount is 2s.

$\therefore$ the original amount is 16s.

Check: Lunch costs $\frac{1}{4}$ of 16s., =4s., leaving 12s.; tea costs $\frac{1}{6}$ of 12s., =2s. leaving 10s.

EXERCISE 127

1. If $\frac{2}{5}$ of a journey takes 36 min., how long will the rest of it take at the same rate?

2. If I take $1\frac{1}{2}$ more minutes to walk $\frac{3}{4}$ of a mile than $\frac{2}{3}$ of a mile, how long do I take to walk a mile?

3. $\frac{7}{12}$ by weight of a certain alloy is copper. Find in lb. the weight of a lump of the alloy which contains 1 cwt. of copper.

[4] If it costs £28 to fill $\frac{5}{12}$ of a cellar with coal, what will it cost to fill $\frac{2}{3}$ of the cellar?

5. A, B, C own a business between them. A owns $\frac{1}{5}$ of it, and B's share is twice C's share. What fraction of the business does B own?

[6] A man loses $\frac{2}{5}$ of his capital one year and $\frac{1}{4}$ of what remains the next year. What fraction of his original capital is still left?

[7] One-tenth of a post is painted red, $\frac{2}{3}$ of the remainder is painted white, and the rest black. What fraction of the post is black?

8. A man spends $\frac{1}{10}$ of his income on rent and $\frac{2}{3}$ of the remainder in other ways. This leaves £135. What is his income?

9. A money prize is divided between A, B, C; A receives $\frac{2}{5}$ of the prize, B receives $\frac{5}{9}$ of the remainder. If C's share is 8s., find the value of the prize.

[10] $\frac{7}{15}$ of the water in a tank, which is full, is used on one day, and $\frac{5}{6}$ of the remainder on the next day. If 20 gall. of water are then left, how much does the tank hold?

11. A man left $\frac{5}{16}$ of his estate to his wife, $\frac{7}{11}$ of the rest to his son, and the balance, £3200, to charity. What did the son receive?

[12] One-quarter of a field is too rough to use; two-fifths of the remainder is kept for cricket, and this leaves $13\frac{1}{2}$ acres for other games. What is the area of the field?

*13. One-eighth of a plank is damaged; a man cuts off three-quarters of the sound part, and this leaves $3\frac{1}{2}$ ft. still to be used. What length of the plank was damaged?

14. A car loses $\frac{1}{4}$ of its value in its first year, and in the second year loses $\frac{1}{8}$ of its value at the beginning of that year. At the end of the second year it is worth £140; what was its value when new?

*15. A and B own a business between them and the ratio of A's share to B's share is 11 : 9. If B sells $\frac{2}{3}$ of his share to A for £720, find the value of the business, and the percentage of the business then owned by A.

MISCELLANEOUS EXAMPLES

EXERCISE 128

1. A bowler takes 109 wickets for 1564 runs. Find the average number of runs per wicket, to 1 place of decimals.

2. A swimming-bath can be filled by two pipes in 15 hr., and by one of them alone in 24 hr. How long will it take if the second pipe is used by itself?

[3] A train averages 42 mi. per hour for a journey of 140 mi. What increase must be made in the average speed to reduce the time by 18 min.?

[4] A man goes $\frac{4}{5}$ of a journey by train, and then $\frac{5}{8}$ of the remainder by bus. This leaves him a quarter of a mile still to go. What is the length of the journey?

5. In what ratio must eggs costing a shilling for 10 be mixed with eggs costing 1s. 4d. a dozen to obtain a mixture costing 2s. 1d. per score?

6. A batsman has an average of 28·3 runs for 31 innings, 4 times not out. What must he score in his next innings, if he gets out, to raise his average to 30?

[7] A boy spent $\frac{5}{12}$ of his money and then had left 1s. 6d. more than what he had spent. How much had he at first?

8. 1 c.c. of a liquid A weighs 0·6 gm. and 1 c.c. of a liquid B weighs 0·75 gm. If equal weights of A and B are mixed together, find the weight of 1 c.c. of the mixture, correct to $\frac{1}{100}$ gm.

9. A can do a piece of work in 8 days, which takes B 10 days and takes C 15 days. All start together, but after 2 days A stays away. How long will B and C take to finish the job?

10. The expenses of a party of 7 men for 14 days are £90, and of another party of 10 men for 7 days are £64. Find the average cost per man per day for all the men.

*11. A liquid X contains 38% alcohol and a liquid Y contains 71% alcohol. In what ratio must X and Y be mixed to obtain a liquid containing 50% alcohol?

*12. One tap fills $\frac{2}{3}$ of a bath in the same time that another tap fills $\frac{3}{8}$ of the bath. If both are turned on, the bath is filled in 12 min.; how long will each tap take by itself?

[13] What is the average annual profit for 5 years' working if for the first 2 years the losses are £142, £75, and for the next 3 years the profits are £96, £217, £508?

*14. Tea at 1s. 10d. per lb. is mixed with tea at 2s. 6d. per lb. in the ratio 5 : 3. In what ratio must this mixture be mixed with tea at 2s. 11d. per lb. to give a mixture worth 2s. 5d. per lb.?

THREE-MINUTE AND FOUR-MINUTE ORAL PRACTICE

ORAL PRACTICE 17–24 (Ch. IV–XII)

[Nothing must be written down except the answer]

Oral Practice 17 (3 min.)

1. $2\frac{1}{4} - \frac{7}{8}$.　　**2.** $1 - (0.63 + 0.36)$.　　**3.** $0.01 \div 0.4$.

4. $2\frac{1}{4}$d. × 24, in s. d.　　　**5.** Ratio of 7s. 6d. to 10s.

6. What % is 12 oz. of 1 lb.?　　**7.** $7\frac{1}{2}\%$ as a fraction.

8. Decrease 2s. 6d. in the ratio 3 : 5.

9. Cost of 21 lb. of sugar if 14 lb. cost 3s.

10. A salary of £350 a year is increased by 10%; what does it become?

Oral Practice 18 (3 min.)

1. $\frac{1}{3} \times \frac{1}{2} + \frac{1}{2}$.　　**2.** $\frac{0.2}{0.4} + \frac{0.3}{0.6}$.　　**3.** $(0.03)^2$.　　**4.** $\frac{1}{2\frac{1}{4}}$ of 2s.

5. Ratio of 10 oz. to $2\frac{1}{2}$ lb.　　**6.** $\frac{1}{30}$ as a percentage.

7. 65% of 1 ton, in cwt.　　　**8.** Divide 2 ft. in the ratio 5 : 7.

9. $\frac{4}{9}$ of a number is 36; what is the number?

10. C.P. 4s.; S.P. 5s.; what is the gain per cent.?

Oral Practice 19 (3 min.)

1. $\frac{3}{5} \div 1\frac{1}{2}$.　　**2.** 0.0709×1.2.　　**3.** $0.1 \div 0.001$.　　**4.** $\frac{1}{7}$ of £3 16s. 5d.

5. Ratio of 1320 yd. to 1 mi.　　**6.** 80% of 15s.

7. What % is 36 of 80?

8. In what ratio must £80 be increased to become £100?

9. A man spends 85% of his income; what fraction of his income does he save?

10. C.P. £2; gain $12\frac{1}{2}\%$; what is the S.P.?

Oral Practice 20 (3 min.)

1. Add : 2·73　　**2.** 11×9.19.　　　　**3.** $0.23 \div 23$.
　　　　0·69　　**4.** $\frac{3}{8}$ of 1 ton, in cwt., qr.
　　　　1·08　　**5.** Ratio of 150 m. to 1 km.

6. $8\frac{1}{3}\%$ as a fraction.   **7.** 24 is 60% of what number?

8. Decrease 1 lb. 4 oz. in the ratio 7 : 10.

9. If 10% is deducted from a bill for 35 shillings, how much remains to be paid?

10. What is the ratio of the S.P. to the C.P. for a gain of 20 per cent.?

Oral Practice 21 (4 min.)

1. $\dfrac{1}{3\frac{3}{4}} \times 3$.   **2.** $(0.2)^4$.   **3.** $156 \div 1.2$.   **4.** $11\frac{3}{4}$d. $\times 36$, in s. d.

5. Increase 75 by 20%.   **6.** $66\frac{2}{3}\%$ of 2 yd., in yd., ft.

7. What % is $2\frac{1}{2}$ cwt. of 1 ton?

8. The scale of a map is 1 : 100,000; what length in km. is represented by 12·6 cm. on the map?

9. 4s. is divided into 3 shares in the ratios 7 : 3 : 2; what is the largest share?

10. S.P. 2s.; gain 20%; what is the C.P.?

Oral Practice 22 (4 min.)

1. Add : 1·617
      5·42
      3·504
      2·059

2. $1 - \dfrac{1}{2\frac{1}{2}}$.

3. $(0.12)^3$.

4. $0.028 \div 14$.

5. £1 5s. $\times 48$.

6. Decrease 72 by $16\frac{2}{3}\%$.

7. What is the ratio of the areas of two squares, sides 8 in. and 1 ft., respectively?

8. 18 gall. of oil cost 16s.; what is the cost of 27 gall.?

9. The duty on an article is 30% of its value. If the duty is 12s., what is the value?

10. Petrol costs 1s. 3d. per gallon; what does the price become if it rises 10%?

Oral Practice 23 (4 min.)

1. $0.75 \times 1\frac{1}{3}$.   **2.** 1.01×0.11.   **3.** Subtract : 3·001

4. £2 4s. $\times 35$.   **5.** 125% of 12s.   2·207

6. What % is 14 of 35?   **7.** Decrease £1 by 15%.

8. Find 3 integers proportional to 1s. 9d., 1s., 2s. 3d.

9. Two weights are in the ratio, 8 : 5; the larger is 1 lb., what is the smaller in oz.?

10. S.P. 6s.; loss 2s.; what is the loss per cent.?

Oral Practice 24 (4 min.)

1. $1 \div (\frac{1}{2} + \frac{1}{3})$.   **2.** $0 \cdot 129 \times 0 \cdot 12$.   **3.** 4s. 11d. $\times 7$, in s. d.

4. $3 \div 0 \cdot 01$.   **5.** 17% of 50.   **6.** Ratio of 1d. per oz. to 1s. per lb.

7. Express 3 Kg. $\div 200$ in grams.

8. What is the error per cent. in saying that a road is 4 mi. long, if its real length is 5 mi.?

9. The scale of a map is 2 in. to the mile; how many acres are represented by 1 sq. in. on the map?

10. The perimeter of a triangle is 12 cm., and the ratios of the sides are $5 : 6 : 9$; find the length of the shortest side.

TESTS IN COMPUTATION

TESTS 9–16 (Ch. IV–XII)

Test 9

1. $(2\frac{1}{4} - 3\frac{2}{3} + 5\frac{1}{6}) \div (2\frac{1}{4} - 3\frac{5}{8} + 2\frac{1}{3})$.

2. (i) $0 \cdot 3098 \times 0 \cdot 01015$;   (ii) $1 \cdot 72 \div 0 \cdot 1075$.

3. Cost of 73 articles at £2 14s. 7d. each.

4. Increase £7 in the ratio $11 : 6$.

5. (i) What is $4\frac{1}{2}\%$ of £3 15s.?   (ii) What percentage is $11\frac{1}{4}$ of 36?

6. An article costs 13s. 4d. and is sold at a gain of $22\frac{1}{2}\%$; find the selling price.

Test 10

1. Express 13 cwt. 1 qr. 21 lb. as a fraction of 15 cwt.

2. (i) $0 \cdot 01 \times 1 \cdot 01 \times 0 \cdot 11$;   (ii) $9 \cdot 9176 \div 0 \cdot 01771$.

3. Cost of 12,000 articles at 7s. $8\frac{1}{2}$d. each.

4. Cost of 3 tons 12 cwt. of coal at £2 3s. 4d. per ton.

5. (i) Express $\frac{28}{40}$ as a percentage.

     (ii) Find the number of which 81 is $67\frac{1}{2}$ per cent.

6. By how much %, to 1 place of decimals, does 8435 exceed 7942?

Test 11

1. Arrange in descending order of magnitude:

$$\frac{5}{7}, \ \frac{17}{24}, \ \frac{84}{125}, \ \frac{0 \cdot 073}{0 \cdot 11}, \ \frac{1}{1\frac{3}{8}}.$$

2. (i) $(0 \cdot 04)^3 \times (0 \cdot 15)^2$;   (ii) $123 \cdot 7236 \div 0 \cdot 4017$.

3. Cost of 670 articles at 17s. $8\frac{1}{2}$d. each.

4. Taking 1 km. $= 0 \cdot 6214$ mi., express 835 m. in yards, to the nearest yard.

5. Divide £100 into three shares proportional to 8, 5, 3.

6. (i) What percentage is 16s. $4\frac{1}{2}$d. of £1?

  (ii) If $7\frac{1}{2}\%$ is deducted from a bill, £6 18s. 9d. remains to be paid. How much was the bill?

Test 12

1. $2\frac{3}{4} + \frac{1}{4}(1\frac{2}{3} - \frac{1}{6}) \div (4\frac{1}{8} - 7\frac{5}{12} + 4\frac{1}{6})$.

2. (i) $1 \cdot 0101 \times 0 \cdot 01101$; (ii) $26 \cdot 44528 \div 0 \cdot 004195$.

3. Cost of 2 tons 11 cwt. 2 qr. at £5 13s. 4d. per ton.

4. Express $0 \cdot 5673$ ch. in yd., ft., in., to nearest inch.

5. (i) Find the ratio of 7 cwt. 2 qr. to 1 ton.

  (ii) What percentage is $4\frac{1}{2}$d. of 5 shillings?

6. Find to the nearest penny $7\frac{3}{4}\%$ of £65 12s.

Test 13

1. Express 18s. $4\frac{3}{4}$d. as the decimal of £1, to 4 places.

2. (i) $0 \cdot 3728 \times \frac{17}{25}$; (ii) $0 \cdot 0124 \div 0 \cdot 775$.

3. $\frac{2}{15}(\frac{2}{3} - \frac{1}{6}) \div (\frac{2}{21} \times 3\frac{1}{2} - \frac{2}{3} + \frac{1}{2 \cdot 4})$.

4. Find the pay for 365 days at 17s. 10d. per day.

5. (i) What percentage is £2 10s. of £3 6s. 8d.?

  (ii) Find to the nearest £100 the value of $2\frac{3}{4}\%$ of £3,685,240.

6. An article is sold for 24s. 6d. at a gain of 40%; find the cost price.

Test 14

1. Express $0 \cdot 03729$ mi. in yd., ft., in., to the nearest inch.

2. (i) $\dfrac{(0 \cdot 15)^2}{(0 \cdot 9)^2} - \dfrac{(0 \cdot 12)^2}{(0 \cdot 8)^2}$; (ii) $1 \div 0 \cdot 987$, to 2 places.

3. Cost of 2 mi. 3 fur. 7 ch. at £3 11s. 8d. per mile.

4. Find the ratio of 2 tons 12 cwt. 28 lb. to 4 tons 10 cwt. 84 lb.

5. Add: $133\frac{1}{3}\%$ of 2 yd.; 145% of 5 ft.; $62\frac{1}{2}\%$ of 1 ch.; answer in yd., ft., in.

6. The population of a town decreases from 63,573 to 59,184. Find the decrease per cent., to 1 place of decimals.

Test 15

1. $(\frac{1}{2} - \frac{1}{8})(\frac{1}{10} - \frac{1}{14}) \div (\frac{1}{2} - \frac{1}{8} + \frac{1}{10} - \frac{1}{14})$.

2. (i) $0\cdot90807 \times 0\cdot07089$; (ii) $0\cdot02 \div 3108$, correct to 8 places.

3. Cost of 12,000 articles at $11\frac{3}{4}$d. each.

4. Find to the nearest penny the cost of 3 qr. 16 lb. 10 oz. at £125 per cwt.

5. 56% of a sum of money is £47 16s. 8d.; find the value of 18% of the same sum.

6. An article is sold for £37 16s. at a loss of 16%; find the loss.

Test 16

1. Evaluate to 2 places of decimals, $\frac{117}{259} - \frac{19}{203}$.

2. (i) $\frac{0\cdot8 \times 0\cdot027 \times 0\cdot35}{0\cdot032 \times 2\cdot1 \times 0\cdot1}$; (ii) $6\frac{1}{4}\%$ of 7 tons 3 cwt.

3. Express 42 ch. 17 yd. 1 ft. as a decimal of 1 fur., to 4 places.

4. Find the cost of $472\frac{3}{4}$ tons at £84 15s. 8d. per ton.

5. What percentage, correct to 1 place of decimals, is £1 17s. 10d. of £3 5s. 6d.?

6. What sum of money, to the nearest £1000, exceeds £3,584,265 by $23\frac{1}{4}\%$?

TESTS 17–24 (Ch. IV–XV)

Test 17

1. (i) $4\frac{1}{2} \times 4\frac{2}{3} \div (5\frac{1}{2} + 3\frac{1}{4})$; (ii) $0\cdot1702 \div 0\cdot46$.

2. Find the cost of 724 articles at 16s. $8\frac{1}{2}$d. each.

3. (i) What percentage is 4d. of 1s. 3d.?
(ii) Find the ratio of 17 lb. 8 oz. to 18 lb. 2 oz.?

4. Express $0\cdot1355$ days in hr., min., sec., to nearest sec.

5. A beam of timber 7 ft. 6 in. long, 1 ft. 4 in. wide, 8 in. deep, weighs 240 lb. Find the weight of the timber per cu. ft.

6. In what time will the simple interest on £62 10s. amount to £6 11s. 3d. at $3\frac{1}{2}\%$ p.a.?

Test 18

1. (i) $(1\frac{7}{10} - \frac{3}{4}) \div (1\frac{1}{5} \times 3\frac{1}{3})$; (ii) $7\cdot5 \div 0\cdot0625$.

2. $\frac{2}{7}$ of £3 4s. 9d. $+ \frac{11}{24}$ of 10s. $+ \frac{3}{4}$ of 1 guinea.

3. (i) What is $37\frac{1}{2}\%$ of 28 tons 12 cwt.?

(ii) A man's salary is £450 a year. He spends 85% of his salary; how much does he save each year?

4. Find the rate payable on property valued at £1230, if the rate is 1s. $2\frac{1}{2}$d. in the £.

5. The circumference of a circle is 2 ft. 9 in. Find the area of the circle, to the nearest sq. in. [Take $\pi = \frac{22}{7}$.]

6. Find, correct to the nearest penny, the simple interest on £173 14s. for $1\frac{1}{2}$ years at $3\frac{1}{2}\%$ p.a.

Test 19

1. (i) $17\frac{5}{6} - 10\frac{1}{3} + 3\frac{1}{7}$ of 8·4; (ii) $13\cdot9472 \div 0\cdot184$.

2. (i) Express 11s. $7\frac{1}{2}$d. as a decimal of £5.

(ii) Find, correct to the nearest penny, 39% of 1 guinea.

3. $4\frac{1}{4}$ lb. of tea cost 7s. $9\frac{1}{2}$d.; find the cost per lb.

4. Find the cost of 186 articles at 3s. $10\frac{1}{2}$d. each.

5. A poultry-run is 86 ft. long, 32 ft. wide, and is surrounded with netting $4\frac{1}{2}$ ft. high. Find the cost of the netting at $3\frac{1}{2}$d. per sq. yd.

6. By selling an article for £3 12s. a man loses 4%. For what must he sell it to gain 24%.

Test 20

1. (i) $30\cdot05 \times 0\cdot0346$; (ii) $0\cdot65 \times 1\cdot08 \div 3\cdot9$.

2. Arrange in ascending order of magnitude: $\frac{5}{16}$, $\frac{9}{32}$, $\frac{2}{7}$, 0·28.

3. A man earns 19s. 6d. for $3\frac{1}{4}$ hr. work; how much does he earn per hour?

4. (i) 15% of a number is 84. What is the number?

(ii) The weekly wage bill in a factory is £248. What will it become if all wages are raised by $1\frac{1}{4}\%$?

5. Find the cost of matting for a floor 31 ft. 6 in. long, 22 ft. 6 in. wide, at 2s. 4d. per sq. yd.

6. At what rate % p.a. will the interest on £870 amount to £13 1s. in 4 months?

Test 21

1. (i) $5\frac{1}{2} \times 0\cdot8 \div 12\frac{1}{2}$; (ii) Express 0·1375 of 1 mi. in yards.

2. (i) Find the ratio of 1 yd. 4 in. to 2 yd. 2 ft.

(ii) Find the value of $102\frac{1}{2}\%$ of 12s. 6d.

3. Taking 1 gall. $= 277 \cdot 27$ cu. in., express 10 gall. in cu. ft., correct to 2 places of decimals.

4. A bankrupt pays at the rate of 14s. 6d. in the £. How much will a creditor lose to whom he owes £1845?

5. Divide £1 into 3 parts proportional to 2, 3, 7.

6. A solid cylindrical metal bolt is $1\frac{1}{2}$ in. in diameter and 5 in. long. Find its weight to the nearest oz., if the metal weighs $3\frac{1}{2}$ oz. per cu. in. [Take $\pi = \frac{22}{7}$.]

Test 22

1. (i) $(\frac{1}{5} + \frac{1}{3} - \frac{1}{2}) \div (\frac{2}{5} - \frac{1}{4} + \frac{1}{2})$; (ii) $0 \cdot 64 \times 0 \cdot 035 \div 0 \cdot 14$.

2. (i) Express 7s. 3d. as a percentage of 9s. 8d.

    (ii) Express $0 \cdot 0043$ ton in lb., oz., to nearest oz.

3. Find, to the nearest penny, the cost of 3 tons 12 cwt. 3 qr. at £1 14s. 8d. per ton.

4. The rent of a house is £132 a year, and rates at 8s. 9d. in the £ are demanded on $\frac{5}{8}$ of the annual rent. Find the amount of the rates.

5. Divide £5 10s. between A, B, C so that A's share is $\frac{5}{8}$ of C's share and B's share is $\frac{2}{3}$ of C's share.

6. A sheet of lead $9 \cdot 6$ m. long, $2 \cdot 25$ m. wide weighs 1935 kg. Find the thickness of the sheet, correct to $\frac{1}{10}$ mm., given that 1 c.c. of lead weighs $11 \cdot 4$ gm.

Test 23

1. (i) $1 \div (4\frac{3}{4} - \frac{1}{4} \text{ of } 7\frac{1}{5})$; (ii) $0 \cdot 002769 \div 0 \cdot 156$.

2. (i) Find the ratio of £1 2s. to £1 16s. 8d.

    (ii) Find, to the nearest penny, $26\frac{1}{2}\%$ of £1 11s. 2d.

3. How many pieces, each $0 \cdot 15$ yd. long, can be cut from $4\frac{1}{4}$ yd. of tape, and how much remains over?

4. The population of a town was 42,732 in 1921 and increased by $8\frac{1}{3}\%$ in the next 10 years. What was it in 1931?

5. A man obtained 60 st. of potatoes from a plot of ground 90 ft. long, 24 ft. wide. What was the average yield in tons per acre?

6. The diameter of a garden roller is 2 ft. 6 in., and the roller is $3\frac{1}{2}$ ft. wide. What area, to the nearest sq. yd., does it roll over in 24 revolutions? [Take $\pi = \frac{22}{7}$.]

Test 24

1. (i) What must be added to $\frac{3}{8}$ of $\frac{5}{7}$ to make $\frac{9}{14}$ of $1\frac{3}{4}$?

(ii) What whole number is nearest to $\dfrac{7\cdot47 \times 4\cdot82}{0\cdot45}$?

2. (i) Express $3\frac{1}{4}$d. as a decimal of 4s. 2d.

(ii) Find, correct to the nearest penny, the value of 145% of £2 17s. 10d.

3. 36% of the contents of a chest of tea is worth £4 10s.; what is the value of 64% of the contents?

4. A steamer travels at 22 knots; find its speed in miles per hour. [1 knot = 6080 ft. per hour.]

5. An alloy is made of copper weighing 550 lb. per cu. ft. and tin weighing 440 lb. per cu. ft.; the alloy contains 2 parts of copper to 5 parts of tin, *by weight*. Find the weight per cu. ft. of the alloy.

6. A tank containing water is 4 ft. 6 in. long, 3 ft. 4 in. wide. How many inches, correct to $\frac{1}{10}$ in., does the water-level fall, when 20 gall. are drawn out of the tank? [1 gall. = 277·3 cu. in.]

TESTS 25–32 (Ch. X–XVII)

Test 25

1. (i) Find the value of $22\frac{1}{2}$% of 11s. 8d.

(ii) Find the ratio of 17s. 9d. to £2 19s. 2d.

2. Find the rent for 52 weeks at 13s. $10\frac{1}{2}$d. a week.

3. Find, correct to the nearest penny, the simple interest on £173 17s. for 8 mo. at $4\frac{1}{4}$% p.a.

4. Goods are bought at £8 a ton and sold at $1\frac{1}{4}$d. per lb.; find the gain per cent.

5. In 1930, £748,187 was paid under the Workman's Compensation Act for 2667 fatal accidents. Find, to the nearest £, the average amount paid per accident.

6. A plot of ground 80 yd. long, 32 yd. wide has a fence round it, and a pathway 4 ft. 6 in. wide is made round the edge of it inside the fence. Find the cost of the path at $1\frac{1}{2}$d. per sq. ft.

Test 26

1. (i) $\dfrac{9\cdot3 - 7\cdot9}{2\cdot2 \div 50\cdot9}$; (ii) Express $\dfrac{103}{125}$ as a percentage.

2. In a sale, a discount of 1s. 8d. in the £ is given on the marked price. If the reduced price of a piano is £71 10s., what is its marked price?

3. Find the simple interest on £138 for 14 months at $3\frac{3}{4}\%$ p.a.

4. The number of men unemployed on 28th September 1931 was 2,070,639, and on 22nd August 1932 was 2,289,045. Find the increase per cent., to the nearest whole number.

5. A man paid $62\frac{1}{2}\%$ of the cost of a dinner-party. What did the party cost if he paid £4 2s. 6d.?

6. The diameter of the cross-section of a tube railway tunnel is 11 ft. 6 in. Find the area of the cross-section, to the nearest sq. ft. [Take $\pi = 3\cdot14$.]

Test 27

1. (i) Find the ratio of 3 qr. 16 lb. to $7\frac{1}{2}$ cwt.

(ii) Divide £1620 into two parts such that one is 70% greater than the other.

2. Evaluate correct to 4 places of decimals :

$$\frac{1}{7} + \frac{1}{2}\cdot\frac{1}{7^2} + \frac{1}{3}\cdot\frac{1}{7^3} + \frac{1}{4}\cdot\frac{1}{7^4} + \cdots$$

3. Find the pay for 365 days at 17s. $4\frac{1}{2}$d. per day.

4. A man can do $\frac{7}{18}$ of a piece of work in 35 hr.; how long will he take to do 60% of it at the same rate?

5. A photograph 16·4 cm. wide, 12·7 cm. high, is mounted on a card 22·6 cm. wide, 17·3 cm. high. Find the area of the part of the card left uncovered.

6. Find, to the nearest penny, the true present worth of a bill for £274 due in 7 months time, interest being reckoned at 4% p.a.

Test 28

1. $\dfrac{3\frac{7}{8} + 2\frac{5}{16} - 5\frac{1}{32}}{6\frac{1}{8} \times 2\frac{2}{5} + 1\frac{1}{4}}$;
    2. $\dfrac{36 \times 0\cdot003 \times 0\cdot0035}{0\cdot63 \times 0\cdot8}$,

3. Find, to the nearest penny, the cost of 11 cwt. 1 qr. 16 lb. at £45 per ton.

4. The profits of a business for 1934 exceeded those for 1933 by 26%. The profits were £4620 for 1934; find the profits for 1933.

5. In what time will the interest on £1320 amount to £28 17s. 6d. at $3\frac{3}{4}\%$ p.a.?

6. A cylindrical watering-can is 1 ft. 9 in. high and 8 in. in diameter. Find its capacity, to the nearest $\frac{1}{10}$ gall. [Take $\pi = \frac{22}{7}$, and 1 gall. = 277 cu. in.]

Test 29

1. $\pi = 3.1415926\ldots$ and $e = 2.7182818\ldots$; find, correct to 4 figures, the value of (i) $\pi + e$; (ii) $\pi - e$.

Find, correct to 3 figures, the value of $\pi \div e$.

2. On a map of scale 4 in. to the mile, an estate occupies an area of 9.37 sq. in. Find the actual area, to the nearest acre.

3. Subtract $\frac{3}{7}$ of $2\frac{1}{2}$ guineas from $87\frac{1}{2}\%$ of £1 10s.

4. The weight of a lorry is 12% of the load it carries. Find in lb. the weight of the lorry if the combined weight of the lorry and its load is 2 tons.

5. Find, to the nearest penny, the true discount on a bill for £608 due in 4 months time, reckoning interest at $4\frac{1}{2}\%$ p.a.

6. From a circular disc of diameter 5 in., a semicircular portion of diameter 3 in. is removed. Find the area of the upper surface of the remainder, correct to 3 figures. [$\pi = 3.142$.]

Test 30

1. In the period June–August 1934, 9,570,000 telegrams were despatched in Great Britain, and for the corresponding period in 1935, after the reduction in cost, 12,240,000 telegrams were despatched. Find the increase per cent. to the nearest whole number.

2. Evaluate, correct to 5 places of decimals:

$$\frac{1}{3} - \frac{1}{3} \cdot \frac{1}{3^3} + \frac{1}{5} \cdot \frac{1}{3^5} - \frac{1}{7} \cdot \frac{1}{3^7} + \cdots.$$

3. The average breadth of a railway is 32 yd. How many acres are required per mile of railway?

4. Divide £12 into 4 parts proportional to 3, 5, 11, 13.

5. A bankrupt's liabilities are £29,570 and his assets are £3850 10s. How much in the £ can the bankrupt pay? Answer to a farthing.

6. A speculator lost 35% of his capital in one operation, and lost 40% of the remainder in a second operation. If he then had £1560, how much had he at first?

Test 31

1. Taking 1 m. = 1·09363 yd., find to the nearest foot, the difference between 16·1 km. and 10 mi.

2. A grocer sells 4 lb. 10 oz. of butter for 6s. 2d.; find the sale price per lb. If the grocer bought the butter at £5 16s. 8d. per cwt., find his gain per cent.

3. Street accidents in Great Britain increased from 156,793 in 1930 to 181,077 in 1931. Find the increase per cent., to the nearest whole number.

4. Gunpowder is composed (by weight) of 75% nitre, 10% sulphur, 15% charcoal. Find in cwt. the amount of each substance used in making $1\frac{1}{2}$ tons of gunpowder.

5. The catalogue price of an article is £36; this is subject to a discount of $22\frac{1}{2}\%$, and the price so reduced is subject to a further discount of $12\frac{1}{2}\%$. What is the final price?

6. A halfpenny may be regarded as a circular cylinder of diameter 1 in., thickness $\frac{1}{16}$ in., and weight $\frac{1}{5}$ oz.; find, correct to $\frac{1}{10}$ oz., the weight per cu. in. of the alloy of which it is made. [Take $\pi = 3\cdot14$.]

Test 32

1. An express is timed to leave Swindon at 3.45 p.m. and to arrive at Paddington (77·3 mi. away) at 4.50 p.m.; find its average speed in miles per hour, to the nearest mile.

2. The Chancellor of the Exchequer received for the 7 yr. 1925 to 1931 the following amounts of "Conscience Money": £1427 1s.; £2931 18s. 4d.; £10,745 5s. 8d.; £14,985 16s. 7d.; £7594 13s. 6d.; £2116 7s. 6d.; £1195. Find the average annual receipt from this source, to the nearest penny.

3. A bankrupt pays at 7s. $8\frac{3}{4}$d. in the £. How much will a man receive, to whom he owes £1348?

4. A grocer buys tea at £150 per ton and retails it at 1s. 8d. per lb.; but there is a wastage of 7% of the weight in the retail trading. Find the grocer's gain per cent.

5. If a man's capital increases each year by 20% of its value at the beginning of the year, find the percentage increase in 3 years.

6. A swimming-bath 100 ft. long, 40 ft. wide, is being filled at the rate of 120 gall. of water per minute. At what rate in inches per hour, correct to $\frac{1}{100}$ in., does the water-level rise? [1 gall. = 277·3 cu. in.]

REVISION PAPERS

PAPERS 25–32 (Ch. I–XII)

Paper 25

1. (i) Simplify $(\frac{5}{6} - \frac{4}{9}) \div (1\frac{5}{8} + \frac{3}{5} \div \frac{4}{9})$.

(ii) Divide 0·0280719 by 0·843.

2. (i) Find the value of $\frac{3}{7}$ of £2 12s. 6d.

(ii) Find the cost of 173 articles at £2 16s. each.

3. (i) What percentage is 24 of 40?

(ii) What is $4\frac{1}{2}\%$ of £75?

4. Find the area of a path 8 ft. wide which surrounds a rectangular lawn, 18 yd. long, 13 yd. wide.

5. £196 is shared between A, B, C, so that A gets twice as much as B, and B gets twice as much as C. What does C get?

6. A tailor allows a customer to deduct 10% from the amount of a bill for cash. If the customer settles the bill by paying £12 3s. cash, find the original amount.

Paper 26

1. (i) Express 67320 in prime factors.

(ii) Divide 24 yd. 1 ft. 9 in. by 15.

2. (i) How many articles at 4s. 7d. each can be bought for £4, and how much money remains?

(ii) Find the cost of 126 tons at £2 6s. 3d. per ton.

3. (i) What percentage is $4\frac{1}{2}$d. of 1s.?

(ii) The duty on a watch is 35% of its value. What is the duty on a watch valued at £7 10s.?

4. Express in acres, correct to 2 places of decimals, the area of a field 140 yd. long, 86 yd. broad.

5. The railway fare for 36 people for 60 mi. is £11 5s.; find the fare for 80 people for 40 mi. at the same rate.

6. A man buys goods for £475 and sells them for £532. Find his gain per cent.

Paper 27

1. (i) The height of Everest is 29,142 ft. Express this in mi., yd.

(ii) Find the square root of 27225.

2. (i) Taking 1 m. = 39·37 in., express 3 m. 65 cm. in ft., in., to the nearest inch.

(ii) Find the cost of 3 tons 7 cwt. 2 qr. at £2 6s. 8d. per ton.

3. (i) Find the ratio of 7 cwt. 2 qr. to 1 ton.

(ii) Express 62½% as a fraction, and $\frac{97}{125}$ as a percentage.

4. The population of a town increases from 11,200 to 13,100. Find the increase per cent., to the nearest whole number.

5. A metal sheet, 8·75 in. long, 3·2 in. wide, weighs 10½ oz. If it is cut down so as to be 8 in. long, 3 in. wide, what will it weigh?

6. By selling a car for £132, I lose 28%. What is my loss?

Paper 28

1. (i) By what must 3⅓ be multiplied to give 9⅛?

(ii) Express 17s. 10¾d. as a decimal of £1, correct to 4 places.

2. (i) Divide £422 4s. 8d. by 53.

(ii) Find the cost of 3 yd. 1 ft. 8 in. at £1 5s. 6d. per yard.

3. (i) Find the value of 1¼% of £266 13s. 4d.

(ii) 73 boys in a school get measles, and this is just less than 28% of the school. How many are there in the school?

4. A man owes £176, and only possesses £33 1s. 6d.; at what rate in the £, correct to the nearest penny, can he pay his creditors?

5. The diagram represents the top of a metal sheet ⅔ in. thick. The corners are right-angled and the dimensions are shown in inches. Find the volume of the sheet in cu. in., and its weight if the metal weighs 4·8 oz. per cu. in.

6. The speed of a tube train at various times after the start is as follows :—

Time in seconds	2	4	6	8	10	12
Speed in m.p.h.	9	17	23	27·5	30	30

Represent these facts by a graph, and estimate (i) the time when the train first attains a speed of 20 m.p.h., (ii) its speed 3 sec. after the start.

Paper 29

1. (i) Simplify $(\frac{1}{4} + \frac{3}{8} + \frac{5}{12}) \div (\frac{2}{15} + \frac{1}{20} + \frac{7}{30})$.
   (ii) Express 0·4283 mi. in ch., yd., ft., to the nearest foot.

2. (i) Find the cost of 247 yd. at 3s. 11¾d. per yard.
   (ii) If 1 rupee = 1s. 6d., express 32 rupees 12 annas 2 pice in
        £. s. d., to the nearest penny, given that 1 rupee = 16
        annas = 64 pice.

3. (i) 36% of a certain number is 117; find the number.
   (ii) A boy's height increased from 5 ft. 2 in. to 5 ft. 3¾ in.
        in a year. Find the increase per cent., to one place of
        decimals.

4. How long will a column of soldiers 450 yd. long take to pass
a given point if the rate of marching is 120 paces of 30 in. each
per minute?

5. On a map of scale 4 in. to the mile an estate has an area of
12·35 sq. in. Find its area in acres.

6. A grocer buys 15 tons of sugar for £350 and sells it at 2¾d.
per lb. Find his gain per cent. At what price would he have to
sell it to gain 40 per cent.?

Paper 30

1. (i) Find the H.C.F. of 25245 and 64350.
   (ii) Divide 0·0028213 by 0·634.

2. (i) Find the dividend on £532 at 2s. 10d. in the £.
   (ii) The weekly output of 1,124,000 miners is 4,813,000 tons
        of coal. Find to the nearest cwt. the weekly output per
        miner.

3. (i) What percentage is £1 10s. 9d. of £6 16s. 8d.?
   (ii) After a man's salary had been increased by 8%, it became
        £378 a year. What was the increase in his salary?

4. How long does a train 72 yd. long, travelling at 30 mi. an hour,
take to pass completely through a station 126 yd. long?

5. A metal box without a lid is 15 cm. long, 11 cm. wide, 5 cm.
high, measured externally, and the metal is 5 mm. thick. Find the
weight of the box if 1 c.c. of the metal weighs 7·2 gm.

6. A obtains 35% of the total, 160 marks, assigned to a paper;
B is ahead of A by 25% of A's marks, C is ahead of B by 20% of
B's marks. What percentage of the total did C get?

Paper 31

1. (i) Express $\frac{4}{7} + \frac{1}{12}$ as a decimal, correct to 3 places.

(ii) Find the value of $(0\cdot05)^3 \times (0\cdot16)^2 \div 0\cdot2$.

2. (i) A locomotive uses $5\frac{1}{4}$ tons of coal at £1 18s. 6d. per ton for a journey of 240 mi. Find the cost per mile, to the nearest $\frac{1}{10}$d.

(ii) Find to the nearest penny the cost of 4 cwt. 3 qr. 21 lb. at £1 16s. 9d. per cwt.

3. (i) When railway fares were increased in the ratio 7 : 4, the fare for a journey became 24s. 6d.; what was the increase?

(ii) A length is stated to be 5 cm. when it is really 6·25 cm.; find the error per cent.

4. A gas company charges 1s. $2\frac{1}{2}$d. per therm. If 100 cu. ft. of gas are equivalent to 0·45 therm, find to the nearest penny the cost of 3800 cu. ft. of gas.

5. £7 11s. 8d. is paid for a job which three men working separately can do in 8, 10, and 15 days respectively. If all work together, how should the payment be shared between them?

6. In 1933, a house is rated at £80, and the rate payable is 8s. 4d. in the £. How much has to be paid? In 1934, the amount at which the house is rated is increased by 5%, and the rate is decreased by 10%. Find the decrease per cent. in the amount to be paid.

Paper 32

1. (i) Divide 9 cwt. 1 qr. 15 lb. 5 oz. by 89.

(ii) Taking 1 m. as 40 in., find to the nearest whole number the number of ares in 1 ac. [1 are = 100 sq. m.]

2. Find correct to the nearest penny:

(i) the value of $7\frac{3}{4}\%$ of £5 17s. 3d.;

(ii) the cost of 2 tons 17 cwt. 1 qr. 10 lb. at £3 11s. 6d. per ton.

3. (i) What sum exceeds 16s. 8d. by 24 per cent.?

(ii) The income of the Southern Railway fell from £6,960,000 in 1922 to £6,090,000 in 1923. Find the decrease per cent.

4. An elastic spring is held at one end; its natural length is 12 cm., and its stretched lengths when different weights are attached to the other end are as follows :—

Weight in gm.	20	50	70	100
Length in cm.	13	14·5	15·5	17

Illustrate these facts by a graph and find (i) the length of the spring when a weight of 85 gm. is attached, (ii) the weight which will stretch it to a length of 14·8 cm.

5. 10 men can construct a motor track 220 yd. long, 10 yd. wide, in 6 days of 8 hr. each. How many men will be required to construct a similar track 18 mi. long, 12 yd. wide in 72 days of 9 hr. each?

6. A property is divided between A, B, C so that the shares of A, B are in the ratio 5 : 3, and the shares of B, C are in the ratio 4 : 3. If A receives £825 more than C, how much does B receive?

PAPERS 33-40 (Ch. I-XIV)

Paper 33

1. Express 6552 × 1150 in prime factors. Find the least whole number by which it must be multiplied to give a perfect square.

2. A "bag" of white pepper contains 168 lb. (i) How many bags go to the ton? (ii) What is the cost per bag at 1s. 7d. per lb.?

3. Find the value of $4\frac{3}{4}\%$ of £75.

4. My household expenses in 1930 were: Food £300, clothing £140, rent £70, sundries £190. In 1934, the costs of food and clothes had increased by 50% and 40% respectively, and sundries by £24; the rent was unchanged. Find the new total expenditure and the increase per cent.

5. Find the amount of wood used to make an open box, 25 cm. long, 14 cm. wide, 8 cm. high, external measurements, the wood being 5 mm. thick.

6. Find the length of the circumference of a circle of diameter 5 in., correct to $\frac{1}{10}$ in., and the area of the circle, correct to $\frac{1}{10}$ sq. in. [Take $\pi = 3\cdot142$.]

Paper 34

1. If oranges are reduced from 1s. 6d. a dozen to 1s. 3d. a dozen, how many more can be bought for 7s. 6d.?

2. Arrange in ascending order of magnitude :

$$\frac{5}{11}, \quad \frac{7}{18}, \quad \frac{3\cdot4}{7\cdot5}, \quad \frac{1}{2\cdot5}, \quad \frac{0\cdot5}{1\cdot2}.$$

3. On a map whose scale is 1 in. to the mile the area of an estate is $3\frac{1}{2}$ sq. in. Find its actual area in acres.

4. A tradesman accepts £50 8s. cash for a bill for £52 10s. What percentage of the bill did he deduct for cash?

5. A bankrupt owes £1250 to A and £2300 to B; his assets are £2710. Three-fifths of his debt to A is first paid in full, and the remainder of his assets are then used to pay the rest of what he owes A and what he owes B at the same rate in the £. How much does B receive?

6. Find the volume of a circular cylinder of diameter 3 in., and height 8 in., correct to $\frac{1}{10}$ cu. in.; and find the area of its curved surface correct to $\frac{1}{10}$ sq. in. [Take $\pi = 3\cdot142$.]

Paper 35

1. Edinburgh is 390 mi. from London. How much time is saved by going by air at 120 mi. an hour instead of by train at 54 mi. an hour?

2. (i) What percentage is 13s. 6d. of £1?
    (ii) A man buys 140 eggs at 3s. 3d. per score and 180 eggs at 2s. 1d. a dozen, and sells the whole at 5 for 1s. Find his gain per cent.

3. A motorist uses 389 gall. of petrol in driving 8253 mi. and his expenditure on petrol is at the rate of 7d. every 9 mi. Find the average cost of the petrol per gall. to the nearest $\frac{1}{2}$d.

4. I can buy cigarettes at 100 for 4s. 8d. or at 30 for 1s., but each of the second kind contains only $\frac{3}{4}$ of the amount of tobacco in the first kind. Which kind should I buy to obtain the greater amount of tobacco for a given sum of money, and how much more weight per cent. shall I get by doing so?

5. A coal cellar measures 12 ft. by 7 ft. by 8 ft. If 90 lb. of coal go to the cu. ft., find the cost of filling the cellar at £2 5s. a ton.

6. Find correct to the nearest inch the diameter of a wheel whose rim is 85 in. long. [Take $\pi = 3\cdot14$.]

Paper 36

1. The following tickets were sold for a pageant : 1189 at £1 1s.; 1622 at 10s. 6d.; 2411 at 5s.; 778 at 2s. 6d. What was the total amount paid and the average price per ticket?

2. 1 cwt. of artificial manure is sufficient for 1000 sq. yd. of land. Find in cwt. lb., to the nearest lb., how much is sufficient for a field of area 5 ac. 3½ ro.

3. (i) What percentage is scored by a boy who obtains 81 marks out of 150?

(ii) A man gains 20% by selling an article for 19s.; what did it cost?

4. There are 20 members of a committee, and the ratio of the number of men to the number of women is 3 : 1. How many women must be added to the committee to make the ratio of men to women 3 : 2?

5. A room is 16 ft. long, 12 ft. wide, 9 ft. high. Find the cost of the wall-paper needed for it, allowing 84 sq. ft. for window space, etc., if the paper costs 4s. 9d. per piece, each piece being 12 yd. long, 28 in. wide.

6. A cylindrical telegraph pole is 10 in. in diameter and 24 ft. high. If the wood weighs 48 lb. per cu. ft., find the weight of the pole to the nearest lb. [Take $\pi = 3\cdot142$.]

Paper 37

1. (i) Divide £173 19s. 6d. by 197.

(ii) The duty on cigarettes is 14s. 7d. per lb.; how much is it per cwt.?

2. A grocer buys tea at £7 per cwt. and sells it at 1s. 10½d. per lb. What is his gain per cent.? At what rate must he sell it to gain 60%?

3. A gramophone record, price 1s. 6d., contains two dance tunes, each of which takes 2½ min. to play. What does the dance music cost by the hour, if records are worn out after being played 100 times?

4. In firing at a target, A scores 2 hits in every 3 shots, B 3 hits in every 4 shots, C 4 hits in every 5 shots. Each fires the same number of shots and the target is hit altogether 931 times. How many shots were fired altogether? How many hits did A score?

5. Find to the nearest gallon how much water is required to fill a cistern 6 ft. by 4 ft. by 3 ft.   [1 cu. ft. = 6·23 gall.]

6. The bore (internal diameter) of an iron pipe is 7 cm. and the iron is 5 mm. thick.   If the pipe is 40 cm. long and if the iron weighs 7·2 gm. per c.c., find in kg., correct to $\frac{1}{100}$ kg., the weight of the pipe.   [Take $\pi = 3·142$.]

Paper 38

1. (i) The area of Denmark is 15,000 sq. mi. and its population is 3,600,000.   Find the population per sq. mi.

(ii) A car runs 2640 yd. in $2\frac{1}{2}$ min.   Find its average speed in miles per hour.

2. A path from the foot to the top of a hill ascends for 600 yd. at a gradient of 1 in 18, then for 300 yd. at 1 in 12, then for 150 yd. at 1 in 9, and lastly 200 yd. at 1 in 8.   Find the height of the hill in feet.

3. When railway fares were increased in the ratio 7 : 4, the fare for a certain journey was increased by 16s. 6d.; what was the new fare?

4. A man X leaves a town P at 1 p.m. and travels to a town Q, 40 mi. away, going at 20 m.p.h. for 1 hr. and at 10 m.p.h. for the rest of the way.   Another man Y leaves Q at 2 p.m. and motors to P at 30 m.p.h.   Draw the travel graphs of X and Y, and find when and where the two men pass one another.

5. Water flows at 2 m.p.h. through a pipe whose cross-section is of area 7 sq. in.   How long will it take to fill a cistern, 7 ft. by 4 ft. by 2 ft. 9 in., if the pipe is kept full?

6. The inner edge of a circular running-track is 400 m. long. Find the diameter of this circle to the nearest metre, and the area enclosed by it in hectares to the nearest are.   [1 are = 1 sq. Dm.; take $\pi = 3·14$.]

Paper 39

1. (i) An engine uses 4 cwt. of fuel every 3 hr.; how long will $2\frac{1}{2}$ tons of fuel last?

(ii) A man who takes 7 steps in 3 sec. walks 6·5 km. per hour; find the length of his stride to the nearest cm.

2. How much is produced by a rate of 5s. $8\frac{1}{2}$d. in the £, on a rateable value of £348,600?

3. An 18-carat gold watch-chain weighs 940 grains (18 parts out of every 24 are pure gold). If the price of gold rises from £4 4s. per oz. to £7 per oz., find the increase in value of the gold in the chain. [1 oz. = 480 grains.]

4. The air-pressure on the screen of a car for various speeds is as follows :—

Speed in m.p.h. . .	10	20	30	40	45	50
Pressure in lb. per sq. ft.	0·4	1·6	3·6	6·4	8·1	10

Represent these facts by a graph and find (i) the pressure when the speed is 35 m.p.h., (ii) the speed when the pressure is 3 lb. per sq. ft.

5. The outside measurements of an open wooden tray of rectangular shape to hold foolscap are $15\frac{1}{2}$ in. by $10\frac{1}{2}$ in. by $2\frac{3}{4}$ in.; the wood is $\frac{5}{16}$ in. thick. Find to the nearest cu. in. the volume of wood used in making the tray.

6. A cylinder closed at both ends is 12 cm. long, and 4 cm. in diameter. Find the area of its total external surface. [Take $\pi = \frac{22}{7}$.]

Paper 40

1. (i) Multiply £1 2s. 6d. by $7\frac{4}{15}$.

    (ii) How many weekly bills of £3 7s. 6d. can be paid out of £55, and how much is left over?

2. A man walks from A to B in 1 hr. 34 min. The road is level for 4576 yd. and then rises uniformly to B. His speed is 4 m.p.h. on the level and 3 m.p.h. uphill. Find in yards the distance from A to B.

3. The municipal rates in 2 towns X, Y amount respectively to 6s. 3d., 7s. in the £; out of these rates the amounts spent on Education are respectively 1s., 1s. $3\frac{3}{4}$d. in the £. Find the ratios of the Education rate to the total rate in each town, and express the last ratio also as a percentage.

4. A tradesman makes a profit of 40% by selling an article for 3s. 6d. If he sells $\frac{3}{4}$ of his stock of these articles at 3s. 6d. each and the rest at 2s. each, find his gain % on the whole transaction.

5. Cloth 50 in. wide costs 4s. 6d. per yard. Find the cost of a dozen curtains each $7\frac{1}{2}$ ft. long, 100 in. wide, made of this material.

6. The floor of a hall is a rectangle 60 ft. long, 30 ft. wide. The side walls are 12 ft. high and the cross-section of the ceiling is a semicircle which springs from the side walls. Find the volume of the hall to the nearest 100 cu. ft., and the area of the ceiling to the nearest 10 sq. ft. [Take $\pi = 3\cdot142$.]

PAPERS 41–48 (Ch. I–XVII)

Paper 41

1. (i) Simplify $(\frac{4}{7} + \frac{2}{13}) \div (1 + \frac{4}{7} \times \frac{2}{13})$.

(ii) Divide £1 into 3 parts proportional to 2, 5, 9.

2. A car travels 1056 yd. in $1\frac{1}{2}$ min. Express this speed in miles per hour.

3. In 1928, the rateable value of Oxford was £734,450 and rates were paid at 7s. 8d. in the £. How much altogether was paid? The population was 80,500; find the amount paid per head to the nearest penny.

4. Carpet 27 in. wide is sold at 5s. 6d. per yard length. Find the cost of the carpet for a piece 16 ft. 6 in. long, 11 ft. 3 in. wide.

5. Find, correct to the nearest penny, the simple interest on £284 for 16 mo. at $4\frac{1}{2}\%$ p.a.

6. In what ratio must coal at 32s. per ton be mixed with coal at 44s. per ton to make the mixture worth 36s. 6d. per ton?

Paper 42

1. (i) Express $\frac{0\cdot3}{3\cdot75}$ as a percentage.

(ii) B exceeds A by 60%; C exceeds B by $12\frac{1}{2}\%$; find the ratio of A to C.

2. An advertisement containing 43 words costs £1; find the charge per word correct to the nearest penny.

3. A bankrupt pays at the rate of 16s. 3d. in the £. How much will a man receive, if he is owed £45 13s. 4d. by the bankrupt? What percentage of the bankrupt's debts remain unpaid?

4. If the diameter of the wheel of a car, travelling at 30 mi. an hour, is $2\frac{1}{4}$ ft., find the number of revolutions per minute made by the wheel. [Take $\pi = \frac{22}{7}$.]

5. If the simple interest on £425 for $2\frac{1}{2}$ yr. is £47 16s. 3d., find the rate per cent. p.a.

6. An English aspirin tablet contains 5 grains of aspirin, and a foreign tablet contains 150 mg. of aspirin. How many foreign tablets, to the nearest whole number, contain as much aspirin as 50 English tablets? [7000 grains = 1 lb.; 2·2 lb. = 1 kg.]

Paper 43

1. (i) Simplify $\dfrac{5\frac{1}{7} - 3\frac{5}{14}}{2\frac{1}{2} + 3\frac{3}{4}} \times 79\frac{1}{2}$.

(ii) Find the value of $2\frac{1}{4}\%$ of £41 16s., to the nearest penny.

2. Taking 35 yd. equal to 32 m., express 7 mi. in km.

3. The number of S.O.S. messages broadcast by the B.B.C. was 858 in 1933, and 889 in 1934. 44·75% were successful in 1933, how many was this? 503 messages were successful in 1934, what percentage, correct to 3 figures, was this?

4. Find the weight of a rectangular metal plate 6·4 cm. long, 4·5 cm. wide, 6 mm. thick, if the metal weighs 7·5 gm. per c.c.

5. Find, to the nearest penny, the true discount on a bill for £2526 due in 3 months time, reckoning interest at 7% p.a.

6. A well can be pumped dry in $1\frac{1}{2}$ hr. by two pumps which discharge respectively 80 gall., 120 gall. per min. If the smaller pump is used alone, the water sinks at 1 in. per min.; how deep is the well?

Paper 44

1. (i) Find the cost of 87 tons of coal at £1 17s. 8d. per ton.
(ii) The duty on an article is $17\frac{1}{2}\%$ of its value. If the duty is 12s. 10d., find the value.

2. Find the cost to the nearest penny of 39,765 articles at 12s. 6d. per thousand.

3. 1 cwt. of condensed milk is equivalent to 35 gall., and 1 cwt. of powder-milk to 95 gall. In 1931, 483,600 cwt. of condensed milk and 352,700 cwt. of powder-milk were imported. To how many gallons, correct to 3 figures, was the total imported equivalent?

4. Find, to the nearest penny, the simple interest on £453 18s. for 2½ yr. at 3½% p.a.

5. Find, to the nearest gallon, the amount of water in a cylindrical tank 6 ft. in diameter, if the water is 3 ft. 4 in. deep. [Take 1 cu. ft. = 6¼ gall., and π = 3·142.]

6. A man makes a profit of 20% by selling an article for 15s.; he sells ¾ of his stock at this price and the rest at 10s. each. Find his gain per cent. on the whole transaction.

Paper 45

1. Find, to 3 places of decimals, the values of $\frac{17}{6}$, $\frac{82}{29}$, $\frac{9\pi}{10}$, and arrange them in ascending order of magnitude.

2. (i) The area of the British Dominions is 14,200,000 sq. mi.; find, correct to 2 figures, what percentage this is of the area of the Earth, 55,500,000 sq. mi.

(ii) Find, correct to 1 figure, the error per cent. in the following rule: to convert metres to inches, subtract $\frac{1}{60}$ of the number and multiply the remainder by 40. [1 m. = 39·37 in.]

3. Planks 4 in. wide, 3 ft. 6 in. high are placed side by side to form a fence round a piece of ground 24 yd. long, 20 yd. wide. Find the length of the planking required, and the cost at 1s. 6d. per sq. ft.

4. In what ratio by volume must two metals, one weighing 485 lb. per cu. ft., the other 520 lb. per cu. ft., be combined to obtain an alloy weighing 506 lb. per cu. ft.?

5. Find the sum of money which will amount in 7 months time to £230 5s. at 4% p.a.

6. A starts a business with £4000, and at the end of 4 mo. takes in B with £3000, and 3 mo. later C joins with £5000. The profits 1 yr. from the start are £242 10s. Find A's share if the profits are divided so that the shares are proportional to the "£-months" of capital each has in the business.

Paper 46

1. (i) Simplify $\frac{5\frac{1}{15}}{15} - \frac{15}{2\frac{1}{1}} \div 1\frac{5}{17} - (\frac{5\frac{1}{15}}{15} - \frac{15}{5\frac{1}{1}}) \div 1\frac{5}{17}$.

   (ii) Express 0·007 as a percentage of 0·25.

2. Find the cost of 126 linen sheets at 28s. 6d. per pair.

3. Railway receipts for a certain year were as follows: from passenger traffic £2,487,700; from goods traffic £3,440,800; find to the nearest integer what percentage of the receipts came from goods traffic.

4. If £760 10s. amounts in 3 yr. at simple interest to £897 7s. 10d., find the rate per cent. p.a.

5. Find to the nearest gm. the weight of 12 m. of wire, diameter 3 mm., if the wire weighs 8 gm. per c.c. [Take $\pi = 3\cdot14$.]

6. A boy, engaged to work for 30 days, is paid 5s. for each day he works and is fined 6d. for each day he stays away. At the end he receives £5 11s. 6d.; how many days did he work?

Paper 47

1. (i) Express 1s. $5\frac{1}{2}$d. as a percentage of 3s. 6d.

   (ii) Express 1 ft. 5 in. in cm., correct to 3 figures, given that 1 yd. = 0·9144 m.

2. 8 tons 2 cwt. 2 qr. of coke cost £14 12s. 6d.; find the cost per ton.

3. A non-stop train leaves London at 10.30 a.m. and travels *via* Taunton (143 mi. from London) to Plymouth (226 mi. from London), arriving at 2.37 p.m. At what time to the nearest minute does it pass Taunton, assuming that it travels at a uniform speed.

4. Which of the following approximations are obviously wrong? Give reasons.

   (i) $\sqrt{0\cdot4816} \simeq 0\cdot2194$; (ii) $(4\cdot86)^3 \simeq 111\cdot7$;

   (iii) $(0\cdot3397)^2 \simeq 1\cdot154$; (iv) $\frac{27^2 \times 7 \times 23}{8 \times 22 \times 277} \simeq 2\cdot41$.

5. A tank, 7 ft. 6 in. long, 5 ft. 4 in. wide, contains 700 gall. of water. Find the depth of the water. [Take 1 cu. ft. = $6\frac{1}{4}$ gall.]

6. A man buys a house for £1450 and rents it so that, after allowing £9 a year for insurance and repairs, he obtains interest at 6% p.a. on his money. Find the rent.

Paper 48

1. (i) Express $\frac{5}{7} - \frac{4}{13}$ as a decimal, correct to 3 figures.

    (ii) Find the duty on an article valued at £6 4s. if duty is charged at the rate of 8s. 4d. in the £.

2. 120 cartridges cost 15s. 6d. Find the cost per million, if there is a reduction of 30% in the price for this quantity.

3. Simplify $\left\{ \dfrac{2\frac{1}{12} \times 4\frac{2}{7}}{1\frac{7}{8}} - \dfrac{3\frac{1}{5} + 5\frac{1}{4}}{5\frac{1}{2} - 4\frac{1}{5}} \right\} \div \{ 1\frac{1}{36} \times (7\frac{1}{5} - \frac{1}{4} \text{ of } 4\frac{4}{5}) \}$.

4. An open rectangular tank is made of cement, the walls and base being 6 in. thick. Externally, the tank is 10 ft. long, 7 ft. wide, 3 ft. high. Find its weight in tons if the concrete weighs 168 lb. per cu. ft.

5. A shopkeeper allows a discount of $17\frac{1}{2}\%$ on the marked price of a chair for cash in a sale. The sale price is £2 17s. 9d.; find the marked price.

6. A can do a piece of work in 21 days, B can do it in $31\frac{1}{2}$ days, and C in 63 days. How long will it take if all work together? If £30 is paid for the work, how much should each receive?

PART III

CHAPTER XVIII

SQUARE ROOT AND USE OF TABLES

The graph printed below represents the squares of numbers from 0 to 10. It may be used to read off approximate values of square roots of numbers between 0 and 100.

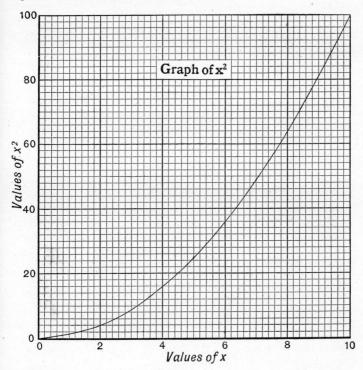

Graph of x^2

Values of x^2 (vertical axis)

Values of x (horizontal axis)

For Oral work. Use the graph to write down approximate values of: (i) $3 \cdot 4^2$, $6 \cdot 8^2$, $8 \cdot 6^2$, $9 \cdot 2^2$; (ii) the numbers whose squares are 34, 52, 74, 88; (iii) the square roots of 46, 58, 92, 12.

Finding Square Roots. The problem of finding the square root of, say, 1369 is equivalent to finding the length of a square containing 1369 units of area.

Since $30^2 = 900$ and $40^2 = 1600$, the side of the required square is

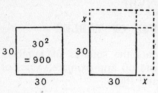

between 30 and 40 units long. We therefore start with a square whose side is 30 units long and find the breadth of the border which will convert it into a square of area 1369 units.

Area of required border
$$= (1369 - 900) \text{ units} = 469 \text{ units}.$$

If the breadth of the border is x units, the area of the border is $x(30 \times 2 + x)$ units; therefore $(60 + x)x = 469$.

The value of x is found by trial: x is small compared with 60, ∴ $60x \fallingdotseq 469$; $x \fallingdotseq 469 \div 60 \fallingdotseq 7$; but $67 \times 7 = 469$, exactly;

∴ the required border is 7 units wide;
∴ $\sqrt{1369} = 37$, exactly.

The reader should verify that $37 \times 37 = 1369$.

Example 1.   Find the square root of 69169.

Mark off 69169 in periods of *two* digits *starting from the decimal point*, in this case from the right.

The greatest integer whose square is not more than 6 is 2; write 2 in the first period of the answer and 2^2, that is 4, under the 6, and subtract. Bring down the digits 91 from the next period. Write down *twice* 2, that is 4, and find the approximate value of $291 \div 40$, that is 7. $47 \times 7 = 329$, but this is too large; $46 \times 6 = 276$.

```
          2| 6| 3
       6|91|69
       4
   46)291
       276
  523) 1569
       1569
```

Write 6 in the trial divisor and the second period of the answer, 276 under 291, and subtract. Bring down the digits 69 from the next period. Write down *twice* 26, that is 52, and find the approximate value of $1569 \div 520$, that is 3. $523 \times 3 = 1569$. Write 3 in the trial divisor and in the third period of the answer.

$$\sqrt{69169} = 263, \text{ exactly.}$$

The reader should verify that $263 \times 263 = 69169$.

Example 2. Find the square root of 165649.

Mark off the number in periods of two digits, starting from the decimal point.

Since $4^2 = 16$, write 4 in the first period of the answer.

Write down twice 4, $= 8$, and use 80 as trial divisor for the second stage of the work, with 56 as dividend; $81 \times 1 = 81$, and this is too big. We therefore put 0 in the second period of the answer and bring down the next two digits, 49, and then use 800 as trial divisor with 5649 as dividend.

$$\therefore \ \sqrt{165649} = 407, \text{ exactly.}$$

```
         4|   1
       16|56|49
       16
    80)   56

         4| 0| 7
       16|56|49
       16
      807)  5649
            5649
            ————
```

EXERCISE 129

Find the square roots of:

1. 529.   **[2]** 841.   **3.** 1156.   **4.** 1444.   **[5]** 2209.

[6] 3249.   **7.** 3721.   **[8]** 7396.   **[9]** 9801.   **10.** 53361.

11. 64009.   **[12]** 137641.   **13.** 117649.   **[14]** 15129.   **15.** 97969.

[16] 169744. **17.** 157609.   **18.** 277729.   **[19]** 405769.   **20.** 556516.

21. 4284900. **[22]** 9548100. **23.** 166464.   **[24]** 369664.

*25. 4704561. ***26.** 17749369. ***27.** 9418761. ***28.** 36012001.

Square Root of a Decimal. The same method can be used for finding the square root of a decimal.

Example 3. Find the square root of 0·0019l844.

Mark off the number in periods of two digits, *starting from the decimal point.*

Put the decimal point in the answer above the decimal point in the given number.

The period 00 after the decimal point gives 0 in the answer after the decimal point; then proceed as with whole numbers.

$$\therefore \ \sqrt{0\cdot00191844} = 0\cdot0438, \text{ exactly.}$$

```
      0·| 0| 4| 3| 8
      0·|00|19|18|44
         16
       83)  318
            249
      868)  6944
            6944
            ————
```

Square Root of a Vulgar Fraction. Since $\frac{5}{7} \times \frac{5}{7} = \frac{25}{49}$, the square root of $\frac{25}{49}$ is $\frac{5}{7}$. Thus the square root of a fraction may be found by taking the square root of its numerator and denominator. The square root of a mixed number may be found by expressing it as an improper fraction. For example,

$$\sqrt{7\tfrac{1}{9}} = \sqrt{\tfrac{64}{9}} = \frac{\sqrt{64}}{\sqrt{9}} = \frac{8}{3} = 2\tfrac{2}{3}.$$

EXERCISE 130 (Oral)

State the square roots if exact, or otherwise the first significant figure of the square roots, of the following:—

1. 0·25. **2.** 0·72. **3.** 0·05. **4.** 0·64. **5.** 0·8.

6. 0·09. **7.** 0·9. **8.** 0·4. **9.** 0·04. **10.** 1·21.

11. 2·5. **12.** 0·01. **13.** 0·1. **14.** 0·0061. **15.** 0·005.

16. 1·44. **17.** 0·144. **18.** 4·9. **19.** 0·0049. **20.** 0·016.

21. 0·000,04. **22.** 0·0004. **23.** 0·000,01. **24.** 0·000,005.

EXERCISE 131

Find the square roots of:

1. 6·76. **2.** 15·21. **3.** 0·2704. **4.** 0·0784.

5. 0·003364. **6.** 0·023104. **7.** 1·2996. **8.** 0·014161.

9. 1552·36. **10.** 0·111556. **11.** 25·8064. **12.** 0·368449.

13. 50·2681. **14.** 64·6416. **15.** 0·00041616. **16.** 0·091809.

17. $\frac{16}{25}$. **18.** $\frac{121}{400}$. **19.** $\frac{529}{1681}$. **20.** $\frac{2916}{4761}$. **21.** $\frac{1}{8464}$.

22. $12\frac{1}{4}$. **23.** $13\frac{4}{9}$. **24.** $6\frac{30}{49}$. **25.** $1\frac{9}{16}$. **26.** $52\frac{101}{289}$.

Example 4. Find correct to 3 significant figures the square root of 1440.

To obtain the square root correct to 3 figures, it is necessary to have 4 periods, and these are formed by inserting zeros after the decimal point.

$$\begin{array}{r} 3\ |\ 7\cdot|\ 9\ |\ 4 \\ \hline 14\ |40\cdot|00|00 \\ 9 \\ \hline 67)\ \ 540 \\ 469 \\ \hline 749)\ 7100 \\ 6741 \\ \hline 7584)\ 35900 \end{array}$$

∴ $\sqrt{1440} = 37\cdot9$, correct to 3 figures.

Example 5. Find correct to 2 places of decimals the square root of $2\frac{17}{23}$.

To obtain the square root correct to 2 places of decimals, it is necessary to have 3 periods, *i.e.* 6 decimal places, after the decimal point:

$2\frac{17}{23} = 2\cdot739130 \ldots$

$\sqrt{2\frac{17}{23}} = 1\cdot66$, correct to 2 places.

$$\begin{array}{r} 1\cdot|\ 6\ |\ 5\ |\ 5 \\ \hline 2\cdot|73|91||30 \\ 1 \\ \hline 26)173 \\ 156 \\ \hline 325)\ 1791 \\ 1625 \\ \hline 3305)\ 16630 \\ 16525 \end{array}$$

Example 6. Find correct to 2 places of decimals the value of $\frac{1}{\sqrt{3}}$.

$\sqrt{3}$ means the number which when multiplied by itself makes 3, that is $\sqrt{3} \times \sqrt{3} = 3$;

$$\therefore \frac{1}{\sqrt{3}} \times \frac{1}{\sqrt{3}} = \frac{1}{3}; \quad \therefore \frac{1}{\sqrt{3}} \text{ is the square root of } \frac{1}{3}.$$

We therefore find the square root of $\frac{1}{3}$;
$$\frac{1}{3} = 0.3333 \ldots;$$
$$\therefore \frac{1}{\sqrt{3}} = 0.58, \text{ correct to 2 places.}$$

```
      0.| 5 | 7 | 7
      0.|33|33|33
         25
   107)  833
         749
  1147)  8433
```

Alternatively, $\frac{1}{\sqrt{3}} = \frac{1 \times \sqrt{3}}{\sqrt{3} \times \sqrt{3}} = \frac{\sqrt{3}}{3}.$

We therefore find the square root of 3; the reader should show that $\sqrt{3} = 1.732 \ldots$;

$$\text{then } \frac{1}{\sqrt{3}} \simeq \frac{1.732}{3} \simeq 0.577, \text{ as before.}$$

This process is called *rationalising the denominator*.

For example, to find the value of $\frac{\sqrt{7}}{\sqrt{11}}$

either say $\frac{\sqrt{7}}{\sqrt{11}} = \sqrt{\frac{7}{11}} = \sqrt{0.6363 \ldots}$, and work out the square root;

or say $\frac{\sqrt{7}}{\sqrt{11}} = \frac{\sqrt{7} \times \sqrt{11}}{\sqrt{11} \times \sqrt{11}} = \frac{\sqrt{77}}{11};$ then work out the square root of 77, and divide it by 11.

Do *not* work out separately $\sqrt{7}$ and $\sqrt{11}$: this would involve, besides finding *two* square roots, an awkward long division.

EXERCISE 132

Find, correct to 3 significant figures, the square roots of:

1. 2.   **2.** 20.   **3.** 10.   **[4]** 0.3.   **[5]** 7.4.   **6.** 0.74.

[7] 0.3942.   **8.** 0.03942.   **[9]** 532.1.   **[10]** 960.   **11.** 0.09477.

[12] 0.8168.   **[13]** 8627.   **14.** 0.00909.   **15.** 0.104.   **[16]** 64.05.

Find, correct to the number of decimal places indicated in brackets, the square roots of:

[17] 7.094 (2).   **[18]** 0.6085 (3).   **19.** 0.1 (3).

[20] 0.0932 (3).   **21.** 0.001656 (4).   **22.** 0.00036 (3).

[23] $4\frac{1}{4}$ (2).   **24.** $25\frac{4}{9}$ (2).   **25.** $\frac{1}{11}$ (3).

*26. $\frac{13}{17}$ (2).   ***27.** $3\frac{11}{23}$ (2).   ***28.** $\frac{7}{109}$ (3).

Express the following fractions so that their denominators do not
contain $\sqrt{\ }$ signs :—

29. $\dfrac{1}{\sqrt{2}}$. **30.** $\dfrac{6}{\sqrt{3}}$. **[31]** $\dfrac{\sqrt{5}}{\sqrt{15}}$. **32.** $\dfrac{\sqrt{18}}{\sqrt{10}}$.

Evaluate, correct to 3 significant figures :

33. $\dfrac{1}{\sqrt{5}}$. **[34]** $\dfrac{3}{\sqrt{7}}$. **[35]** $\dfrac{1}{\sqrt{1\frac{1}{2}}}$. **36.** $\dfrac{\sqrt{2}}{\sqrt{5}}$.

[37] $\dfrac{\sqrt{6}}{\sqrt{8}}$. ***38.** $\dfrac{\sqrt{1\cdot2}}{\sqrt{0\cdot5}}$. ***39.** $\dfrac{10}{\sqrt{5}}+\dfrac{6}{\sqrt{3}}$. ***40.** $\dfrac{2}{\sqrt{6}}+\dfrac{3}{\sqrt{24}}$.

Use of Tables. Approximate values of the squares and square-
roots of numbers may be found by using printed tables, the degree
of accuracy depending on the number of significant figures given
by the tables. Decimal points are usually omitted from the tables
and must be inserted by making a rough estimate of the answer.

Table of Squares. The arrangement of the tables is best explained by taking an example.

By direct multiplication, $237^2 = 237 \times 237 = 56169$.

This result can be obtained, correct to 4 figures, from 4-figure
tables. In the table of squares, look for the number 23 in the left-
hand column; the figures in the "23" row, together with the head-
ings at the top of the page, are :

MAIN COLUMNS

		0	1	2	3	4	5	6	7	8	9
23		5290	5336	5382	5429	5476	5523	5570	5617	5664	5712

There is also at the end of this row a column of "mean differences"
whose use will be explained later.

In the "23" row, under the 7 in the main columns, we find the
figures 5617; this means that *the first* 4 *significant figures* in 237^2
are 5617.

Since $200^2 = 40,000$ and $300^2 = 90,000$, the square of 237 lies
between 40,000 and 90,000,

$$\therefore\ 237^2 = 56,170 \text{ correct to } 4 \text{ figures.}$$

This statement can be checked by comparing it with the exact value
56,169 obtained by direct multiplication.

The figures obtained in working out the square of 23·7 are exactly the same as those obtained in working out the square of 237, the only difference being the position of the decimal point.

Since $20^2 = 400$ and $30^2 = 900$, the square of 23·7 lies between 400 and 900; therefore from the tables

$$23·7^2 = 561·7, \text{ correct to 4 figures.}$$

Similarly $2·37^2 = 5·617$, $0·237^2 = 0·05617$, etc., to 4 figures.

EXERCISE 133 (Oral)

Find from 4-figure tables the squares, to four figures, of:

1. 47. **2.** 4·7. **3.** 72. **4.** 720. **5.** 8·3. **6.** 290.

7. 3100. **8.** 2·3. **9.** 0·24. **10.** 660. **11.** 4·13 **12.** 72·5.

13. 619. **14.** 1·76. **15.** 2870. **16.** 31·6. **17.** 3·17. **18.** 0·346.

19. 0·895. **20.** 695. **21.** 0·327. **22.** 5040. **23.** 0·0101.

24. 0·703. **25.** 0·094. **26.** 0·0633. **27.** 70·8. **28.** 3180.

29. 897. **30.** 0·709.

Mean Difference Column. We now proceed to explain how 4-figure tables are used to find approximately the squares of numbers of *four* significant figures.

Example 7. Use tables to find approximately the value of $2·374^2$.

An extract from a table of squares showing the "23" row was given on p. 278; at the end of this row in the tables, the mean differences for that row are added:

					1	2	3	4	5	6	7	8	9
23	.	.	.	.	.	5	9	14	19	23	28	33	38	42

From the main columns, we have

$$2·37^2 = 5·617 \text{ and } 2·38^2 = 5·664.$$

$$\therefore \text{ the value of } 2·374^2 \text{ lies between } 5·617 \text{ and } 5·664.$$

Under the heading 4 in the mean differences, we find 19, which means that 19 must be added to 5617 to obtain the first 4 significant figures in $2·374^2$.

$$2·37^2 = 5·617$$
$$Diff. \text{ for } 4 \qquad 19$$
$$\therefore 2·374^2 = \overline{5·636}$$

But direct multiplication shows that $2·374^2 = 5·635876$, so that the result given by the tables is actually correct to 4 figures. In general, when mean difference columns are used, the 4th figure is not absolutely reliable, but the error will not usually be more than a unit in the fourth figure; this fact may be indicated by writing the result in the form, $2·374^2 = 5·63\,(6)$.

EXERCISE 134 (Oral)

Find to 4 significant figures, as given by 4-figure tables, the squares of:

1. 3·826.	**2.** 38·12.	**3.** 387·4.	**4.** 3868.	**5.** 6·453.
6. 0·6427.	**7.** 0·06472.	**8.** 64·84.	**9.** 9·031.	**10.** 90·76.
11. 9058.	**12.** 0·09011.	**13.** 80·04.	**14.** 5308.	**15.** 400·7.
16. 0·7047.	**17.** 1·798.	**18.** 0·1656.	**19.** 14·88.	**20.** 0·02067.
21. 3·162.	**22.** 3·163.	**23.** 0·3108.	**24.** 3187.	**25.** 0·2009.
26. 30·08.	**27.** 100·7.	**28.** 1009.	**29.** 8487.	**30.** 920·8.
31. 0·9907.	**32.** 90·01.	**33.** 4·5753.	**34.** 16·367.	**35.** 227·84.
36. 0·30523.				

Table of Square Roots. If a number is multiplied by 10 the digits in its square root are altered, but if it is multiplied by 100 the digits remain the same. For example, it can be shown that, correct to 4 figures,

$$\sqrt{692} = 26\cdot31; \quad \sqrt{6\cdot92} = 2\cdot631; \quad \sqrt{0\cdot0692} = 0\cdot2631;$$
but $$\sqrt{6920} = 83\cdot19; \quad \sqrt{69\cdot2} = 8\cdot319; \quad \sqrt{0\cdot692} = 0\cdot8319.$$

For this reason, tables of square roots are arranged on pairs of pages: on one page the reading corresponding to 692 is 2631 and on the other page it is 8319; decimal points are usually omitted. It is therefore necessary to find by inspection, or by the square root rule, the *first* significant figure of the square root and the position of the decimal point.

Example 8. Use square root tables to find to 4 figures, (i) $\sqrt{537}$; (ii) $\sqrt{53\cdot7}$.

(i) The rule shows that $\sqrt{537} = 2 * \cdot *$.

Look on the page where the square root of 537 starts with 2. $\quad \dfrac{2}{5} \bigg| \dfrac{* \cdot}{37\cdot}$

∴ $\sqrt{537} = 23\cdot1(7)$, to 4 figures.

(ii) The rule shows that $\sqrt{53\cdot7} = 7 \cdot *$.

Look on the page where the square root of 537 starts with 7. $\quad \dfrac{7\cdot}{53\cdot} \bigg| \dfrac{*}{70}$

∴ $\sqrt{53\cdot7} = 7\cdot32(8)$, to 4 figures.

The mean difference column is used in the same way for square roots as for squares.

Example 9.   Use tables to find $\sqrt{0.1138}$, to 4 figures.

Look on the page where the square root starts with 3.

0·	3	*
0·	11	38

When mean differences are used, the 4th figure is not reliable.   Here, the result is more likely to be correct to 4 figures, if 1138 is treated as $1140-2$, instead of $1130+8$.

The rule for square root gives

$$\sqrt{0.1138} = 0.33734$$

to 5 figures, so that the second result is actually correct to 4 figures.

$$\sqrt{0.113} \simeq 0.3362$$
Diff. for 8 $\qquad$ 12
$$\sqrt{0.1138} \simeq \overline{0.3374}$$

$$\sqrt{0.114} \simeq 0.3376$$
Subtract diff. for 2 $\qquad$ 3
$$\sqrt{0.1138} \simeq \overline{0.3373}$$

EXERCISE 135 (Oral)

Find to 4 significant figures, as given by 4-figure tables, the square roots of :

1. 2·6.   **2.** 26.   **3.** 268.   **4.** 0·268.   **5.** 73.   **6.** 730.

7. 7340.   **8.** 0·0734.   **9.** 616.   **10.** 59·7.   **11.** 0·923.   **12.** 0·0864.

13. 50·7.   **14.** 3040.   **15.** 0·00529.   **16.** 0·000609.   **17.** 17·43.

18. 1·743.   **19.** 356·4.   **20.** 0·3564.   **21.** 707·4.   **22.** 60·86.

23. 92050.   **24.** 0·9407.   **25.** 0·3863.   **26.** 4·007.   **27.** 5718.

28. 0·05074.   **29.** 77060.   **30.** 80·46.   **31.** 0·04297.   **32.** 0·1093.

33. 0·09176.   **34.** 57387.   **35.** 0·20738.   **36.** 815·67.

Pythagoras' Theorem.   Examine the following diagrams :

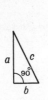 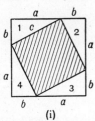 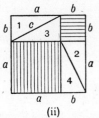

(i)   (ii)

In (i), the shaded portion of the square is a square whose side is the hypotenuse of the triangle ; and in (ii) the shaded portion is made up of two squares whose sides are the other two sides of the triangle.   Hence it follows that

The area of the square on the hypotenuse of a right-angled triangle is equal to the sum of the areas of the squares on the other two sides.

But the areas of these squares are c^2 sq. in., a^2 sq. in., b^2 sq. in.,

$$\therefore\ c^2 = a^2 + b^2.$$

Example 10. If the lengths of the sides of a rectangle are 4·7 in., 3·2 in., find to $\frac{1}{100}$ in. the length of a diagonal.

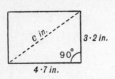

If the length of a diagonal is c in.,

$$c^2 = 4·7^2 + 3·2^2$$
$$= 22·09 + 10·24 \text{ (table of squares)}$$
$$= 32·33$$
$$\therefore c = \sqrt{32·33} = 5·686 \text{ (table of square roots)}$$

∴ the length of the diagonal is 5·69 in., to $\frac{1}{100}$ in.

Example 11. A room is 17 ft. long, 14 ft. wide, 9 ft. high. Find the distance from a corner A of the floor to the opposite corner N of the ceiling.

Suppose the diagonal AC of the floor is x ft. long and the diagonal AN of the room is y ft. long.

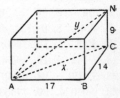

From the right-angled triangle ABC,

$$x^2 = 17^2 + 14^2 ;$$

∴ from the right-angled triangle ACN,

$$y^2 = x^2 + 9^2 ;$$

$$\therefore y^2 = 17^2 + 14^2 + 9^2 = 289 + 196 + 81 = 566 ;$$

$$\therefore y = \sqrt{566} = 23·79 \text{ (table of square roots)} ;$$

∴ AN is 23·8 ft., to 3 figures.

Notice that it is unnecessary to find the value of x.

EXERCISE 136

[Give answers correct to 3 significant figures, unless otherwise stated]

Find the length of a side of a square field of area:

1. 8000 sq. yd.   **[2]** 13750 sq. yd.   **[3]** $\frac{1}{20}$ sq. km.   **4.** 1 ac.

[5] 160 sq. ch.   **[6]** 4 ac. 3 ro.   **7.** Half a sq. mile.

In Nos. 8–11, the length of the hypotenuse of a right-angled triangle is c in., and the lengths of the other sides are a in., b in.

[8] If $a = 5·2$, $b = 7·8$, find c.   **9.** If $a = 4·73$, $b = 6·14$, find c.

10. If $b = 5·67$, $c = 8·06$, find a.   **[11]** If $a = 23·26$, $c = 37·08$, find b.

[12] The sides of a rectangle are 7·85 cm., 6·42 cm. long, find the length of a diagonal.

13. The length of a diagonal of a rectangular courtyard is 23·7 yd., and the length of one side is 18·8 yd.; find the perimeter.

14. A ladder 14 ft. 6 in. leans against a wall, and the foot of the ladder is 5 ft. 9 in. from the wall. How high up the wall does the ladder reach, to the nearest inch? If the foot of the ladder is pulled out an extra foot from the wall, how far to the nearest inch does the top slide down the wall?

*15. The equal sides AB, AC of an isosceles triangle ABC are 8·54 cm. long, and BC = 6·08 cm. Find the distance of A from BC.

16. An awning over a shop-front is 10 ft. long and the lower edge is 4 ft. below the level of the upper edge. Find the distance of the lower edge from the wall of the shop.

*17. A pendulum 5 ft. long is swinging to and fro. If the horizontal distance between the extreme positions of its tip is 1 ft. 6 in., find the height the tip rises, to the nearest $\frac{1}{10}$ in.

18. A room is 15 ft. long, 13 ft. wide, $8\frac{1}{2}$ ft. high. Find the distance from a corner of the floor to the opposite corner of the ceiling.

[19] The area of a square field is $2\frac{1}{2}$ ac. Find in yards the length of a diagonal.

20. Find the length of the diagonal of a match-box, 6 cm. by 3 cm. by 2 cm.

[21] What is the length of the longest straight thin rod, measuring a whole number of inches, that can be put into a rectangular box whose internal measurements are 6 ft. by 5 ft. by 4 ft.?

*22. The area of a rectangular field is 5 ac., and its length is 3 times its breadth; find its perimeter in yards.

*23. The lengths of the sides of a rectangle are in the ratio 2 : 3, and the length of a diagonal is 5 ft. Find perimeter in feet.

*24. A pyramid of height 7·5 in. stands on a square base of side 4 in.; find the length of a slant edge, given that the slant edges are equal.

Table of Reciprocals. Any two numbers whose product is 1 are called *reciprocals* of one another. Thus 7 and $\frac{1}{7}$, $\frac{8}{11}$ and $1\frac{1}{8}$, $2\frac{1}{3}$ and $\frac{3}{7}$, are pairs of reciprocals.

The reciprocal of 4 is $\frac{1}{4}$, that is 0·25; and the reciprocals of 40, 400, 4000, etc., are 0·025, 0·0025, 0·00025, etc.; also the reciprocals of 0·4, 0·04, etc., are 2·5, 25, etc. Thus, as a number gets larger, its reciprocal gets smaller, and as a number gets smaller, its reciprocal gets larger.

Example 12.   Find the reciprocal of 0·365 to 4 figures.

The reciprocal of 0·365 is $\dfrac{1}{0\cdot365}$;

$$\dfrac{1}{0\cdot3}\bigg|_{65} \simeq \dfrac{10}{3} \simeq 3.$$

By long division, $\dfrac{1}{0\cdot365} = 2\cdot740$, to 4 figures.

It is, however, quicker to look up the result in a table of reciprocals which is arranged on the same plan as tables of squares, etc.

In a table of reciprocals in the " 36 " row under the heading 5 in the main columns, we find the figures 2740; the position of the decimal point must be found by making a rough approximation as above,

$$\therefore \text{ from the tables, } \dfrac{1}{0\cdot365} = 2\cdot740 \text{ to 4 figures.}$$

```
                27397
        365)1000
            730
           2700
           2555
           1450
           1095
           3550
           3285
           2650
```

Example 13.   Find from tables the reciprocal of 0·3654, to 4 figures.

The reciprocal of 0·3654 is *less* than the reciprocal of 0·365, and therefore the difference given in the mean difference columns must be *subtracted*.

When mean differences are used, the 4th figure is not reliable.

Reciprocal of 0·365 $\simeq$ 2·740
Subtract diff. for 4   3
Reciprocal of 0·3654 $\simeq$ 2·737

$$\therefore \dfrac{1}{0\cdot3654} \simeq 2\cdot73(7).$$

Example 14.   Find the reciprocal of 18460 to 4 figures.

$$\dfrac{1}{1}\bigg|_{8460} \simeq \dfrac{0\cdot0001}{2}$$
$$\simeq 0\cdot000,05;$$

Number	Reciprocal
184	5435
Subtract diff. for 6	18
1846	5417

$$\therefore \dfrac{1}{18460} \simeq 0\cdot000,054,1(7).$$

EXERCISE 137 (Oral)

Find to 4 significant figures, as given by 4-figure tables, the values of:

1. $\dfrac{1}{2\cdot8}$.   2. $\dfrac{1}{28}$.   3. $\dfrac{1}{0\cdot28}$.   4. $\dfrac{1}{2800}$.   5. $\dfrac{1}{2\cdot9}$.

6. $\dfrac{1}{290}$.   7. $\dfrac{1}{77}$.   8. $\dfrac{1}{707}$.   9. $\dfrac{1}{43\cdot6}$.   10. $\dfrac{1}{0\cdot527}$.

11. $\dfrac{1}{0\cdot0816}$. **12.** $\dfrac{1}{6090}$. **13.** $\dfrac{1}{0\cdot409}$. **14.** $\dfrac{1}{10\cdot1}$. **15.** $\dfrac{1}{0\cdot106}$.

16. $\dfrac{1}{0\cdot0204}$. **17.** $\dfrac{1}{2\cdot645}$. **18.** $\dfrac{1}{2\cdot648}$. **19.** $\dfrac{1}{0\cdot4916}$. **20.** $\dfrac{1}{54\cdot73}$.

21. $\dfrac{1}{187\cdot4}$. **22.** $\dfrac{1}{1754}$. **23.** $\dfrac{1}{17570}$. **24.** $\dfrac{1}{0\cdot1354}$. **25.** $\dfrac{1}{23\cdot06}$.

26. $\dfrac{1}{0\cdot2036}$. **27.** $\dfrac{1}{20080}$. **28.** $\dfrac{1}{0\cdot02017}$. **29.** $\dfrac{1}{10\cdot63}$. **30.** $\dfrac{1}{1\cdot003}$.

31. $\dfrac{1}{0\cdot01004}$. **32.** $\dfrac{1}{0\cdot1107}$.

Miscellaneous Examples

Example 15. Find the value of $\dfrac{7}{27\cdot68}$ to 3 figures.

From tables, $\quad \dfrac{1}{27\cdot68} \simeq 0\cdot03612$;

$$\therefore \ \frac{7}{27\cdot68} \simeq 0\cdot03612 \times 7 \simeq 0\cdot2528 \simeq 0\cdot253.$$

Example 16. Evaluate to 3 figures,

$$\frac{3}{\sqrt{47\cdot15}} + \sqrt{\left\{\frac{1}{(6\cdot15)^2} - \frac{1}{(13\cdot24)^2}\right\}}.$$

From square root tables and table of reciprocals,

$$\frac{3}{\sqrt{47\cdot15}} \simeq \frac{3}{6\cdot867} = \frac{1}{2\cdot289} \simeq 0\cdot4369;$$

also $\qquad \dfrac{1}{(6\cdot15)^2} - \dfrac{1}{(13\cdot24)^2} \simeq \dfrac{1}{37\cdot82} - \dfrac{1}{175\cdot3}$

$$\simeq 0\cdot02645 - 0\cdot005704 \simeq 0\cdot02075$$

$$\therefore \ \text{expression} \simeq 0\cdot4369 + \sqrt{0\cdot02075} \simeq 0\cdot4369 + 0\cdot1441$$

$$\simeq 0\cdot581, \text{ to 3 figures.}$$

EXERCISE 138

Find, to 3 significant figures, the values of:

1. $\dfrac{3}{17\cdot87}$. **[2]** $\dfrac{11}{400\cdot8}$. **3.** $\dfrac{1}{\sqrt{16\cdot74}}$. **4.** $\sqrt{\dfrac{3}{40\cdot96}}$.

5. $\dfrac{1}{(0\cdot4071)^2}$. **[6]** $\dfrac{5}{\sqrt{0\cdot1107}}$. **7.** $\dfrac{0\cdot03}{\sqrt{0\cdot02}}$. **[8]** $\dfrac{25}{(12\cdot7)^2}$.

9. $\dfrac{1}{27\cdot38} + \dfrac{1}{19\cdot03}$. **[10]** $\dfrac{1}{2072} - \dfrac{1}{9163}$.

11. If $\dfrac{1}{u} + \dfrac{1}{v} = \dfrac{1}{f}$, find f if $u = 8\cdot63$, $v = 6\cdot07$.

[12] If $\dfrac{1}{u} - \dfrac{1}{v} = \dfrac{1}{f}$, find f if $u = 27 \cdot 4$, $v = 40 \cdot 8$.

13. If $\dfrac{1}{a^2} + \dfrac{1}{b^2} = \dfrac{1}{c^2}$, find c if $a = 3 \cdot 84$, $b = 4 \cdot 07$.

Find, to 3 significant figures, the values of :

[14] $\dfrac{1}{\sqrt{4 \cdot 93}} + \dfrac{1}{\sqrt{6 \cdot 48}}$.   15. $\dfrac{4}{(3 \cdot 817)^2} + \dfrac{5}{\sqrt{130 \cdot 4}}$.

*16. $\sqrt{(1 - \tfrac{1}{7})} + \sqrt{(1 + \tfrac{1}{8})}$.   *17. $(6 \cdot 307)^4 + (5 \cdot 213)^4$.

18. Given 1 ft. $= 0 \cdot 3048$ m., express 1 m. in feet.

[19] Given 1 kg. $= 2 \cdot 205$ lb., express $\tfrac{1}{4}$ lb. in kg.

20. Given 1 cm. $= 0 \cdot 3937$ in., express 1 sq. cm. in sq. in., and express 1 sq. in. in sq. cm.

*21. Find the smallest integer greater than 146290 which is a perfect square.

22. Find, to one significant figure, the error per cent. in taking $\sqrt{3}$ as $1\tfrac{3}{4}$.

[23] Express 100 yd. as a percentage of 1 mi., to 4 figures.

*24. The lengths of the two shorter sides of a right-angled triangle are $\sqrt{2}$ in., $\sqrt{3}$ in.; find the perimeter of the triangle, correct to $\tfrac{1}{100}$ in.

CHAPTER XIX

INDICES AND LOGARITHMS

Positive Integral Indices

If n is any positive integer, a^n is an abbreviation for

$$a \times a \times a \times \ldots, n \text{ factors.}$$

Example 1. Simplify (i) $a^3 \times a^4$;   (ii) $a^6 \div a^2$;   (iii) $(a^2)^3$.

   (i) $a^3 \times a^4 = (a \times a \times a) \times (a \times a \times a \times a) = a^7$.

   (ii) $a^6 \div a^2 = \dfrac{a \times a \times a \times a \times a \times a}{a \times a} = a \times a \times a \times a = a^4$.

   (iii) $(a^2)^3 = a^2 \times a^2 \times a^2 = (a \times a) \times (a \times a) \times (a \times a) = a^6$.

EXERCISE 139 (Oral)

Obtain from first principles the simplest forms of:

1. $a^2 \times a^3$.　　**2.** $b^5 \div b^2$.　　**3.** $(c^3)^2$.　　**4.** $d^9 \div d^3$.

Write down the simplest forms of:

5. $a^4 \times a^2$.　　　**6.** $b^6 \div b^3$.　　　**7.** $c \times c^4$.　　　**8.** $d^5 \div d$.

9. $(e^4)^2$.　　　　**10.** $f^2 \times f^6$.　　**11.** $g^5 \times g^3$.　　**12.** $(h^5)^3$.

13. $k^8 \div k^4$.　　　**14.** $(l^2)^4$.　　　**15.** $m^8 \div m^2$.　　**16.** $n^5 \times n^5$.

What general formulæ include the following special cases?

17. $a^3 \times a^4 = a^7$; $a^2 \times a^6 = a^8$; $a^4 \times a^7 = a^{11}$.

18. $a^6 \div a^2 = a^4$; $a^8 \div a^3 = a^5$; $a^{10} \div a^4 = a^6$.

19. $(a^2)^3 = a^6$; $(a^5)^2 = a^{10}$; $(a^3)^4 = a^{12}$.

20. What is the square of x^6?

21. By what must y^4 be multiplied to give y^{12}?

22. By what must z^{10} be divided to give z^2?

The examples in Exercise 139 illustrate the following facts: If m and n are positive integers,

$$a^m \times a^n = a^{m+n}; \quad a^m \div a^n = a^{m-n}, \ m \text{ greater than } n; \quad (a^m)^n = a^{mn}.$$

If m is not a positive integer, the symbol a^m has not yet been defined in this book; for example, no meaning has yet been given here to such symbols as $9^{\frac{1}{2}}$, 5^{-2}, 6^0. We shall now find out what meaning must be given to such symbols if the law, $a^m \times a^n = a^{m+n}$, remains true for *all* values of m and n.

Example 2.　What meaning must be given to $9^{\frac{1}{2}}$?

$$9^{\frac{1}{2}} \times 9^{\frac{1}{2}} = 9^{\frac{1}{2}+\frac{1}{2}} = 9^1 = 9;$$

∴ $9^{\frac{1}{2}}$ is the number which when multiplied by itself gives 9;

$$\therefore \ 9^{\frac{1}{2}} = \sqrt{9} = 3.$$

Example 3.　What meaning must be given to $8^{\frac{1}{3}}$?

$$8^{\frac{1}{3}} \times 8^{\frac{1}{3}} \times 8^{\frac{1}{3}} = 8^{\frac{1}{3}+\frac{1}{3}+\frac{1}{3}} = 8^1 = 8.$$

∴ $8^{\frac{1}{3}}$ is the cube root of 8;　∴ $8^{\frac{1}{3}} = \sqrt[3]{8} = 2$.

Example 4. What is the meaning of $a^{\frac{3}{4}}$?

$$a^{\frac{3}{4}} \times a^{\frac{3}{4}} \times a^{\frac{3}{4}} \times a^{\frac{3}{4}} = a^{\frac{3}{4}+\frac{3}{4}+\frac{3}{4}+\frac{3}{4}} = a^3;$$

$\therefore$ $a^{\frac{3}{4}}$ is the fourth root of a^3; $\therefore$ $a^{\frac{3}{4}} = \sqrt[4]{(a^3)}$.

But since $a^{\frac{3}{4}} = a^{\frac{1}{4}} \times a^{\frac{1}{4}} \times a^{\frac{1}{4}}$ and since $a^{\frac{1}{4}} = \sqrt[4]{a}$, it follows that $a^{\frac{3}{4}} = (\sqrt[4]{a})^3$; thus $\sqrt[4]{(a^3)} = (\sqrt[4]{a})^3$.

For example, $16^{\frac{3}{4}} = \sqrt[4]{(16^3)} = \sqrt[4]{(16 \times 16 \times 16)}$
$= \sqrt[4]{(8 \times 2 \times 8 \times 2 \times 8 \times 2)} = \sqrt[4]{(8 \times 8 \times 8 \times 8)} = 8;$

but it is simpler to say, $16^{\frac{1}{4}} = \sqrt[4]{16} = 2;$

$$\therefore 16^{\frac{3}{4}} = (\sqrt[4]{16})^3 = 2^3 = 8,$$

that is, take the root first, if the result is exact.

Example 5. What meaning must be given to 10^{-2}?

$$10^3 \times 10^{-2} = 10^{3-2} = 10^1 = 10;$$

but $10^3 \times \dfrac{1}{10^2} = 10$, $\therefore$ $10^{-2} = \dfrac{1}{10^2}$

Example 6. What is the meaning of a^{-5}, where a is not zero?

$$a^6 \times a^{-5} = a^{6-5} = a^1 = a;$$

but $a^6 \times \dfrac{1}{a^5} = a$, $\therefore$ $a^{-5} = \dfrac{1}{a^5}.$

Example 7. What meaning must be given to 6^0?

$$6^3 \times 6^0 = 6^{3+0} = 6^3; \quad \therefore 6^0 = \frac{6^3}{6^3} = 1.$$

Similarly $10^0 = 1$, and more generally $a^0 = 1$, if a is not zero.

Example 8. Find the value of (i) $(\frac{3}{4})^{-2}$; (ii) $9^{-1\cdot5}$.

(i) The method of Example 5 shows that
$$(\tfrac{3}{4})^{-2} = 1 \div (\tfrac{3}{4})^2 = 1 \div \tfrac{9}{16} = \tfrac{16}{9}.$$

(ii) Similarly $9^{-1\cdot5} = 1 \div 9^{1\cdot5};$
but $9^{1\cdot5} = 9^1 \times 9^{0\cdot5} = 9 \times 9^{\frac{1}{2}} = 9 \times \sqrt{9} = 9 \times 3 = 27;$
$$\therefore 9^{-1\cdot5} = \tfrac{1}{27}.$$

EXERCISE 140 (Oral)

1. Write down, as powers of x, the squares of x^4, x^5, and the square roots of x^8, x^{10}, x^9.

2. What is x^n if

(i) $x^n \times x^n = x^6$;   (ii) $x^n \times x^n = x^5$;   (iii) $x^n \times x^n = x$?

3. What is x^n if

(i) $x^n \times x^n \times x^n = x^6$;   (ii) $x^n \times x^n \times x^n = x^2$;

(iii) $x^n \times x^n \times x^n = x$;   (iv) $(x^n)^3 = x^5$?

4. Write down, as powers of a, the cube roots of a^{12}, a^4, a.

5. Simplify $b^{\frac{2}{3}} \times b^{\frac{2}{3}} \times b^{\frac{2}{3}}$.   What is the meaning of $x^{\frac{2}{3}}$?

6. Simplify $(b^{\frac{4}{3}})^3$.   What is the meaning of $x^{\frac{4}{3}}$?

Show how to find the meanings of:

7. $a^{\frac{1}{4}}$.   **8.** $b^{\frac{5}{6}}$.   **9.** $c^{\frac{3}{2}}$.   **10.** $d^{1\frac{2}{3}}$.

Write down the numerical values of:

11. $16^{\frac{1}{2}}$.   **12.** $27^{\frac{1}{3}}$.   **13.** $8^{\frac{2}{3}}$.   **14.** $9^{1\frac{1}{2}}$.   **15.** $81^{\frac{1}{4}}$.

16. $16^{1\frac{1}{4}}$.   **17.** $32^{\frac{3}{5}}$.   **18.** $81^{\frac{3}{4}}$.

19. What is x^n if

(i) $x^5 \times x^n = x^8$;   (ii) $x^5 \times x^n = x^6$;   (iii) $x^5 \times x^n = x^5$;

(iv) $x^5 \times x^n = x^3$;   (v) $x^5 \times x^n = x$;   (vi) $x^5 \times x^n = 1$?

20. Write down as powers of x, that is in the form x^n, and also simplify in the ordinary way:

(i) $\dfrac{x^3}{x^5}$;   (ii) $\dfrac{x^2}{x^6}$;   (iii) $\dfrac{x}{x^6}$;   (iv) $\dfrac{x^3}{x^3}$.

21. Simplify $a^5 \times a^{-3}$; what is the meaning of a^{-3}?

22. Simplify $b^4 \times b^{-1}$; what is the meaning of b^{-1}?

23. Simplify $c^2 \times c^0$; what is the meaning of c^0?

Write down the numerical values of:

24. 3^{-2}.   **25.** 4^{-1}.   **26.** 5^0.   **27.** 2^{-3}.   **28.** $9^{-\frac{1}{2}}$.   **29.** $16^{-\frac{1}{2}}$.

30. $8^{-\frac{1}{3}}$.   **31.** $27^{-\frac{1}{3}}$.   **32.** $8^{-\frac{2}{3}}$.   **33.** $(\frac{1}{5})^{-2}$.   **34.** $(\frac{1}{2})^{-1}$.   **35.** $(\frac{1}{4})^0$.

Express with root signs:

36. $10^{\frac{1}{2}}$.   **37.** $10^{\frac{1}{4}}$.   **38.** $10^{0.5}$.   **39.** $10^{0.75}$.   **40.** $10^{1.5}$.

41. $10^{1.75}$.   **42.** $10^{-\frac{1}{2}}$.   **43.** $10^{-\frac{1}{3}}$.

Write down the numerical values of:

44. $100^{1 \cdot 5}$.   **45.** $100^{-0 \cdot 5}$.   **46.** $32^{0 \cdot 2}$.   **47.** $32^{0 \cdot 8}$.

48. $(0 \cdot 2)^{-1}$.   **49.** $(0 \cdot 1)^{-2}$.   **50.** $(0 \cdot 027)^{\frac{1}{3}}$.   **51.** $(0 \cdot 027)^{-\frac{2}{3}}$.

The methods used in Examples 2–7, p. 287, may be used to establish the following results :—

   (i) If p, q are any positive integers,

$$a^{\frac{1}{q}} = \sqrt[q]{a}; \quad a^{\frac{p}{q}} = \sqrt[q]{(a^p)} = \sqrt[q]{(a)^p}.$$

   (ii) If n is any number, and a is not zero, $a^{-n} = \dfrac{1}{a^n}$.

   (iii) If a is not zero, $a^0 = 1$.

Powers of 10. Since $10^{\frac{1}{2}} = \sqrt{10}$, the value of $10^{\frac{1}{2}}$ can be calculated to as many decimal places as desired by using the square-root process.

$$\text{Thus } 10^{\frac{1}{2}} = \sqrt{10} = 3 \cdot 162 \ldots;$$
$$\text{similarly } 10^{\frac{1}{4}} = \sqrt{10^{\frac{1}{2}}} = \sqrt{3 \cdot 162} \ldots = 1 \cdot 779 \ldots$$
$$\text{and } 10^{\frac{1}{8}} = \sqrt{10^{\frac{1}{4}}} = \sqrt{1 \cdot 779} \ldots = 1 \cdot 333 \ldots$$
$$\text{Also } 10^{\frac{3}{4}} = \sqrt[4]{10^3} = \sqrt[4]{1000} = \sqrt{31 \cdot 62} \ldots = 5 \cdot 623 \ldots,$$

and in a similar way we can find approximate values $10^{\frac{3}{8}}$, of $10^{\frac{5}{8}}$, $10^{\frac{7}{8}}$; also $10^0 = 1$.

We therefore have the following table of values which can be used to draw the graph of 10^x:—

x	0	0·125	0·25	0·375	0·5	0·625	0·75	0·875	1
10^x	1	1·33	1·78	2·37	3·16	4·22	5·62	7·50	10

EXERCISE 141 (Oral)

[*Use the printed graph of 10^x for the following examples*]

Write down the values of:

   1. $10^{0 \cdot 2}$.   **2.** $10^{0 \cdot 7}$.   **3.** $10^{0 \cdot 42}$.   **4.** $10^{0 \cdot 84}$.

Express as powers of 10:

   5. 2.   **6.** 3.   **7.** 6.   **8.** 7·8.   **9.** 1·5.

   10. Find the values of a, b, c, N in the following argument :—

$$2 \cdot 8 = 10^a; \quad 3 \cdot 2 = 10^b;$$
$$\therefore \ 2 \cdot 8 \times 3 \cdot 2 = 10^a \times 10^b = 10^{a+b} = 10^c = N.$$

Check the result by ordinary multiplication.

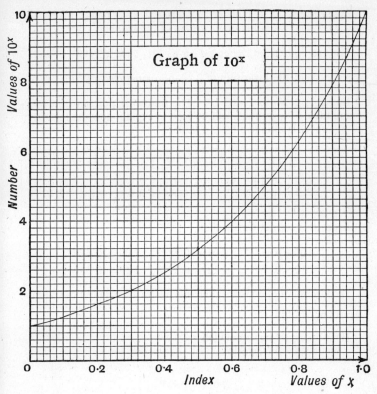

Graph of 10^x

11. Use the method of No. 10 to find approximately:

(i) $4·6 \times 1·6$; (ii) $2·7^2$.

12. Find the values of a, b, c, N in the following argument:—

$$8·5 = 10^a; \quad 3·8 = 10^b;$$

$$\therefore \ 8·5 \div 3·8 = 10^a \div 10^b = 10^{a-b} = 10^c = N.$$

Check the result by ordinary division.

13. Use the method of No. 12 to find approximately:

(i) $7·4 \div 2·9$; (ii) $8·2 \div 6·6$.

Find the values of a, b, N in the following arguments:—

14. $8 = 10^a$; $\therefore \ \sqrt{8} = 10^b = N$. 15. $6 = 10^a$; $\therefore \ \sqrt{6} = 10^b = N$.

16. $9 = 10^a$; $\therefore \ \sqrt[3]{9} = 10^b = N$.

Logarithms. If a number is expressed as a power of 10, the *index* is called the common *logarithm* of the number.

For example, from the graph on p. 291, $2 \backsimeq 10^{0\cdot30}$:

∴ the logarithm of 2 is approximately 0·30.

Numbers between 1 and 10. The following portion of a four-figure table of logarithms will be used to explain how the logarithm of a number is obtained from a table :—

	0	1	2	. . .	9	1 2 3	. . .	7 8 9
2·0	·3010	·3032	·3054	. . .	·3201	2 4 6	. . .	15 17 19
2·1	·3222	·3243	·3263		·3404	2 4 6	. . .	14 16 18

From this extract we see that

$$2{\cdot}00 = 10^{\cdot3010}, \quad 2{\cdot}01 = 10^{\cdot3032}, \quad 2{\cdot}09 = 10^{\cdot3201},$$
$$2{\cdot}10 = 10^{\cdot3222}, \quad 2{\cdot}12 = 10^{\cdot3263}, \quad 2{\cdot}19 = 10^{\cdot3404}.$$

The logarithms of numbers given to 4 figures are obtained by using the column of mean differences in the ordinary way : for example, to find the logarithm of 2·013,

	Number	Logarithm
The working set out here in full	2·01	·3032
should be done mentally.	*Diff.* for 3	6
	2·013	·3038

$$2{\cdot}013 = 10^{\cdot3038}.$$

To save space, the decimal points in the left-hand column and in the main columns are usually omitted in printed tables and must be supplied by the reader. The extract given above is usually printed in the form :

	0	1	2	. . .	9	1 2 3	. . .	7 8 9
20	·3010	3032	3054	. . .	3201	2 4 6	. . .	15 17 19
21	·3222	3243	3263	. . .	3404	2 4 6	. . .	14 16 18

Since $1 = 10^0$ and $10 = 10^1$, the logarithm of any number between 1 and 10 lies between 0 and 1, and is therefore of the form 0·****, and the figures printed in the four-figure columns are the figures of the logarithm which follow the decimal point, though the decimal point is usually not printed.

EXERCISE 142 (Oral)

Use tables to express as powers of 10 :

1. 3·2.	**2.** 6·4.	**3.** 9·6.	**4.** 3.	**5.** 9.
6. 2·5.	**7.** 5.	**8.** 4·1.	**9.** 8·2.	**10.** 7·7.
11. 4·26.	**12.** 6·95.	**13.** 3·04.	**14.** 5·60.	**15.** 1·11.
16. 1·07.	**17.** 1·20.	**18.** 9·06.	**19.** 4·44.	**20.** 6·03.
21. 2·563.	**22.** 2·568.	**23.** 7·451.	**24.** 7·468.	**25.** 4·645.
26. 4·657.	**27.** 4·678.	**28.** 4·606.	**29.** 6·347.	**30.** 6·358.
31. 8·876.	**32.** 9·708.	**33.** 7·067.	**34.** 7·004.	**35.** 5·081.
36. 5·005.	**37.** 3·050.	**38.** 3·005.	**39.** 1·086.	**40.** 1·074.
41. 1·003.	**42.** 1·048.	**43.** 1·006.	**44.** 1·995.	

The same tables may be used by reversing the process to find the value of any given power of 10.

Example 9. Find the value of

$$\text{(i) } 10^{.7076}; \quad \text{(ii) } 10^{.7143}; \quad \text{(iii) } 10^{.7148}.$$

(i) Look for the figures 7076 in the four-figure columns; these occur in the "51" row in the column headed 0; therefore the significant figures in the value of $10^{.7076}$ are 510; but the value of $10^{.7076}$ lies between 10^0 and 10^1, that is between 1 and 10;

$$\therefore \ 10^{.7076} = 5·100, \text{ to 4 figures.}$$

(ii) The figures 7143 occur in the "51" row in the column headed 8,
$$\therefore \ 10^{.7143} = 5·180, \text{ to 4 figures.}$$

(iii) The actual figures 7148 do not occur in the four-figure columns;

$$10^{.7143} = 5·180 \quad \text{and} \quad 10^{.7152} = 5·190,$$

$$\therefore \text{ the value of } 10^{.7148} \text{ lies between 5·180 and 5·190.}$$

The difference between 7143 and 7148 is 5, and in the column of mean differences for this row 5 occurs under the column headed 6,

$$\therefore \ 10^{.7148} = 5·186, \text{ to 4 figures.}$$

Note. Whenever mean differences are used in 4-figure tables, the 4th figure is not reliable ; *this may be indicated by enclosing the 4th figure in brackets.*

Example 10. Find the value of

$$\text{(i) } 10^{\cdot0135}; \quad \text{(ii) } 10^{\cdot9543}.$$

(i) The figures less than 0135 which are nearest to it and occur in the four-figure columns are 0128.

$$10^{\cdot0128} = 1\cdot030 \text{ to 4 figures.}$$

The difference between 0128 and 0135 is 7; but 7 does not occur in the column of mean differences for this row, we therefore take the nearest difference, namely 8, which is in the column headed 2.

$$\therefore \ 10^{\cdot0135} = 1\cdot03(2) \text{ to 4 figures.}$$

(ii) From the tables, $10^{\cdot9542} = 9\cdot000$, to 4 figures.

For this row, the difference 1 occurs in two columns, namely, those headed 2 and 3; we cannot therefore tell whether it is better to take the value as $9\cdot002$ or as $9\cdot003$; the result may be written

$$10^{\cdot9543} = 9\cdot00(2).$$

EXERCISE 143 (Oral)

Use logarithm tables to find the values of :

1. $10^{\cdot6232}$.	**2.** $10^{\cdot7709}$.	**3.** $10^{\cdot7782}$.	**4.** $10^{\cdot5428}$.
5. $10^{\cdot5514}$.	**6.** $10^{\cdot7059}$.	**7.** $10^{\cdot9106}$.	**8.** $10^{\cdot9713}$.
9. $10^{\cdot7016}$.	**10.** $10^{\cdot574}$.	**11.** $10^{\cdot781}$.	**12.** $10^{\cdot9042}$.
13. $10^{\cdot4019}$.	**14.** $10^{\cdot5258}$.	**15.** $10^{\cdot7581}$.	**16.** $10^{\cdot8642}$.

Use logarithm tables to find the numbers whose logarithms are :

17. $\cdot4835$.	**18.** $\cdot7040$.	**19.** $\cdot7801$.	**20.** $\cdot9052$.	**21.** $\cdot5255$.
22. $\cdot6603$.	**23.** $\cdot2753$.	**24.** $\cdot1992$.	**25.** $\cdot2011$.	**26.** $\cdot6105$.
27. $\cdot7138$.	**28.** $\cdot7621$.	**29.** $\cdot8455$.	**30.** $\cdot9034$.	**31.** $\cdot9701$.
32. $\cdot0298$.	**33.** $\cdot0314$.	**34.** $\cdot0025$.	**35.** $\cdot003$.	**36.** $\cdot9546$.

Multiplication and Division

Example 11. Find the value of $3\cdot18 \times 2\cdot17$.

Rough Estimate : $3 \times 2 = 6$.

$$3\cdot18 \times 2\cdot17 = 10^{\cdot5024} \times 10^{\cdot3365} = 10^{\cdot5024 + \cdot3365}$$
$$= 10^{\cdot8389} = 6\cdot90(1) \text{ or } 6\cdot90(2)$$

$$\begin{array}{r} \cdot5024 \\ \cdot3365 \\ \hline \cdot8389 \end{array}$$

Example 12.   Find the value of $8 \cdot 37 \div 5 \cdot 09$.

Rough Estimate : $8 \div 5 = 1 \cdot 6$.

$$8 \cdot 37 \div 5 \cdot 09 = 10^{\cdot 9227} \div 10^{\cdot 7067} = 10^{\cdot 9227 - \cdot 7067}$$

$$= 10^{\cdot 2160} = 1 \cdot 64(4) \text{ or } 1 \cdot 64(5).$$

$$\begin{array}{r} \cdot 9227 \\ \cdot 7067 \\ \hline \cdot 2160 \end{array}$$

Note. To obtain the 4th figure accurately, it is necessary to use 5-figure tables; the error in the 4th figure obtained from 4-figure tables will usually be small. But in the exercises that follow, the reader is asked to give the answer to *four* figures, "as given by 4-figure tables," in order to make it easier to check the accuracy of his use of the tables. **The fourth figure should be enclosed in brackets to show its approximate character.**

EXERCISE 144

Find the value to 4 figures, as given by 4-figure tables, of :

1. $2 \cdot 36 \times 3 \cdot 24$.	**[2]** $2 \cdot 73 \times 3 \cdot 18$.	**3.** $4 \cdot 19 \times 1 \cdot 84$.
4. $3 \cdot 624 \times 2 \cdot 315$.	**5.** $5 \cdot 278 \times 1 \cdot 406$.	**[6]** $2 \cdot 073 \times 4 \cdot 108$.
7. $2 \cdot 086 \times 4 \cdot 104$.	**[8]** $7 \cdot 263 \times 1 \cdot 173$.	**9.** $3 \cdot 708 \times 2 \cdot 046$.
10. $8 \cdot 67 \div 3 \cdot 29$.	**[11]** $7 \cdot 49 \div 4 \cdot 08$.	**12.** $9 \cdot 07 \div 2 \cdot 61$.
13. $7 \cdot 408 \div 2 \cdot 165$.	**[14]** $9 \cdot 032 \div 4 \cdot 705$.	**15.** $8 \cdot 007 \div 6 \cdot 503$.
16. $9 \cdot 804 \div 5 \cdot 073$.	**17.** $7 \cdot 006 \div 1 \cdot 088$.	**18.** $6 \cdot 704 \div 5 \cdot 908$.
*19. $1 \cdot 78 \times 2 \cdot 04 \times 2 \cdot 56$.	***20.** $7 \cdot 03 \times 6 \cdot 74 \div 8 \cdot 26$.	

Numbers greater than 10

Number		expressed as power of 10
$7 \cdot 243$		$10^{\cdot 8599}$
$72 \cdot 43$	$= 7 \cdot 243 \times 10^1$	$10^{\cdot 8599} \times 10^1 = 10^{1 \cdot 8599}$
$724 \cdot 3$	$= 7 \cdot 243 \times 10^2$	$10^{\cdot 8599} \times 10^2 = 10^{2 \cdot 8599}$
7243	$= 7 \cdot 243 \times 10^3$	$10^{\cdot 8599} \times 10^3 = 10^{3 \cdot 8599}$
72430	$= 7 \cdot 243 \times 10^4$	$10^{\cdot 8599} \times 10^4 = 10^{4 \cdot 8599}$

Thus, so long as the order of the digits of a number is unaltered, the decimal portion of the logarithm, called its **mantissa,** *remains the same.*

The integral portion of the logarithm, called its **CHARACTERISTIC, is** obtained by counting the number of digits between the decimal point and where it would be in the standard form.

For example, for 7|24·3, two digits, the characteristic is 2 ;
              for 7|2430, four digits, the characteristic is 4.

Example 13. Express 72428 as a power of 10.

$$72428 \simeq 72430, \text{ to 4 figures,}$$
$$\simeq 10^{4 \cdot 8599}$$

Example 14. Find the value of $10^{5 \cdot 5748}$.

From the tables, $10^{\cdot 5748} = 3 \cdot 757$,

Move the figures 5 places to the left, $\therefore 10^{5 \cdot 5748} = 375700$.

The 4th figure in 375700, here printed in italics, may be underlined, when written, to show that it is only approximate.

EXERCISE 145 (Oral)

Read off the characteristics of the logarithms of the numbers :

1. 72.　　**2.** 694.　　**3.** 8850.　　**4.** 11·17.　　**5.** 7·916.

6. 15720.　　**7.** 823000.　　**8.** 61944·72.　　**9.** 12,000,000.

State the number of digits to the left of the decimal point in the numbers whose logarithms are :

10. 1·8627.　**11.** 3·0145.　**12.** 2·6158.　**13.** 4·2717.　**14.** 3·162.

15. 5·7018.　**16.** 0·9824.　**17.** 0·0104.　**18.** 3·85.　　**19.** 4·2.

EXERCISE 146 (Oral)

Use tables to write down to 4 figures the logarithms of :

1. 26.　　**2.** 380.　　**3.** 62·4.　　**4.** 7480.　　**5.** 41·72.

6. 3212.　　**7.** 814·7.　　**8.** 10·04.　　**9.** 200·3.　**10.** 53,700.

11. 428,300.　　**12.** 2,007,000.　　**13.** 1000.　　**14.** 100,000.

15. 10^7.　　**16.** 1.　　　　**17.** 63,748.　　**18.** 371·62.

19. 800,735.　　**20.** $5 \cdot 163 \times 10^8$.

Use tables to write down to 4 figures the numbers whose logarithms are :

21. 1·5843.　**22.** 2·7275.　**23.** 3·8865.　**24.** 2·4771.　**25.** 4·9304.

26. 5·9562.　**27.** 7·847.　　**28.** 6·932.　**29.** 2·5256.　**30.** 1·6687.

31. 3·4777.　**32.** 1·3018.　**33.** 4·6029.　**34.** 2·0025.　**35.** 5·702.

36. 3·787.　　**37.** 2·0000.　**38.** 5·0000.　**39.** 1·1.　　**40.** 4·4.

Example 15.   Find the value of $816\cdot3 \times 37\cdot42$.

Rough Estimate: $800 \times 40 = 32000$.

$$816\cdot3 \times 37\cdot42 = 10^{2\cdot9119} \times 10^{1\cdot5731}$$
$$= 10^{4\cdot4850} = 30550.$$

$$\begin{array}{r} 2\cdot9119 \\ 1\cdot5731 \\ \hline 4\cdot4850 \end{array}$$

Example 16.   Find the value of $816\cdot3 \div 37\cdot42$.

Rough Estimate: $800 \div 40 = 20$.

$$816\cdot3 \div 37\cdot42 = 10^{2\cdot9119} \div 10^{1\cdot5731}$$
$$= 10^{1\cdot3388} = 21\cdot8(2).$$

$$\begin{array}{r} 2\cdot9119 \\ 1\cdot5731 \\ \hline 1\cdot3388 \end{array}$$

Example 17.   Find the value of $(37\cdot06)^4$.

Rough Estimate: $40^4 = 2,560,000$.

$$(37\cdot06)^4 = (10^{1\cdot5689})^4 = 10^{1\cdot5689\times4}$$
$$= 10^{6\cdot2756} = 1,886,000.$$

$$\begin{array}{r} 1\cdot5689 \\ 4 \\ \hline 6\cdot2756 \end{array}$$

Example 18.   Find the value of $\sqrt[3]{561\cdot4}$.

$$\sqrt[3]{561\cdot4} = (10^{2\cdot7493})^{\frac{1}{3}} = 10^{2\cdot7493\times\frac{1}{3}}$$
$$= 10^{\cdot9164} = 8\cdot24(9).$$

$$\begin{array}{r} 3\underline{\smash{|2\cdot7493}} \\ \cdot9164 \end{array}$$

Rough Check: $8^3 = 512$; $9^3 = 729$.

We shall now repeat Example 15, to show how the work may be arranged, after the principles have been grasped; for other examples of this method of arrangement, see pp. 298, 304.

Example 19.   Find the value of $816\cdot3 \times 37\cdot42$.

Rough Estimate: $800 \times 40 = 32,000$.

$\therefore \ 816\cdot3 \times 37\cdot42 = 3\cdot055 \times 10^4$
$ = 30550.$

Number	Logarithm
816·3	2·9119
37·42	1·5731
Product	4·4850

Logarithmic Notation.   The fact that the logarithm of 2 is $\cdot3010$ is often written in the form, $\log 2 = \cdot3010$; and in general if $x = 10^p$, that is, if p is the logarithm of x, then $\log x = p$.

Examples 15–19 illustrate the following general properties:—

$$\log(xy) = \log x + \log y; \quad \log\left(\frac{x}{y}\right) = \log x - \log y; \quad \log(x^n) = n \log x.$$

EXERCISE 147

Find the value to 4 figures, as given by 4-figure tables, of:

1. $53 \cdot 2 \times 67 \cdot 4$.   **[2]** $724 \times 15 \cdot 3$.   **3.** $6070 \times 1 \cdot 08$.

[4] $84 \cdot 3 \div 9 \cdot 15$.   **5.** $387 \div 71 \cdot 6$.   **6.** $4130 \div 8 \cdot 62$.

[7] $268 \cdot 3 \times 37 \cdot 4$.   **[8]** $409 \cdot 3 \times 64 \cdot 9$.   **9.** $20 \cdot 72 \times 18 \cdot 37$.

[10] $627 \cdot 4 \div 8 \cdot 36$.   **11.** $5070 \div 21 \cdot 68$.   **[12]** $61320 \div 483 \cdot 4$.

13. $36828 \times 4 \cdot 073$.   **14.** $50 \div 3 \cdot 0643$.   **[15]** 4527×3406.

16. $1000 \div 28 \cdot 447$.   **17.** $10 \cdot 73 \times 2004$.   **[18]** $73600 \div 909$.

19. $(21 \cdot 76)^2$.   **[20]** $(7 \cdot 294)^3$.   **21.** $(10 \cdot 71)^4$.

22. (i) $\sqrt{7 \cdot 34}$; (ii) $\sqrt{73 \cdot 4}$.   **23.** (i) $\sqrt[3]{618}$; (ii) $\sqrt[3]{61 \cdot 8}$; (iii) $\sqrt[3]{6 \cdot 18}$.

[24] $\sqrt{453 \cdot 6}$.   **[25]** $\sqrt[3]{507 \cdot 3}$.   **[26]** $\sqrt[4]{8672}$.   **[27]** $\sqrt[3]{10 \cdot 43}$.

28. $\sqrt[4]{200 \cdot 7}$.   **[29]** $\sqrt[5]{40 \cdot 78}$.   **30.** $\sqrt[3]{100}$.   **[31]** $\sqrt[4]{1000}$.

If the expression is complicated, the working may be arranged in the more concise form illustrated by the following examples:—

Example 20. Find the value of $\dfrac{65130 \times 37 \cdot 14}{793 \cdot 2 \times 4 \cdot 186}$.

Rough Estimate: $\dfrac{60,000 \times 40}{800 \times 4} = \dfrac{600,000}{800} \simeq 700$.

Number	Logarithm		Number	Logarithm
65130	4·8138		793·2	2·8994
37·14	1·5699		4·186	·6218
Numerator	6·3837		Denominator	3·5212
Denominator	3·5212			
Expression	2·8625			

$\therefore$ expression $= 7 \cdot 286 \times 10^2 = 728 \cdot (6)$.

Example 21. Find the value of $\dfrac{(35 \cdot 41)^3 \times 4 \cdot 783}{34 \cdot 65 \times \sqrt{41 \cdot 8}}$.

Number	Logarithm	
$(35 \cdot 41)^3$	$1 \cdot 5491 \times 3$	4·6473
4·783		·6797
Numerator		5·3270
34·65		1·5397
$\sqrt{41 \cdot 8}$	$1 \cdot 6212 \times \frac{1}{2}$	·8106
Denominator		2·3503
Expression		2·9767

Rough Estimate:

$\dfrac{30^3 \times 5}{30 \times 6} \simeq 30^2 = 900$.

5·3270
2·3503
2·9767

$\therefore$ expression $= 9 \cdot 478 \times 10^2$

$= 947 \cdot (8)$.

EXERCISE 148

Find the value to 4 figures, as given by 4-figure tables, of :

1. $4·62 \times 20·7 \times 35·8$.   **[2]** $83·6 \times 1·07 \times 155$.

[3] $1732 \times 8·04 \times 23·69$.   **4.** $80·72 \times 11·01 \times 3·141$.

5. $\dfrac{31·73 \times 6·482}{7·918}$.   **[6]** $\dfrac{520·4 \times 8·065}{97·53}$.   **7.** $\dfrac{7324}{16·42 \times 39·81}$.

[8] $\dfrac{800·6}{7·152 \times 9·038}$.   **9.** $\dfrac{4·045 \times 1760}{49·13 \times 50·5}$.   **[10]** $\dfrac{76·03 \times 908}{101·2 \times 6·317}$.

11. $\dfrac{(19·42)^2}{8·73 \times 6·04}$.   **[12]** $\dfrac{7073 \times 8500}{(362·5)^2}$.   **13.** $\dfrac{(161·3)^3 \times 4·03}{(285·1)^2 \times 30}$.

14. $\dfrac{(27·3)^2 \times (4·17)^3}{(11·01)^3}$.   **[15]** $\left(\dfrac{17·46 \times 10·8}{13·47}\right)^2$.   **[16]** $\left(\dfrac{7134}{85·07 \times 26·92}\right)^3$.

17. $\sqrt{\dfrac{793·4}{86·13}}$.   **[18]** $\sqrt[3]{\dfrac{8·427}{5·913}}$.   **19.** $\dfrac{\sqrt{874·2}}{\sqrt[3]{75·13}}$.   **[20]** $\dfrac{\sqrt{635·4}}{11·6 \times 1·07}$

21. $\dfrac{39·6 \times 4005}{\sqrt[3]{83470}}$.   ***22.** $\dfrac{31·72 \times \sqrt{84·26}}{(5·73)^2 \times 2·645}$.   **23.** $\dfrac{18·07 \times \sqrt[3]{364·2}}{3·006 \times \sqrt{240·5}}$

[24] $1\frac{1}{8} \times 3·142 \times (4·102)^3$.   **25.** $2 \times \sqrt[3]{100} \div \sqrt[4]{1000}$.

*26. $\sqrt{\left(\dfrac{90·13 \times 7·518}{4·126 \times 11·02}\right)}$.   ***27.** $\dfrac{\sqrt{42·17} \times \sqrt[3]{121·4}}{3·061 \times \sqrt[4]{90·9}}$.

*28. $\dfrac{16·34 \times 107·4 \times \sqrt{919·5}}{46·03 \times 3·108 \times (1·807)^2}$.   ***29.** $\dfrac{(8·17)^2}{10·3} + \dfrac{(2·617)^2}{1·059}$.

EXERCISE 149

[*Take* $\log \pi = 0·4971$.   *Give answers to* 3 *significant figures*]

1. Find in acres the area of a rectangular field, 215 yd. long, 164 yd. wide.

2. Find the volume of a rectangular block 17·3 cm. long, 12·8 cm. wide, 10·4 cm. high.

[3] Given 1 m. = 39·37 in., express 1 ch. in metres.

4. The population of England and Wales in 1921 was 37,885,000 and the number of houses was 7,811,000; what was the average number living in every 100 houses?

[5] How many times is Mont Blanc (15,781 ft.) as high as Snowdon (3571 ft.)?

[6] Given 1 kg. $=2 \cdot 205$ lb., express 50 lb. in kg.

7. The world production of tea in 1930 was 813,500 tons, of which 287,500 tons came from India and Ceylon. What percentage was this?

[8] If 1 c.c. of lead weighs $11 \cdot 4$ gm., find the weight of a cuboid of lead, $7 \cdot 45$ cm. by $5 \cdot 08$ cm. by $3 \cdot 16$ cm.

9. If a cuboid of iron $6 \cdot 13$ cm. by $4 \cdot 95$ cm. by $2 \cdot 05$ cm. weighs 462 gm., find the weight of 1 c.c. of iron.

*10. In Egyptian measures, 1 Fedden $=24$ qirats, and 1 qirat $=209 \cdot 3$ sq. yd.; express 1 Fedden in acres.

[11] Entertainment tax yielded £6,952,088 in 1931 and £7,868,908 in 1932. Find the increase per cent.

12. The Trades Union membership was 3,388,286 in 1926 and 2,060,043 in 1931. Find the decrease per cent.

13. The area of a circle, radius r in., is A sq. in. where $A = \pi r^2$, and $r = \sqrt{\left(\dfrac{A}{\pi}\right)}$. (i) Find A if $r = 4 \cdot 163$; (ii) find r if $A = 10$.

[14] The time of a complete oscillation of a pendulum l ft. long is t sec. where $t = 2\pi\sqrt{\left(\dfrac{l}{g}\right)}$ and $l = \dfrac{gt^2}{4\pi^2}$ and $g = 32 \cdot 2$. (i) Find l if $t = 2 \cdot 35$; (ii) find t if $l = 40$.

15. The weight of a brass cylinder, height h cm., base-diameter d cm. is w gm. where $w = 2 \cdot 09 d^2 h$. (i) Find w if $d = 2 \cdot 516$, $h = 127 \cdot 4$; (ii) find h if $w = 856 \cdot 4$, $d = 3 \cdot 85$.

*16. Find k from the formula, $w = \pi k l (D + d)(D - d)$ if $w = 4528$, $l = 10 \cdot 7$, $D = 6 \cdot 31$, $d = 4 \cdot 92$.

*17. Find in yards the diameter of a circular enclosure of area $2\frac{1}{4}$ ac.

*18. The volume of a cube is 7 cu. in., find the area of its surface.

[19] The skating record for 500 m. is $42 \cdot 6$ sec. If 1 m. $= 39 \cdot 37$ in., express the average speed in miles per hour.

[20] Find the number of acres in 1 sq. km., given that 1 m. $= 39 \cdot 37$ in.

*21. If $\frac{4}{3}\pi r^3 = 100$, find the value of $4\pi r^2$.

*22. If 1 litre contains $61 \cdot 04$ cu. in., express 1 ft. in cm.

*23. Evaluate $\dfrac{a^2 + b^2 - c^2}{ab}$ if $a = 7{\cdot}65$, $b = 6{\cdot}48$, $c = 5{\cdot}19$.

24. Evaluate $\sqrt{\{s(s-a)(s-b)(s-c)\}}$ if $a = 3{\cdot}15$, $b = 4{\cdot}27$, $c = 5{\cdot}14$, and $s = \frac{1}{2}(a + b + c)$.

*25. Evaluate $\sqrt{\{(ab + cd)(ad + bc)\}}$ if $a = 17{\cdot}03$, $b = 21{\cdot}42$, $c = 18{\cdot}16$, $d = 22{\cdot}07$.

Positive Numbers less than 1

Example 22. Find the logarithm of $0{\cdot}0648$.

$$0{\cdot}0648 = 6{\cdot}48 \div 10^2 = 10^{{\cdot}8116} \div 10^2$$
$$= 10^{{\cdot}8116 - 2} = 10^{-2 + {\cdot}8116}.$$

Similarly, $\quad 0{\cdot}648 = 6{\cdot}48 \div 10 = 10^{{\cdot}8116} \div 10^1 = 10^{-1 + {\cdot}8116}$

and $\quad 0{\cdot}000648 = 6{\cdot}48 \div 10^4 = 10^{{\cdot}8116} \div 10^4 = 10^{-4 + {\cdot}8116}.$

Logarithms of numbers between 0 and 1 are negative, but are always written so that the decimal portion is positive; for example, the logarithm of $0{\cdot}0648$ is taken as $-2 + {\cdot}8116$, instead of $-1{\cdot}1884$, and for brevity is written $\bar{2}{\cdot}8116$, the "minus" being placed above the 2 to show that it refers only to the 2 and not to ${\cdot}8116$. But at first it is best to write out such logarithms in full when making any calculations and to speak of "minus 2 plus point 8116," although later the shorter phrase "bar 2 point 8116" will be used.

Thus for any number between 0 *and* 1, *the characteristic is* **negative** *and is obtained by* **counting the number of digits between the decimal point and where it would be in the standard form.**

For example, for $0{\cdot}6|48$, one digit, the characteristic is -1;

for $0{\cdot}0006|48$, four digits, the characteristic is -4.

Notice that this is the same rule as that given on p. 295 for numbers greater than 10.

There is *no* logarithm of a *negative* number.

Example 23. Find the number whose logarithm is

$$\text{(i) } \bar{3}{\cdot}6749; \quad \text{(ii) } \bar{1}{\cdot}3027.$$

(i) $10^{{\cdot}6749} = 4{\cdot}73$,

    Move the figures 3 places to the right, $\therefore 10^{\bar{3}{\cdot}6749} = 0{\cdot}00473$.

(ii) $10^{{\cdot}3027} = 2{\cdot}008$,

    Move the figures 1 place to the right, $\therefore 10^{\bar{1}{\cdot}3027} = 0{\cdot}200(8)$.

EXERCISE 150 (Oral)

[*It is suggested that the characteristics of the logarithms of the numbers in Nos. 1–16 should be read off, before Exercise 150 is taken.*]

Find the logarithms of:

1. 0·342.	**2.** 0·0483.	**3.** 0·0076.	**4.** 0·902.
5. 2·04.	**6.** 0·0075.	**7.** 10·01.	**8.** 0·0003.
9. 0·0025.	**10.** 0·101.	**11.** 0·001.	**12.** 0·0704.
13. 0·04503.	**14.** 0·4013.	**15.** 0·007138.	**16.** 0·01101.
17. $\frac{4}{5}$.	**18.** $\frac{3}{400}$.	**19.** $\frac{1}{300}$.	**20.** $\frac{7}{250}$.
21. $4·03 \times 10^{-5}$.	**22.** $6·104 \times 10^{-6}$.	**23.** 428×10^{-10}.	

Find the numbers whose logarithms are:

24. $-1 + 0·5922$.	**25.** $-2 + 0·8645$.	**26.** $-4 + 0·9085$.
27. $-1 + 0·4771$.	**28.** $-2 + 0·6085$.	**29.** $-3 + 0·7067$.
30. $-1 + 0·8476$.	**31.** $-5 + 0·9703$.	**32.** $-1 + 0·5229$.
33. $-4 + 0·2939$.	**34.** $-2 + 0·1650$.	**35.** $-3 + 0·1315$.
36. $\bar{2}·3016$.	**37.** $\bar{1}·0425$.	**38.** $\bar{3}·0055$.	**39.** $\bar{2}·0028$.
40. $\bar{1}·0000$.	**41.** $\overline{10}·7782$.	**42.** $\overline{15}·699$.	**43.** $\bar{1}·9990$.
44. $\bar{2}·06$.	**45.** $\bar{2}·0000$.	**46.** $\bar{4}·44$.	**47.** $\bar{3}·044$.

Some preliminary practice in working with negative characteristics is desirable. The working given in the illustrative examples may be abbreviated as soon as the processes are understood.

Example 24. Express with the decimal portion positive:

(i) $2·89 + \bar{5}·47$;　(ii) $\bar{3}·76 + \bar{1}·58$.

(i)
$$
\begin{array}{r}
2 + ·89 \\
-5 + ·47 \\
\hline
-3 + 1·36 \\
\hline
\bar{2}·36
\end{array}
$$

(ii)
$$
\begin{array}{r}
-3 + ·76 \\
-1 + ·58 \\
\hline
-4 + 1·34 \\
\hline
\bar{3}·34
\end{array}
$$

In *subtraction*, the reader should use for the decimal portion his ordinary method, it may be either of those given below; for the *integral* portion, if there is any difficulty, it is best to use the rule "change the sign of the lower line and add."

Example 25. Express with the decimal portion positive:

(i) $\bar{4}\cdot21 - 1\cdot73$;   (ii) $\bar{2}\cdot63 - \bar{5}\cdot87$.

			Equal Additions		Decomposition
(i)	$-4 + \cdot21$	becomes	$-4 + 1\cdot21$	or	$-5 + 1\cdot21$
	$1 + \cdot73$		$2 + 0\cdot73$		$1 + 0\cdot73$
			$-6 + 0\cdot48$		$-6 + 0\cdot48$
			$\bar{6}\cdot48$		$\bar{6}\cdot48$

In the subtraction, the integer -6 is obtained by changing the sign of the lower line and adding: $-2 - 4 = -6$; $-1 - 5 = -6$.

			Equal Additions		Decomposition
(ii)	$-2 + \cdot63$	becomes	$-2 + 1\cdot63$	or	$-3 + 1\cdot63$
	$-5 + \cdot87$		$(-5 + 1) + 0\cdot87$		$-5 + 0\cdot87$
			$2 + 0\cdot76$		$2 + 0\cdot76$
			$2\cdot76$		$2\cdot76$

In the "equal additions" method, $(-5 + 1) = -4$, change the sign of the lower line and add: $+4 - 2 = 2$.

Example 26. Express with the decimal portion positive:

(i) $\bar{2}\cdot76 \times 4$;   (ii) $\bar{6}\cdot42 \div 3$;   (iii) $\bar{4}\cdot52 \div 3$.

(i) $(-2 + \cdot76) \times 4 = -8 + 3\cdot04 = -5 + \cdot04 = \bar{5}\cdot04$.

(ii) $(-6 + \cdot42) \div 3 = -2 + \cdot14 = \bar{2}\cdot14$.

(iii) $(-4 + \cdot52) \div 3$; since -4 is not exactly divisible by 3, it must be expressed as $-6 + 2$;

$(-4 + \cdot52) \div 3 = (-6 + 2\cdot52) \div 3 = -2 + \cdot84 = \bar{2}\cdot84$.

EXERCISE 151

Express with the decimal portion positive:

1. $\bar{2}\cdot3 + \bar{1}\cdot4$.   **2.** $\bar{5}\cdot2 + 3\cdot6$.   **3.** $\bar{3}\cdot6 + \bar{2}\cdot8$.   **4.** $\bar{4}\cdot7 + 2\cdot8$.

5. $\bar{2}\cdot7 + 4\cdot8$.   **6.** $\bar{3}\cdot9 + 2\cdot7$.   **7.** $\bar{3}\cdot8 - \bar{1}\cdot5$.   **8.** $\bar{4}\cdot7 - 1\cdot2$.

9. $4\cdot6 - \bar{3}\cdot2$.   **10.** $2\cdot7 - 5\cdot4$.   **11.** $\bar{4}\cdot5 - \bar{2}\cdot8$.   **12.** $\bar{3}\cdot4 - 1\cdot6$.

13. $3\cdot2 - \bar{2}\cdot5$.   **14.** $4\cdot2 - 6\cdot7$.   **15.** $1 - \bar{1}\cdot32$.   **16.** $0 - 2\cdot8$.

17. $0 - 3\cdot4$.   **18.** $\bar{3}\cdot1 - \bar{7}\cdot8$.   **19.** $\bar{2}\cdot3 \times 2$.   **20.** $\bar{2}\cdot4 \times 3$.

21. $\bar{3}\cdot9 \times 4$.   **22.** $\bar{6}\cdot8 \div 2$.   **23.** $\bar{9}\cdot6 \div 3$.   **24.** $\bar{3}\cdot4 \div 2$.

25. $\bar{5}\cdot5 \div 3$.   **26.** $\bar{1}\cdot4 \div 3$.   **27.** $\bar{7}\cdot7 \div 3$.   **28.** $\bar{1}\cdot6 \div 4$.

29. $\bar{6}\cdot8 \div 4$.   **30.** $\bar{2}\cdot4 \div 5$.   **31.** $\bar{3} \div 5$.   **32.** $\bar{4}\cdot5 \div 7$.

33. $\bar{2}\cdot2 \div 9$.   **34.** $3\cdot7 \times (-2)$.   **35.** $\bar{2}\cdot6 \times (-3)$.   **36.** $3\cdot6 \div (-2)$.

37. $\bar{3}\cdot6 \div (-2)$.   **38.** $\bar{5}\cdot8 \div (-3)$.   **39.** $3 \div (-5)$.

Example 27. Evaluate 0.000645×82.3.

Rough Estimate: $0.0006 \times 80 = 0.048$.

Number	Logarithm
0.000645	$\bar{4}.8096$
82.3	1.9154
Expression	$\bar{2}.7250$

$$
\begin{array}{r}
-4 + .8096 \\
1 + .9154 \\
\hline
-3 + 1.7250 \\
\hline
-2 + .7250
\end{array}
$$

∴ expression $= 0.0530(9)$.

Example 28. Evaluate $429.3 \div 0.00736$.

Rough Estimate: $\dfrac{400}{0.007} = \dfrac{400000}{7} \backsim 50,000$.

Number	Logarithm
429.3	2.6328
0.00736	$\bar{3}.8669$
Expression	4.7659

$$
\begin{array}{r}
2 + .6328 \\
-3 + .8669 \\
\hline
4 + .7659
\end{array}
$$

∴ expression $= 58,330$.

Example 29. Evaluate $(0.08644)^3$:

Rough Estimate: $(0.09)^3 = 0.000729$.

Number	Logarithm	
$(0.08644)^3$	$\bar{2}.9367 \times 3$	$\bar{4}.8101$

∴ expression $= 0.000645(8)$.

$$
\begin{array}{r}
-2 + 0.9367 \\
3 \\
\hline
-6 + 2.8101 \\
\hline
\bar{4}.8101
\end{array}
$$

Example 30. Evaluate $\sqrt[4]{0.5173}$.

Number	Logarithm	
$\sqrt[4]{0.5173}$	$\bar{1}.7138 \div 4$	$\bar{1}.9284$

∴ expression $= 0.848(0)$.

$$
\begin{array}{r}
-1 + .7138 \\
4\,\overline{)\,-4 + 3.7138} \\
\hline
-1 + 0.9284 \\
\hline
\bar{1}.9284
\end{array}
$$

Rough Check: $(0.8)^4 = (0.64)^2 \backsim (0.6)^2 = 0.36$

$(0.9)^4 = (0.81)^2 \backsim (0.8)^2 = 0.64$.

EXERCISE 152

Find the value to 4 figures, as given by 4-figure tables, of :

1. 0.243×3.12.   **[2]** 0.816×4.37.   **3.** 0.729×56.2.

[4] 0.215×0.186.   **5.** 0.743×0.814.   **[6]** 0.315×617.

[7] 0.0863×0.924.   **8.** 0.0072×0.091.   **[9]** 0.000389×47.4.

10. $614 \cdot 3 \times 0 \cdot 03617$. **[11]** $0 \cdot 8172 \times 0 \cdot 5049$. **12.** $0 \cdot 06194 \times 1 \cdot 032$.

13. $0 \cdot 542 \div 3 \cdot 67$. **[14]** $0 \cdot 618 \div 8 \cdot 04$. **15.** $0 \cdot 847 \div 0 \cdot 623$.

[16] $6 \cdot 71 \div 0 \cdot 426$. **17.** $83 \cdot 7 \div 0 \cdot 00217$. **[18]** $729 \div 0 \cdot 0564$.

19. $37 \cdot 4 \div 0 \cdot 0684$. **[20]** $0 \cdot 463 \div 0 \cdot 0852$. **[21]** $3 \cdot 67 \div 529$.

22. $42 \cdot 71 \div 6832$. **[23]** $10 \cdot 74 \div 2007$. **24.** $0 \cdot 3007 \div 0 \cdot 0942$.

25. $1 \div 0 \cdot 03716$. **[26]** $100 \div 0 \cdot 7054$. **[27]** $\frac{2}{3} \div 0 \cdot 0807$.

28. $(0 \cdot 284)^2$. **[29]** $(0 \cdot 717)^2$. **[30]** $(0 \cdot 0846)^2$. **31.** $(0 \cdot 372)^3$.

32. $(0 \cdot 0513)^4$. **[33]** $(0 \cdot 463)^5$. **[34]** $(0 \cdot 724)^{10}$. **[35]** $(0 \cdot 006)^4$.

36. $\sqrt{(0 \cdot 0863)}$. **37.** $\sqrt{(0 \cdot 5167)}$. **[38]** $\sqrt{(0 \cdot 007)}$. **[39]** $\sqrt{(0 \cdot 104)}$.

40. $\sqrt[3]{(0 \cdot 009)}$. **41.** $\sqrt[3]{(0 \cdot 615)}$. **[42]** $\sqrt[3]{(0 \cdot 0485)}$. **[43]** $\sqrt[4]{(0 \cdot 732)}$.

[44] $\sqrt[5]{(0 \cdot 00704)}$. **45.** $\sqrt[6]{(0 \cdot 00039)}$. **46.** $(0 \cdot 473)^{\frac{2}{3}}$. **[47]** $(0 \cdot 0066)^{\frac{2}{3}}$.

Example 31. Find to 3 figures the value of

$$\frac{(0 \cdot 05871)^3 \times \sqrt{(0 \cdot 7128)}}{5\frac{2}{3} \times (0 \cdot 8136)^4 \times \sqrt[3]{(0 \cdot 6915)}}.$$

Number	Logarithm	
$(0 \cdot 05871)^3$	$\bar{2} \cdot 7687 \times 3$	$\bar{4} \cdot 3061$
$\sqrt{(0 \cdot 7128)}$	$\bar{1} \cdot 8530 \div 2$	$\bar{1} \cdot 9265$
Numerator		$\bar{4} \cdot 2326$
$5\frac{2}{3} = 5 \cdot 667$		$\cdot 7533$
$(0 \cdot 8136)^4$	$\bar{1} \cdot 9104 \times 4$	$\bar{1} \cdot 6416$
$\sqrt[3]{(0 \cdot 6915)}$	$\bar{1} \cdot 8398 \div 3$	$\bar{1} \cdot 9466$
Denominator		$\cdot 3415$
Expression		$\bar{5} \cdot 8911$

$$\bar{4} \cdot 2326$$
$$\cdot 3415$$
$$\overline{\bar{5} \cdot 8911}$$

∴ expression $= 0 \cdot 0000778$, to 3 figures.

Example 32. Find to 3 figures the value of $\dfrac{1}{\sqrt[4]{(0 \cdot 326)}}$.

Number	Logarithm	
1		$\cdot 0000$
$\sqrt[4]{0 \cdot 326}$	$\bar{1} \cdot 5132 \div 4$	$\bar{1} \cdot 8783$
Expression		$0 \cdot 1217$

∴ expression $= 1 \cdot 323 = 1 \cdot 32$, to 3 figures.

If the calculation of the logarithm is itself difficult, as in the next example, the working should be set out in full.

L   20

Example 33.   Find, to 3 figures, the value of $(0.0728)^{-1.6}$.

Number	Logarithm
$(0.0728)^{-1.6}$	$\bar{2}.8621 \times (-1.6)$

$$(-2 + 0.8621) \times (-1.6) = (-1.1379)(-1.6)$$
$$= 1.8206.$$

$$\begin{array}{r} 1.1379 \\ 1.6 \\ \hline 1.1379 \\ .68274 \\ \hline 1.82064 \end{array}$$

∴ expression $= 10^{1.8206} = 66.16 = 66.2$, to 3 figures.

EXERCISE 153

Find the value to 4 figures, as given by 4-figure tables, of:

1. $0.387 \times 0.473 \times 7.08$.   [2] $0.01031 \times 0.2074 \times 1.702$.

3. $\dfrac{6.314 \times 0.7285}{37.62}$.   [4] $\dfrac{0.5178}{4.917 \times 14.97}$.   5. $\dfrac{17.35 \times 3.628}{0.4271 \times 0.00726}$.

[6] $\dfrac{4007 \times 0.0275}{0.9193 \times 1.063}$.   7. $\dfrac{(0.7356)^2}{3.142 \times 0.0867}$.   8. $\dfrac{\sqrt{0.07324}}{16.81 \times 53.46}$.

[9] $\dfrac{(0.3274)^3 \times 15.07}{(0.0728)^2 \times 37}$.   10. $\dfrac{1.57 \times 23.6 \times 108}{11.04 \times 0.827 \times 0.33}$.

11. $\sqrt{\left(\dfrac{6.372 \times 15.08}{8307}\right)}$.   [12] $\dfrac{16.39 \times \sqrt{(0.8372)}}{247.3 \times (1.634)^2}$.

13. $\dfrac{496 \times \sqrt{(0.7065)}}{(11.01)^2 \times 0.0301}$.   *14. $\dfrac{\sqrt{(0.7164)} \times \sqrt{(0.4285)}}{(2.073)^2}$.

15. $(0.7054)^{\frac{3}{4}}$.   [16] $(0.0107)^{\frac{2}{5}}$.   17. $(0.6362)^{-1.2}$.

[18] $(0.8072)^{4.8}$.   [19] $(0.835)^{-1.1}$.   *20. $(0.1)^{0.1}$.

[21] $(0.009)^{-1.5}$.   22. $(0.076)^{-0.6}$.   *23. $\sqrt{(0.624)^{-3}}$.

[24] $(12.8)^{-\frac{1}{4}}$.   25. $(0.075)^{-\frac{1}{3}}$.   [26] $(0.62)^{-\frac{3}{5}}$.

Find the value to 3 figures, of:

*27. $\dfrac{(0.438)^2}{12.3} + \dfrac{(0.057)^2}{0.342}$.   *28. $\dfrac{1.7246 - \sqrt{(0.8143)}}{\sqrt[4]{(0.05361)}}$.

*29. $\dfrac{\frac{3}{4} \times 107 \div \sqrt{(0.434)}}{0.808 \times 0.01}$.   *30. $\dfrac{\sqrt{(0.7254)} + \sqrt[3]{(1.072)}}{(3.625)^2 + (1.081)^2}$.

Index Problems.   The general properties of logarithms were stated on p. 297; the relation, $\log(x^n) = n \log x$, is useful in problems where the value of an index is required.

Example 34. It can be proved, see p. 340, that the amount of £P at R% per annum compound interest after n years is $£P\left(1 + \frac{R}{100}\right)^n$. Use this formula to find after how many years £160 will amount to £500 at $3\frac{1}{2}$% p.a., compound interest.

After n years, £160 amounts to $£160(1 + \frac{3.5}{100})^n$;

$\therefore\ 160(1 \cdot 035)^n = 500$; $\therefore\ \log 160 + \log (1 \cdot 035)^n = \log 500$;

$\therefore\ n \log 1 \cdot 035 = \log 500 - \log 160$;

$\therefore\ n \times 0 \cdot 0149 = 2 \cdot 6990 - 2 \cdot 2041 = 0 \cdot 4949$;

$\therefore\ n = \dfrac{0 \cdot 4949}{0 \cdot 0149} = 33 \cdot 2$;

Number	Logarithm
0·4949	$\bar{1}$·6945
0·0149	$\bar{2}$·1732
n	1·5213

$\therefore$ the length of time is 33 yr., to nearest year.

Note. It is suggested that the reader should check the value of n by long division as the double use of logarithms may be confusing.

EXERCISE 154

Find the value of x in Nos. 1–6:

    1. $2^x = 100$.   **[2]** $3^x = 1000$.   **3.** $5^x = \sqrt{175}$.   **4.** $9^x = \frac{3}{4}$.

    [5] $(1 \cdot 1)^x = 2$.   ***6.** $(0 \cdot 8)^x = 0 \cdot 05$.

Simplify, without using logarithm tables:

  *7. $\dfrac{\log 9}{\log 3}$.   ***8.** $\dfrac{\log 125}{\log 5}$.   ***9.** $\dfrac{\log \sqrt{7}}{\log 7}$.

  *10. $\log 4 + \log 25$.   ***11.** $\log 6\frac{1}{4} + \log 1\frac{3}{5}$.

  12. If $pv^n = 475$, find n when $p = 3 \cdot 62$, $v = 98 \cdot 5$.

  [13] If $h = 391Q^n$, find n when $h = 7 \cdot 95$, $Q = 0 \cdot 125$.

  14. Find the least integral value of n for which $(0 \cdot 95)^n$ is less than $0 \cdot 1$.

Find the value of x in Nos. 15–17:

  15. $x \log 5 = 10$.   ***16.** $\log x - \log 2 = \log 3$.

  17. $x(\log 417 - \log 31) = 2 + \log 3 \cdot 82$.

  18. In how many years will £150 invested at 4% p.a. compound interest amount to £250?

  19. In how many years will a sum of money invested at 5% p.a. compound interest be doubled?

  *20. The present population of a country is 24,650,000. If the population increases at 3% p.a., obeying the compound interest law, after how many years will it become 35 millions?

MISCELLANEOUS EXAMPLES

EXERCISE 155

[Give answers to 3 figures.   Take log $\pi = 0.4971$]

1. Evaluate $2\pi\sqrt{\left(\dfrac{l}{g}\right)}$ if $l = 62.5$, $g = 981$.

2. In 1931 the Inland Revenue collected £481,628,508 at a cost of £7,967,787. What percentage is the cost of collection of the sum collected?

[3] 1 sea mile = 1·854 km.; 1 statute mile = 1·609 km. What is the speed in m.p.h. of a train which travels 40% faster than a ship doing 25 knots?

*4. If $x^2 = y^2 - z^2$, find x when $y = 1.247$, $z = 0.816$.

5. Find r if $\pi r^2 = 1$.

[6] Evaluate $\sqrt{\left(\dfrac{1.27\text{M}}{h \times \text{S}}\right)}$ when $\text{S} = 8.9$, $\text{M} = 2.51$, $h = 15$.

*7. Evaluate $0.2476 \times 10^{1.7254}$.

*8. Evaluate $\left(\dfrac{1}{6.39} - \dfrac{1}{12.14}\right)^2$.

9. Evaluate $xy^2 \div \sqrt{z}$ when $x = 4.732$, $y = 0.1785$, $z = 276.3$.

10. 1 litre of water weighs 2·205 lb. and 1 pt. of water weighs 1·25 lb. Express 1 pt. in litres.

[11] Taking 1 sq. mi. = 2·589 sq. km., express 1 ft. in cm.

12. The volume V cu. dm. of a cone, base diameter d dm., height h dm., is given by $\text{V} = \frac{1}{12}\pi d^2 h$. (i) Find V if $d = 0.472$, $h = 0.357$; (ii) find d if $\text{V} = 35$, $h = 3.57$.

[13] Find in tons the weight of water which falls on a 20-acre field in a rainfall of $\frac{3}{4}$ in., assuming that 1 cu. ft. of water weighs 62·3 lb.

*14. Evaluate $\dfrac{0.15 + (0.15)^{\frac{2}{3}}}{1.15} \times 3.046$.

15. Evaluate $\sqrt{\left\{\dfrac{(s-c)(s-a)}{s(s-b)}\right\}}$ when $a = 12.05$, $b = 9.17$, $c = 12.74$, and $s = \frac{1}{2}(a + b + c)$.

16. Find x from the formula, $kx = 5.602 \log\left(\dfrac{\text{P}}{\text{W}}\right)$ when $k = 0.74$, $\text{P} = 56.8$, $\text{W} = 39.3$.

17. A sum of money invested at r per cent. per annum compound interest is doubled after n years where $n = \log 2 \div \log\left(1 + \dfrac{r}{100}\right)$. Find n if $r = 2\frac{3}{4}$.

18. An iceberg loses every day 5% of its volume at the beginning of that day by melting. After how many days will its volume be halved?

*19. The safe width of a dam at a depth of x ft. below water-level is $\sqrt{\left\{\dfrac{0.05x^3}{9 + 0.03x}\right\}}$ ft. How wide should it be at a depth of $17\frac{1}{2}$ ft.?

[20] The horse-power of the engines required to drive a ship of T tons at a speed of K knots is $0.0042K^3 \times \sqrt[3]{T^2}$. Find the horse-power for a vessel of 30,700 tons with a maximum speed of 25·4 knots.

*21. Evaluate $\dfrac{ab + cd}{ac + bd}$ when $a = 2.47$, $b = 0.365$, $c = 3.06$, $d = 0.972$.

[22] If $pv^n = 372$, find n when $p = 2.87$, $v = 86.4$.

CHAPTER XX

HARDER MENSURATION

Areas

If ABCD is a parallelogram on the same base and between the same parallels as the rectangle ABHK, the areas of the parallelogram and rectangle are equal.

Area of parallelogram ABCD = area of ABHK
$$= AB \times BH.$$

This fact is often expressed in the form:

area of parallelogram = base × height.

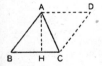

If ABCD is a parallelogram and if AH is its height, area of $\triangle$ ABC
$$= \tfrac{1}{2} \text{ area of ABCD}$$
$$= \tfrac{1}{2} \text{ BC} \times \text{AH}.$$

This fact is often expressed in the form:

area of triangle = $\tfrac{1}{2}$ base × height.

The area of a triangle can also be expressed in terms of the lengths of its sides :

If the lengths of the sides are a, b, c in., and if the semi-perimeter is s in., that is if $s = \frac{1}{2}(a+b+c)$, it can be proved that the area of the triangle is

$$\sqrt{\{s(s-a)(s-b)(s-c)\}}\ \text{sq. in.}$$

If the parallel sides AB, DC of the trapezium ABCD are of lengths a, b in. and at a distance h in. apart,

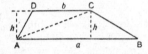

area of $\triangle$ ABC $= \frac{1}{2}\ ah$ sq. in.,
area of $\triangle$ ACD $= \frac{1}{2}\ bh$ sq. in.,
$\therefore$ area of trapezium ABCD
$= (\frac{1}{2}ah + \frac{1}{2}bh)$ sq. in. $= \frac{1}{2}(a+b)h$ sq. in.

This fact is often expressed in the form :

area of trapezium = average width × height.

Example 1. Find the area of the isosceles triangle, whose sides are of lengths 7·4 cm., 7·4 cm., 6·2 cm.

The altitude AD bisects the base BC, $\therefore$ BD $= 3\cdot1$ cm.;
but $AD^2 + DB^2 = AB^2$,

$\therefore$ AD $= \sqrt{(7\cdot4^2 - 3\cdot1^2)}$ cm. $= \sqrt{(54\cdot76 - 9\cdot61)}$ cm.
$\qquad = \sqrt{(45\cdot15)}$ cm. $= 6\cdot720$ cm.

$\therefore$ area of $\triangle$ ABC $= (\frac{1}{2} \times 6\cdot2 \times 6\cdot72)$ sq. cm.
$\qquad = (3\cdot1 \times 6\cdot72)$ sq. cm.
$\qquad = 20\cdot8$ sq. cm., to 3 figures.

Example 2. Find in acres the area of a triangular field, whose sides are of lengths 366 yd., 407 yd., 485 yd.

Denoting the lengths by a, b, c, we have

		Number	Logarithm
		629	2·7987
$a = 366$	$s = 629$	263	2·4200
$b = 407$	$s-a = 263$	222	2·3464
$c = 485$	$s-b = 222$	144	2·1584
$2s = a+b+c = 1258$	$s-c = 144$		9·7235 ÷ 2
$\therefore$ area $= \sqrt{\{629 \times 263 \times 222 \times 144\}}$ sq. yd.		area (sq. yd.)	4·8617
but 4840 sq. yd. $= 1$ ac.,		4840	3·6848
$\therefore$ area $= 15\cdot0$ ac., to 3 figures.		area (ac.)	1·1769

Note. $(s-a) + (s-b) + (s-c) = 3s - a - b - c = 3s - 2s = s$. The values obtained for $s-a$, $s-b$, $s-c$, should be checked by verifying that their sum is s. Here, $263 + 222 + 144 = 629$.

EXERCISE 156

[Do not give answers to more than 3 figures.   Logarithm tables
should be used, where suitable]

In Nos. 1–14, AH, CK are altitudes of the
parallelogram ABCD.

Find the area of ABCD, if :

1. BC = 8 cm., AH = 5 cm.

[2] AB = 3 in., CK = 4 in.

3. AD = 2·34 in., AH = 1·56 in.

[4] CD = 7·28 cm., CK = 9·46 cm.

5. If the area of ABCD is 28·46 sq. in., and if BC = 7·35 in., find
the length of AH.

[6] If the area of ABCD is 37·24 sq. cm., and if CK = 8·14 cm.,
find the length of AB.

7. If BC = 4·76 in., CD = 3·28 in., AH = 2·84 in., find the area of
ABCD and the length of CK.

*8. If CD = 5·74 cm., AH = 2·85 cm., CK = 3·92 cm., find the
area of ABCD and the length of AD.

Find the area of the triangle ABC, if :

9. BC = 7 in., AH = 5 in.   **[10]** AB = 6·14 cm., CK = 8·72 cm.

[11] BC = 3·45 in., AH = 4·85 in.

12. AB = 10·17 cm., CK = 12·08 cm.

13. If the area of △ ABC is 8·32 sq. in., and if BC = 6·35 in., find
the length of AH.

[14] If the area of △ ABC is 59·7 sq. cm., and if CK = 13·4 cm.,
find the length of AB.

Find the area of a triangle, whose sides are :

15. 5 in., 5 in., 6 in.   **[16]** 7 cm., 7 cm., 6 cm.

17. 3·64 in., 3·64 in., 4·96 in.   ***18.** Each 7·5 cm.

19. Find the area of a rhombus whose diagonals are of lengths
3·9 in., 4·7 in.   [The diagonals cut at right angles.]

20. The parallel sides of a trapezium are 1·47 ft., 1·15 ft., and are
0·85 ft. apart.   Find the area of the trapezium.

[21] The parallel sides of a trapezium are 4·36 cm., 3·18 cm., and
its area is 18·72 sq. cm.; find the distance between the parallel sides.

22. The end wall of a barn consists of a rectangle 25 ft. wide, 14 ft. high, surmounted by an isosceles triangle. The ridge of the roof is 17 ft. above the ground. Find the area of the wall.

*23. AH, CK are perpendiculars to the diagonal BD of the quadrilateral ABCD. If AH=4·63 in., CK=2·84 in., BD=5·37 in., find the area of ABCD.

*24. DP, CQ are the perpendiculars from D, C to AB. If DP=238 yd., CQ=316 yd., AP=95 yd., PQ=174 yd., QB=82 yd., find in acres the area of ABCD.

*25. ABCD is a quadrilateral, right-angled at A and at B; AD=3 in., BC=2·2 in., CD=1·7 in. Find (i) the area of ABCD, (ii) the area of △BCD, (iii) the length of the perpendicular from B to DC produced.

Find the area of a triangle and the length of its greatest altitude, if the sides are:

26. 5 cm., 6 cm., 7 cm.   [**27**] 4·6 in., 5·3 in., 6·9 in.

28. 207 yd., 246 yd., 291 yd. (area in acres).

[**29**] 7·36 ch., 8·49 ch., 9·15 ch. (area in acres).

*30. The parallel sides of a trapezium are 7·5 in., 3·9 in.; and the other sides are each 2·6 in. Find its area.

Volumes. If a solid has a uniform cross-section, and if this cross-section is a triangle, quadrilateral, or any polygon, the solid is called a **prism**; if the cross-section is circular or oval, the solid is called a **cylinder**.

As explained in Chapter XIII, see p. 190, the volume is obtained by the rule:

Volume of prism =area of base × height
                    =**area of cross-section × distance between end-faces.**

The diagrams represent a wedge (a triangular prism), and a lean-to shed (a prism whose cross-section parallel to an end-face is a trapezium).

Example 3. The surface of the water in a swimming-bath is a rectangle 155 ft. long, 40 ft. wide, and the depth of the water increases uniformly from $3\frac{1}{2}$ ft. at one end to $10\frac{1}{2}$ ft. at the other end. Find the volume of water in the bath.

The side-face of the bath in contact with the water is a trapezium, parallel sides $3\frac{1}{2}$ ft., $10\frac{1}{2}$ ft., at a distance 155 ft. apart.

Therefore the area of side-face of bath in contact with the water is $\frac{1}{2}(3\frac{1}{2}+10\frac{1}{2}) \times 155$ sq. ft.

But the water is in the form of a prism, of cross-section equal to area of side-face, and of width 40 ft.;

$$\therefore \text{ volume of water} = \frac{1}{2}(3\frac{1}{2}+10\frac{1}{2}) \times 155 \times 40 \text{ cu. ft.}$$
$$= \frac{1}{2} \times 14 \times 155 \times 40 \text{ cu. ft.}$$
$$= 43{,}400 \text{ cu. ft.}$$

EXERCISE 157

[Give answers to 3 figures. Logarithm tables should be used where suitable]

1. A triangular set square is 5 mm. thick and its two shorter sides measure 22·5 cm., 38·7 cm. Find its volume.

[**2**] The cross-section of a trough 7 ft. long is a triangle whose sides are 3 in., 4 in., 5 in. Find how much water it can hold.

3. The heights of the front and back walls of a lean-to shed are $8\frac{1}{2}$ ft. and $10\frac{1}{2}$ ft., and are 7 ft. apart. The shed is 16 ft. long. Find its volume.

4. The cross-section of a trench, 24 ft. long, is a trapezium 3 ft. 6 in. wide at the bottom and 5 ft. 4 in. wide at the top. The trench is 6 ft. 3 in. deep. Find in cu. ft. the volume of soil removed in making it.

[**5**] A rectangular brass plate 4·6 in. wide, 0·15 in. thick weighs 3 lb. Find its length if the brass weighs 528 lb. per cu. ft.

[**6**] The depth of water in a swimming-bath increases uniformly from $2\frac{1}{2}$ ft. at one end to $8\frac{1}{2}$ ft. at the other end. The bath is 120 ft. long and 35 ft. wide. Find the volume of the water.

7. Find the air-space in a hall, 60 ft. long, whose cross-section has the dimensions shown in the diagram.

8. The base of a prism, 15 cm. long, is an isosceles triangle, sides 5 cm., 5 cm., 6 cm. Find (i) its volume, (ii) the total area of its surface.

9. The cross-section of a writing-desk, 3 ft. wide, is shown in the diagram; three of the corners are right-angled. Find its volume in cu. ft.

10. The depth of water in a swimming-bath increases uniformly from 3 ft. at one end to 10 ft. at the other end. The bath is 80 ft. long and 30 ft. wide. Find the number of gallons of water in the bath. [1 cu. ft. $= 6\frac{1}{4}$ gall.]

11. Find the number of gallons of water left in the bath described in No. 10, when the water is allowed to run out until only half the floor remains covered.

[12] The base of a metal prism is an equilateral triangle, side 12 cm., and the height of the prism is 35 cm. Find (i) the total area of its surface, (ii) its weight in Kg., if 1 c.c. of the metal weighs 8·45 gm.

*13. The base of a reservoir is a horizontal rectangle 100 yd. long, 50 yd. wide. The two shorter end-faces are vertical and the two longer side-faces are inclined outwards at 45° with the vertical. Find the volume of water in gallons when the depth is 6 ft. [1 gall. $= 277\cdot3$ cu. in.]

[14] The diagram represents the cross-section of a barn, 45 ft. long; the three marked corners are right-angled. Find the volume of the barn.

*15. The cross-section of a prism, 8 in. high, is a triangle whose sides are 6 in., 7 in., 9 in. Find its volume.

16. A vessel of uniform horizontal cross-section contains water to a depth of 16 cm. When 50 marbles, each of volume 0·876 c.c., have been dropped into it, the depth is observed to be 18·65 cm. Find the area of the cross-section.

*17. A trough is 15 ft. long; its cross-section is an isosceles trapezium, 27 in. wide at the top, 9 in. wide at the bottom, and its slant edges are each 15 in. Find the amount of water in cu. ft. the trough will hold.

*18. Water is discharged at 3500 gall. per min. from a reservoir of surface area 7200 sq. ft. into one with surface area 5600 sq. ft. The sides of both reservoirs are vertical planes. By how much does the difference of the levels of the two surfaces alter in 15 min.? [1 cu. ft. $= 6\frac{1}{4}$ gall.]

If the base of a solid is a polygon ABCDE . . ., and if the other faces are triangles VAB, VBC, VCD, . . . with a common vertex V, the solid is called a **pyramid**, with ABCDE . . . as *base* and V as *vertex*; and the distance VK of the vertex V from the plane of the base is called the *height* of the pyramid. The form of a pyramid is best explained by the use of models. If the lines joining the vertex to the corners of the base are all equal, the solid is called a *right* pyramid, and each of these lines is called a *slant edge* of the pyramid. It can be proved that

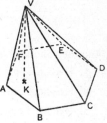

$$\text{Volume of pyramid} = \tfrac{1}{3} \times \text{area of base} \times \text{height.}$$

Example 4. The base ABCD of a right pyramid, vertex V, is a rectangle, 4·4 in. by 3·6 in., and the length of a slant edge is 3·9 in. Find (i) the volume of the pyramid, (ii) the total area of its surface.

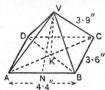

(i) If the diagonals AC, BD of the base cut at K, VK is the height of the pyramid. Let VK $= h$ in., KC $= x$ in., then AC $= 2x$ in.

Since $\angle$ ABC $= 90°$, $(2x)^2 = 4·4^2 + 3·6^2 = 19·36 + 12·96$;
$$\therefore 4x^2 = 32·32; \quad \therefore x^2 = 8·08.$$

Since $\angle$ VKC $= 90°$, $h^2 + x^2 = 3·9^2 = 15·21$; $\therefore h^2 = 15·21 - 8·08 = 7·13$;
$$\therefore h = \sqrt{7·13} = 2·670.$$

	Logarithms
$\therefore$ volume $= \tfrac{1}{3} \times$ area of base $\times$ height	·6435
$= \tfrac{1}{3} \times (4·4 \times 3·6) \times 2·670$ cu. in.	·0792
$= (4·4 \times 1·2 \times 2·670)$ cu. in.	·4265
$= 14·1$ cu. in., to 3 figures.	1·1492

(ii) As in Example 1, p. 310, the height VN of the isosceles triangle VAB is given by

VN $= \sqrt{(3·9^2 - 2·2^2)}$ in. $= \sqrt{(15·21 - 4·84)}$ in. $= \sqrt{10·37}$ in. $= 3·220$ in.
$$\therefore \text{ area of } \triangle \text{VAB} = (\tfrac{1}{2} \times 4·4 \times 3·220) \text{ sq. in.} = 7·084 \text{ sq. in.}$$

Similarly, area of $\triangle$ VBC $= \tfrac{1}{2} \times 3·6 \times \sqrt{(3·9^2 - 1·8^2)}$ sq. in.
$$= 1·8 \times \sqrt{(15·21 - 3·24)} \text{ sq. in.}$$
$$= (1·8 \times 3·460) \text{ sq. in.} = 6·228 \text{ sq. in.}$$
$$\therefore \text{ area of four faces} = 2(7·084 + 6·228) \text{ sq. in.} = 26·62 \text{ sq. in.}$$

But area of base ABCD $= (4·4 \times 3·6)$ sq. in. $= 15·84$ sq. in.
$\therefore$ total area of surface $= (26·62 + 15·84)$ sq. in. $= 42·5$ sq. in., to 3 figures.

EXERCISE 158

[Do not give answers to more than 3 figures.   Use logarithm tables where suitable]

Find the volume of a pyramid, given :

1. Height, 5 in.; square base, side 3 in.

[**2**] Height, 6 cm.; rectangular base, 4 cm. by 5 cm.

3. Height, 8 cm.; triangular base, sides 3 cm., 4 cm., 5 cm.

4. Find the height of a pyramid of volume 100 cu. in., if its base is a square, side 5 in.

5. Find the area of the base of a pyramid of volume 48 cu. cm., if its height is 8 cm.

Find the volume of a right pyramid, given :

6. Slant edge, 13 cm.; rectangular base, 6 cm. by 8 cm.

[**7**] Slant edge, 2 in.; square base, side 2 in.

8. Height, 9 cm.; base, equilateral triangle, side 8 cm.

*****9.** Height, 1 ft.; triangular base, sides 5 in., 6 in., 7 in.

10. The volume of a right pyramid whose base is 4 in. square is 32 cu. in.; find its height and the length of a slant edge.

[**11**] The volume of a right pyramid, 8 in. high, standing on a square base, is 96 cu. in.; find the length of a side of the base and of a slant edge.

Find the total area of the surface of a right pyramid, given :

12. Height, 4 cm.; square base, side 6 cm.

[**13**] Height, 5 in.; rectangular base, 4 in. by 6 in.

14. Find the volume of a right pyramid standing on a square base, if its height is 6 in. and the length of its slant edge is 8 in.

*****15.** In a cubical tank, each edge 4 ft., there is a solid metal pyramid, 4 ft. high, whose base is a square of side 3 ft.   The tank is filled with water.   If the pyramid is removed, find the distance the water-level sinks.

Circles and Cylinders. The mensuration of the circle has been discussed in Chapter XIV, see p. 195. The principal formulæ are repeated here for the convenience of the reader:

For a *circle*, radius r in.,

$$\text{circumference} = 2\pi r \text{ in.}; \quad \text{area} = \pi r^2 \text{ sq. in.}$$

For a *circular cylinder*, radius r in., height h in.,

$$\text{area of curved surface} = 2\pi rh \text{ sq. in.}; \quad \text{volume} = \pi r^2 h \text{ cu. in.}$$

Calculations are generally shortened by using logarithms: $\log \pi = 0\cdot4971$.

Example 5. The diameter of the section of a steel wire, weighing 492 lb. per cu. ft., is 0·104 in. Find, to 3 figures, the weight of a mile length of the wire.

The radius of the cross-section is 0·052 in., therefore the area of the cross-section is $\pi \times (0\cdot052)^2$ sq. in.

Logarithms

∴ the volume of a length of 1 mi. of wire is

$\{\pi \times (0\cdot052)^2 \div 144\} \times 1760 \times 3$ cu. ft.

∴ the weight of a length of 1 mi. of wire

$$= \frac{\pi \times (0\cdot052)^2 \times 5280}{144} \times 492 \text{ lb.}$$

$= 153\cdot2$ lb. $= 153$ lb., to 3 figures.

$\overline{2}\cdot7160 \times 2$
$\overline{3}\cdot4320$
$\cdot4971$
$3\cdot7226$
$2\cdot6920$
$4\cdot3437$
$2\cdot1584$
$2\cdot1853$

N.B. *Obtain a numerical expression for the result before using logarithms.*

Example 6. A cylindrical tankard holds 1 qt. If its height equals the radius of its base, find the height in inches to $\frac{1}{100}$ in., given that 1 gall. $= 277\cdot27$ cu. in.

If the radius of the base is r in., the height is r in.;

∴ the volume $= (\pi r^2 \times r)$ cu. in.

∴ $\pi r^3 = 277\cdot27 \div 4 = 69\cdot32$;

∴ $r^3 = 69\cdot32 \div \pi$; ∴ $r = \sqrt[3]{(69\cdot32 \div \pi)} = 2\cdot804$;

∴ the height is 2·80 in., to $\frac{1}{100}$ in.

Logarithms

$1\cdot8408$

$\cdot4971$

$3\,|\,\overline{1\cdot3437}$

$\cdot4479$

Example 7. A length of 2400 ft. of paper is wrapped on a wooden cylinder of radius 3 in.; the thickness of the paper is $\frac{1}{120}$ in. Find the radius of the whole roll to $\frac{1}{100}$ in.

If the radius of the whole roll is r in., the area of the cross-section of the roll is πr^2 sq. in.; but the area of the cross-section of the wooden cylinder is $\pi \times 3^2$ sq. in.;

∴ area of cross-section of paper $= (\pi r^2 - 9\pi)$ sq. in.

But the cross-section of the paper is a rectangle 2400 ft. long, $\frac{1}{120}$ in. deep.

∴ $\pi r^2 - 9\pi = 2400 \times 12 \times \frac{1}{120} = 240$;

∴ $\pi r^2 = 240 + 9\pi$;   ∴ $r^2 = \frac{240}{\pi} + 9$;

∴ $r^2 = 76.40 + 9 = 85.40$;   ∴ $r = \sqrt{(85.40)} = 9.241$.

Logarithms
2·3802
·4971
1·8831

∴ the radius of the whole roll is 9·24 in., to $\frac{1}{100}$ in.

EXERCISE 159

[*Give answers to 3 figures; $\log \pi = ·4971$; 1 gall. = 277·3 cu. in.*]

1. Find (i) the circumference, (ii) the area of a circle of radius 13·62 in.

2. Find (i) the radius, (ii) the area of a circle whose circumference is 100 yd.

[3] Find in yards (i) the radius, (ii) the circumference of a circle whose area is 1 ac.

[4] Find the number of revolutions of a wheel of a car, 33 in. in diameter, when the car travels 1 mi.

5. A circular hole of diameter 7·5 cm. is punched in a tin sheet 9 cm. long, 8 cm. wide. Find the area of the upper surface of the sheet.

*6. Taking the mean distance of the Earth from the Sun to be $1·51 \times 10^8$ km. and the length of the year to be $365\frac{1}{4}$ days, find the speed of the Earth in its orbit (assumed circular) in miles per hour. [1 mi. = 1·609 km.]

7. A cylindrical ruler, 1·5 in. in diameter, is 18 in. long. Find its volume.

[8] Find the weight of a cylindrical iron bar, 5·27 dm. long, 6·4 cm. in diameter, if the iron weighs 7·72 gm. per c.c.

9. Find the inside area in sq. ft. of a wall 4 ft. 9 in. high, enclosing a circular courtyard, diameter 65 ft.

10. An oil drum, diameter 2 ft. 3 in., holds 50 gall. Find its height.

[11] Find the area of the ring bounded by two concentric circles, radii 15·7 cm., 21·4 cm. respectively.

[12] An open jam-jar is 4·5 in. in diameter and 5·5 in. high, external measurements. Find the total area of the external surface.

13. A circular lead disc of radius $10\frac{1}{2}$ in. weighs 824·6 oz. Find its thickness if 1 cu. in. of lead weighs 6·52 oz.

[14] Find the perimeter of a semicircular plate of radius 3·85 in.

15. The section of a tunnel $1\frac{1}{4}$ mi. long is a semicircle 23 ft. in diameter. Find in sq. yd. the area of the internal curved surface.

16. The volume of a cylinder 6 in. long is 1 cu. in. Find the diameter of the cross-section.

[17] A cylindrical boiler holds 176 gall. and is 3 ft. long. Find its internal radius in inches.

*18. Find the area of sheet tin required to make a closed cylindrical tin 4 in. in diameter, 9 in. high, if the lid overlaps $\frac{1}{2}$ in. all round. [No allowance is to be made for the join up the side of the tin.]

*19. A cylindrical tin holds 1 pt. A second tin is half the height but $1\frac{1}{2}$ times the diameter of the first; how much does it hold?

20. Water flows at 6 ft. per second through a pipe of diameter $2\frac{1}{2}$ in. How many hours will it take to fill a tank 40 ft. long, 30 ft. broad, 8 ft. deep if the pipe remains full?

[21] A tank 12 ft. by 8 ft. by 6 ft. is filled in 2 hr. by a pipe through which water flows at 3 ft. per second. Find the diameter of the pipe.

22. Find the weight in cwt. of 100 ft. of lead pipe, internal diameter 1 in., and 0·2 in. thick, if 1 cu. ft. of lead weighs 708 lb.

[23] Find in sq. yd. the area of a path 3 ft. wide which runs round a circular pond of area $\frac{1}{2}$ ac.

*24. Paper 3000 ft. long, $\frac{1}{100}$ in. thick, is wrapped round a cylinder, radius 3 in. Find the radius of the whole roll in inches.

*25. 5 mi. of paper is wound on to a roller, diameter 6 in., the complete roll being 3 ft. in diameter. Find the thickness of the paper in inches.

Circular Cone. Cut out a sector of a circle and fold it into the form of a funnel. The surface so obtained is called a *circular cone* : we can regard it as a right pyramid with a circular base.

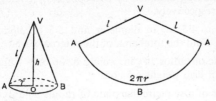

If V is the vertex of the cone, and if O is the centre of the base and AB a diameter of the base, the line VO is called the *axis* of the cone and its length is called the *height* of the cone; VA is called a slant side of the cone and its length is called the *slant length* or the *slant height* of the cone.

If a cut is made along VA and if the curved surface is then folded flat, we obtain a sector of a circle, centre V, radius VA, as shown.

If the slant length of the cone is *l* in., and if the base-radius is *r* in., then VA =*l* in. and arc ABA of sector =$2\pi r$ in.

Since the circumference of the complete circle, of which the sector is a part, is $2\pi l$ in., the area of the sector is $\dfrac{2\pi r}{2\pi l}$ of this complete circle.

$$\therefore \text{ area of sector} = \frac{2\pi r}{2\pi l} \text{ of } \pi l^2 \text{ sq. in.} = \pi r l \text{ sq. in.}$$

$$\therefore \textbf{ area of curved surface of cone} = \pi \textbf{rl sq. in.}$$

Also since a cone may be regarded as a pyramid, its volume is given by the rule, $\frac{1}{3}$ area of base × height ;

$$\therefore \textbf{ volume of cone} = \tfrac{1}{3}\pi\textbf{r}^2\textbf{h cu. in.}$$

By Pythagoras, the values of *l*, *r*, *h* are connected by the relation,

$$\textbf{r}^2 + \textbf{h}^2 = \textbf{l}^2.$$

EXERCISE 160

[Give answers to 3 figures; log π = ·4971]

Find the volume of a circular cone, given :

1. Height, 4 in.; area of base, 15 sq. in.

[2] Height, 8 cm.; radius of base, 3 cm.

3. Height, 3 in.; slant length, 5 in.

4. Height, 5 in.; perimeter of base, 8 in.

[5] Height, 6·14 in.; slant length, 8·36 in.

Find the area of the curved surface of a circular cone, given:

6. Slant length, 8 cm.; base-radius, 6 cm.

[7] Slant length, 13 cm.; height, 12 cm.

*8. Slant length, 7 in.; perimeter of base, 15 in.

9. Height, 8 in.; base-diameter, 1 ft.

*10. Slant length, 9·5 in.; height, 7·2 in.

11. Find the height of a cone whose base-radius is 4·72 in., and whose volume is 56·8 cu. in.

12. The length of the arc of a sector of a circle is 6 cm. and the radius of the circle is 4 cm.; find the area of the sector.

[13] The area of a sector of a circle of radius 5 in. is 20 sq. in.; find the length of the arc of the sector.

14. The base of a conical tent is 15 ft. in diameter and the height is 9 ft. Find (i) the volume of the tent, (ii) the area of the canvas used for making it.

*15. Find the height of a cone if the area of the curved surface is 100 sq. in. and the base-radius is 4·5 in.

16. A conical block of silver has a slant edge of 20 in. and base-radius 12 in. How many coins $\frac{1}{8}$ in. thick and $1\frac{1}{2}$ in. in diameter can be made from it?

*17. A conical tent of capacity 600 cu. ft. stands on a circular base of area 160 sq. ft. Find in sq. ft. the area of the canvas.

*18. The inside of a glass is an inverted cone, height 5 in.; diameter of top 3 in.; it contains $\frac{1}{8}$ pt. of wine. What is the depth at the centre? Use the fact that the depth is proportional to the diameter of the surface of the wine; if the depth is $5x$ in., the diameter of the surface is $3x$ in. [1 gall. = 277·3 cu. in.]

The Sphere. An object shaped like a tennis ball is called a sphere.

If the radius of a sphere is r inches, it can be proved that

$$\text{area of surface of sphere} = 4\pi r^2 \text{ sq. in.;}$$
$$\text{volume of sphere} = \tfrac{4}{3}\pi r^3 \text{ cu. in.}$$

21

Example 8. The volume of a sphere is 8 cu. in.; find, to **3** figures, the area of its surface.

	Number	Log.
	6	·7782
	π	·4971
	$6 \div \pi$	·2811
	$\sqrt[3]{(6 \div \pi)}$	·0937
	$\{\sqrt[3]{(6 \div \pi)}\}^2$	·1874
	4	·6021
	π	·4971
	Area	1·2866

If the radius of the sphere is r in.,

$$\tfrac{4}{3}\pi r^3 = 8; \quad \therefore \ r^3 = \tfrac{6}{\pi}; \quad \therefore \ r = \sqrt[3]{(\tfrac{6}{\pi})}.$$

$\therefore$ area of surface $= 4\pi r^2$ sq. in.

$\qquad = 4\pi \left(\sqrt[3]{\tfrac{6}{\pi}}\right)^2$ sq. in.

$\qquad = 19\cdot34$ sq. in.

$\therefore$ area of surface $= 19\cdot3$ sq. in., to 3 figures.

Example 9. A hollow copper sphere weighs 10 lb. and its external diameter is 6 in. If the cavity is spherical, find its radius, to 3 figures, given that 1 cu. ft. of copper weighs 548·2 lb.

If the radius of the cavity is r in., the volume of the cavity is $\tfrac{4}{3}\pi r^3$ cu. in.; also the volume of the sphere is $\tfrac{4}{3}\pi \times 3^3$ cu. in.;

$\therefore$ the volume of the copper is $(\tfrac{4}{3}\pi \times 27 - \tfrac{4}{3}\pi r^3)$ cu. in.;

but 1 cu. in. of copper weighs $(548\cdot2 \div 1728)$ lb.,

$\therefore$ the weight of the copper is $\{\tfrac{4}{3}\pi(27 - r^3) \times 548\cdot2 \div 1728\}$ lb.

	Logarithms	
$\therefore \ \tfrac{4}{3}\pi(27 - r^3) \times 548\cdot2 \div 1728 = 10;$	1·4771	·6021
$\therefore \ 27 - r^3 = \frac{10 \times 3 \times 1728}{4 \times \pi \times 548\cdot2} = 7\cdot523;$	3·2375	·4971
	4·7146	2·7390
$\therefore \ r^3 = 27 - 7\cdot523 = 19\cdot477;$	3·8382	3·8382
$\therefore \ r = \sqrt[3]{19\cdot48} = 2\cdot690.$	0·8764	

$\therefore$ the radius of the cavity is 2·69 in., to 3 figures.

$3)\overline{1\cdot2896}$

$\qquad \overline{\cdot4299}$

EXERCISE 161

[Give answers to 3 figures; $\log \pi = \cdot4971$]

Find the volume and area of the surface of a sphere, given:

1. Radius, 2·63 in.   **[2]** Diameter, 7·28 cm.

Find the radius of a sphere, given:

3. Volume, 4256 cu. cm.   **[4]** Area of surface, 9·84 sq. in.

5. Find the volume of a sphere whose surface is 74·5 sq. cm.

[6] Find the surface of a sphere whose volume is 48·72 cu. in.

7. 8 spheres, each of radius 1 in., are fitted into a hollow cube, side 4 in., internal measurements. Find the volume of the unoccupied space inside the cube.

8. A cylindrical tank 4 ft. in diameter contains water to a depth of 3 ft.; a solid metal sphere, diameter 3 ft., is placed in it. Find in inches the rise of the water-level.

[9] 10 dozen lead spheres, each of diameter 3 in., are melted and recast in the form of a cylinder 1 ft. in diameter. Find its height.

10. A hemispherical bowl, diameter 6 in., full of water, is emptied into an empty cylindrical glass, diameter 4 in., both measurements being internal. Find the depth of water in the glass.

11. A cylindrical measuring-glass contains water up to the mark 12·6 c.c. When a solid metal sphere is dropped into it, the water rises to the mark 14·7 c.c. Find the diameter of the sphere.

12. Find the total area of the surface of a solid hemisphere of diameter 6·58 in.

[13] Find the weight of a solid lead hemisphere of diameter 5 cm., if 1 c.c. of lead weighs 11·4 gm.

14. Shrapnel bullets are spherical and weigh 41 to the lb. and are made of metal weighing 682 lb. per cu. ft. Find the diameter of a bullet in inches.

15. Find in lb. the weight of a hollow iron ball, external diameter 1 ft., thickness 1 in., if i cu. ft. of iron weighs 748 lb.

*16. The external diameter of a hollow metal sphere is 12 cm. and its thickness is 2 cm. Find the radius of a solid sphere made of the same material and having the same weight as the hollow sphere.

*17. A hollow metal sphere of radius 3 in. weighs 20 lb. If the cavity is spherical, find its radius, given that the metal weighs 448 lb. per cu. ft.

18. A gasometer is in the form of a cylinder with a hemispherical cap; its height is 30 ft. at the sides and its diameter is 28 ft., internal measurements. Find in cu. ft. the volume of gas it holds.

*19. A conical vessel has a hemispherical lid. The total height when closed is 18 cm. and the maximum girth is 48 cm. Find (i) the volume, (ii) the total area of the surface of the vessel.

*20. A test-tube consists of a hollow cylindrical tube joined to a hemispherical bowl of the same internal radius. The whole tube holds 304 c.c. of water, and the water in the cylindrical portion falls 1 cm. if 19·7 c.c. of water are removed. Find the internal radius and the length of the cylindrical portion of the tube.

Similar Figures and Similar Solids. Two plane figures or two solids are called *similar* if the larger can be regarded as a magnification of the smaller; that is, if all corresponding angles are equal and if the ratio of any two corresponding lengths is constant, this constant being equal to the (linear) magnification.

Thus if the sides of a rectangle, 6 in. by 9 in., are magnified in the ratio $\frac{5}{3}$, we obtain a rectangle, 10 in. by 15 in., which is said to be similar to the original rectangle.

$$\text{The ratio of their areas} = \frac{10 \times 15}{6 \times 9} = \frac{5}{3} \times \frac{5}{3} = \left(\frac{5}{3}\right)^2;$$

thus the ratio of their areas equals the square of the magnification. It can be proved geometrically that if any two plane figures are similar, *the ratio of the area of the larger to the area of the smaller is equal to the square of the magnification*; that is, the square of the ratio of the length of any line in the larger figure to the length of the corresponding line in the smaller figure.

For example, if two triangles are similar, the ratio of their areas equals the square of the ratio of corresponding sides, or the square of the ratio of corresponding altitudes.

Any two circles are similar; the ratio of their areas equals the square of the ratio of their radii. If the radii are a in., b in., ratio of areas $= \frac{\pi a^2}{\pi b^2} = \left(\frac{a}{b}\right)^2$.

If the edges of a rectangular block, 6 in. by 9 in. by 12 in., are magnified in the ratio $\frac{5}{3}$, we obtain a rectangular block, 10 in. by 15 in. by 20 in., which is said to be similar to the original rectangular block.

The ratio of their volumes $= \frac{10 \times 15 \times 12}{6 \times 9 \times 12} = \frac{5}{3} \times \frac{5}{3} \times \frac{5}{3} = \left(\frac{5}{3}\right)^3;$ thus the ratio of their volumes equals the cube of the magnification. Also since their surfaces are composed of similar figures, the ratio of the areas of their surfaces equals the square of the magnification.

It can be proved geometrically that if any two solids are similar, *the ratio of the volume of the larger to the volume of the smaller is equal to the cube of the magnification*, and that *the ratio of the area of the surface of the larger to that of the smaller is equal to the square of the magnification*.

Example 10. Two solid spheres, diameters 4 in., 5 in., are made of the same material. The smaller weighs 120 lb., find the weight of the larger.

$$\frac{\text{Weight of larger}}{\text{Weight of smaller}} = \frac{\text{Volume of larger}}{\text{Volume of smaller}} = (\tfrac{5}{4})^3;$$

∴ weight of larger $= \{120 \times (\tfrac{5}{4})^3\}$ lb. $= \frac{120 \times 125}{64}$ lb. $= 234\tfrac{3}{8}$ lb.

Example 11. Two similar solids are in the form of a hemisphere surmounted by a cone; their heights are 20 in. and 30 in. It costs 45 shillings to gild the larger; how much does it cost to gild the smaller?

$$\frac{\text{Cost for smaller}}{\text{Cost for larger}} = \frac{\text{Area of surface of smaller}}{\text{Area of surface of larger}} = (\tfrac{20}{30})^2 = \tfrac{4}{9};$$

∴ cost for smaller $= (45 \times \tfrac{4}{9})$s. $= 20$s. $= £1$.

Example 12. An estate is represented by an area of 1·2 sq. in. on a map whose scale is $\frac{1}{50,000}$. By what area is it represented on a map whose scale is $\frac{1}{20,000}$?

The second map is an *enlargement* of the first map, and the magnification is $\tfrac{5}{2}$.

Therefore an area of 1·2 sq. in. on the first map is enlarged into an area of $1·2 \times (\tfrac{5}{2})^2$ sq. in. on the second map.

∴ area on second map $= (0·3 \times 25)$ sq. in. $= 7·5$ sq. in.

EXERCISE 162

Find the ratio of the areas of two similar triangles, given :

1. Two corresponding sides are 4 in., 6 in.

[2] Two corresponding altitudes are 15 cm., 6 cm.

3. Their perimeters are 120 yd., 144 yd.

Find the ratio of (i) the volumes, (ii) the areas of the surfaces of :

4. Two spheres, diameters 3 in., 4·5 in.

[5] Two similar solid cylinders, girths 15 cm., 12 cm.

6. Two similar solid cones, heights 9 in., 15 in.

7. The weight of a cube, edge 8 cm., is 320 gm.; find the weight of a cube, edge 1 dm., of the same material.

[8] The weight of a sphere, diameter 8 in., is 160 lb.; find the weight of a sphere, diameter 5 in., of the same material.

9. A water-can, height 15 in., diameter 10 in., holds $4\frac{1}{2}$ gall. How much does a can of the same shape, 10 in. high, hold?

[10] Two similar tankards are respectively 5 in. and 7 in. high; the smaller holds a pint; how much does the larger hold?

11. It costs 36s. to gild a sphere of diameter $4\frac{1}{2}$ in.; how much will it cost to gild a sphere of diameter $7\frac{1}{2}$ in.?

*12. A plaster model of a statue is 2 ft. high and weighs 24 lb. If the statue is 9 ft. high and is made in stone which is $2\frac{1}{2}$ times as heavy as the plaster, find the weight of the statue in tons.

[13] The areas of two circles are 9·6 sq. in. and 15 sq. in.; find the ratio of their diameters.

14. The volumes of two spheres are 500 c.c. and 108 c.c.; find the ratio of (i) their diameters, (ii) the areas of their surfaces.

15. The tobacco in a tin 6 in. high lasts me 8 days. How long will the tobacco in a tin of the same shape 9 in. high last me?

16. The ratio of the areas of the surfaces of two hemispheres is 5 : 4. Find in the form $n : 1$, giving n to 3 figures, the ratio of (i) their diameters, (ii) their volumes.

[17] The ratio of the volumes of two similar cones is 3 : 2. Find in the form $n : 1$, giving n to 3 figures, the ratio of (i) their heights, (ii) the areas of their surfaces.

18. A golf course occupies 185 acres. By what area is it represented on a map of scale (i) 2 inches to the mile, (ii) 1 inch to the mile?

*19. An estate is represented by an area of 3·75 sq. in. on a map whose scale is $\frac{1}{10,000}$. By what area is it represented on a map whose scale is $\frac{1}{25,000}$?

*20. If the surface of a soap bubble increases by 21%, find the percentage increase in (i) its diameter, (ii) its volume.

*21. If 1 pt. of water is poured into a conical vessel, the depth of the water is 4 in. How much more water must be added to make the depth 6 in.?

*22. If 1 pt. of water is poured into a conical vessel, the area of the wet surface is 40 sq. in.; what is the increase in the area of the wet surface if 7 more pints are added?

*23. A tank can be filled by a 3-in. pipe in 40 min. How long will it take if a 4-in. pipe is used, the rate of flow being the same?

MISCELLANEOUS EXAMPLES

EXERCISE 163

[Give answers to 3 figures. Logarithm tables should be used where suitable]

1. A bushel of grass seed, costing 2s. per lb., weighs 25 lb. Find the cost of seed for a lawn 78 ft. by 36 ft. if 8 bushels are required per acre.

[2] ABCD is a field. B is 284 yd. east of A; C is 215 yd. north of B; D is 194 yd. west of C. Find in acres the area of the field.

3. The unshaded part of the square in the diagram consists of a square and four equal trapeziums. Find its area.

4. Find the area of the figure represented in the diagram if all the corners, except two, are right-angled.

[5] A corridor is 20 yd. long, 7 ft. 6 in. wide. It is covered with carpet at 6s. 3d. per sq. yd. down the middle, with a margin 18 in. wide along each side which is laid with wooden blocks $4\frac{1}{2}$ in. by 9 in. at £2 10s. per 100. Find the cost of (i) the carpet, (ii) the blocks.

6. The internal length and breadth of a petrol can are $9\frac{7}{8}$ in., $5\frac{3}{4}$ in. Find the depth of a can which holds $2\frac{1}{4}$ gall. [1 gall. $=277\cdot3$ cu. in.]

7. A railway embankment is 20 ft. wide at the top, 40 ft. wide at the bottom, and 11 ft. high. Find the number of tons required for 50 yd. of embankment, assuming that 1 cu. ft. of earth weighs 120 lb.

[8] The base of a wooden wedge 9 in. long is a triangle whose sides are 2 in., 4 in., 4 in. long. Find the weight of the wedge if 1 cu. in. of the wood weighs $0\cdot365$ oz.

[9] Find the radius of a circle whose circumference is $8\cdot34$ cm.

10. Find the circumference of a circle whose area is 20 sq. yd.

11. A cylindrical tank, without a cover, holds 100 litres. The internal diameter is 40 cm.; find the total area of the internal surface.

*12. Find the area of the quadrilateral ABCD, given that AB = 6 in., BC = 8 in., CD = 9 in., DA = 7 in., ∠ ABC = 90°.

13. A rectangular area on a map measures 2·87 in. by 4·18 in. approximately and represents an area of 58,000 sq. yd. Find the scale of the map in the form, 1 : *n*.

14. The diagram represents the vertical section of a bridge, in the form of a rectangle from which a semicircle has been removed. The bridge is 14 ft. wide and is made of material weighing 112 lb. per cu. ft. Find the weight of the bridge in tons, and the cost of painting the curved surface under the bridge at 1s. 3d. per sq. yd.

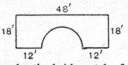

[15] A circular cylinder, height 20 cm., diameter 12 cm., is half-full of water. If 6 circular discs, each 4 cm. in diameter and 3 mm. thick, are dropped into it and totally submerged, find the rise of the water-level.

16. Find the volume of a circular cone if its height is 6·54 in. and the diameter of its base is 8·28 in.

*17. The length of the arc of a sector of a circle, of radius 5 in., is 18 in. If the sector is folded to form the curved surface of a cone (without overlap), find (i) the base-radius of the cone, (ii) the area of the curved surface of the cone, (iii) the height of the cone.

18. A circular cylinder, internal diameter 8 in., height 10 in., contains water to a depth of 6 in.; two solid lead spheres each of diameter 4 in. are placed in it. Find the height the water-level rises.

*19. The base of a tank is a square ABCD, side 5 ft., and the tank is 3 ft. high. It contains water to a depth of 2 ft., the base being horizontal. The tank is now tilted slowly about the edge BC until the edge AD is in the surface of the water. How much water has run out?

*20. A piece of ground in the shape of a rectangle 100 yd. by 80 yd., with a semicircle on each short side as diameter, is surrounded by a running-track 15 ft. wide. The track is to be covered to a depth of 3 in. with cinders weighing 70 lb. per cu. ft. Find in tons the weight of the cinders required.

CHAPTER XXI

SPECIFIC GRAVITY

The **mass** of a unit of volume of a substance is called its **density**. Any units may be selected, but must be specified. Masses are estimated by using the fact that the ratio of the masses of two bodies is equal to the ratio of their weights at the same place. The statement that a body weighs 2 lb. is an abbreviation for the statement that its weight equals the weight of a body of mass 2 lb. at the same place.

Thus for copper, 1 cu. in. weighs 5·1 oz., 1 cu. cm. weighs 8·8 gm.; therefore the density of copper can be given as

5·1 oz. per cu. in.   or   8·8 gm. per cu. cm.

For many purposes it is useful to compare the weight of a substance with the weight of the same volume of water. In the metric system the weight of 1 gm. was chosen as the weight of 1 c.c. of water (at 4° C.),

∴ *the density of water is* 1 *gm. per c.c.*

In British units, it is found that 1 cu. ft. of water weighs about 1000 oz., or, more accurately, 62·3 lb. (weighed in air at ordinary temperature),

∴ *the density of water is* 62·3 *lb. per cu. ft.*

The **ratio** of the weight of any volume of a substance to the weight of an equal volume of water (at 4° C.) is called the **specific gravity** of the substance. Since the specific gravity is a ratio, it does not depend on the units chosen. The abbreviation for specific gravity is sp. gr.

For example, the statement that "the sp. gr. of silver is 10·5" means that any volume of silver is 10·5 times as heavy as the same volume of water.

Since 1 c.c. of water weighs 1 gm., 1 c.c. of silver weighs 10·5 gm.; since 1 cu. ft. of water weighs 62·3 lb., 1 cu. ft. of silver weighs (62·3 × 10·5) lb.

Example 1. A sheet of plate glass is 15 in. long, 8 in. wide, and $\frac{1}{4}$ in. thick. Find its weight, to the nearest oz., if the density of the glass is 1·63 oz. per cu. in.

The volume of the glass $= (15 \times 8 \times \frac{1}{4})$ cu. in. $= 30$ cu. in.;
∴ its weight $= (1·63 \times 30)$ oz. $= 49$ oz., to nearest oz.

Example 2. The density of steel is 486 lb. per cu. ft.; find, to 2 figures, its specific gravity.

1 cu. ft. of steel weighs 486 lb.

1 cu. ft. of water weighs 62·3 lb.

∴ sp. gr. of steel $=\frac{486}{62\cdot3}=7\cdot8$ to 2 figures.

Logarithms
2·6866
1·7945
‾‾‾‾‾‾
·8921

Example 3. A rectangular tin, 16 cm. by 12 cm., contains petrol (sp. gr. 0·68) to a depth of 25 cm. Find, to 2 figures, the weight of the petrol.

1 c.c. of water weighs 1 gm.,   ∴ 1 c.c. of petrol weighs 0·68 gm.

But volume of petrol $=(16\times12\times25)$ c.c. $=4800$ c.c.

∴ weight of petrol $=(0\cdot68\times4800)$ gm. $=3264$ gm.

$=3\cdot3$ kg., to 2 figures.

Example 4. Find, to the nearest cu. in., the volume of a lump of lead weighing 50 lb., given that the sp. gr. of lead is 11·4.

1 cu. ft. of water weighs 62·3 lb.,

∴ 1 cu. ft. of lead weighs $(62\cdot3\times11\cdot4)$ lb.;

∴ $(62\cdot3\times11\cdot4)$ lb. is the weight of 1728 cu. in. of lead.

∴ 50 lb. is the weight of $\frac{1728\times50}{62\cdot3\times11\cdot4}$ cu. in.,

that is, 121·6 cu. in.;

∴ volume $=120$ cu. in., to 2 figures.

3·2375 | 1·7945
1·6990 | 1·0569
‾‾‾‾‾ | ‾‾‾‾‾
4·9365 | 2·8514
2·8514 |
‾‾‾‾‾ |
2·0851 |

Example 5. A flask when empty weighs 16·3 gm., when full of water weighs 61·7 gm., and when full of spirit weighs 52·6. Find, to 2 figures, the sp. gr. of the spirit.

The weight of the empty flask $=16\cdot3$ gm.,

∴ the weight of the water in the flask $=(61\cdot7-16\cdot3)$ gm. $=45\cdot4$ gm.;
and the weight of the *same volume* of spirit $=(52\cdot6-16\cdot3)$ gm. $=36\cdot3$ gm.

∴ the ratio of the weight of a certain volume of spirit to the weight of the *same volume* of water

$$=\tfrac{36\cdot3}{45\cdot4}=0\cdot7995.$$

1·5599
1·6571
‾‾‾‾‾
1·9028

∴ the sp. gr. of the spirit $=0\cdot80$, to 2 figures.

Note. It was unnecessary to state the volume of the alcohol in the flask, because the specific gravity is the ratio of the weight of *any volume* to the weight of the *same volume* of water. A flask used in this way to find the specific gravity of a substance is called a *specific gravity bottle*.

The *approximate* data contained in the following table should be used, where necessary, in Exercise 164 :—

Specific Gravity Table

Platinum, 21·2	Wrought iron, 7·75	Glycerine, 1·25
Gold, 19·3	Tin, cast iron, 7·25	Ebony, 1·20
Mercury, 13·6	Plate-glass, 2·75	Alcohol, 0·78
Lead, 11·4	Aluminium, 2·65	Petrol, 0·68
Silver, 10·5	Sulphur, 2·05	Elm, 0·55
Copper, 8·85	Sulphuric acid, 1·85	Cork, 0·24

1 cu. ft. of water weighs 62·3 lb.
1 gall. of water weighs 10 lb.

EXERCISE 164

[Give answers to 2 figures]

1. Find the weight of a rectangular block of wood, 8 in. by 6 in. by 5 in., if the density is 0·45 oz. per cu. in.

2. Find the weight of a rectangular block of stone, 40 cm. by 35 cm. by 3·6 cm.; sp. gr. 2·6.

3. A rectangular metal block, 4 cm. by 3 cm. by 2 cm., weighs 195·4 gm.; find the sp. gr. of the metal.

4. A cubic foot of a metal weighs 516·7 lb.; find its specific gravity.

5. A block of ebony weighs 62·4 gm.; find its volume in c.c.

6. A lump of gold weighs 38 oz.; find its volume in cu. in.

[7] A metal bar, sp. gr. 7·18, has a circular cross-section of diameter 4·8 cm., and is 1 m. long. Find its weight.

[8] A cylindrical wooden stick 91 cm. long is 1·8 cm. in diameter and weighs 170 gm. Find the sp. gr. of the wood.

9. A rectangular block of limestone, 23 ft. by 14 ft. by 10 ft., weighs 210 tons. Find its specific gravity.

[10] A solid silver cone is 6 in. high and the diameter of its base is 3 in.; find its weight in oz.

[11] The diameter of a lead sphere is 2·8 cm.; find its weight.

12. The outer diameter of a pipe is 5·6 cm. and its bore (*i.e.* internal diameter) is 4·9 cm. If the material is of sp. gr. 7·4, find the weight of a length of 10 m. of pipe.

[13] A cylindrical tank, 10 ft. high, 6 ft. in diameter, inside measurements, is full of petrol. Find in lb. the weight of the petrol.

14. A cylindrical tube is 10 cm. long and holds 66 gm. of mercury when full. Find the internal diameter of the tube.

[15] The external dimensions of a closed wooden box (sp. gr. 0·65) are as follows: length 3 ft., breadth 2 ft., depth 1 ft. 8 in. If the wood is $\frac{1}{2}$ in. thick, find in lb. the weight of the box.

[16] A barometer tube 125 cm. long has internal diameter 1·2 cm.; find the cost of filling it with mercury at 10s. 6d. per kg.

17. Some metal shot weighing 48 gm. are dropped into a tall cylindrical glass, diameter 2 cm., half-full of water. If the water-level rises 1·4 cm., find the sp. gr. of the metal.

18. A flask weighs 23 gm. when empty, 141·7 gm. when full of water, and 102·6 gm. when full of another liquid. Find the sp. gr. of the liquid.

[19] A bottle weighs 7 oz. when empty, 18 oz. when full of water, and 17·1 oz. when full of oil. Find the sp. gr. of the oil.

20. A flask weighs 15 gm. when empty and weighs 84·3 gm. when full of water. Find its weight when full of alcohol.

*21. 20 equal ball-bearings and a small stoppered bottle full of water together weigh 53·62 gm. If the ball-bearings are placed inside the bottle which is then filled up with water, the weight is 49·87 gm. Find the volume of 1 ball-bearing.

*22. If 8 c.c. of a liquid, sp. gr. 0·65, are mixed with 12 c.c. of a liquid, sp. gr. 0·85, find the sp. gr. of the mixture, assuming there is no chemical action.

*23. The composition by *weight* of a mixture is 30% water, 70% alcohol. Find the sp. gr. of the mixture.

*24. A bottle when empty weighs 32 gm. and when full of sulphuric acid weighs 115·6 gm. What will it weigh when full of alcohol?

*25. An alloy is made of two metals, sp. gr. 18 and sp. gr. 10. Find its sp. gr. if (i) equal volumes, (ii) equal weights, of the two metals are used.

The Principle of Archimedes. It is assumed that the meaning of Archimedes' Principle will be demonstrated *experimentally*; the illustrative examples given below indicate its applications. The Principle may be stated as follows :—

If a body is immersed, wholly or partially, in a fluid, the upward (vertical) thrust which the fluid exerts on the body is equal to the weight of the fluid displaced.

Example 6. A block of wood, sp. gr. 0·7, of volume 120 c.c. is floating in water. Find the volume of the submerged portion of the block.

The weight of water displaced = the weight of the block
$$= (120 \times 0·7 \text{ gm.}) = 84 \text{ gm.};$$
∴ the volume of the water displaced is 84 c.c.
∴ the volume of the submerged portion of the block is 84 c.c.

Example 7. A lump of metal weighs 73 gm. in air and appears to weigh 63·5 gm. in water and 64·7 gm. in another liquid. Find the sp. gr. of (i) the metal, (ii) the other liquid.

The upward thrust of the water on the lump
$$= (73 - 63·5) \text{ gm.} = 9·5 \text{ gm.};$$
∴ the weight of a volume of water equal to the volume of the lump is 9·5 gm.

$$\therefore \text{ sp. gr. of metal} = \frac{\text{weight of any volume of metal}}{\text{weight of } same \text{ volume of water}}$$

$$= \frac{73 \text{ gm.}}{9·5 \text{ gm.}} = \frac{73}{9·5} = 7·7.$$

The upward thrust of the other fluid on the lump
$$= (73 - 64·7) \text{ gm.} = 8·3 \text{ gm.};$$
∴ the weight of a volume of the fluid equal to the volume of the lump is 8·3 gm.; but the weight of the *same* volume of water is 9·5 gm.

$$\therefore \text{ sp. gr. of other fluid} = \frac{8·3 \text{ gm.}}{9·5 \text{ gm.}} = \frac{8·3}{9·5} = 0·87.$$

EXERCISE 165

[*Give answers to 2 figures; 1 cu. ft. of water weighs 62·3 lb.*]

1. A block of wood floats in water so that the volume of the submerged portion is 36 c.c.; find the weight of the block.

[2] A block of wood floats in a liquid of sp. gr. 0·8 so that the volume of the submerged portion is 55 c.c.; find the weight of the block.

3. A wooden cuboid, 5 cm. by 4 cm. by 3 cm., sp. gr. 0·65, is floating in water. Find the volume of water displaced.

4. A block of wood floats in water so that the volume of the submerged portion is 10 cu. in.; find the weight of the block.

5. A body is floating in a liquid of sp. gr. 1·35 and the volume of the portion submerged is 8·5 cu. in.; find the weight of the body.

*6. A body of weight 100 lb. floats in water with ⅗ of its volume below the surface. Find the volume of the body in cu. ft.

[7] A lead cuboid, sp. gr. 11·4, measures 2 cm. by 3 cm. by 4 cm. Find its weight (i) in air, (ii) in water, (iii) in glycerine, sp. gr. 1·25.

8. A lump of brass weighs 10 lb. Find its apparent weight in glycerine, sp. gr. 1·25, given that 1 cu. ft. of brass weighs 520 lb.

9. A lump of stone weighs 65 gm., and its apparent weight in water is 35 gm. Find (i) its volume, (ii) its sp. gr., (iii) its apparent weight in a liquid of sp. gr. 1·4.

[10] A body weighs 157 gm. in air and 99 gm. in water. Find (i) its sp. gr., (ii) its apparent weight in a liquid of sp. gr. 0·8.

[11] A body, sp. gr. 7·40, weighs 135 gm. in air. Find its weight (i) in water, (ii) in a liquid of sp. gr. 0·65.

12. Find the apparent weight in spirit, sp. gr. 0·78, of a copper cylinder 4·7 cm. long, 0·68 cm. in diameter, if the sp. gr. of the copper is 8·85.

CHAPTER XXII

COMPOUND INTEREST

The connection between simple and compound interest was explained in Chapter XV, see p. 208. The following examples indicate the method for computing the amount of a sum of money lent at compound interest. To obtain results correct to the nearest penny, it is necessary to keep 5 places of decimals, working in £, so that the final result can be written down correct to 3 places.

Example 1. Find the compound interest on £317 for 3 yr. at 4% per annum, payable yearly.

The interest on £317 for 1 yr. is $\frac{4}{100}$ of £317; therefore the interest is obtained by multiplying 317 by 4 and *starting two places to the right* when writing down the result.

(a) Interest for 2nd year is obtained by multiplying 329·68 by 4, and *starting two places to the right*.

(b) Interest for 3rd year is obtained by multiplying 342·8672 by 4, and starting 2 places to the right. But as only 5 places of decimals are retained we put a comma after the 7 in 342·8672 and multiply 342·867 by 4; since, however, $2 \times 4 = 8$, we may carry 1 from the place that has been omitted, although usually the final answer (correct to 3 places) is not affected if we omit to do so.

	£317	Princ. 1st year.
	12·68	Int. 1st year.
(a)	329·68	Princ. 2nd year.
	13·187 2	Int. 2nd year.
(b)	342·867,2	Princ. 3rd year.
	13·714 69	Int. 3rd year.
	356·581 89	Amount, 3 yr.
	317	*Deduct* 1st Princ.
	39·581 89	Comp. Int.

∴ compound interest = £39·582 to 3 places = £39 11s. 8d., to nearest penny.

Example 2. Find the amount at $2\frac{3}{4}$% compound interest, payable yearly, of £427 9s. 7d. (i) for 2 yr., (ii) for $2\frac{1}{2}$ yr.

First express 9s. 7d. as a decimal of £1 to 5 places;
$$9s.\ 7d. = 9·58333s. = £0·47917.$$

(a) Interest at 1% is $\frac{1}{100}$ of £427·47917 = £4·2747917; therefore interest at $\frac{1}{2}$% is obtained by dividing the Principal by 2 and starting two places to the right.

(b) Interest at $\frac{1}{4}$% is half the interest at $\frac{1}{2}$%; we therefore divide line (a) by 2.

(c) The interest for the final half-year is taken to be half the interest for one more year and is therefore calculated at the rate of $\frac{1}{2}$ of $2\frac{3}{4}$%, that is $1\frac{3}{8}$% of the Principal for the 3rd year.

(d) $\frac{1}{4}$% is $\frac{1}{4}$ of the 1% line; $\frac{1}{8}$% is $\frac{1}{2}$ of the $\frac{1}{4}$% line.

	£427·479,17	Princ. 1st year.
	8·549 58	Int. 2%.
(a)	2·137 39	Int. $\frac{1}{2}$%.
(b)	1·068 69	Int. $\frac{1}{4}$%.
	439·234,83	Princ. 2nd year.
	8·784 70	Int. 2%.
	2·196 17	Int. $\frac{1}{2}$%.
	1·098 08	Int. $\frac{1}{4}$%.
	451·313,78	Amount, 2 yr.
(c)	4·513 13	Int. 1%.
(d)	1·128 28	Int. $\frac{1}{4}$%.
	·564 14	Int. $\frac{1}{8}$%.
	457·519 33	Amount, $2\frac{1}{2}$ yr.

∴ amount after 2 yr. = £451·314, to 3 places
= £451 6s. 3d., to nearest penny,
and amount after $2\frac{1}{2}$ yr. = £457·519, to 3 places
= £457 10s. 5d., to nearest penny.

In the previous examples, the interest has been taken to be payable at yearly intervals. If, however, it is payable for shorter periods, the amount at the end of each period must be calculated.

Example 3. Find the compound interest on £287 15s. for $1\frac{1}{2}$ yr. at $4\frac{1}{2}\%$ per annum, interest being payable half-yearly.

The rate $4\frac{1}{2}\%$ per annum is equivalent to $(\frac{1}{2}$ of $4\frac{1}{2})\%$ per half-year, that is $2\frac{1}{4}\%$ half-yearly. We therefore calculate the compound interest for 3 half-yearly periods at $2\frac{1}{4}\%$ per period.

The $\frac{1}{4}\%$ line is found by dividing the Principal by 4 and starting two places to the right; as a check, observe that it is $\frac{1}{8}$ of the 2% line.

£287·75	Princ. 1st period.
5·7550	Int. 2%.
·71937	Int. $\frac{1}{4}\%$.
294·224,37	Princ. 2nd period.
5·884 49	
·735 56	
300·844,42	Princ. 3rd period.
6·016 89	
·752 11	
307·613 42	Amount, 3 periods.
287·75	*Deduct* 1st Princ.
19·863 42	Comp. Int.

$$\therefore \text{ compound interest} = £19{\cdot}863, \text{ to 3 places}$$
$$= £19 \text{ 17s. 3d., to nearest penny.}$$

Note. As a rough check, it is advisable to note that the corresponding items of the interest increase steadily from period to period; a rough estimate is obtained by calculating the simple interest on £300 for $1\frac{1}{2}$ years at $4\frac{1}{2}\%$ p.a.

Example 4. A man invests £6500 for 3 years at $4\frac{1}{2}\%$ p.a. compound interest, compounded yearly. Income tax at 4s. in the £ is deducted at the end of each year. Find the amount at the end of the third year.

Allow for the income tax deduction by altering the rate $\%$.

$$\text{Nominal rate } \% = 4\frac{1}{2};$$
$$\text{but deduction} = \tfrac{1}{5} \text{ of yearly interest};$$
$$\therefore \text{ net rate } \% = \tfrac{4}{5} \text{ of } 4\frac{1}{2} = 3\frac{3}{5}.$$

We therefore calculate the compound interest at the rate of $3\frac{3}{5}\%$ p.a.; the reader should now use the ordinary method to show that the net amount after 3 years is £7227 11s. 6d., to the nearest penny.

Example 5. A man borrows £400 at 4% p.a. compound interest, compounded yearly, and repays £33 at the end of each year.   Find the amount of the loan outstanding at beginning of the fourth year.

	£400	Princ. 1st period.
	16	Int. 4%.
Deduct	416	
	33	1st repayment.
	383·	Princ. 2nd period.
	15·32	
Deduct	398·32	
	33	2nd repayment.
	365·32	Princ. 3rd period.
	14·6128	
Deduct	379·9328	
	33	3rd repayment.
	346·9328	Outstanding loan.

∴ outstanding loan = £346 18s. 8d. to nearest penny.

EXERCISE 166

[Give answers correct to the nearest penny]

Find the compound interest (payable yearly) on the following
    sums for the stated periods and rates of interest :—

1. £240; 2 yr.; 4%.   [2] £370; 2 yr.; 3%.

3. £462; 2 yr.; 5%.   [4] £537; 2 yr.; 6%.

5. £328 10s.; 3 yr.; 6%.   [6] £271 4s. 6d.; 3 yr.; 4%.

[7] £108 8s. 7d.; 3 yr.; 5%.   8. £348 14s.; 2 yr.; $3\frac{1}{2}$%.

9. £92 11s. 8d.; 2 yr.; $5\frac{1}{4}$%. [10] £273 14s. 4d.; 2 yr.; $4\frac{3}{4}$%.

11. £473; $2\frac{1}{2}$ yr.; 6%.   [12] £547; $2\frac{1}{2}$ yr.; 5%.

[13] £819; $2\frac{1}{4}$ yr.; 7%.   14. £372; $2\frac{3}{4}$ yr.; 6%.

Find the amount at compound interest of :

[15] £2013 for $2\frac{1}{2}$ yr. at $3\frac{1}{2}$%, payable yearly.

[16] £9278 7s. 6d. for $2\frac{3}{4}$ yr. at 2%, payable yearly.

17. £285 for 1 yr. at 5% p.a., payable half-yearly.

[18] £473 for $1\frac{1}{2}$ yr. at $4\frac{1}{2}$% p.a., payable half-yearly.

19. £639 for 1 yr. at 6% p.a., payable quarterly.

[20] £5720 for 1 yr. at 5% p.a., payable quarterly.

M   22

Find the difference between the simple and compound interest (payable yearly) on the following sums for the stated periods and rates of interest :—

21. £350; 3 yr.; 3%.   [22] £220; 4 yr.; 5%.

23. £195 6s.; 3 yr.; 4%.   [24] £407 14s.; 3 yr.; $4\frac{1}{2}$%.

25. A district contains 64,000 inhabitants. If the population increases at the rate of $2\frac{1}{2}$% per annum, find the number of inhabitants at the end of 3 yr.

26. A man invests £2500 at 4% p.a., compounded yearly. Income tax at 5s. in the £ is deducted at the end of each year. Find the amount at the end of the third year.

[27] A man invests £850 at 3% p.a., compounded yearly. Income tax at 4s. in the £ is deducted at the end of each year. Find the amount at the end of the third year.

28. Find, as the decimal of £1, the compound interest on £1 for 3 yr. at 5% p.a., payable yearly. Hence find what sum will amount to £5556 12s. in 3 yr. at 5% p.a. compound interest.

29. Which is the better price for a property, £16,000 paid at once or £19,500 paid in 4 years' time, allowing $5\frac{1}{4}$% per annum compound interest?

*30. One moneylender charges interest at 24% per annum, payable monthly, and a second moneylender charges interest at 30% per annum, payable every 2 months. If a man borrows £100 from each of them, how much will he owe each at the end of 4 months? [Each month is reckoned as $\frac{1}{12}$ of a year.]

31. A man borrowed £500 at 5% p.a., the interest for any year being calculated on the total sum owing at the beginning of that year. He paid back £150 at the end of each of the first two years. What did he owe at the end of the third year?

[32] Find, as the decimal of £1, the difference between the simple and compound interest on £1 for 2 yr. at 3%, payable yearly. Hence find the sum on which the difference between the simple and compound interest for 2 yr. at 3% is £30 12s.

33. A man borrowed £650 on January 1, 1930, and repaid equal instalments of £243 on December 31 of each of the years 1930, 1931, 1932. Reckoning compound interest at 6% p.a., find how much had still to be paid at the end of 1933.

[34] A Corporation **borrowed** £40,000 at 5% p.a. compound interest, and repaid £4500 at the end of each year.   How much was still owing at the beginning of the 5th year?

*35. A man borrows £500 and pays it off in two equal instalments, one at the end of 1 yr. and the other 1 yr. later.   Find the size of each instalment to the nearest shilling, allowing compound interest at 4% p.a., payable yearly.

Compound Interest Formula

Example 6.   Find an expression for the amount of £250 at 3% p.a. compound interest for 12 yr.

£100 becomes £103 in 1 year's time,

∴ £1 becomes £1·03 in 1 year's time,

that is, £1 has been made 1·03 times larger.

∴ £250 becomes £250 × 1·03 in 1 year's time.

If this sum of money remains at interest for another year, it is again made 1·03 times larger,

∴ in 2 years £250 becomes £250 × 1·03 × 1·03, that is, £250$(1·03)^2$;

and in 3 years £250 becomes £250$(1·03)^2$ × 1·03, that is, £250$(1·03)^3$;

and so on.

Thus in 12 years, £250 becomes £250$(1·03)^{12}$.

If this amount is evaluated by 4-figure tables, the value of 12 times log 1·03 will only be correct to 2 or 3 places of decimals.   We therefore use 7-figure tables, which give (p. 342), log 1·03 = 0·0128372;

∴ 12 log 1·03 = 0·1540464.

∴ *Amount* = £356·4 = £356 8s.;

but in this result, the number of shillings is not reliable.

Number	Logarithm
250	2·3979
$(1·03)^{12}$	0·1540
Amount	2·5519

If 7-figure tables are used throughout, we have

Amount = £356·440

= £356 9s. to nearest shilling.

Number	Logarithm
250	2·3979400
$(1·03)^{12}$	0·1540464
Amount	2·5519864

From the compound interest tables on p. 342, we have

Amount = £(250 × 1·42576) = £356·44 = £356 9s. to nearest shilling.

Similarly in 9 years, reckoning compound interest,

at 3% p.a.,   £P becomes £P$(1·03)^9$;

at 4% p.a.,   £P becomes £P$(1·04)^9$;

at 2½% p.a.,   £P becomes £P$(1·025)^9$.

Oral Work. Read off expressions for what £400 becomes

(i) in 7 years at 2% p.a. compound interest;

(ii) in 8 years at 5% p.a. compound interest;

(iii) in 10 years at $3\frac{1}{2}$% p.a. compound interest;

(iv) in 15 years at $4\frac{1}{4}$% p.a. compound interest.

Hence we have the general formula:

The amount of £P for n years at r% p.a., compound interest, compounded yearly, is

$$£P\left(1+\frac{r}{100}\right)^n.$$

This is called the *compound interest law* and applies to any quantity which increases or decreases so that the amount at the end of each period of constant length bears a constant ratio to the amount at the beginning of that period; this ratio is called the *growth factor* if it is greater than 1, and the *decay factor* if less than 1.

For example, if the population of a town increases steadily by 2% p.a. of the amount at the beginning of each year, the yearly *growth factor* is $(1+\frac{2}{100})$, $=1 \cdot 02$, and the population after n yr. is $(1 \cdot 02)^n$ times the population at the beginning of that period. Similarly, if the value of the machinery in a factory depreciates steadily by 8% p.a. of its value at the beginning of each year, the yearly *decay factor* is $(1-\frac{8}{100})$, $=0 \cdot 92$, and the value after n yr. is $(0 \cdot 92)^n$ times its value when new.

EXERCISE 167 (Oral)

1. Write down as a decimal the growth factor or multiplying factor for 1 year for the following annual percentage increases:

4%; 3%; $2\frac{1}{2}$%; $5\frac{1}{4}$%; 10%; $3\frac{3}{4}$%.

2. Write down as a decimal the decay factor for 1 year for the following annual percentage decreases:

5%; 4%; $3\frac{1}{2}$%; $6\frac{1}{4}$%; 10%; $12\frac{3}{4}$%.

3. Write down the rate per cent. increases which are equivalent to the following growth factors:

$1 \cdot 02$; $1 \cdot 045$; $1 \cdot 0575$; $1 \cdot 2$; $1 \cdot 0325$.

4. Write down the rate per cent. decreases which are equivalent to the following decay factors:

$0 \cdot 96$; $0 \cdot 88$; $0 \cdot 975$; $0 \cdot 75$; $0 \cdot 9825$.

If compound interest is reckoned at $r\%$ p.a., compounded yearly, the annual **multiplying factor** is R, where $R = 1 + \dfrac{r}{100}$, and the amount of £P after n years may then be written **£PR^n**.

Example 7. Find the sum of money which will amount to £3500 in 20 yr. at 4% p.a., compound interest.

If the sum of money is £P, the amount in 20 yr. at 4% p.a. is $£P(1\cdot04)^{20}$;

$\therefore P(1\cdot04)^{20} = 3500$;

$\therefore P = 3500 \div (1\cdot04)^{20} \simeq 1597$.

$\therefore$ the sum is approximately £1597, where the 4th figure is not reliable.

$1\cdot04$	$\cdot017033$ (p. 342)
$(1\cdot04)^{20}$	$\cdot34066$
3500	$3\cdot5441$
$(1\cdot04)^{20}$	$\cdot3407$
P	$3\cdot2034$

Alternatively, from the compound interest table on p. 342, £1 amounts to £2·19112 in 20 yr. at 4% p.a.;

$\therefore$ the sum which amounts to £3500 $= £\dfrac{3500}{2\cdot19112}$, $= £1597\cdot4$.

Thus in this case the 4th figure obtained by using logarithms happens to be correct.

Example 8. At what rate per cent. p.a. will £480 amount to £677 in 10 yr. at compound interest?

If the rate $\%$ p.a. is r, the annual multiplying factor is $1 + \dfrac{r}{100}$;

$\therefore$ if $R = 1 + \dfrac{r}{100}$, the amount of £480 in 10 yr. is $£480R^{10}$, and this is £677.

$\therefore R^{10} = 677 \div 480$; $\therefore R = \sqrt[10]{(677 \div 480)}$;

$\therefore R = 1\cdot035$;

$\therefore$ the rate $\%$ p.a. is $3\frac{1}{2}\%$ approximately.

677	$2\cdot8306$
480	$2\cdot6812$
quotient	$0\cdot1494$
$1 + \dfrac{r}{100}$	$0\cdot0149$

Example 9. In what time will £725 amount to £975 at $3\frac{1}{2}\%$ p.a. compound interest?

The annual multiplying factor is $1\cdot035$, $\therefore$ if £725 amounts to £975 in n yr.,

$$725(1\cdot035)^n = 975;$$
$$\therefore \log 725 + n \log 1\cdot035 = \log 975;$$
$$\therefore 2\cdot8603 + n \times 0\cdot01494 = 2\cdot9890; \therefore n \times 0\cdot01494 = 0\cdot1287.$$
$$\therefore n = \frac{0\cdot1287}{0\cdot01494} = 8\cdot61;$$

$\therefore$ the time is approximately 8·6 yr.

$\bar{1}\cdot1096$
$\bar{2}\cdot1744$
$0\cdot9352$

Example 10. In what time will a sum of money double itself at 4% p.a. compound interest?

The annual multiplying factor is 1·04, ∴ if £1 amounts to £2 in n yr.,

$$(1·04)^n = 2; \quad ∴ \quad n \log 1·04 = \log 2;$$

$$∴ \quad n \times 0·01703 = 0·3010; \quad ∴ \quad n = \frac{0·3010}{0·01703} = 17·7;$$

$$\begin{array}{r} \bar{1}·4786 \\ \bar{2}·2311 \\ \hline 1·2475 \end{array}$$

∴ the time is approximately 17·7 yr.

Note. It can be proved by methods of advanced algebra that a sum of money at r per cent. per annum compound interest doubles itself in approximately $(70\frac{1}{2} \div r)$ years.

TABLE FOR THE AMOUNT OF £1 AT COMPOUND INTEREST

Year	$2\frac{1}{2}$%	3%	$3\frac{1}{2}$%	4%	5%	6%
1	1·02500	1·03000	1·03500	1·04000	1·05000	1·06000
2	1·05063	1·06090	1·07123	1·08160	1·10250	1·12360
3	1·07689	1·09273	1·10872	1·12486	1·15763	1·19102
4	1·10381	1·12551	1·14752	1·16986	1·21551	1·26248
5	1·13141	1·15927	1·18769	1·21665	1·27628	1·33823
6	1·15969	1·19405	1·22926	1·26532	1·34010	1·41852
7	1·18869	1·22987	1·27228	1·31593	1·40710	1·50363
8	1·21840	1·26677	1·31681	1·36857	1·47746	1·59385
9	1·24886	1·30477	1·36290	1·42331	1·55133	1·68948
10	1·28008	1·34392	1·41060	1·48024	1·62889	1·79085
11	1·31209	1·38423	1·45997	1·53945	1·71034	1·89830
12	1·34489	1·42576	1·51107	1·60103	1·79586	2·01220
20	1·63862	1·80611	1·98979	2·19112	2·65330	3·20714
30	2·09757	2·42726	2·80679	3·24340	4·32194	5·74349

The following 7-figure logarithms are supplied here for use in Exercise 168 :—

No.	Log.	No.	Log.	No.	Log.
1·025	·0107239	1·035	·0149403	1·05	·0211893
1·03	·0128372	1·04	·0170333	1·06	·0253059

EXERCISE 168

Find (i) by logarithms, (ii) by using the compound interest table, the approximate amounts of the following sums, at compound interest for the stated periods and rates :—

1. £100; 8 yr.; 3%. [2] £500; 12 yr.; 5%.

[3] £650; 20 yr.; 4%. 4. £374; 11 yr.; $3\frac{1}{2}$%.

5. £1250; 10 yr.; 5%. [6] £9275; 7 yr.; $2\frac{1}{2}$%.

Find by logarithms the approximate amounts of the following sums, at compound interest for the stated periods and rates :—

[7] £724; 15 yr.; 4%. 8. £3050; 24 yr.; $3\frac{1}{2}$%.

Find by logarithms the approximate value of the compound interest on the following sums for the stated periods and rates :—

9. £638; 11 yr.; $3\frac{1}{2}$%. [10] £590; 14 yr.; $2\frac{1}{2}$%.

Find by logarithms the approximate sum of money which amounts at compound interest to :

11. £850 in 9 yr. at 4%. [12] £640 in 14 yr. at 5%.

13. £3500 in 16 yr. at $2\frac{1}{2}$%. [14] £4075 in 25 yr. at 6%.

Find by logarithms the approximate rate per cent. if :

15. £600 amounts to £821 in 8 yr., compound interest.

[16] £140 amounts to £271 in 15 yr., compound interest.

[17] £3960 amounts to £8000 in 16 yr., compound interest.

In what time, at compound interest, will :

[18] £320 amount to £405 at 4% p.a.?

19. £437 amount to £845 at $3\frac{1}{2}$% p.a.?

20. Any sum of money double itself at 5% p.a.?

*21. A Savings Certificate costs 16s. and is worth 24s. at the end of 10 yr. What rate % p.a. compound interest is allowed? How long would it take 16s. to increase to £5 at the same rate?

[22] The value of port wine increases by 5% every year at a compounded rate. If its value is £2 10s. a dozen when laid down, find its value 15 yr. later.

23. The value of a machine depreciates each year by 10% of its value at the beginning of that year. Its value when new is £750; find its value when it is 8 yr. old.

*24. Use the compound interest table on p. 342 to draw graphs showing the amount of £100 at any time in the first 12 yr. at (i) $2\frac{1}{2}$% p.a., (ii) 5% p.a. Draw on the same diagram the corresponding simple interest graphs.

25. The value of a machine depreciates from £1800 to £680 in 12 yr. Find the yearly decay factor, assuming it to be constant.

*26. The population of a town increased from 37,526 in 1911 to 61,473 in 1931. Find the yearly growth factor assuming it to be constant. If the growth factor has been constant, what was the population in 1901?

CHAPTER XXIII

HARDER PERCENTAGE

Practice in the use of percentage factors is desirable.

Example 1. The sales of a book in 1931 exceeded those in 1930 by 10%, and the corresponding successive yearly percentage increases for 1932 and 1933 were 15% and 20%. By what percentage did the sales in 1933 exceed those in 1930?

If C copies were sold in 1930, and if C_1, C_2, C_3 copies were sold in 1931, 1932, 1933,

$$C_1 = C \times \tfrac{110}{100}; \quad C_2 = C_1 \times \tfrac{115}{100} = C \times \tfrac{110}{100} \times \tfrac{115}{100};$$

$$C_3 = C_2 \times \tfrac{120}{100} = C \times \tfrac{110}{100} \times \tfrac{115}{100} \times \tfrac{120}{100}; \quad \therefore C_3 = C \times \tfrac{1518}{1000};$$

$$\therefore C_3 \text{ exceeds C by } 51 \cdot 8\%;$$

$$\therefore \text{ the sales in 1933 exceed those in 1930 by } 51 \cdot 8\%.$$

In actual practice, when there are several multiplying factors, the intermediate steps may be omitted. But it must be noted that *the successive percentages* **cannot be added together**; *they are not percentages of the same thing.*

Example 2. If a dealer charges £2 15s. for a chair, he gains $37\frac{1}{2}\%$; at what price must he sell it to gain 45%?

C.P.	1st S.P.	2nd S.P.
100	$137\frac{1}{2}$	145

$$\therefore \text{ 2nd S.P.} = \frac{145}{137\frac{1}{2}} \text{ of 1st S.P.}$$

$$= \frac{290}{275} \text{ of 55s.} = 58\text{s.}$$

∴ the chair must be sold for £2 18s. to gain 45%.

Example 3. A tradesman marks an article at 40% above cost price, but gives a discount of 1s. in the £ on the marked price. What is his gain per cent.? He also offers 21 of the articles for the price of 20, allowing the same discount. Find his gain per cent. in this case.

C.P. £100	Marked Price £140	Discount 140s. or £7	Net S.P. £133

∴ the tradesman gains 33%.

(ii) When he sells 21 articles for the price of 20 articles, if the cost price is £(100×21), the net sale price is £(133×20),

∴ if the cost price is £100, the net sale price is £$\frac{133 \times 20}{21}$,

that is £$\frac{380}{3}$, or £$126\frac{2}{3}$;

∴ the tradesman gains $26\frac{2}{3}\%$.

Example 4. When the cost of coal increases by 40%, a man reduces his annual consumption by 20%. Find the percentage change in his annual expenditure on coal.

First expenditure :

100 tons at 100 units of money per ton cost 10,000 units of money.

Second expenditure :

80 tons at 140 units of money per ton cost 11,200 units of money.

∴ expenditure increases by $\frac{1200}{10000} \times 100$ per cent., *i.e.* by 12%.

Example 5. A sold a car to B at a profit of 40%, B sold it to C at a profit of 60%, C sold it to D at a loss of 25%. If D paid £187 more than it cost A, find the profit A made.

Start with a car which cost A £100, then

B's C.P.	C's C.P.	D's C.P.
£140	£($\frac{160}{100}$ × 140)	£($\frac{75}{100}$ × $\frac{160}{100}$ × 140), *i.e.* £168.

∴ D paid £68 more than A's C.P. if this was £100,

∴ D paid £187 more than A's C.P. if this was £($\frac{187}{68}$ × 100);

∴ A's profit was $\frac{40}{100}$ of £($\frac{187}{68}$ × 100),

that is £110.

EXERCISE 169

1. A makes a car for £240 and sells it to B at a profit of 25%: B sells it to C at a profit of 30%. How much does C pay for it?

2 The value of a machine is £5000 when new, and depreciates each year by 10% of its value at the beginning of that year. Find its value when 3 years old.

[3] If a man sells his house for £4500 he loses £300. What must he sell it for to gain 20%?

4. If a dealer sold a table for £14, he would gain 12%. Find his gain per cent. if he sells it for £15.

5. If a man sells a chair for 27s., he gains 8%. Find his loss per cent. if he sells it for 22s.

[6] If a man sells a horse for 100 guineas, he gains 12½%. What profit or loss per cent. would he have made if he had sold it for 90 guineas?

7. By selling an article for 38s., a man loses 5%; for what must he sell it to gain 10%?

[8] By selling an article for 29 guineas a man loses 13%; for what must he sell it to make a profit of 15%?

[9] The length of a rod when cut down by 10% is 3 ft. What would its length have become if it had been cut down by 20%?

10. After the price of an article is reduced from 1s. to 6½d., the seller still makes a profit of 30%. What profit per cent. did he make at first?

[11] A merchant gains 15% by selling an article for £8 12s. 6d.; what must he sell it for to double his profit?

[12] By selling 5 lb. of tea for 11s. 6d., a grocer gains 15%; find his gain per cent. if he sells 12 lb. of the same tea for 27s.

[13] By selling sugar at £40 per ton a man makes a profit of 20%; at what price per lb. must he sell it to make a profit of 26%?

14. The value of a bottle of port increases every 10 yr. (up to 30 yr.) by 50% of its value at the beginning of each period. What is the percentage increase in its value (i) in 20 yr., (ii) in 30 yr.?

15. A car depreciates in value by 25% for the first year and for each later year by 20% of its value at the beginning of that year. Find the percentage decrease in value after the first 4 years.

16. A shopkeeper sells $\frac{9}{10}$ of his stock at 25% profit and the rest at 5% loss. What is his gain per cent. on the whole?

[17] A man buys an estate at 18% below the amount at which it has been valued and sells it at 10% above the valuation. His profit was £1358, what did he pay for the estate?

18. A tradesman sells an article for 1s. 2½d. at a profit of 45%. When the cost price is reduced 1d., he reduces the selling price by 1d. Find his new profit per cent.

19. A manufacturer makes an article at a cost of £3 2s. 6d.; he catalogues it at 60% above cost price and allows a trade discount of 30% off the catalogue price and a cash discount of 2½% off the price so reduced. What profit does he make per article?

[20] A manufacturer sells an article to a tradesman at a profit of 60%, and the tradesman retails it for £3 4s. at a profit of 20%. Find the cost of manufacture.

21. A manufacturer sells a car to a dealer at a profit of 30%, the dealer sells it to a customer at a profit of 40%; the customer sells it to a friend for £364 at a loss of 20%. Find the cost of manufacture of the car.

22. A manufacturer makes a profit of 20% by selling an article to the retailer for £15. If the cost of manufacture increases by 60% and if the price paid by the retailer is increased by 66⅔%, find the profit made by the manufacturer.

[23] A commodity costing £9 10s. per cwt. is sold retail at 2s. 3d. per lb., but there is a wastage of 5%. Find the profit per cent.

*24. An article costs 3s. to make; the manufacturer sells it to a retailer who makes a profit of 20% by selling it for 5s. Find the ratio in which the total profit of 2s. was shared between the manufacturer and retailer.

25. The export of cotton piece goods in 1920 exceeded the export in 1919 by 12% in quantity and by $43\frac{1}{2}$% in value. Find the average percentage increase in price of a given quantity of the goods.

26. If the price of petrol rises 20%, by how much per cent. must a motorist reduce his consumption so as not to increase his expenditure?

*27. A man saves 20% of his income. If his expenditure increases by 35%, how much per cent. must his income be increased so that he may save 10% of it?

*28. A manufacturer catalogues his goods at 80% above cost of production. He sells to a distributor allowing him 40% discount off catalogue prices, and the distributor allows the retailer 25% off catalogue prices. What is the percentage profit made by (i) the manufacturer, (ii) the distributor?

*29. When the price of coal rose 20%, a householder reduced his annual consumption by 20%; his yearly expenditure then became £36, what was it before?

*30. The cost of producing an article is made up as follows : cost of labour 65%, cost of material 35%. It is sold at a profit of 50%. If the cost of labour increases by 20%, and if the selling price is increased by 30%, the profit is still 50%; find the percentage change in the cost of material.

Mixtures. Inverse problems on mixtures were discussed in Chapter XVII, see p. 240; some rather harder examples (direct and inverse) are given in Exercise 170.

Example 6. In what ratio must tea at 1s. 9d. per lb. be mixed with tea at 2s. 7d. per lb. so that a profit of 36% is made by selling the tea at 2s. 10d. per lb.?

$$2s.\ 10d. = \tfrac{136}{100}\text{ of cost price of 1 lb.,}$$
$$\therefore \text{ cost price of 1 lb.} = \tfrac{100}{136}\text{ of 34d., that is 25d.}$$

∴ tea at 21d. per lb. is mixed with tea at 31d. per lb. so that the mixture is worth 25d. per lb.

On every 1 lb. of tea at 21d., the gain is $(25-21)$d., $=4$d.

On every 1 lb. of tea at 31d., the loss is $(31-25)$d., $=6$d.

∴ gains and losses balance if 3 lb. of tea at 21d. per lb. are mixed with 2 lb. of tea at 31d. per lb.

∴ the tea at 1s. 9d. per lb. must be mixed with the tea at 2s. 7d. per lb. in the ratio 3 : 2.

EXERCISE 170

1. What profit per cent. is made by selling at 3s. per lb. a mixture of 60 lb. of tea costing 3s. per lb. with 10 lb. costing 2s. per lb.?

2. 96 lb. of tea at 1s. 8d. per lb. are mixed with 128 lb. at 1s. 3d. per lb. At what rate per lb. must the mixture be sold to gain 40%?

[3] What is the profit per cent. made by purchasing coffee whole-sale at £8 10s. per cwt., mixing with it 10% of its weight of chicory at £2 10s. per cwt., and retailing the mixture at 2s. 1d. per lb.?

[4] A grocer mixes 50 lb. of tea costing 11d. per lb. and 150 lb. costing 1s. 7d. per lb. At what price per lb., to the nearest penny, must he sell the mixture to gain 30%?

5. There are two casks of spirit containing 25% and 15% respectively of water. If 2 gall. of the first are added to 3 gall. of the second, what percentage of the mixture is water?

[6] The cost of a dinner and a dance ticket is £1 7s. If the dinner costs 16% more than the dance ticket, what is the cost of the dinner?

7. x-carat gold means that x parts of every 24 parts by weight of the material are pure gold. How many grams of pure gold must be mixed with 100 gm. of 15-carat gold to produce 18-carat gold?

8. Tea at 2s. 2d. per lb. is blended with tea at 3s. 6d. per lb. and the mixture is sold at 3s. 8d. per lb. at a profit of 10%. In what ratio are the teas mixed?

[9] Tea at 1s. 6d. per lb. is blended with tea at 2s. 8d. per lb. so that a profit of 50% is made by selling the mixture at 3s. 3d. per lb. In what ratio are the teas mixed?

10. A dairyman buys milk at $2\frac{1}{2}$d. per quart and dilutes it with water so that he makes a profit of 60% by selling the mixture at 1s. per gallon. In what ratio are the milk and water mixed?

*11. Receipts on railway tickets from 1st and 3rd class passengers are in the ratio 2 : 21, and the ratio of a 1st class to a 3rd class fare is 12 : 7. What percentage of passengers travel 1st class?

12. The composition by weight of two alloys for railway-carriage bearings is as follows :—

> English : copper 22%, tin 67%, antimony 11%.
> French : copper 82%, tin 18%.

If the English and French alloys are mixed in the ratio 3 : 1 by weight, what percentage of copper is there in the mixture?

*13. The values of 3 articles are as 5 : 6 : 7; the third remains constant, but the first two increase so that the values become as 7 : 6 : 5. Find the increase per cent. in value of the first two.

*14. In a battle the casualties were 16% of the total strength. 35% of the officers and 15% of other ranks were casualties. Find the ratio of the number of officers to the number of other ranks.

15. In what ratio must coffee costing £9 6s. 8d. per cwt. be mixed with chicory costing £3 5s. 4d. per cwt. so as to make $12\frac{1}{2}$% profit by selling the mixture at 1s. 6d. per lb.?

*16. At a modern school 90% of the pupils learn French, 85% of them learn German, and 65% of them learn Spanish. What is the least percentage that learn all three languages?

17. A, B, C invest £8000, £4000, £2000 respectively in a business. A and B receive respectively 20% and 10% of the annual profits as salaries, and the remainder is shared between A, B, C in proportion to the capitals they invested. If the profits are £3200, what does each receive?

*18. A tradesman buys 200 lb. of fruit; 10% of it is unsaleable, and the rest is sold at 1s. per lb., but in order to "turn the scales" he has to put $16\frac{1}{4}$ oz. instead of 1 lb. into the scale-pan. If he makes a profit of 15%, what did he pay altogether for the fruit to the nearest shilling?

*19. Five men agree to complete a piece of work in 48 days working 8 hr. a day. One ceased work at the end of 12 days and a second at the end of 15 days. The rest then agreed to work 9 hr. a day. By what percentage (to the nearest unit) must they increase their rate of work to finish in the specified time?

*20. A box when empty weighs 10 lb. It will hold 50 lb. of clothes or 180 lb. of books. What will it weigh when packed full of clothes and books if (i) 20% of the volume is occupied by books and the rest by clothes, (ii) 20% of the weight of the contents is made up by books and the rest by clothes?

CHAPTER XXIV

SHARES AND STOCKS

If a man has saved money, he can put it in the Post Office Savings Bank and will then receive interest at $2\frac{1}{2}\%$ p.a.; he is not, however, allowed to deposit more than £500 in any one year. If he has more money to spare and wishes to invest it and thereby receive interest, he will probably buy shares in a company. The daily newspapers contain lists of shares of every sort of company and the prices at which they can be bought. Suppose he buys what are called Woolworth's 6% preference (£1) shares, he is entitled each year to ($\frac{6}{100}$ of £1) interest on each share he has bought, and this will be paid to him by the Woolworth Company as long as they are making sufficient profit to enable them to do so.

If he looks in the newspapers, he may find that the price of this (£1) share is actually 30 shillings, but the share is still called a (£1) share although its cash value is 30 shillings, and £1 is called its "nominal" value, that is its *name*. *There is no connection between* **nominal** *value and* **cash** *value*.

Example 1. Woolworth's 6% preference (£1) shares stand at 30 shillings. Find (i) the cost of 90 shares; (ii) the yearly interest on 90 shares; (iii) the cash obtained by selling 70 shares; (iv) the number of shares that can be bought for £120 cash; (v) the yearly interest obtained by investing £90 cash.

(i) 1 (£1) share costs 30s., $=£\frac{3}{2}$ cash;

$\therefore$ 90 shares cost $£\frac{3}{2} \times 90$, $=£135$ cash.

(ii) The yearly interest on 1 (£1) share is $£\frac{6}{100}$;

$\therefore$ the yearly interest on 90 (£1) shares is $£(\frac{6}{100} \times 90)$, $=£5$ 8s.

(iii) 1 (£1) share is sold for 30s., $=£\frac{3}{2}$ cash;

$\therefore$ 70 (£1) shares are sold for $£(\frac{3}{2} \times 70)$, $=£105$ cash.

(iv) $£\frac{3}{2}$ cash buys 1 (£1) share;

$\therefore$ £120 cash buys $(\frac{2}{3} \times 120)$ shares, that is 80 shares.

(v) If a man invests $£\frac{3}{2}$ cash, he buys 1 (£1) share, on which the yearly interest is $£\frac{6}{100}$.

$\therefore$ if he invests $£\frac{3}{2}$ cash, he receives $£\frac{6}{100}$ interest;

$\therefore$ if he invests £90 cash, he receives $£(\frac{6}{100} \times \frac{2}{3} \times 90)$ interest; that is £3 12s. interest.

A man can buy or sell shares just as he can buy or sell eggs or motor-cars, but he can usually only buy them through a stock-broker, and the price may alter from day to day according to the demand for the shares. When a man has bought some shares of a company, his name is registered as the owner of those shares, which are numbered just like Treasury notes or cloak-room tickets, and he receives a piece of paper from the company recording the fact that he owns certain shares of specified numbers; this piece of paper is called a *share certificate*, and is the only thing which is given to him to show that the shares belong to him; and when he wishes to sell the shares, he merely sends this share certificate to a stockbroker, who will then sell the shares for whatever value they may have at the time. Shares are bought either for income or for capital appreciation (*i.e.* increase in value due to a rise in their price). And shares are sold either because the money is required for some purpose or because it is believed that the money can be invested to greater advantage elsewhere.

A share is said to *stand at a premium* if its *cash* value is greater than its *nominal* value. Thus Woolworth's 6% (£1) preference shares *at* 30s. stand at "10s. premium," because the cash value exceeds the nominal value by 10s.

A share is said to *stand at par*, if its *cash* value is the same as its *nominal* value; that is, for example, if the cash value of a (10s.) share is 10s.

A share is said to *stand at a discount*, if its *cash* value is less than its *nominal* value; for example, when Moss' Empires 5% (£1) preference shares were standing at 13s. 3d., they were at 6s. 9d. discount.

If the price of a share is quoted in the form, "at $1\frac{3}{4}$," this means that the price is £1$\frac{3}{4}$; if the price is quoted in shillings or pence, this is stated explicitly. A quotation such as 12s. to 12s. 3d. means that a seller receives 12s. per share and that a buyer pays 12s. 3d. per share.

Questions about shares are answered merely by using unitary method or proportion, and present no difficulty if the meaning of the data is understood.

The phrase, a (5s.) share at 4s. paying a dividend of $4\frac{1}{2}$% p.a., means that

(i) the *cash* value of 1 (5s.) share is 4s.

(ii) the yearly interest on 1 (5s.) share is $\dfrac{4\frac{1}{2}}{100}$ of 5s.

(iii) an investment of 4s. *cash* yields $\dfrac{4\frac{1}{2}}{100}$ of 5s. yearly interest.

It is essential to remember that the yearly interest is the quoted percentage of the *nominal* value of the share; the nominal value is a fixed sum, the cash value may vary from hour to hour. In order to distinguish clearly between cash values and nominal values, it is advisable to insert the word "cash" where actual money is involved, and the word "share" where the nominal value is mentioned.

If the amount of the dividend is expressed as a percentage of the *cash* value, the result is called the *yield* of the investment. Unless the shares stand at par, the yield is not the same as the rate per cent. of the dividend declared.

Example 2. A man buys (10s.) shares standing at 18s. Find the yield on his investment if a dividend of 12% is declared.

1 (10s.) share costs 18s. cash and the dividend on it is $\frac{12}{100}$ of 10s.

∴ by investing 18s. cash, he receives $(10 \times \frac{12}{100})$s. interest;

∴ by investing 100s. cash, he receives $(10 \times \frac{12}{100} \times \frac{100}{18})$s. interest, that is $\frac{20}{3}$s. interest.

∴ the yield on his investment is $6\frac{2}{3}\%$.

Example 3. By investing £300 in (10s.) shares paying 8%, a man obtained a dividend of £15. At what price did the shares stand.

The dividend from 1 (10s.) share is $\frac{8}{100}$ of 10s., $= \frac{4}{5}$s.;

∴ a dividend of (15×20)s. is obtained from $(15 \times 20 \div \frac{4}{5})$ shares;

∴ $(15 \times 20 \times \frac{5}{4})$ shares cost £300,

∴ 1 share cost $£(300 \times \frac{4}{15 \times 20 \times 5})$, $= £\frac{4}{5}$, $= 16$s.

∴ the shares stood at 16s.

EXERCISE 171 (Oral)

Write down the cost of and the income from

1. 200 (£1) shares at 2, dividend 12% p.a.

2. 100 (10s.) shares at 8s., dividend 4% p.a.

Write down the number of shares that can be bought and the income obtained, by investing

3. £200 in (£1) shares at 10s., paying 2% p.a.

4. £600 in (£1) shares at 3, paying 20% p.a.

23

Write down the sum of money obtained by selling

5. 40 (£1) shares at 12s.

6. 1000 (10s.) shares at 8s.

Write down the price of the following shares :—

7. 100 (10s.) shares cost £20.

8. 60 (5s.) shares cost £30.

Write down the yield obtained by investing in

9. (£1) shares at 2, paying 8% p.a.

10. (10s.) shares at 5s., paying 3% p.a.

EXERCISE 172

Find the cost of and the income from the following preference shares :—

1. 60 Boots 7% (£1) shares at 27s.

[2] 120 Lyons 5% (£1) shares at 25s. 3d.

3. 150 Hodsman 8% (10s.) shares at 13s. 6d.

4. 50 Guest Keen 5% (£5) shares at $6\frac{1}{4}$.

[5] 180 London Tin $7\frac{1}{2}$% (10s.) shares at 14s. 2d.

Find the number of shares that can be bought and the income obtained by investing :

6. £50 in (£1) shares at 25s., paying 8%.

[7] £72 in (5s.) shares at 9s., paying 12%.

8. £210 in (2s.) shares at 1s. 6d., paying $3\frac{3}{4}$%.

[9] £1350 in (£1) shares at $2\frac{1}{4}$, paying 12%.

10. £240 in (£5) shares at 8, paying 9%.

Find the sum of money obtained by selling :

11. 100 Dunlop 7% (£1) shares at 31s.

12. 250 Trust Houses 6% (£1) shares at $1\frac{1}{4}$.

[13] 420 Polikoff 8% (10s.) shares at 8s. 9d.

14. 160 United Tea 5% (£5) shares at $3\frac{3}{8}$.

[15] 1240 Lawes 7% (10s.) shares at 7s. 9d.

Find the yield obtained by investing money in

16. (£1) shares at $1\frac{1}{2}$, paying 9%.

[**17**] (10s.) shares at 8s., paying 4%.

18. (2s.) shares at 3s. 9d., paying $12\frac{1}{2}$%.

19. (£5) shares at $8\frac{3}{4}$, paying $10\frac{1}{2}$%.

[**20**] (5s.) shares at 84s., paying 120%.

21. A man bought 160 (5s.) shares for £34. At what price did the shares stand? At what premium or discount were they quoted?

[**22**] A man sold 600 (10s.) shares for £515. At what price did the shares stand? At what premium or discount were they quoted?

23. A man who owns 250 (£1) shares receives from them a dividend of £20. What is the rate % of the dividend?

[**24**] A man who owns 1400 (10s.) shares receives from them a dividend of £42. What is the rate % of the dividend?

25. By investing £360 in (£1) shares paying 3%, a man obtained a dividend of £12; at what price did the shares stand?

[**26**] By investing £700 in (10s.) shares paying 8%, a man obtained a dividend of £40; at what price did the shares stand?

[**27**] By investing £600 in (5s.) shares paying 9%, a man obtained a dividend of £33 15s.; at what price did the shares stand?

28. London Brick 8% (£1) shares stand at 36s., and Rio Tinto 5% (£5) shares stand at $4\frac{1}{4}$. Which investment gives the larger yield?

Share Transactions. A stockbroker is merely a commission-agent who arranges to buy and sell shares for his clients.

For arranging the transaction, the stockbroker charges his client a commission, called *brokerage*, which varies according to the price of the share, the number of shares involved, and other considerations.

If the price of a (£1) share is, say, 22s. 8d., and if the broker's commission is 2d. a share, a man who is buying the shares pays (22s. 8d. + 2d.), that is 22s. 10d., for each share; but a man who is selling the shares receives only (22s. 8d. − 2d.), that is 22s. 6d., for each share.

There are also other charges which affect the transaction, viz. a transfer duty which is a Government tax, the stamp on the contract, and the registration fee charged by the company; *but these charges will be ignored in the Exercises in this book unless specially mentioned.* Further, it will be assumed that the brokerage has been included in the named prices of the shares unless the contrary is stated.

Example 4. A man sells 720 El Oro mining (5s.) shares at 6s. 3d. and invests the proceeds in Odhams Press (4s.) shares at 11s. 3d. How many Odhams Press shares does he buy?

1 El Oro share is sold for $6\frac{1}{4}$s. cash;

$\therefore$ 720 El Oro shares are sold for $(6\frac{1}{4} \times 720)$s. cash.

$\therefore$ he invests $(6\frac{1}{4} \times 720)$s. cash in O.P. shares at $11\frac{1}{4}$s.

$\frac{45}{4}$s. cash buy 1 O.P. share,

$\therefore$ $(\frac{25}{4} \times 720)$s. cash buy $\frac{4}{45} \times \frac{25}{4} \times 720$ O.P. shares, $=400$ shares;

$\therefore$ he buys 400 Odhams Press shares.

Example 5. A man sells 360 Grocery (10s.) shares paying 12% at 21s., and invests the proceeds in Tin (5s.) shares paying $4\frac{1}{4}$% at 3s. 6d. Find the change in his income.

1st Income : The interest on 1 Grocery (10s.) share is $\frac{12}{100}$ of 10s.;

$\therefore$ the interest on 360 Grocery (10s.) shares is $(\frac{12}{100} \times 10 \times 360)$s., $=432$s.

Selling out : He sells 1 Grocery (10s.) share for 21s. cash;

$\therefore$ he sells 360 Grocery (10s.) shares for 21×360s. cash.

$\therefore$ he invests (21×360)s. cash in (5s.) Tin shares at $3\frac{1}{2}$s., paying $4\frac{1}{4}$%.

2nd Income : For each (5s.) Tin share he buys, he pays $3\frac{1}{2}$s. cash and receives $\frac{4\frac{1}{4}}{100}$ of 5s. interest;

$\therefore$ if he invests $\frac{7}{2}$s. cash, he receives $(\frac{17}{400} \times 5)$s. interest.

$\therefore$ if he invests (21×360)s. cash, he receives $(\frac{17}{400} \times 5 \times \frac{2}{7} \times 21 \times 360)$s. interest, that is 459s. interest.

$\therefore$ his income is increased by $(459 - 432)$s., that is £1 7s.

Note. This example shows that it is not necessary to find the number of shares bought in the second transaction, if we merely wish to know the change of income.

Example 6. A man sells 180 Tarmac (£1) shares at 22s. 6d. and then buys 200 Hotel (10s.) shares at 18s. 8d. Brokerage is charged at the rate of 2d. per share on the sale and at 1d. per share on the reinvestment. Find the cash balance due to him.

1 Tarmac share is sold for 22s. 6d., but the brokerage charge is 2d.,

∴ net receipt from sale of 1 Tarmac share is 22s. 4d.

∴ net receipt from sale of 180 shares is (22s. 4d.) × 180, = £201.

1 Hotel share costs 18s. 8d., but there is also a brokerage charge of 1d.

∴ net cost of 1 Hotel share is 18s. 9d.

∴ net cost of 200 Hotel shares is (18s. 9d.) × 200, = £187 10s.

∴ cash balance due to man is £201 − £187 10s., = £13 10s.

Note. When shares are sold and the proceeds *at once* reinvested, the brokerage on the reinvestment is charged at half the ordinary rate.

EXERCISE 173

1. A man sells 700 Ciro Pearls (5s.) shares at 4s. 6d. and invests the proceeds in Gamage (10s.) shares at 17s. 6d. How many Gamage shares does he buy?

[2] A man sells 450 Gaumont British (10s.) shares at 13s. 4d. and invests the proceeds in Sears (5s.) shares at 15s. How many Sears shares does he buy?

3. A man sells 550 Humber (10s.) shares at 16s. and with the proceeds can just buy 600 Celanese (10s.) shares. At what price do the Celanese shares stand?

[4] A man sells 150 Ford Motor (£1) shares at 29s. 4d. and with the proceeds can just buy 1600 Maypole (2s.) shares. At what price do the Maypole shares stand?

[5] A man bought 450 (10s.) shares at 6s. 6d. and sold them when they had risen to 8s. 4d. How much did he gain?

6. A man bought 320 (£1) shares at $1\frac{1}{4}$ and sold them when they had fallen to $\frac{7}{8}$. How much did he lose?

7. A man invested £330 in Bradford (£1) shares at 13s. 9d. and sold them at 15s. 3d. How many shares did he buy and how much profit did he make?

8. A man invested £765 in Geevor (5s.) shares at 14s. 2d.; he received one dividend of 20%, and then sold the shares at 13s. 9d. How much did he gain or lose?

9. A man sold 500 (£1) shares, paying 5%, at 18s. and invested the proceeds in (10s.) shares, paying $7\frac{1}{2}$%, at 12s. 6d. How many (10s.) shares did he buy and what was the change of income?

[10] A man sold 420 (£5) shares, paying 7%, at $8\frac{3}{4}$ and invested the proceeds in (10s.) shares, paying 9%, at 24s. 6d. How many (10s.) shares did he buy and what was the change of income?

11. A man invested £990 in (£1) shares, paying 10%, at 27s. 6d.; he sold the shares at 32s. and invested the proceeds in (10s.) shares, paying 5%, at 9s. How many (10s.) shares did he buy and what was the change of income?

*12. A man bought some (£1) shares at 15s. $7\frac{1}{2}$d., and after 4 months sells them at 16s. 1d. Express the profit from the transaction as a rate per cent. per annum of the money invested.

*13. A man bought 25 (£1) shares at $4\frac{7}{8}$; he received a dividend of 9s. 6d. per share and a bonus of one additional share (on which no dividend was paid) for every five shares held by him. He then sold all his shares at $4\frac{1}{8}$. Find the profit (including the dividend) he made by the transaction and express it as a percentage of the money he invested, to 2 figures.

*14. The year's profits of a company are £35,250. From this amount, interest is first paid at $5\frac{1}{2}$% on 150,000 (£1) preference shares, and then £10,000 is set aside as a reserve. The remainder is distributed among the 200,000 (£1) ordinary shares of the company. What dividend is paid on the ordinary shares?

*15. A company has a nominal capital of 12,000 (£10) shares, all issued. Its profits for the year are £15,000, of which £6000 is set aside as a reserve and the remainder is distributed among the shareholders. What dividend is paid on the shares? What percentage will a man obtain on his money who had bought 30 (£10) shares for £480?

Find, allowing for brokerage, (i) the cost of buying, (ii) the proceeds from selling:

16. 150 (£1) shares at 18s. 6d., brokerage 1d. per share.

[17] 240 (10s.) shares at 8s. 3d., brokerage $\frac{1}{2}$d. per share.

18. 1800 (2s.) shares quoted at 1s. 7d. to 1s. 8d., brokerage $\frac{1}{4}$d. per share.

[19] 720 (5s.) shares quoted at 11s. 3d. to 11s. 6d., brokerage $\frac{1}{2}$d. per share.

20. A man sells 360 (10s.) shares at 11s. 6d. and buys 150 (£1) shares at 27s. 4d., brokerage being 1d. per share on each transaction. How much cash does he have to pay to balance the account?

[21] A man sells 120 (£1) shares at 28s. 2d. and buys 150 (£1) shares at 22s. 3d., brokerage being 2d. per share on the sale and 1d. per share on the reinvestment. What cash balance is due to the man?

Stocks. It is often necessary for Governments, City Corporations, Railways, Public Utility concerns, etc., to borrow large sums of money either to repay old loans or to develop new enterprises, and such sums are usually raised by an Issue of Stock redeemable within a fixed period and bearing interest at a fixed rate per annum.

For example: In April 1934 the Liverpool Corporation raised a loan by an Issue of £4,000,000 Stock. This Stock could be bought in units of £100, and entitled the holders to £3 per cent. interest a year (payable half-yearly) on the amount of their holding. The Corporation promised to redeem the loan at par in 1964, and claimed the right to redeem at par any time after 1954 if they should wish to do so.

The price at which each unit of £100 Stock was offered for sale was, however, £96 10s. cash. These facts are expressed shortly by the phrase:

Liverpool 3% Stock, 1954/1964 at 96½.

The whole Loan was called an Issue of £4,000,000 *Stock*, for which the public paid £3,860,000 cash (*i.e.* £96 10s. for every £100 Stock), and will eventually receive in repayment £4,000,000 cash.

One important difference between Stock and Shares is that whereas Shares must always be bought and sold in whole numbers, Stock, once it has been issued, can in many cases be bought and sold in fractional amounts. In such cases, half of £100 Stock is called £50 Stock and costs half the price of £100 Stock; one-third of £100 Stock is called £33 6s. 8d. Stock and costs one-third of the price of £100 Stock, and so on.

In most respects calculations involving £100 Stock are the same as for 100 (£1) Shares. There is no more difficulty in working out questions about Stocks than there is about Shares, provided only the meaning of the description of a stock is clearly understood.

The phrase "Liverpool 3% stock at $96\frac{1}{2}$" means

  (i) £100 Liverpool *stock* costs £$96\frac{1}{2}$ *cash*;
  (ii) The holder of £100 Liverpool *stock* receives £3 *cash*, yearly interest;
  (iii) £$96\frac{1}{2}$ *cash* invested in Liverpool stock yields £3 *cash*, yearly interest;

or we may say that, for the Liverpool 3% stock,

  (i) The *cash* value of £100 *stock* is £$96\frac{1}{2}$;
  (ii) The yearly interest on £100 *stock* is £3 *cash*;
  (iii) An investment of £$96\frac{1}{2}$ *cash* yields £3 *cash* yearly interest.

Further, the phrase "£500 Liverpool 3% stock" means £500 stock of the Liverpool 3% loan; its value is *not* £500 cash, but, if the stock stands at $96\frac{1}{2}$, is £$(96\frac{1}{2} \times 5)$ cash.

It is important to insert the word *stock* where it is implied, and the word *cash* where money is involved, although the form of a statement often makes the distinction between cash and stock clear. Thus, in the statement that "a man invests £300 in a 5% stock," the word *invests* makes it obvious that the £300 is cash and not stock; and in the statement that "a man sells £400 of a 3% stock," the word *sells* makes it obvious that the £400 is stock and not cash. The phrase "£600 Belgium 7% stock," where the £600 is stock and not cash, is often expressed in the form "£600 *of* a 7% stock," and it must be realised that in this form of the phrase the £600 is stock, not cash.

The procedure for buying and selling stock is exactly the same as for shares, and the charges on the transaction, viz. the broker's commission called *brokerage*, the Government tax, stamps, and transfer expenses, operate as for shares.

If the price of a stock is 85, and if the brokerage is "$\frac{1}{4}$ per cent.," a man who buys £100 stock pays £85 cash for the stock and £$\frac{1}{4}$ for the broker's commission, and therefore £100 stock costs him altogether £$85\frac{1}{4}$ cash; while a man who sells £100 stock obtains £85 cash for the stock, but is charged £$\frac{1}{4}$ for brokerage, and therefore receives only £$84\frac{3}{4}$ cash from the sale of £100 stock.

A quotation such as $41\frac{1}{4}$–$41\frac{3}{4}$ for a stock means that a man who is buying £100 stock has to pay £$41\frac{3}{4}$ cash for it, but that a man who is selling £100 stock receives only £$41\frac{1}{4}$ cash for it. If brokerage is $\frac{1}{8}$ per cent., a buyer pays altogether £$(41\frac{3}{4} + \frac{1}{8})$ cash for £100 stock, and a seller receives altogether £$(41\frac{1}{4} - \frac{1}{8})$ cash for £100 stock, disregarding stamp duty, etc.

Example 7. Find the cost of £1500 War Loan $3\frac{1}{2}\%$ stock at 104.

£100 War Loan stock costs £104 cash;

∴ £1500 War Loan stock costs £(104 × 15) cash = £1560 cash.

Note. War Loan $3\frac{1}{2}\%$ stock is the name of the stock. In order to find out how much £1500 stock costs, it is unnecessary to be told that it is a $3\frac{1}{2}\%$ stock; that fact merely enables us to find the income obtained from any amount of the stock.

Example 8. A man invests £450 in Indian $2\frac{1}{2}\%$ stock at 69. Find, to the nearest penny, how much stock he buys and the income from it.

(i) £69 cash buys £100 stock,

∴ £450 cash buys £$(100 \times \frac{450}{69})$ stock, ≏ £652·174 stock;

∴ he buys £652 3s. 6d. Indian $2\frac{1}{2}\%$ stock.

(ii) £100 stock yields £$2\frac{1}{2}$ cash, income,

∴ £652·174 stock yields £$(\frac{5}{2} \times \frac{652\cdot174}{100})$ income;

∴ the income = £16·304, cash, = £16 6s. 1d., to nearest penny.

Alternatively, the income may be found as follows :—

£69 cash buys £100 stock on which the income is £$2\frac{1}{2}$ cash;

∴ £69 cash invested yields £$2\frac{1}{2}$ cash, income,

∴ £450 cash invested yields £$(\frac{5}{2} \times \frac{450}{69})$ income;

∴ the income = £$\frac{375}{23}$ = £16 6s. 1d., to nearest penny.

This example refers to a stock of which it is possible to buy or sell any fraction of £100 stock; the amount purchased was £652·174 stock, approximately; but this is expressed in the form £652 3s. 6d. *stock*, obtained by reducing £0·174 to shillings and pence.

Example 9. A man holds £87 13s. 10d. Local Loans 3% stock. What is his net income from it, after income tax at 5s. in the £ has been deducted. If he sells the stock at 91, what does he receive?

(i) 13s. 10d. = 13·833...s. = £0·6917...; ∴ he holds £87·6917 stock.

£100 stock yields £3 cash, gross income; but $\frac{1}{4}$ of £3 is deducted for income tax;

∴ £100 stock yields $\frac{3}{4}$ of £3 cash, net income;

∴ £87·6917 stock yields £$(\frac{9}{4} \times 0\cdot876917)$ cash, net income;

∴ his net income = £1·973, to 3 places of decimals;

= £1 19s. 6d., to nearest penny.

(ii) £100 stock is sold for £91 cash,

∴ £87·6917 stock is sold for £$(91 \times \frac{87\cdot6917}{100})$ cash,

∴ he receives £79·799 cash, = £79 16s. 0d. cash, to nearest penny.

Example 10. A man buys Japan 5% stock at 80. Find the yield on his investment.

£80 cash buys £100 stock on which the income is £5 cash.

∴ £80 cash invested yields £5 cash, income;

∴ £100 cash invested yields £$(5 \times \frac{100}{80})$ cash, =£$6\frac{1}{4}$ cash, income.

∴ the yield on the investment is $6\frac{1}{4}$ per cent.

Note. The yield of a stock is often expressed in the form, £ s. d. per cent.; here it could be written £6 5s. per cent.

Example 11. By investing £345 in a $4\frac{1}{2}$% stock, a man obtains an income of £15. Find the price of the stock (that is, the cost of £100 stock).

£$4\frac{1}{2}$ is the income on £100 stock,

∴ £15 is the income on £$\left(100 \times \dfrac{15}{4\frac{1}{2}}\right)$ stock;

∴ £$\left(100 \times \dfrac{15}{4\frac{1}{2}}\right)$ stock costs £345 cash,

∴ £100 stock costs £$\left(345 \times \dfrac{4\frac{1}{2}}{15}\right)$ cash, =£$103\frac{1}{2}$ cash.

∴ the price of the stock is $103\frac{1}{2}$.

EXERCISE 174 (Oral)

Write down the cost of and the income derived from

1. £300 of 4% stock at 80.

2. £200 of 6% stock at 120.

How much stock can be bought, and what is the income obtained, by investing

3. £240 in 7% stock at 120?

4. £300 in 3% stock at 60?

Write down the amount of the proceeds from selling

5. £500 of 4% stock at 90.

6. £300 of $5\frac{1}{2}$% stock at 108.

Write down the prices of the following stocks:

7. £400 of 3% stock costs £320.

8. £1000 of 6% stock costs £1100.

Write down the yield obtained by investing in

9. 3% stock at 50.   10. 6% stock at 120.

EXERCISE 175

[Give answers correct to the nearest penny]

Find the cost of and the income derived from the following :—

1. £300 Consols 4% stock at 112.

[2] £250 Portugal 3% stock at 72.

3. £825 Italian $3\frac{1}{2}$% stock at 36.

4. £560 New Zealand 6% stock at 107.

[5] £145 7s. 6d. Indian 3% stock at 80.

How much stock can be bought, and what is the net income obtained, after deduction of income tax at 4s. in the £, by investing :

6. £1000 in Nigeria 6% stock at 125?

[7] £600 in Irish Land 3% stock at 90?

8. £1400 in Belgium 7% stock at 112?

9. £285 in Port of London 3% stock at 89?

[10] £420 in Canada $2\frac{1}{2}$% stock at $92\frac{1}{2}$?

Find the proceeds obtained by selling :

11. £750 Japan 6% stock at 90.

[12] £1400 Peru 6% stock at 18.

13. £427 10s. Consols $2\frac{1}{2}$% stock at 80.

[14] £254 13s. 6d. Conversion $4\frac{1}{2}$% stock at 111.

Find, in the form £ s. d. per cent., the yield from the following stocks :—

15. German 7% stock at 75.   [16] Italian $3\frac{1}{2}$% stock at 35.

17. Consols $2\frac{1}{2}$% stock at 80.

[18] London County $4\frac{1}{2}$% stock at 111.

19. Find the price of a 5% stock if it yields 4% on an investment.

[20] Find the price of a $4\frac{1}{2}$% stock if it yields $7\frac{1}{2}$% on an investment.

21. Find the price, to the nearest £, of a $4\frac{3}{4}$% stock if it yields £3 11s. per cent.

22. By investing £456 in a $3\frac{1}{2}$% stock a man obtained an income of £19.   Find the price of the stock.

[23] By investing £2704 in a $2\frac{3}{4}\%$ stock a man obtained an income of £104.   Find the price of the stock.

24. Find the total cost of £720 Chinese 5% stock at 75 and £675 Egyptian 4% stock at 108.   What is the total income derived from this investment?

25. Which investment gives the higher yield: 5% New Zealand stock at 115 or 6% Nigeria stock at 125?

*26. What sum must be invested in a 4% stock at 114 to give a net income of £120 after income tax at 5s. in the £ has been deducted?

*27. A man invests a certain sum of money in a 3% stock at 75, twice that sum of money in a $3\frac{1}{2}\%$ stock at 80, and three times that sum of money in a 5% stock at 90.   Find the average yield per cent. on the whole investment, to 3 figures.

Find, allowing for brokerage, (i) the cost of buying, (ii) the proceeds from selling:

28. £1600 stock at 86, brokerage $\frac{1}{2}$ per cent.

[29] £2800 stock at $53\frac{1}{2}$, brokerage $\frac{1}{4}$ per cent.

30. £560 stock quoted at $58\frac{1}{2}$–59, brokerage $\frac{1}{4}$ per cent.

[31] £2500 stock quoted at $109\frac{1}{2}$–$110\frac{1}{2}$, brokerage $\frac{1}{2}$ per cent.

[32] £3200 stock quoted at $17\frac{3}{4}$–$18\frac{1}{4}$, brokerage $\frac{1}{8}$ per cent.

*33. A man paid £306 for £400 stock.   At what price did the stock stand if brokerage was $\frac{1}{4}$ per cent.?

*34. A man received £837 from the sale of £720 stock.   At what price did the stock stand if brokerage was $\frac{1}{2}$ per cent.?

Miscellaneous Transactions: Sales and Reinvestments

Example 12.   A man invests £396 in a 4% stock at 82 and sells out when the stock has risen to 88.   Find his profit, if brokerage is charged at the rate of $\frac{1}{2}$ per cent. on each transaction.

Allowing for brokerage, he pays $£82\frac{1}{2}$ cash for each £100 stock he buys and he receives $£87\frac{1}{2}$ cash for each £100 stock he sells; he therefore gains $£(87\frac{1}{2}-82\frac{1}{2})$ cash, $=£5$ cash, on each $£82\frac{1}{2}$ he invests.

If he invests $£82\frac{1}{2}$ cash, he gains £5 cash;

∴ if he invests £396 cash, he gains $£\left(5\times\dfrac{396}{82\frac{1}{2}}\right)$ cash.

∴ his profit $=£(5\times396\times\frac{2}{165})$ cash $=£24$ cash.

Example 13. A man sells £3150 of 7% stock at 112, and invests the proceeds in 3% stock at 72. Find the change in his income.

The phrase, £3150 of 7% stock, means £3150 *stock*.

1st Income : In his first holding, £100 stock yields £7 income,

∴ £3150 stock yields £$(7 \times \frac{3150}{100})$ income, =£220 10s. income.

Selling out : He sells £100 stock for £112 cash,

∴ he sells £3150 stock for £$(112 \times \frac{3150}{100})$ cash;

∴ he invests £$(112 \times \frac{3150}{100})$ cash in 3% stock at 72.

2nd Income : £72 cash invested yields £3 income,

∴ £$(112 \times \frac{3150}{100})$ cash invested yields £$(3 \times 112 \times \frac{3150}{100} \times \frac{1}{72})$ income, that is £147 income.

∴ his loss of income =£220 10s. − £147, =£73 10s.

Example 14. A man held £4200 of 3% stock. He sold out at 76 and invested the proceeds in a $4\frac{1}{2}$% stock, and thereby increased his income by £7. Find the price of the $4\frac{1}{2}$% stock.

In the 3% stock, £100 stock yields £3 income,

∴ £4200 stock yields £(3×42) income, =£126 income.

∴ his income from the $4\frac{1}{2}$% stock is £$(126 + 7)$, =£133.

£100 of 3% stock is sold for £76 cash.

∴ £4200 of 3% stock is sold for £(76×42) cash.

∴ he obtains an income of £133 by investing £(76×42) cash.

∴ he obtains an income of £$4\frac{1}{2}$ by investing £$\left(76 \times 42 \times \frac{4\frac{1}{2}}{133}\right)$ cash.

But £$4\frac{1}{2}$ is the income on £100 stock,

∴ £100 stock costs £$\left(76 \times 42 \times \frac{4\frac{1}{2}}{133}\right)$ cash, =£108 cash.

∴ the price of the $4\frac{1}{2}$% stock is 108.

MISCELLANEOUS EXAMPLES

EXERCISE 176

1. A man sells £840 Greek 7% stock at 39 and invests the proceeds in Siamese 6% stock at 105. How much Siamese stock does he buy?

[2] A man sells £552 L.M.S. 4% preference at 80 and invests the proceeds in Kenya 5% stock at 115. How much Kenya stock does he buy?

3. A man invests £180 in Roumanian 4% stock at 24 and sells out when it has fallen to $16\frac{1}{2}$. What does he lose?

[4] A man invests £315 in Polish 7% stock at 84 and sells out when it has risen to $93\frac{1}{4}$. What does he gain?

5. A man has £25,200 on deposit at a bank at $2\frac{1}{2}$%. If he withdraws this money and invests it in 4% stock at 84, find the change of income.

[6] A man invests £8190 in 3% stock at 91. He sells out £6000 stock at $93\frac{1}{2}$ and the rest when it has fallen to 85. How much does he gain or lose?

7. A man sold £20,000 of a 4% Canadian stock at 90 and invested the proceeds in 7% Belgian stock at 108. Find the change of income.

[8] A man invested £2000 in a 4% stock at 80. Later, he sold out at 84 and invested the proceeds in a $5\frac{1}{2}$% stock at 105. Find the change of income.

[9] A man sold £2500 of $2\frac{1}{2}$% stock at 56 and invested the proceeds in 5% stock at 98. Find the change of income, to the nearest penny.

10. A man invested £500 in a 6% stock at 80. When it has risen to 104, he sells out and reinvests in a $4\frac{1}{2}$% stock at 90. Find the change of income.

*11. A man invested £10,000 in 3% stock at 75. When the stock has risen to 78 he sells out and invests in bank shares on which a dividend of £8 per share is paid. His income is unchanged; find the price of a bank share.

12. A man's income from a $4\frac{1}{2}$% stock is £130 10s. How much money will he obtain if he sells his holding of this stock at 92?

[13] A man invests £3300 in 3% stock at 88, and when the stock has risen to 90 he sells out enough stock to buy a car. His income is thereby diminished by 10 guineas a year. What did the car cost? How much stock does he still hold?

14. A man sells his holding of $4\frac{1}{2}$% Brazil stock at $88\frac{3}{4}$, and after buying 200 (10s.) shares at 34s. 6d. has £10 in hand. If the dividend on the shares is 20%, find the change of income.

15. The difference of income derived from investing a certain sum in 3% stock at 63 and the same sum in $4\frac{1}{2}$% stock at 105 is £22 10s. What is the sum?

16. A man received a half-year's dividend of £12 10s. 3d. from his holding of a $6\frac{1}{2}$% stock. If income-tax at 6s. in the £ was deducted from the dividend before it was paid to him, find how much of the $6\frac{1}{2}\%$ stock he held.

[17] A man sells some 4% stock at 84 and invests the proceeds in 5% stock at 96, thereby increasing his yearly income by £3. How much 4% stock did he sell?

18. A man sold £9000 of 3% stock at 91 and invested the proceeds in a 4% stock, thereby increasing his income by £76 13s. 4d. Find the price of the 4% stock.

[19] A man has an income of £52 10s. from a $3\frac{1}{2}\%$ stock. He sells his holding at 80 and invests the proceeds in a 5% stock, thereby increasing his income by £27 10s. Find the price of the 5% stock.

20. A man invested £2220 in a 4% stock at $92\frac{1}{2}$, and later sold out at a profit of £200. At what price did he sell the stock?

*21. By selling £3500 of $3\frac{1}{2}\%$ stock at 73 and investing the proceeds in a 4% stock, a man increased his income by £10 a year. If brokerage is reckoned at $\frac{1}{8}$ per cent. on each transaction, find the price of the 4% stock.

*22. A man bought £100 of $3\frac{1}{2}\%$ stock at $79\frac{1}{2}$, and £100 of 4% stock at $88\frac{5}{8}$, and £200 of 6% stock. Find the price of the 6% stock if the average yield on his investment was 5%.

*23. A man had a net income of £340 from 5% War Bonds, after deduction of income tax at 3s. in the £. He then sold one-half of his War Bonds at 95 and invested the proceeds in $7\frac{1}{2}\%$ stock at 114. What is his new net income after deducting income tax at 3s. in the £?

*24. A man invests £30,155, partly in $3\frac{1}{2}\%$ stock at 86 and the rest in $4\frac{1}{2}\%$ stock at 99. He divides the money so as to obtain the same income from each stock. Find the total income.

CHAPTER XXV

MISCELLANEOUS PROBLEMS

Change of Units. The statement that the speed of a car is 40 mi. an hour does not mean that it will actually travel 40 mi. in the next hour, or 20 mi. in the next half-hour, etc., but that *if* it should continue to move at the same rate as at present it would then travel 40 mi. in 1 hr.

Example 1. Express a speed of 30 mi. an hour in feet per second.

30 mi. $=(30 \times 1760 \times 3)$ ft.; 1 hr. $=(60 \times 60)$ sec.;

∴ a speed of 30 m.p.h. $=$ a speed of $\frac{30 \times 1760 \times 3}{60 \times 60}$ ft. per sec.

$=$ a speed of 44 ft. per sec.

Note. This result may be used to convert any speed given in m.p.h. to the equivalent speed in ft. per sec.; thus

17 m.p.h. $=(\frac{17}{30}$ of 44) ft. per sec.

Nautical speeds are measured in *knots*; a speed of 1 knot means a speed of 1 nautical mile per hour; a nautical mile is $\frac{1}{60}$ of a degree of latitude, and near the British Isles is taken as 6080 ft. If, however, the speed of a boat is given in "miles per hour," the word *mile* is used as an abbreviation for "statute mile," *not* "nautical mile" unless otherwise stated.

Example 2. Given that 1 m. $=39\cdot37$ in. and 1 gall. $=277\cdot3$ cu. in., express 1 litre in pints to 3 figures.

1 litre $=1000$ c.c. and $(100)^3$ c.c. $=1$ cu. m. $=(39\cdot37)^3$ cu. in.;

∴ 1 litre $=\frac{(39\cdot37)^3}{1000}$ cu. in.;

but 1 gall. $=277\cdot3$ cu. in.,

∴ 1 litre $=\frac{(39\cdot37)^3}{1000 \times 277\cdot3}$ gall. $=\frac{(39\cdot37)^3 \times 8}{1000 \times 277\cdot3}$ pts.

$=1\cdot76$ pt., to 3 figures.

1·5952	
4·7856	3
·9031	2·4430
5·6887	5·4430
5·4430	
0·2457	

N.B.—*Do not perform any numerical calculation until it is necessary to do so.*

Example 3. Find the cost per yard, to the nearest penny, if 1 metre of cloth costs 18 fr. 50 c., given 1 m. $=39\cdot37$ in., £1 $=78$ fr. 40 c.

[*First write down the given statement.*]

1 metre costs 18·5 fr.

[*Next change to British units.*]

$\frac{39\cdot37}{36}$ yd. cost £$\frac{18\cdot5}{78\cdot4}$;

∴ 1 yd. costs £$\frac{18\cdot5}{78\cdot4} \times \frac{36}{39\cdot37}$

1·2672	1·8943
1·5563	1·5952
2·8235	3·4895
3·4895	
1·3340	

Rough Estimate: £$\frac{20}{80}$, that is 5s., therefore 4-figure logarithms can be used.

∴ 1 yd. costs £0·2158, that is 4s. 4d., to nearest penny.

EXERCISE 177

[Give answers to 3 figures]

1. Express a speed of 23 m.p.h. in ft. per sec.

[2] Express a speed of 17 ft. per sec. in m.p.h.

3. Express a speed of 18 knots in m.p.h., taking 1 nautical mile as 6080 ft.

[4] Express a speed of 45 m.p.h. in metres per second. [1 in. =2·540 cm.]

5. Taking 1 cu. ft. =6·228 gall., express 1 pt. in cu. in.

6. Taking 1 gall. =277·3 cu. in. and 1 ft. =0·3048 m., express 1 gall. in litres.

7. A metal weighs 524 lb. per cu. ft., find its weight in gm. per c.c. [1 oz. =28·35 gm.; 1 in. =2·540 cm.]

[8] A liquid weighs 0·726 kg. per cu. dm., find its weight in oz. per cu. in. (Use the data in No. 7.)

[9] Find the cost per yard, to the nearest penny, if 1 metre of cloth costs 21·75 fr., if £1 =76·25 fr., given 1 m. =39·37 in.

10. Express in francs per kg. the price of butter costing 1s. 7½d. per lb., if £1 =75·4 fr., given 1 kg. =2·205 lb.

11. Find the cost per pint, to the nearest penny, if 1 litre costs 27·5 fr., if £1 =72·75 fr., given 1 gall. =4·546 litres.

[12] Find the cost per sq. ft., to the nearest penny, if 1 sq. m. costs 128·5 fr., if £1 =74·35 fr., given 1 m. =39·37 in.

13. On a day when £1 is worth 75·85 fr. and is worth 36·35 pesetas, express the value of 350 pesetas in francs.

[14] On a day when £1 is worth 77·85 francs and is worth 57·55 lire, express the value of 100 francs in lire.

15. Express a price of 3s. 6d. per sq. ft. in francs per sq. dm., when £1 =77·85 francs. [1 ft. =0·3048 m.]

[16] Taking 1 sq. yd. =0·8361 sq. m. and 1 gall. =277·3 cu. in., express 1 gall. in litres.

17. A liquid weighs 7·63 lb. per gallon; find its weight in kg. per litre. [1 lb. =453·6 gm.; 1 cu. ft. =6·228 gall.; 1 in. =2·540 cm.]

*18. Express in £ per acre the price of land which costs 24,650 francs per Hectare when £1 = 77·85 francs. [1 Ha. = 100 ares = 100 sq. Dm.; 1 km. = 0·6214 mi.]

*19. 1 c.c. of water weighs 1 gm.; express the weight of 1 gall. of water in lb., taking 1 cm. = 0·3937 in., 1 cu. ft. = 6·228 gall., 1 lb. = 0·4536 Kg.

*20. The pressure on a containing wall is 1·275 tons per sq. ft.; express it in lb. per sq. in.

*21. Express in Kg. per sq. cm. a pressure of 36·85 lb. per sq. in. [1 lb. = 0·4536 Kg., 1 in. = 2·540 cm.]

*22. On April 17, 1934, the London exchange on Paris was 78·25 francs to £1 and the London exchange on New York was 5·15 dollars to £1, and the Paris exchange on New York was 15·08 francs to the dollar. A man in London has to pay 100,000 dollars in New York; what is the difference in £ between paying it direct and paying it through Paris?

*23. A man in London has to pay 10,000 pesetas in Madrid. He can buy pesetas in London at 37·72 ptas. to the £, or he can buy francs in London at 78·25 francs to the £ and pesetas in Paris at 48·35 ptas. per 100 francs. What is the difference of cost in £ between paying direct and paying through Paris?

Relative Velocity. If a motorist travelling at 42 m.p.h. is overtaking a cyclist travelling at 12 m.p.h. in the same direction, the motorist gains on the cyclist at the rate of (42 − 12) m.p.h., that is at 30 m.p.h. Therefore if the motorist first sees the cyclist when he is 1 mi. away, it will take him $\frac{1}{30}$ hr. to catch up the cyclist. We say that the velocity of the motorist *relative* to the cyclist is 30 m.p.h.

If, however, the motorist and cyclist are approaching one another at these respective speeds, the distance between them decreases at the rate of (42 + 12) m.p.h., that is at 54 m.p.h. Therefore if, as before, the motorist first sees the cyclist when he is 1 mi. away, it will be only $\frac{1}{54}$ hr. before they pass one another; and in this case we say that the velocity of the motorist *relative* to the cyclist is 54 m.p.h.

Thus, if two people are travelling in the same direction, the velocity of one relative to the other is equal to the *difference* of their actual velocities; but if they are travelling towards one another, the velocity of one relative to the other is equal to the *sum* of their actual velocities.

Example 4. A train 140 yd. long takes 8 sec. to pass completely over a bridge 36 yd. long. Find the speed of the train.

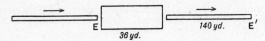

The distance of the point E where the engine reaches the bridge from the position E′ of the engine when the train is just clear of the bridge is (36 + 140) yd., that is 176 yd.

∴ in 8 sec. the engine travels 176 yd.

∴ in 1 hr. the engine travels $\frac{176 \times 60 \times 60}{8 \times 1760}$ mi., = 45 mi.

∴ the train is travelling at 45 m.p.h.

Example 5. A train 120 yd. long, travelling at 45 m.p.h., overtakes another train travelling in the same direction at 36 m.p.h. and passes it completely in 50 sec. Find the length of the second train.

Find also the time they would have taken to pass one another if they had been travelling at these speeds in opposite directions.

(i) The engine A of the first train gains on the engine B of the second train a distance equal to the sum of the lengths of the two trains in passing it completely. [Draw a diagram as in the previous example to illustrate this fact.] From the data it takes 50 sec. to gain this distance.

A gains on B at the rate of (45 − 36) m.p.h.;

∴ in 1 hr. A gains on B 9 mi.

∴ in 50 sec. A gains on B $\frac{9 \times 1760 \times 50}{60 \times 60}$ yd., = 220 yd.

∴ the sum of the lengths of the two trains is 220 yd.;

but the length of the first train is 120 yd.,

∴ the length of the second train is 100 yd.

(ii) If the trains are travelling in opposite directions, the velocity of one relative to the other is (45 + 36) m.p.h., that is 81 m.p.h.; therefore the distance between the engines A and B decrease at the rate of 81 mi. per hour;

∴ the distance decreases by 220 yd. in $\frac{60 \times 60 \times 220}{81 \times 1760}$ sec., = $\frac{50}{9}$ sec.

∴ the time the trains take to pass one another is $5\frac{5}{9}$ sec.

Alternatively, we may argue more shortly as follows:—

When the relative velocity is 9 m.p.h., the time of passing is 50 sec.

∴ when the relative velocity is 81 m.p.h., the time of passing is $\frac{50}{9}$ sec.

Example 6. A steamer can travel at 9 m.p.h. upstream and at 12 m.p.h. downstream. At what speed is the stream running?

If the steamer can travel at u m.p.h. in still water, and if the stream runs at v m.p.h., the speed of the steamer, relative to the land, is $(u-v)$ m.p.h. upstream and is $(u+v)$ m.p.h. downstream.

$$\therefore \quad u-v=9 \quad \text{and} \quad u+v=12;$$
$$\therefore \quad 2v=12-9=3; \therefore v=1\tfrac{1}{2};$$
$$\therefore \text{ the stream runs at } 1\tfrac{1}{2} \text{ m.p.h.}$$

EXERCISE 178

1. A man cycles 8 m.p.h. on the level, 6 m.p.h. uphill, and 12 m.p.h. downhill. If he first rides 3 mi. uphill, then 6 mi. along the level and ends with 2 mi. downhill, find his average speed. Find also his average speed on the return journey.

2. A launch travels $7\tfrac{1}{2}$ m.p.h. upstream and $10\tfrac{1}{2}$ m.p.h. downstream. How long does it take to go (i) 21 mi. upstream and back, (ii) 40 mi. downstream and back?

3. A train is timed to make a journey of 63 mi. at 45 m.p.h. It starts 4 min. late and runs at its proper speed for 30 min. At what rate must it do the rest of the journey to arrive punctually?

4. How long will a train 160 yd. long, travelling at 60 m.p.h., take to pass a train 148 yd. long travelling at 25 m.p.h. in the same direction?

5. A train 88 yd. long moving at 50 m.p.h. overtakes a second train moving at 35 m.p.h. in the same direction and passes it completely in $22\tfrac{1}{2}$ sec. Find the length of the second train. Find also how long the first train takes to pass a passenger in the second train.

[6] A man in a train travelling at 30 m.p.h. notices that a train going in the opposite direction passes him in 9 sec. If the length of this train is 220 yd., find its speed.

7. A man standing on a platform 220 yd. long notices that a train passes him in 6 sec. and passes completely through the station in 21 sec. Find the length of the train and its speed in m.p.h.

[8] A dog pursues at 18 m.p.h. a hare which runs at 14 m.p.h.; the hare has 44 yd. start; after what time will it be caught?

[9] Two cyclists A, B ride together; A stops for 5 min. while B rides on at 10 m.p.h. If A overtakes B after another 10 min., at what speed does he ride?

10. A can row 1 mi. upstream in 20 min. and back to his starting-point in 12 min. How long would he take to row 1 mi. in still water?

[11] In a paper chase, the hares had 20 min. start and ran the whole distance at 9 m.p.h. One of the hounds who ran the same way at 10 m.p.h. arrived 15 min. after the hares. How long was the run?

12. A liner, 814 ft. long, travelling at 20 m.p.h., is overtaken by a torpedo-boat 154 ft. long. A passenger from a porthole on the liner notices that the torpedo-boat takes 7 sec. to pass him. How long would the torpedo-boat take to pass the liner completely if going in the opposite direction?

*13. A man running at 6 m.p.h. takes 40 sec. to get from the rear to the front of a column of men marching at $3\frac{3}{4}$ m.p.h. What is the length of the column?

*14. A steamer is travelling directly away from a fort at 20 m.p.h.; a gun is fired from the fort at intervals of 1 min. At what intervals are the reports of the gun heard on the steamer, if sound travels at 1100 ft. per sec.?

*15. A car travelling at 55 m.p.h. overtook at 3 p.m. a man walking the same way at 4 m.p.h., and met at 3.5 p.m. another man walking in the opposite direction at $4\frac{1}{2}$ m.p.h. At what time will the two men meet?

Problems on Clocks and Races

Example 7. In a race of 100 yd., A beats B by 10 yd., and beats C by 13 yd. By how much will B beat C in a race of 120 yd., assuming that A, B, C all run at constant speeds throughout?

In the time that A takes to run 100 yd.,

B runs 90 yd. and C runs 87 yd.;

∴ when B has run 90 yd., C has run 87 yd.,

∴ when B has run 120 yd., C has run $\frac{87 \times 120}{90}$ yd., $=116$ yd.

∴ B beats C by 4 yd. in a race of 120 yd.

Example 8. At what times between 4 o'clock and 5 o'clock are the hands of a clock at right angles?

Imagine that the short hour-hand is prolonged so as to meet the circle round the edge of the clock which is divided into 60 equal arcs or "minute-spaces."

The hands are at right angles when the distance between their tips measured along the circle is 15 minute-spaces.

At 4 o'clock, the tip of the minute-hand is 20 minute-spaces behind the tip of the prolonged hour-hand; therefore it will be 15 minute-spaces *behind* when it has gained 5 minute-spaces on the tip of the prolonged hour-hand, and will be 15 minute-spaces *in front* when it has gained 35 minute-spaces.

In 1 hr. the tip of the minute-hand travels 60 minute-spaces and the tip of the prolonged hour-hand travels 5 minute-spaces;

$\therefore$ the minute-hand gains 55 minute-spaces in 60 min.;

$\therefore$ the minute-hand gains 5 minute-spaces in $\frac{60}{11}$ min., $= 5\frac{5}{11}$ min.,

and the minute-hand gains 35 minute-spaces in $\frac{60 \times 7}{11}$ min., $= 38\frac{2}{11}$ min.,

that is in $38\frac{2}{11}$ min.

$\therefore$ the hands are at right angles at $5\frac{5}{11}$ min. past 4 and at $38\frac{2}{11}$ min. past 4.

EXERCISE 179

1. At what times are the hands of a clock at right angles between (i) 5 p.m. and 6 p.m.; (ii) 7 p.m. and 8 p.m.?

2. At what time are the hands of a clock coincident between 3 p.m. and 4 p.m.?

[**3**] At what time are the hands of a clock opposite one another between 9 p.m. and 10 p.m.?

4. At what times do the hands of a clock contain an angle of 60° between 6 p.m. and 7 p.m.?

5. A clock is set right at 1 p.m. If it gains 1 min. an hour, what is the true time when the clock indicates 6 p.m. the same day?

[**6**] A clock is set right at 9 a.m. If it gains 30 sec. an hour, what is the true time when the clock indicates 9 a.m. the next morning?

[**7**] At 7 a.m. the time by my watch is 6.59, and at 7 p.m. the same day my watch reads 2 min. past seven. What is the right time when my watch shows 7 a.m. the next morning?

8. Two clocks are set right at midday on Monday; one loses 20 sec. an hour, the other gains 4 min. a day. What is the right time when one clock is 9 min. ahead of the other?

9. In a race of 100 yd., A beats B by 10 yd. and beats C by 16 yd. By how much will B beat C in a race of 100 yd.?

10. At billiards, A can give B 20 points in 100, and B can give C 10 points in 100. What is the probable result if A plays C level 100 up, *i.e.* a game of 100 points?

[11] At billiards, A can give B 35 points in 100 and can give C 27 points in 100; C can give D 11 points in 100. What is the probable result if B plays D level 100 up?

*12. In a quarter-mile race, A beats B by 20 yd. and C beats B by 2 sec. If A takes 50 sec. to do the quarter-mile, find whether A or C wins and by what distance, to the nearest foot.

*13 A, B start at the same time and place to ride in opposite directions round a circular track 1 mi. in circumference and pass one another when A has gone 935 yd. How far from the starting-point will B be when A has completed (i) 1 round, (ii) 2 rounds?

*14. Using the data of No. 13, find how far A and B are from the starting-point when they pass one another the second time.

*15. The length along the inner edge of a circular track is $\frac{1}{4}$ mi., and the track is 3 yd. wide. In a cycle race, four times round the track, A keeps on the inside edge and B on the outside edge. If both ride at 24 m.p.h., by how many seconds will A appear to win?

MISCELLANEOUS EXAMPLES

EXERCISE 180

1. Some Christmas cards are bought at 10d. a dozen. One half of them are sold at 2d. each, one quarter of them at $1\frac{1}{2}$d. each, and the rest are wasted. Find the gain per cent.

2. By making 65 out in his last test-match innings, Hobbs brought his average for 58 completed test-match innings to $57\frac{1}{2}$. What would he have had to make to bring it up to 60?

[3] A commodity is catalogued at £2 17s. 6d. per cwt.; if a discount of 15% is allowed, find the cost per lb., correct to $\frac{1}{10}$d.

*4. The sides of a rectangle are measured as 7·4 cm. and 6·2 cm., correct to the nearest mm. Between what limits does the area of the rectangle lie? To how many figures is it justifiable to give the area? Find, to 2 figures, the greatest possible error in taking the area as (7·4 × 6·2) sq. cm.

5. A telegraph pole is 18 ft. high and 1 ft. in diameter. Find its weight, correct to the nearest lb., if the wood weighs 35 lb. per cu. ft.

6. A French car uses 12 litres of petrol in running 100 km. How many miles, to 3 figures, does it run on a gallon of petrol? [1 mi. = 1·609 km.; 1 gall. = 4·546 litres.]

[**7**] A man buys shirts at 4s. 6d. each and sells them at 6s. 3d. each. Find his gain per cent. What would be his gain per cent. in a sale when he allows 10% discount?

[**8**] Find in yards the length of the diagonal of a square field of area 20 ac.

*****9.** A boy runs 55 yd. round a circular track, one-quarter of a mile in circumference. Through what angle has he turned?

10. Electricity is said to be consumed at the rate of 1 watt, if $\frac{1}{1000}$ of a "unit" is used per hour. For a small electric fan, the rate of consumption is 70 watts and for a larger fan is 120 watts. Find, to the nearest penny, the cost of running one fan of each kind for 28 hr. a week for 30 weeks, if electricity costs $1\frac{1}{2}$d. per unit.

[**11**] The side walls of a building, 80 ft. long, are 40 ft. high, and the roof-rafters which form a right angle at the ridge are 15 ft., 20 ft. long. Find (i) the width, (ii) the volume of the building.

*****12.** The gear of a bicycle is 70, that is for each revolution of the pedals the bicycle travels a distance equal to the circumference of a circle of diameter 70 in. If the pedals revolve 18 times in 25 sec., find the speed of the bicycle in miles per hour. [Take $\pi = 3\frac{1}{7}$.]

13. A tap discharges water at 3 cu. ft. per minute into a cylindrical tank, diameter 5 ft.; find in inches per minute, to 3 figures, the rate at which the water-level rises.

14. Calculate, to 3 figures, (i) the number of tons produced per miner, (ii) the value in £ of the coal produced per miner, in the year 1929 from the following data :—

Miners	Tons of coal produced	Total value
985,422	257,907,000	£173,233,000

*****15.** A tradesman marks his goods so that his profit is 40% of the marked price. How much per cent. of the marked price can he deduct for cash so as to gain 40% of the cost price?

[**16**] Each member of a club pays £3 a year subscription, and the expenses of the club are £240 a year. If the expenses increase by 35% and if the number of members is increased to 100, find, to the nearest shilling, what increase must be made in the subscription to cover expenses.

*17. A merchant bought cheese at 6 guineas per cwt. and sold it at 1s. 9d. per lb. Find his gain per cent. if there was a loss in weight of 4 lb. per cwt. in retailing it.

*18. A cricket ground, 120 yd. by $\frac{1}{4}$ mi., is mowed by 3 machines, A, B, C; A and B run at 3 m.p.h. and cut widths of 1 ft. and 3 ft. respectively; C runs at 5 m.p.h. and cuts a width of 3 ft. All start together, but when half the ground is done, B breaks down and the work is finished by A and C. Find the total time taken.

19. A figure is drawn on a rectangular sheet, 24 cm. by 15 cm., of stiff paper, which is found to weigh 4·72 gm. When the figure has been cut out, the rest of the paper is found to weigh 3·65 gm. Find the area of the figure, to the nearest sq. cm.

*20. A submarine can travel at 21 knots on the surface and at 15 knots when submerged. How many hours will it take for a passage of 252 nautical miles if it is submerged (i) for $\frac{3}{4}$ of the distance, (ii) for $\frac{3}{4}$ of the time?

21. The cross-section of a railway tunnel 100 yd. long is a square with a semicircle on the top edge as diameter. The tunnel is 17 ft. high at the centre; find, to 3 figures, the number of tons of material excavated at 2 tons per cu. yd.

[22] The cost of fuel per week of 54 hr. for engines of various horse-powers in a factory is as follows :—

Horse-power .	10	20	50	80	100
Cost . .	4s. 11d.	9s. 3d.	21s. 9d.	31s. 8d.	37s. 6d.

Represent these facts by a graph and estimate the cost per week for an engine of 30 H.P., and the horse-power of an engine which costs 29s. 3d. per week.

[23] In an examination the marks of the boys A, B, C, who were top respectively in the three papers, were : Arithmetic, A 90, B 77, C 62; Algebra, A 49, B 80, C 73; Geometry, A 80, B 64, C 86. The marks are scaled so that the top boy in each subject obtains 100, other marks being calculated to the nearest integer. Find the scaled totals of A, B, C.

[24] A piece of paper 1 mi. long, $\frac{1}{300}$ in. thick, is rolled into the form of a solid cylinder. Find its diameter, correct to $\frac{1}{10}$ in.

25. A shopkeeper marks his goods at 45% above cost, but allows a discount of 10% on the marked prices. What is his net gain per cent.?

*26. Electric power may be paid for either (i) at the rate of 2·35d. per unit for heating and 4·4d. per unit for lighting, or (ii) at 0·65d. per unit for all power, together with a quarterly payment of $2\frac{1}{2}\%$ of the rent of the house. If the quarterly consumption is 261 units for heating and 94 units for lighting, and if the rent is £37, find the cost of each method of payment per quarter, to the nearest penny.

27. In a certain year, income tax was levied as follows: the first £120 of a man's income was free of tax, the next £260 of his income was taxed at 2s. 3d. in the £, and the remainder at 4s. 6d. in the £. What was a man's income who paid £87 15s. in tax?

*28. A policeman, by observing the time a car takes to travel a measured distance, calculates the average speed of the car to be 68 m.p.h. If there may be an error of 5% in the distance and 10% in the time, find, to 2 figures, the limits between which the average speed lies.

29. Water is drawn off from a tank at 20 gall. per minute through a pipe of diameter $1\frac{1}{2}$ in. Find the rate of flow, in ft. per second correct to 2 figures, of the water in the pipe, if the pipe remains full. [1 gall. =277·3 cu. in.]

30. A sells goods to B at a profit of 10%; B sells them to C for £2 7s. 8d., making a profit of 4%. What did the goods cost A?

31. The £10 shares of a company stand at 8 and pay a dividend of 5 per cent. What yield per cent. is obtained by investing in these shares?

32. A man borrows £3000 at 5% p.a. compound interest, reckoned yearly. He pays back £1000 at the end of the first year and £1000 at the end of the second year. How much must he pay at the end of the third year to clear off the debt?

[33] A train X travelling at 31 m.p.h. passes a station at 2 p.m.; a train Y travelling the same way at 56 m.p.h. passes this station at 2.25 p.m. At what time will Y overtake X?

*34. A tyre pressure-gauge is graduated in kg. per sq. cm. A tyre is to be inflated to a pressure of 30 lb. per sq. in.; find, to 3 figures, the reading on the gauge for this pressure.
[1 lb. =453·6 gm., 1 cm. =0·3937 in.]

35. The eight edges of a pyramid on a square base are each 2 in. long. Find, to 3 figures, (i) the height, (ii) the volume, (iii) the total area of the surface of the pyramid.

36. A and B start a business, A contributing £1200 and B £400. After 6 months B contributes an additional £1000. If the profits at the end of the year are £140, what should A receive?

37. A goods train starts from X at 11.30 a.m., travelling at 20 m.p.h., stops for 15 min. at Y, 10 mi. from X, and then proceeds at 20 m.p.h. A passenger train leaves X at 12.10 p.m. and travels at 40 m.p.h., without stopping at Y. Find from a graph when and where it passes the goods train.

[**38**] In a mile bicycle race A beats B by 160 yd. and beats C by 20 sec. If C rides at 20 m.p.h., find the speeds of A and B, assuming them to be uniform.

39. Find the ratio by volume, in the form $n:1$, of lead to tin in an alloy made up of 10 lb. of lead and 3 lb. of tin, given that the specific gravities of the lead and tin are 11·4 and 7·3 respectively. Give n to 2 figures.

40. A bath has two taps A, B and an outlet C. With A turned on, it fills in 15 min.; with A and B turned on, it fills in 10 min.; with B turned on and C opened, the water-level remains stationary. How long will it take to fill the bath with A turned on and C opened?

*41. A man goes from Winchester to London to buy an article which costs 10% less in London than in Winchester. His expenses are 15s., but he makes a clear profit of 24s. by doing so. What did the article cost in Winchester?

*42. A bicycle pump is 0·8 in. in diameter and has a stroke of length 14 in. It takes 35 strokes to pump up a flat tyre; what volume of uncompressed air has been put in? Find the volume of the interior of the tyre when pumped up, if the air which has been put in is compressed in the ratio 7 : 2. Give answers to 2 figures.

43. A lead sphere weighs $\frac{1}{12}$ lb.; find its diameter in in. to 2 figures, if 1 cu. ft. of lead weighs 708 lb.

*44. A man buys 50 ordinary shares at £4 2s. 6d. per share. He receives a dividend of 8s. 6d. per share, and a bonus of one additional share for every 5 shares held by him. He then sells all his shares at £3 16s. 4d. Find his total gain per cent. on his outlay.

45. How much money must be invested in a 4% stock at 115 to yield a net income of £60, after tax at 5s. in the £ has been deducted?

*46. Shop A sells goods at the prices marked on them. Shop B sells at 5% less than the prices marked. Actually B sells for £98 goods that are sold in A for £100. What price does B mark on an article that is sold in A for £9 10s.?

47. A man buys a Savings Certificate for 16s. and after 3 years receives 18s. 3d. for it. At what rate per cent. per annum is compound interest reckoned?

*48. A faulty speedometer records the speed of a car, running at v m.p.h., as $(a+bv)$ m.p.h., where a, b are fixed numbers. The speedometer gives the correct reading when the car is running at 45 m.p.h., but registers 60 m.p.h. when the car's speed is $57\frac{1}{2}$ m.p.h. What is the reading on the speedometer when the car is running at 60 m.p.h.? What is the speed of the car when the speedometer registers 35 m.p.h.?

*49. For a piece of furniture a firm pays sums for material and labour in the ratio 6 : 5, and sells it at a profit of 25%. If I make the same article for myself, the material costs me twice as much as the firm paid, but by avoiding all other expenses I save £1 15s. At what price did the firm sell the article?

*50. In ascending a mountain the difference in height between X and Y is $65620(\log H - \log h)$ ft. where H, h are the barometric readings at X, Y. If the readings at X, Y are 29·85 in., 19·35 in., find the height of Y above X, and the reading at a place half-way up from X to Y.

TESTS IN COMPUTATION

TESTS 33–40 (Ch. XIII–XX)

Test 33

1. If 84% of a sum of money is £9324, what is 116% of the same sum?

2. The population of New York increased from 5,620,048 in 1920 to 6,930,446 in 1930. Find the increase per cent. correct to 3 figures.

3. (i) Find the square root of 0·094864.

(ii) Use tables to evaluate $\sqrt{(2\cdot87^2 + 1\cdot69^2)}$, correct to 3 figures.

4. Use tables to evaluate, correct to 3 figures :

$$\text{(i) } \frac{18\cdot92 \times 7\cdot064}{563\cdot7 \times 0\cdot808}; \qquad \text{(ii) } \frac{(0\cdot7246)^3}{(0\cdot8103)^2}.$$

5. The base of a triangle of area 13·7 sq. yd. is 9·85 yd.; find its height in yards, correct to 3 figures.

6. Find, correct to 3 figures, the length of the circumference of a circle of area 15 sq. in.

Test 34

1. Find the value of $\dfrac{1\frac{7}{8} + \frac{8}{9}}{3\frac{1}{9} - \frac{1}{3}} \div \dfrac{7\frac{1}{2} + 6\frac{5}{7}}{18\frac{1}{2} - 4\frac{3}{14}}$.

2. The population of Soviet Russia was 111,630,000 in 1931; the area of the country is 7,638,000 sq. mi. Find, correct to 3 figures, the average population per sq. mile.

3. (i) Find the square root of 16·5649.

(ii) Use tables to evaluate $\dfrac{1}{4\cdot72} + \dfrac{1}{7\cdot36}$, correct to 3 figures.

4. Use tables to evaluate, correct to 3 figures :

$$\text{(i) } \frac{0\cdot9172 \times 0\cdot0604}{10\cdot79 \times 0\cdot5147}; \qquad \text{(ii) } \sqrt[3]{(0\cdot6218)}.$$

5. A pond of area $3\frac{1}{2}$ ac. is frozen over with ice $2\frac{1}{4}$ in. thick. Find in tons the weight of the ice, correct to 2 figures, given that 1 cu. ft. of ice weighs 57·3 lb.

6. Find, correct to $\frac{1}{100}$ in., the radius of a sphere whose volume is 30 cu. in.

Test 35

1. (i) Find the square root of 101·6064.

(ii) Use tables to evaluate $\frac{2}{\sqrt{7}}$, correct to 3 figures.

2. Find, correct to 3 figures, by how much per cent. 0·3817 exceeds 0·3294.

3. Use tables to evaluate, correct to 3 figures :

(i) $\dfrac{9\frac{1}{2} \times 0\cdot7073}{(0\cdot3174)^2 \times 0\cdot1}$; (ii) $\dfrac{(0\cdot5076)^2}{\sqrt{0\cdot9136}}$.

4. Find in yards, correct to 3 figures, the diameter of a circular pond of area $\frac{3}{4}$ ac.

5. What sum, correct to the nearest penny, will amount to £100 in 10 months at 7% p.a. simple interest?

6. The base of a right pyramid is a square of side 6 in., and each edge is 7 in. long. Find, correct to 3 figures, (i) the height in inches, (ii) the volume in cu. in., of the pyramid.

Test 36

1. (i) *Calculate* the square root of 0·0925, correct to 3 figures.

(ii) Use tables to evaluate $\frac{30}{619} - \frac{20}{827}$, correct to 3 figures.

2. Taking 1 cu. yd. equal to 0·7645 cu. m., express 1 m. in yards, correct to 3 figures.

3. The value of some goods rises in the ratio 20 : 27. If the original value was £17 4s. 8d., find the new value correct to the nearest penny.

4. Use tables to evaluate, correct to 3 figures :

(i) $\dfrac{3\frac{3}{4} \times \sqrt{0\cdot8847}}{17 \times \sqrt[3]{0\cdot7264}}$; (ii) $(0\cdot865)^{2\frac{1}{2}}$.

5. The perimeter of a semicircular plate is 1 ft. Find, correct to 3 figures, (i) its diameter in inches, (ii) its area in sq. in.

6. Find, correct to $\frac{1}{100}$ in., the radius of the base of a circular cone of volume 10 cu. in., if its height is 4 in.

Test 37

1. Coal production in Great Britain in 1932 amounted to 243,882,000 tons and its pithead value was estimated at £165,733,000. Find the average value per ton, to the nearest penny.

2. (i) Find the square root of 309·4081.

(ii) Use tables to evaluate $\sqrt{(13\frac{9}{19})}$, correct to 3 figures.

3. Use tables to evaluate, correct to 3 figures:

(i) $\sqrt{\left\{\dfrac{7\cdot294 \times 0\cdot0085}{607\cdot4 \times 0\cdot2071}\right\}}$;　　(ii) $\dfrac{1}{\sqrt[3]{0\cdot5236}}$.

4. Find the true present worth of a bill for £405 5s. due in $4\frac{1}{2}$ months, reckoning interest at $3\frac{1}{2}\%$ p.a.

5. A cylinder which holds 35 gall. is 1 ft. 10 in. high. Find in inches, to 3 figures, the internal diameter. [1 gall. = 277·3 cu. in.]

6. The area of the surface of a sphere is 2 sq. yd. Find, correct to 3 figures, (i) the radius of the sphere in feet, (ii) the volume of the sphere in cu. feet.

Test 38

1. (i) $\pi = 3\cdot1415926...$, *calculate* the value of $\sqrt{\pi}$, correct to 3 figures.

(ii) Use tables to evaluate $\dfrac{1}{\sqrt{19}} + \dfrac{1}{\sqrt{23}}$, correct to 3 figures.

2. Taking 1 sq. km. equal to 0·3861 sq. mi., express 1 mi. in km., correct to 3 figures.

3. A's income is 11·3% greater than B's income, and B's income is 18·4% less than C's income. Find, correct to 3 figures, by how much per cent. A's income is less than C's income.

If A's income is £1750 a year, find C's income, correct to 3 figures.

4. Use tables to evaluate, correct to 3 figures:

(i) $\sqrt{\left\{\dfrac{2\cdot7}{5+\sqrt{2}}\right\}}$;　　(ii) $(0\cdot426)^{-0\cdot4}$.

5. Water is flowing at 3 mi. an hour out of a pipe of internal diameter 5 in. If the pipe remains full, find, correct to 3 figures, the number of gallons discharged per minute. [1 gall = 277·3 cu. in.]

6. The base of a right pyramid is a square of side 6 in., and the height of the pyramid is 5 in. Find (i) the volume of the pyramid, (ii) the total area of its surface, correct to 3 figures, in sq. in.

Test 39

1. Arrange in ascending order of magnitude:
$$1\tfrac{7}{12}, \quad 4\tfrac{1}{29}, \quad \sqrt{2}.$$

2. In Great Britain there were 623,231 deaths in 1929, and 536,860 deaths in 1930. Find the decrease per cent. in the number of deaths, correct to 3 figures.

3. Use tables to evaluate, correct to 3 figures:

(i) $\dfrac{(0\cdot07284)^2}{\sqrt[3]{(0\cdot06195)}} \times 4\tfrac{23}{87};$ (ii) $\dfrac{\log 305 - \log 273}{\log 6\cdot07}.$

4. Find, correct to the nearest penny, the true discount on a bill for £76 15s. due in 4 mo.; reckoning interest at $4\tfrac{3}{4}\%$ p.a.

5. Find, correct to 3 figures, the area in sq. ft. of a path 5 ft. wide surrounding a circular grass plot of diameter 80 ft.

6. The base of a conical tent is 13 ft. in diameter and its height is 9 ft. Find, correct to 3 figures, (i) the volume of the tent in cu. ft., (ii) the area of canvas used for making it, in sq. ft.

Test 40

1. Express 7 hr. 28 min. 40 sec. as a percentage of 24 hr., correct to 3 figures.

2. (i) $\pi = 3\cdot14159\ldots$, use tables to find the value of $\dfrac{1}{\sqrt{\pi}}$, correct to 3 figures.

 (ii) Find in inches, correct to $\tfrac{1}{10}$ in., the radius of a circle of area of 1 sq. ft.

3. Use tables to evaluate, correct to 3 figures:

(i) $\sqrt[3]{\left\{\dfrac{89\cdot34 \times \sqrt{17}}{10^4 \times 4\cdot006}\right\}};$ (ii) $(0\cdot034)^{0\cdot15}.$

4. Find, correct to 3 figures, the volume in cu. in. of the metal in a tube $2\tfrac{1}{2}$ ft. long, internal diameter $7\tfrac{1}{2}$ in., if the metal is $0\cdot3$ in. thick.

5. Find, correct to 3 figures, the capacity in gallons of a cylindrical tank of diameter 2 ft. 9 in. and height 5 ft. 6 in. [1 gall. $= 0\cdot1604$ cu. ft.]

6. A hollow spherical metal shell has an external diameter of 5 in. and is $\tfrac{1}{4}$ in. thick. Find, correct to 3 figures, (i) the volume in cu. in. of metal used in making it, (ii) the weight of the shell in oz. if the metal weighs 524 lb. per cu. ft.

TESTS 41-48 (Ch. XIX-XXV)

Test 41

1. Find, correct to 2 figures, the error per cent. in taking $\frac{\pi}{4}$ as 1 per cent. greater than $\frac{7}{8}$. $[\pi = 3.1415926 \ldots]$

2. A field, 285 yd. long, 155 yd. wide, is rented at £4 10s. a year. Find, to the nearest penny, the annual rent per acre.

3. Use tables to find, correct to 3 figures:

(i) the value of x if $2^x = 3$;　(ii) the value of $\sqrt{\left\{\frac{(3.602)^5}{0.728 \times \frac{2}{3}}\right\}}$.

4. Find, correct to 2 figures, the weight in kg. of a rectangular wooden beam 4.72 m. long, 0.38 m. wide, 0.26 m. thick, if the specific gravity of the wood is 0.65.

5. Find, correct to the nearest penny, the compound interest on £285 for 3 yr. at 4% p.a.

6. Find the income obtained from investing £1680 in $3\frac{1}{2}\%$ stock at 96.

Test 42

1. To how many places of decimals is $\frac{116}{31}$ an accurate approximation for $\sqrt{14}$?

2. A merchant blends 350 lb. of tea costing 1s. 5d. per lb. with 140 lb. costing 1s. $8\frac{1}{2}$d. per lb. At what price per lb. must he sell the mixture to gain 25%.

3. Use tables to find, correct to 3 figures:

(i) the value of r if $\frac{4}{3}\pi r^3 = 2\frac{1}{4}$;
(ii) the value of n if $(1.05)^n = 1.35$.

4. If American dollars are quoted at 4.865 to the £ and French francs at 74.35 to the £, express the value of 100 French francs in dollars, correct to 3 figures.

5. An ordinary brick measures $8\frac{3}{4}$ in. by $4\frac{1}{2}$ in. by $2\frac{3}{4}$ in., and 500 of these bricks weigh 1 ton 11 cwt. Find the sp. gr. of the material, correct to 2 figures. [1 cu. ft. of water weighs 62.3 lb.]

6. Find the income from, and the cost of, £1650 of $4\frac{1}{2}\%$ stock at $83\frac{1}{2}$.

Test 43

1. A bankrupt is only able to pay 67·3% of his debts. How much in the £ does he pay? Answer to nearest farthing.

2. On a map, a road 850 yd. long is represented by a line of length 1·93 in. What area on the map, correct to 3 figures, represents $1\frac{1}{2}$ ac.?

3. Use tables to find, correct to 3 figures:
   (i) the value of $(0·4615)^3 \times \sqrt{\{(5·138)^2 - (3·816)^2\}}$;
   (ii) the value of πr^2 if $2\pi r = 439·5$.

4. A grocer mixes 150 lb. of tea which costs 1s. 4d. per lb. with 360 lb. of tea which costs 1s. 7d. per lb., and sells the mixture at 1s. 9d. per lb. Find his gain per cent.

5. Two solid lead spheres of radii 3 in., 4 in., are melted together and recast as a single sphere; find its radius, correct to 3 figures.

6. 740 (£1) shares are bought at 23s. 6d. What is the purchase price? What is the yield per cent., correct to 3 figures, on the money invested if a dividend of 1s. 9d. per share is paid?

Test 44

1. A man is paid at the rate of £470 a year (365 days); how much, to the nearest shilling, is due to him after 23 days?

2. Taking 1 gall. $= 277·3$ cu. in. and 1 ft. $= 0·3048$ m., express 1 litre in gallons, correct to 3 figures.

3. Use tables to find, correct to 3 figures:
   (i) the value of n if $4·18 \times (83·4)^n = 500$;
   (ii) the value of $\sqrt[4]{\left(\dfrac{1}{0·6947}\right)} \div \sqrt[3]{\left(\dfrac{1}{0·3}\right)}$.

4. The internal and external diameters of a flat ring are 8·1 cm. and 9·7 cm., and the thickness is 1·24 cm. (i) Find the volume, correct to 3 figures. (ii) If the weight is 27·3 gm., find the specific gravity of the substance, correct to 2 figures.

5. Find, to the nearest penny, the compound interest on £126 for $1\frac{1}{2}$ yr. at 7% p.a., the interest being credited half-yearly.

6. In 1934 Leeds Corporation paid a dividend of $2\frac{1}{2}$% on £750,000 stock and a dividend of 3% on £2,000,000 stock. What was the total amount paid out to stockholders if income tax was deducted at the rate of 4s. 6d. in the £?

Test 45

1. Prove that $\sqrt{101}$ may be taken as $\frac{4030}{401}$, correct to 5 places of decimals.

2. Brass is composed by weight of 167 parts of copper, 27 parts of tin, and 6 parts of zinc. If the copper is worth £27 per ton, the tin £233 per ton and the zinc £22 per ton, find the value of the brass per ton, correct to 3 figures.

3. Use tables to evaluate, correct to 3 figures :

(i) $(0.4873)^{-0.6}$;   (ii) $\dfrac{\sqrt{\{(0.7245)^2 + (0.6083)^2\}}}{4\pi^2}$.

4. The present population of a district is 164,500. If it has increased at the rate of 14 per 1000 per year for the last 3 yr., find, correct to 3 figures, what it was 3 yr. ago.

5. The base of a solid metal right pyramid is a square of side 12 cm., and the height of the pyramid is 9 cm. Find, correct to 3 figures, (i) the weight in kg. if the specific gravity of the metal is 8.52, (ii) the total area of the surface in sq. cm.

6. Find the yield, in £ s. d. per cent., correct to the nearest penny, from an investment in a 4% stock at 93.

Test 46

1. A bankrupt is only able to pay at the rate of 7s. $4\frac{3}{4}$d. in the £. What percentage of his debts, correct to 3 figures, remains unpaid?

2. A metal weighs 573.4 lb. per cu. ft. Find, correct to 3 figures, its specific gravity (i) by taking 1 cu. ft. of water to weigh 62.3 lb., (ii) by taking 1 oz. $=28.35$ gm. and 1 in. $=2.540$ cm.

3. £165 was borrowed on June 1 and repaid with interest on August 10 of the same year (365 days). Reckoning simple interest at $5\frac{1}{2}$% p.a., find the amount repaid correct to the nearest penny.

4. Find, correct to 3 figures :

(i) the value of $\frac{4}{3}\pi r^3$ if $4\pi r^2 = 1$;
(ii) the value of $\frac{3}{4}$ of $(15.37)^{0.4} \times (0.836)^{-0.2}$.

5. A closed hollow metal cylinder has an external diameter of 5 in. and external height of 8 in.; the metal is 0.2 in. thick. Find, correct to 2 figures, (i) the volume of the metal, (ii) the weight of the cylinder if the metal weighs 5.45 oz. per cu. in.

6. In 1934 Derwent Valley Water Board paid a dividend of 5% on £1,250,000 stock and a dividend of $3\frac{1}{2}$% on £1,000,000 stock. What was the total amount paid out to the stockholders if income tax was deducted at the rate of 4s. 6d. in the £?

Test 47

1. Find, correct to 1 figure, the error per cent. in taking $\dfrac{70}{r}$ as the value of $\log 2 \div \log\left(1 + \dfrac{r}{100}\right)$ when $r = 6\frac{1}{2}$.

2. Express, correct to 3 figures, in lb. per sq. in. a pressure of 7·36 kg. per sq. cm., given 1 kg. = 2·205 lb., 1 cm. = 0·3937 in.

3. Find, correct to 2 figures, the value of $e^{2n\mu\pi}$, where $e = 2·718$, $n = 1\frac{3}{8}$, $\mu = 0·645$, $\pi = 3·142$.

4. Two solid lead spheres of radii 6 in., 1 ft., are melted together and recast as a solid circular cylinder of height 1 ft. 6 in. Find in inches the radius of the cylinder. Prove that the total surface of the two spheres is equal to that of the cylinder.

5. Find, correct to the nearest shilling, the sum of money which will amount to £350 in 3 yr. at 4% p.a. compound interest.

6. What yield in £ s. d. per cent., to the nearest penny, did a man who bought Poole Corporation $4\frac{3}{4}$% stock at 115, obtain on his money?

If he invested £5520 in this stock and sold out when the stock rose to $117\frac{1}{2}$, find his profit.

Test 48

1. If pesetas are quoted at 35·85 to the £ and lire at 57·62 to the £, express the value of 100 lire in pesetas, correct to 3 figures.

2. A liquid weighs 8·275 lb. per gallon; find, correct to 3 figures, its weight in kg. per litre. [1 lb. = 453·6 gm.; 1 cu. ft. = 6·228 gall.; 1 in. = 2·540 cm.]

3. Find, correct to 3 figures:

    (i) the value of x if $\log x = 1\frac{3}{4}$; and if $\log x = \frac{1}{4}$;

    (ii) the value of $\dfrac{0·0455}{(2·35)^{1·6}} \times \dfrac{(7·42)^2 \times 75·3}{64·4}$.

4. A sells an article to B at a profit of 20%; B sells it to C at a profit of 10%; C sells it to D at a profit of 50%. If D pays £33 for it, at what price did A sell it?

5. The volume of a circular cone, height 8 in., is 65 cu. in.; find, correct to 3 figures, (i) the diameter of the base, (ii) the length of a slant height of the cone.

6. Find the change of income if a man sells £2600 of $3\frac{1}{2}\%$ stock at 84 and invests the proceeds in $4\frac{1}{4}\%$ stock at 91.

REVISION PAPERS

PAPERS 49–56 (Ch. I–XX)

Paper 49

1. (i) Express in prime factors the L.C.M. of 385, 231, 165, 105.
  (ii) A man sells for a guinea what costs him 17s. 6d.; find his gain per cent.

2. Use logarithms to evaluate, correct to 3 figures:

  (i) $\dfrac{0 \cdot 2079 \times 0 \cdot 0804}{0 \cdot 09072}$;   (ii) $\sqrt[3]{0 \cdot 8514}$.

3. The running record for 440 yd. is 47 sec.; express this speed in miles per hour, correct to 3 figures.

4. Find, correct to $\frac{1}{10}$ yd., the radius of a circular lake of area 5 ac.

5. A swimming-bath is 30 ft. long, 18 ft. wide; it is 4 ft. deep at one end and 8 ft. deep at the other end, and the floor slopes evenly. Find how many gallons of water are required to fill the bath. [1 gall. = 0·1604 cu. ft.]

6. Find in sq. in. to 3 figures, the area of the curved surface of a cone 1 ft. high, base-diameter 10 in.

Paper 50

1. (i) Express £8 3s. 4d. as a fraction of £9 12s. 6d.
  (ii) Divide £1 into 3 parts in the ratios 3 : 4 : 5.

2. Use logarithms to evaluate, correct to 3 figures:

  (i) $\sqrt{\left\{\dfrac{9 \cdot 347 \times 10 \cdot 73}{55 \cdot 09 \times 0 \cdot 173}\right\}}$;   (ii) $(0 \cdot 5621)^{\frac{2}{3}}$.

3. In 1930 the number of deaths due to accidents in England and Wales was as follows: males, 10,922; females, 4838. What percentage, to 3 figures, of the total were males?

4. A tankard is a cylinder of internal diameter 4·3 in. Find to what depth in inches, to 3 figures, a quart of liquid will fill it. [1 gall. = 277·3 cu. in.]

5. Find, correct to $\frac{1}{10}$ sq. in., the area of an equilateral triangle whose sides are each 6 in. long.

6. Find, correct to $\frac{1}{100}$ in., the radius of the base of a circular cone, 9 in. high, if its volume is 345 cu. in.

Paper 51

1. (i) Divide £35 9s. 6d. by $2\frac{3}{4}$.

(ii) B exceeds A by 16%; C exceeds B by 25%; find the ratio of A to C.

2. Use logarithms to evaluate, correct to 3 figures :

(i) $\dfrac{47\cdot326 \times (8\cdot9712)^2}{698\cdot43}$;   (ii) $\dfrac{1}{\sqrt{0\cdot6394}} \times \dfrac{1}{21}$.

3. The areas in sq. mi. of the Pacific, Atlantic, Indian, Arctic oceans are respectively 63,986,000; 30,000,000; 28,350,000; 5,541,600. These form together 96·51 per cent. of the total sea area. Find the total sea area, correct to 3 figures.

4. Find, correct to the nearest penny, the simple interest on £428 for 35 days at $4\frac{5}{8}$% p.a. [Take 1 year = 365 days.]

5. A pump delivers 165 gall. of water per minute through a pipe 3 in. in diameter. Find in feet per second, correct to 3 figures, the rate of flow of water in the pipe, if kept full. [1 gall. = 277·3 cu. in.]

6. Find, correct to $\frac{1}{100}$ in., the diameter of a sphere whose volume is 100 cu. in. Find also the area of the surface of the sphere, to the nearest sq. in.

Paper 52

1. (i) Simplify $(10\frac{1}{2} \times 1\frac{7}{9} - 10\frac{2}{5}) \div (1\frac{9}{16} - 3\frac{1}{4} \div 2\frac{1}{6})$.

(ii) Calculate the square root of 0·09653449.

2. Use logarithms to evaluate, correct to 3 figures :

(i) $\dfrac{0\cdot3086 \times 2\frac{1}{8}}{20\cdot07 \times 1\cdot01}$;   (ii) $\dfrac{\sqrt{0\cdot7162}}{\sqrt[3]{(0\cdot809)^4}}$.

3. In 1931 the population of (Greater) London was 8,202,818 and of New York 6,981,927. By how much %, correct to 3 figures, did the population of London exceed that of New York?

4. A bankrupt's assets are £3526 and his liabilities are £5693. How much can he pay in the £, to the nearest penny?

5. A pianola record is made of paper $\frac{1}{50}$ in. thick: it is 22 yd. long and is rolled up tightly on a cylindrical roller $1\frac{1}{2}$ in. in diameter. Find the radius of the complete roll, to the nearest $\frac{1}{10}$ in.

6. The height of an open cylindrical vessel equals the diameter of its base, both measured internally. Its capacity is 3 qt. Find its height in inches, correct to 3 figures. [1 gall. = 277·3 cu. in.]

Paper 53

1. (i) Find the whole numbers between 1550 and 1800 which are perfect squares.

    (ii) Calculate the square root of 0·01449616.

2. Use logarithms to evaluate, correct to 3 figures:

$$\text{(i)} \quad \frac{0·086}{(0·9134)^3} \div \frac{13}{17}; \qquad \text{(ii)} \quad (0·6135)^{-0·7}.$$

3. In 1930 there were 455,427 deaths in England and Wales, and this was 1·141 per cent. of the population. Find the population, correct to 3 figures. The births were 1·629 per cent. of the population, find the number of births, correct to 3 figures.

4. By selling a commodity at 3s. $4\frac{1}{2}$d. per lb., a merchant gains 17%. What would be his profit per cent. if he increased the price by $2\frac{1}{4}$d. per lb.?

5. A swimming-bath is emptied by three equal pipes, each of diameter 2 in. It is desired to replace them by a single pipe which will empty the bath in the same time as the three pipes, for the same rate of flow. Find the diameter of the single pipe, correct to $\frac{1}{100}$ in.

6. The cross-section of a bar, 6 ft. long, is a trapezium ABCE (parallel sides AB and EC), surmounted by an isosceles triangle DEC (DE = DC). The distances of D and A from EC are $1\frac{1}{2}$ in., $3\frac{1}{2}$ in. respectively; AB = 4 in., EC = 6 in. Find the volume of the bar in cu. ft.

Paper 54

1. (i) Simplify $\dfrac{0\cdot05 \times 0\cdot012}{(0\cdot3)^2} \div 0\cdot25.$ (ii) Find $7\frac{3}{4}\%$ of £45.

2. Use logarithms to evaluate, correct to 3 figures :

$$\text{(i) } \pi\{17\cdot37^2 - 4\cdot08^2\}; \qquad \text{(ii) } (0\cdot3718)^{-0\cdot4}.$$

3. Find in lb., correct to 3 figures, the weight of 1 cu. in. of mercury, if 1 c.c. of mercury weighs 13·60 gm. [1 in. = 2·540 cm.; 1 lb. = 453·6 gm.]

Find also the volume of 1 cwt. of mercury in cu. in., correct to 3 figures.

4. What sum of money will yield £162 interest in $2\frac{1}{2}$ years at $4\frac{1}{2}\%$ p.a. simple interest?

5. A cylindrical tank holds 150 litres; its internal height is 65 cm., find its internal diameter in cm., correct to 3 figures.

6. How many spherical shot, each of diameter $\frac{3}{8}$ in., can be cast from $\frac{1}{2}$ cu. ft. of lead? Answer correct to 3 figures.

Paper 55

1. (i) Divide 8 tons 5 cwt. 3 qr. of coal equally among 17 pensioners.

(ii) A penny weighs $\frac{1}{3}$ oz. and is 1·2 in. in diameter. Find in miles, to 2 figures, the distance 1 ton of pennies placed edge to edge would stretch.

2. Use logarithms to evaluate, correct to 3 figures :

$$\text{(i) } \sqrt{\left\{\dfrac{3\cdot2436 \times (5\cdot321)^2}{19\cdot836}\right\}}; \qquad \text{(ii) } \dfrac{\log 585 - \log 485}{\log 32\cdot6}.$$

3. A bicycle is geared up to x cm. when, for every revolution of a pedal, the bicycle moves forward πx cm. Find, correct to 3 figures, the number of revolutions made by a pedal while a bicycle geared up to 180 cm. is travelling $\frac{3}{4}$ mi. [1 mi. = 1·609 km.]

4. Find the principal which will amount in 4 months to £228 at 4% p.a.

5. A rectangular block of iron has a square base and is 2·6 in. high, it weighs 65 lb. Find, to $\frac{1}{100}$ in., the side of the base, if 1 cu. ft. of iron weighs 444 lb.

6. A solid is composed of a solid circular cone, height 5 cm., base-radius 6 cm., with a solid hemisphere, radius 6 cm., fitted to the base. Find, to 3 figures, (i) the area of the total surface, (ii) the volume of the solid.

Paper 56

1. (i) Express, correct to 3 figures, 14s. 5d. as a decimal of 18s. 9d.

(ii) When the price of an article is reduced in the ratio 7 : 5, the reduction in price is 3s. 6d.; find the reduced price.

2. (i) Use logarithms to evaluate, correct to 3 figures:
$$0 \cdot 000482 \sqrt{(42 \cdot 7)^3} \div \sqrt{(8 \cdot 71 \times 0 \cdot 46)}.$$

(ii) Find n if $724 \times (0 \cdot 273)^n = 5 \cdot 18$.

3. Find in cu. in., to 3 figures, the volume of a lump of lead weighing 20 kg., given that 1 c.c. of lead weighs $11 \cdot 37$ gm. [1 m. $= 39 \cdot 37$ in.]

4. A, B, C, D form a business with a total capital of £11,900. At the end of the year, their shares of the profits are £319, £446 12s., £638, £765 12s. respectively. What amount of capital did each put into the business?

5. The base of a right pyramid is a rectangle 6 in. by 4 in., and each edge of the pyramid is 7 in. long. Find, correct to 3 figures, (i) the volume, (ii) the total area of the surface of the pyramid.

6. A hollow sphere whose radius is 3 in. weighs 28 lb. and is made of metal weighing 448 lb. per cu. ft. Find, correct to 2 figures, the thickness of the metal, assuming it to be uniform.

PAPERS 57–64 (Ch. I–XXV)

Paper 57

1. (i) Taking 1 lb. $= 0 \cdot 4536$ kg., express $9\frac{3}{4}$ oz. in grams, correct to 3 figures.

(ii) By what percentage does a speed of 30 mi. an hour exceed a speed of 11 yd. per second?

2. Evaluate, correct to 3 figures:

(i) $\sqrt{\left\{ \dfrac{(s-b)(s-c)}{s(s-a)} \right\}}$ if $a = 4 \cdot 27, b = 5 \cdot 18, c = 6 \cdot 39, s = \frac{1}{2}(a+b+c)$;

(ii) $12 \div (0 \cdot 7)^{1 \cdot 4}$.

3. Find, correct to the nearest penny, the compound interest on £215 for 3 years at 4% p.a.

4. Two tins have the same volume: one is rectangular, 4·32 in. long, 1·72 in. broad, 0·76 in. high; the other is cylindrical, with base-radius 1·31 in.; find its height, correct to 3 figures.

5. 3·68 c.c. of a liquid of specific gravity 0·92 are mixed with 5·14 c.c. of another liquid of specific gravity 0·78. Find, correct to 2 figures, the specific gravity of the mixture (assuming no chemical reaction).

6. A man invested £630 in $4\frac{1}{2}$% stock at 84. What income did he obtain? Later on, he sold out and made a capital profit of £45. At what price did he sell?

Paper 58

1. (i) By what percentage does $\frac{3}{4}$ exceed $\frac{2}{3}$?

(ii) Find, correct to 1 figure, the difference between $7\frac{2}{3}$ and $\sqrt{59}$.

2. Find:

(i) the value of $1 \div \sqrt[3]{\{(0·867)^2 + (0·405)^2\}}$, correct to 3 figures;

(ii) the least integral value of n for which $(\frac{2}{3})^n$ is less than 0·001.

3. If £100 is allowed to accumulate at 5% p.a. compound interest, the amount, to the nearest £, is as follows :—

Number of years .	0	5	10	12	15
Amount in £ . .	100	128	163	180	208

Represent these facts by a graph, and draw with the same scale and axes a graph showing the amount of £100 at 5% p.a. simple interest. Find from the graph the number of years after which the amount of £100 at 5% p.a. compound interest (i) first exceeds £140, (ii) first exceeds the amount of £100 at 5% p.a. simple interest by £20.

4. The diameter of the base of a solid cone of height 6 in. is 9 in. Find, correct to 3 figures, (i) the volume, (ii) the total area of the surface of the cone.

5. A tradesman marks his goods so that he makes a profit of 15% after giving a discount of $\frac{1}{2}$d. in the shilling off the marked prices. What is the marked price of an article on which his net profit is £1 13s.?

6. A man invests £3564 in a $3\frac{1}{2}$% stock at 88. How much less money need he invest in a $4\frac{1}{2}$% stock at 104 to obtain the same income?

Paper 59

1. (i) Evaluate $\dfrac{(5\cdot4)^2 \times (1\cdot8)^2 \times 125}{(10\cdot8)^2 \times 90 \times 0\cdot25}$;

(ii) Evaluate, correct to 3 figures, $\sqrt[3]{(0\cdot06157)} \div \sqrt{(0\cdot4183)}$.

2. How many seconds will a train 480 ft. long, travelling at 45 mi. an hour, take to pass completely through a station 170 yd. long?

3. A town of 52,270 inhabitants is supplied with water from a reservoir of surface area 7·63 ac. The consumption of water per day is 185 gall. per 100 inhabitants. Find, correct to 2 figures, the fall in inches of the water-level per day in the reservoir, if no water enters it. [1 cu. ft. = 6·23 gall.]

4. Copper weighs 552 lb. per cu. ft.; find its specific gravity, to 3 figures, by using the relations, 1 kg. = 2·205 lb., 1 m. = 39·37 in.

5. Find, correct to 2 figures, the weight in lb. of iron per cu. ft. if the following rule can be used:

The approximate weight of an iron pipe l feet long, t inches thick, and d inches in average diameter (*i.e.* average of internal and external diameters) is 10 ltd pounds.

6. A man holding £2500 of $2\frac{1}{2}$% Consols sold out at 56 and invested the proceeds in a 5% stock at 98. Find the increase in his income, to the nearest penny.

Paper 60

1. (i) Taking 1 gall. = 277·3 cu. in., express 1 qt. $1\frac{1}{2}$ pt. in cu. in., correct to 3 figures.

(ii) Find, without using tables, the square root of 1·6, correct to 3 figures.

2. Evaluate, correct to 3 figures:

(i) $(1\cdot516)^2 - \dfrac{1}{(1\cdot156)^2}$;

(ii) $0\cdot064\{2\cdot3 \log (72 \div 0\cdot35) + 0\cdot25\}$.

3. On a certain day, 10 kg. of potatoes cost 9 francs in Paris and 14 lb. cost 1s. 6d. in London. If £1 = 78·82 francs, how much cheaper, to the nearest shilling, would it have been to buy one ton of potatoes in Paris instead of in London? [1 lb. = 0·4536 kg.]

4. The cross-section of a bridge is a rectangle 56 ft. long, 21 ft. high, from the lower part of which a semicircle of radius 15 ft. has been removed. The bridge is 16 ft. wide and is made of material weighing 112 lb. per cu. ft. Find in tons, to 3 figures, the weight of the bridge. Find also the cost, to the nearest penny, of painting the curved surface of the under portion of the bridge at 6d. per sq. yd.

5. The composition by weight of a mixture is 70% water, 30% glycerine (specific gravity 1·25). Find the percentage composition by volume of the mixture.

6. By selling a certain amount of a $2\frac{1}{2}$% stock at $55\frac{1}{4}$ and investing the proceeds in a 6% stock at $87\frac{3}{4}$, a man increases his income by £100 a year. How much stock does he sell, assuming that brokerage at $\frac{1}{4}$ per cent. is charged on each transaction.

Paper 61

1. (i) Express the distance, 122 km., of Ostend from Brussels as a percentage, correct to 3 figures, of the distance, 145 mi., of Cardiff from London. [1 km. = 0·6214 mi.]

(ii) Evaluate, correct to 3 figures, $\frac{1}{3}\pi r^2 h$, if $r = 7$ and $h = \sqrt{50}$.

2. Two square sheets of metal, one of side 47·3 cm., the other of side 38·6 cm., of the same thickness, were melted down and rolled out into a square sheet of $\frac{3}{4}$ of this thickness. Find, correct to 3 figures, the length of the side of the final sheet.

3. Find, correct to the nearest penny, the compound interest on £254 for 3 years at $3\frac{1}{2}$% p.a.

4. (i) 20 cu. in. of a substance weigh 3 lb. 7$\frac{1}{2}$ oz.; find its specific gravity, to 2 figures. [1 cu. ft. of water weighs 62·3 lb.]

(ii) A metal body weighs 37·3 gm. in air, 28·6 gm. in water, and 21·8 gm. in another liquid. Find, to 2 figures, the specific gravity of (i) the metal, (ii) the other liquid.

5. The cost of manufacturing a certain article can be divided into two parts : the first part (overhead expenses) is the same total sum in the year, whatever number of articles are made; the second part is proportional to the number of articles made. The average cost per article is 6s. when 1000 are made in the year, and is 5s. when 2000 are made in the year. Find the overhead expenses per year, and the average cost per article if 8000 are made in the year.

6. A man buys £300 of $2\frac{1}{4}\%$ stock at $53\frac{3}{4}$ and £600 of 5% stock at $98\frac{1}{8}$. What average rate per cent. does he obtain on the money he invests? Later on, he sells his holding in the first stock at 56 and in the second stock at 92, and invests the proceeds in $3\frac{3}{4}\%$ stock at 75. Find the change of income.

Paper 62

1. (i) Express, correct to 3 figures, a pressure of 135 lb. per sq. in. in kg. per sq. cm. [1 lb. $=0.4536$ kg.; 1 in. $=2.540$ cm.]

(ii) Evaluate, correct to 3 figures, $\sqrt[3]{(0.7018)} \div (\sqrt{5} + \sqrt{11})$.

2. When the cost of food increases by 140%, the consumption per head is reduced by 25%. For how many days can 4 persons be fed for the same money that was required previously for feeding 6 persons for 30 days?

3. A solid iron bar, of circular cross-section 4.74 cm. in diameter, is melted down and recast into a hollow pipe of the same length as the bar and of internal radius 3.16 cm.; find, correct to 3 figures, its external radius.

4. Find, to the nearest £, the amount to which £142 accumulates in 30 years at 3% p.a. compound interest. [log $1.03 = 0.0128372$.]

5. The specific gravity of gold is 19.3 and of copper is 8.9. An alloy is made of 9 parts gold to 2 parts copper (i) by volume, (ii) by weight. Find the specific gravity of each mixture, correct to 2 figures.

6. Two years ago a man received an income of £51 14s. 7d. from a stock when the dividend was paid at the rate of $3\frac{1}{4}\%$. Last year he received an income of £87 10s. 10d. from the same stock; at what rate was the dividend paid? What will he obtain if he sells his holding at $93\frac{1}{2}$?

Paper 63

1. (i) A locomotive consumes $5\frac{1}{4}$ tons of coal at £1 5s. $7\frac{1}{2}$d. per ton, for a journey of 240 mi. Find the cost per mile, correct to $\frac{1}{10}$d.

(ii) In what time would a column of 20 battalions, each 320 ft. long, march completely through a defile $1\frac{1}{2}$ mi. long at the ordinary rate of 75 paces of $2\frac{1}{2}$ ft. each per minute?

2. On a certain day, £1 was worth 4 dollars 77 cents in New York, one dollar was worth 16·07 francs in Paris, and £1 was worth 78·82 francs in London. If a merchant changed £1000 into dollars, then the resulting dollars into francs, and then the resulting francs back into pounds on that day, find to the nearest ten shillings his gain or loss.

3. A cylindrical jar of diameter 11 cm. and of height 11 cm. is half-full of water. A metal sphere of diameter 10·8 cm. is then placed in it. Find in c.c., correct to 2 figures, how much water overflows.

4. A man borrows £575 and is charged interest at 5% each year for the amount owing at the beginning of that year. He repays £200 at the end of the first year, and another £200 at the end of the second year; how much does he still owe at the end of the third year?

5. A body is floating in a liquid of specific gravity 1·24, and the volume of the portion submerged is 52·5 c.c.; find the weight of the body.

6. A man has £3100 of 3% stock; he sells out at $92\frac{1}{4}$ and invests the proceeds in a 5% stock, brokerage being charged at $\frac{1}{4}$ per cent. on each transaction. If his income is thereby increased by £31, find the price of the 5% stock.

Paper 64

1. A man uses 10 lb. 4 oz. of sealing-wax for sealing 5540 envelopes; how much, to the nearest oz., should he use for sealing 7520 envelopes at the same rate? Find, to the nearest penny, the cost of the wax used for 7520 envelopes at 6s. per lb.

2. The rate of exchange varies from 4 dollars $88\frac{3}{8}$ cents to the £ one day to 4 dollars $88\frac{1}{4}$ cents to the £ the next day. How much, to the nearest shilling, will a merchant gain by waiting till the second day to convert 100,000 dollars into English money?

3. A dealer marks his goods at 40% above cost price, but allows customers a discount of 1s. in the £ off the marked price. What profit per cent. does the dealer make?

4. The contents of a cubical chest of tea, internal measurement 2 ft. 3 in. each way, are just sufficient to fill 230 equal cylindrical tin canisters, each 10 in. high. Find in inches, to 3 figures, the radius of a canister.

5. The price of gas is $8\frac{2}{5}$d. a therm; 1 therm = 100,000 units of heat, and 1 cu. ft. of gas gives out 460 units of heat. In 1932 and 1933 a consumer's bills were respectively £12 9s. and £9 16s., although he used the same amount of gas each year, the difference being due to the repair of a leak. Find, correct to 3 figures, the number of cu. ft. of gas wasted in 1932.

6. A man held £2100 of $3\frac{1}{2}$% Metropolitan stock. When it became due to be repaid, he accepted an offer to have it transferred without charge to the new $4\frac{1}{2}$% London County stock at the rate of £103 10s. of the new stock for every £100 of the Metropolitan stock. Find, to the nearest penny, the change in his income, after allowing for income tax deduction at 4s. in the £ in each case.

TABLES

	0	1	2	3	4	5	6	7	8	9	1	2	3	4	5	6	7	8	9
10	·0000	0043	0086	0128	0170	0212	0253	0294	0334	0374	4	8	12	17	21	25	29	33	37
11	·0414	0453	0492	0531	0569	0607	0645	0682	0719	0755	4	8	11	15	19	23	26	30	34
12	·0792	0828	0864	0899	0934	0969	1004	1038	1072	1106	3	7	10	14	17	21	24	28	31
13	·1139	1173	1206	1239	1271	1303	1335	1367	1399	1430	3	6	10	13	16	19	23	26	29
14	·1461	1492	1523	1553	1584	1614	1644	1673	1703	1732	3	6	9	12	15	18	21	24	27
15	·1761	1790	1818	1847	1875	1903	1931	1959	1987	2014	3	6	8	11	14	17	20	22	25
16	·2041	2068	2095	2122	2148	2175	2201	2227	2253	2279	3	5	8	11	13	16	18	21	24
17	·2304	2330	2355	2380	2405	2430	2455	2480	2504	2529	2	5	7	10	12	15	17	20	22
18	·2553	2577	2601	2625	2648	2672	2695	2718	2742	2765	2	5	7	9	12	14	16	19	21
19	·2788	2810	2833	2856	2878	2900	2923	2945	2967	2989	2	4	7	9	11	13	16	18	20
20	·3010	3032	3054	3075	3096	3118	3139	3160	3181	3201	2	4	6	8	11	13	15	17	19
21	·3222	3243	3263	3284	3304	3324	3345	3365	3385	3404	2	4	6	8	10	12	14	16	18
22	·3424	3444	3464	3483	3502	3522	3541	3560	3579	3598	2	4	6	8	10	12	14	15	17
23	·3617	3636	3655	3674	3692	3711	3729	3747	3766	3784	2	4	6	7	9	11	13	15	17
24	·3802	3820	3838	3856	3874	3892	3909	3927	3945	3962	2	4	5	7	9	11	12	14	16
25	·3979	3997	4014	4031	4048	4065	4082	4099	4116	4133	2	3	5	7	9	10	12	14	15
26	·4150	4166	4183	4200	4216	4232	4249	4265	4281	4298	2	3	5	7	8	10	11	13	15
27	·4314	4330	4346	4362	4378	4393	4409	4425	4440	4456	2	3	5	6	8	9	11	13	14
28	·4472	4487	4502	4518	4533	4548	4564	4579	4594	4609	2	3	5	6	8	9	11	12	14
29	·4624	4639	4654	4669	4683	4698	4713	4728	4742	4757	1	3	4	6	7	9	10	12	13
30	·4771	4786	4800	4814	4829	4843	4857	4871	4886	4900	1	3	4	6	7	9	10	11	13
31	·4914	4928	4942	4955	4969	4983	4997	5011	5024	5038	1	3	4	6	7	8	10	11	12
32	·5051	5065	5079	5092	5105	5119	5132	5145	5159	5172	1	3	4	5	7	8	9	11	12
33	·5185	5198	5211	5224	5237	5250	5263	5276	5289	5302	1	3	4	5	6	8	9	10	12
34	·5315	5328	5340	5353	5366	5378	5391	5403	5416	5428	1	3	4	5	6	8	9	10	11
35	·5441	5453	5465	5478	5490	5502	5514	5527	5539	5551	1	2	4	5	6	7	9	10	11
36	·5563	5575	5587	5599	5611	5623	5635	5647	5658	5670	1	2	4	5	6	7	8	10	11
37	·5682	5694	5705	5717	5729	5740	5752	5763	5775	5786	1	2	3	5	6	7	8	9	10
38	·5798	5809	5821	5832	5843	5855	5866	5877	5888	5899	1	2	3	5	6	7	8	9	10
39	·5911	5922	5933	5944	5955	5966	5977	5988	5999	6010	1	2	3	4	5	7	8	9	10
40	·6021	6031	6042	6053	6064	6075	6085	6096	6107	6117	1	2	3	4	5	6	8	9	10
41	·6128	6138	6149	6160	6170	6180	6191	6201	6212	6222	1	2	3	4	5	6	7	8	9
42	·6232	6243	6253	6263	6274	6284	6294	6304	6314	6325	1	2	3	4	5	6	7	8	9
43	·6335	6345	6355	6365	6375	6385	6395	6405	6415	6425	1	2	3	4	5	6	7	8	9
44	·6435	6444	6454	6464	6474	6484	6493	6503	6513	6522	1	2	3	4	5	6	7	8	9
45	·6532	6542	6551	6561	6571	6580	6590	6599	6609	6618	1	2	3	4	5	6	7	8	9
46	·6628	6637	6646	6656	6665	6675	6684	6693	6702	6712	1	2	3	4	5	6	7	7	8
47	·6721	6730	6739	6749	6758	6767	6776	6785	6794	6803	1	2	3	4	5	5	6	7	8
48	·6812	6821	6830	6839	6848	6857	6866	6875	6884	6893	1	2	3	4	4	5	6	7	8
49	·6902	6911	6920	6928	6937	6946	6955	6964	6972	6981	1	2	3	4	4	5	6	7	8
50	·6990	6998	7007	7016	7024	7033	7042	7050	7059	7067	1	2	3	3	4	5	6	7	8
51	·7076	7084	7093	7101	7110	7118	7126	7135	7143	7152	1	2	3	3	4	5	6	7	8
52	·7160	7168	7177	7185	7193	7202	7210	7218	7226	7235	1	2	2	3	4	5	6	7	7
53	·7243	7251	7259	7267	7275	7284	7292	7300	7308	7316	1	2	2	3	4	5	6	6	7
54	·7324	7332	7340	7348	7356	7364	7372	7380	7388	7396	1	2	2	3	4	5	6	6	7

	0	1	2	3	4	5	6	7	8	9	1	2	3	4	5	6	7	8	9
55	·7404	7412	7419	7427	7435	7443	7451	7459	7466	7474	1	2	2	3	4	5	5	6	7
56	·7482	7490	7497	7505	7513	7520	7528	7536	7543	7551	1	2	2	3	4	5	5	6	7
57	·7559	7566	7574	7582	7589	7597	7604	7612	7619	7627	1	2	2	3	4	5	5	6	7
58	·7634	7642	7649	7657	7664	7672	7679	7686	7694	7701	1	1	2	3	4	4	5	6	7
59	·7709	7716	7723	7731	7738	7745	7752	7760	7767	7774	1	1	2	3	4	4	5	6	7
60	·7782	7789	7796	7803	7810	7818	7825	7832	7839	7846	1	1	2	3	4	4	5	6	6
61	·7853	7860	7868	7875	7882	7889	7896	7903	7910	7917	1	1	2	3	4	4	5	6	6
62	·7924	7931	7938	7945	7952	7959	7966	7973	7980	7987	1	1	2	3	3	4	5	6	6
63	·7993	8000	8007	8014	8021	8028	8035	8041	8048	8055	1	1	2	3	3	4	5	5	6
64	·8062	8069	8075	8082	8089	8096	8102	8109	8116	8122	1	1	2	3	3	4	5	5	6
65	·8129	8136	8142	8149	8156	8162	8169	8176	8182	8189	1	1	2	3	3	4	5	5	6
66	·8195	8202	8209	8215	8222	8228	8235	8241	8248	8254	1	1	2	3	3	4	5	5	6
67	·8261	8267	8274	8280	8287	8293	8299	8306	8312	8319	1	1	2	3	3	4	5	5	6
68	·8325	8331	8338	8344	8351	8357	8363	8370	8376	8382	1	1	2	3	3	4	4	5	6
69	·8388	8395	8401	8407	8414	8420	8426	8432	8439	8445	1	1	2	2	3	4	4	5	6
70	·8451	8457	8463	8470	8476	8482	8488	8494	8500	8506	1	1	2	2	3	4	4	5	6
71	·8513	8519	8525	8531	8537	8543	8549	8555	8561	8567	1	1	2	2	3	4	4	5	5
72	·8573	8579	8585	8591	8597	8603	8609	8615	8621	8627	1	1	2	2	3	4	4	5	5
73	·8633	8639	8645	8651	8657	8663	8669	8675	8681	8686	1	1	2	2	3	4	4	5	5
74	·8692	8698	8704	8710	8716	8722	8727	8733	8739	8745	1	1	2	2	3	4	4	5	5
75	·8751	8756	8762	8768	8774	8779	8785	8791	8797	8802	1	1	2	2	3	3	4	5	5
76	·8808	8814	8820	8825	8831	8837	8842	8848	8854	8859	1	1	2	2	3	3	4	5	5
77	·8865	8871	8876	8882	8887	8893	8899	8904	8910	8915	1	1	2	2	3	3	4	4	5
78	·8921	8927	8932	8938	8943	8949	8954	8960	8965	8971	1	1	2	2	3	3	4	4	5
79	·8976	8982	8987	8993	8998	9004	9009	9015	9020	9025	1	1	2	2	3	3	4	4	5
80	·9031	9036	9042	9047	9053	9058	9063	9069	9074	9079	1	1	2	2	3	3	4	4	5
81	·9085	9090	9096	9101	9106	9112	9117	9122	9128	9133	1	1	2	2	3	3	4	4	5
82	·9138	9143	9149	9154	9159	9165	9170	9175	9180	9186	1	1	2	2	3	3	4	4	5
83	·9191	9196	9201	9206	9212	9217	9222	9227	9232	9238	1	1	2	2	3	3	4	4	5
84	·9243	9248	9253	9258	9263	9269	9274	9279	9284	9289	1	1	2	2	3	3	4	4	5
85	·9294	9299	9304	9309	9315	9320	9325	9330	9335	9340	1	1	2	2	3	3	4	4	5
86	·9345	9350	9355	9360	9365	9370	9375	9380	9385	9390	1	1	2	2	3	3	4	4	5
87	·9395	9400	9405	9410	9415	9420	9425	9430	9435	9440	0	1	1	2	2	3	3	4	4
88	·9445	9450	9455	9460	9465	9469	9474	9479	9484	9489	0	1	1	2	2	3	3	4	4
89	·9494	9499	9504	9509	9513	9518	9523	9528	9533	9538	0	1	1	2	2	3	3	4	4
90	·9542	9547	9552	9557	9562	9566	9571	9576	9581	9586	0	1	1	2	2	3	3	4	4
91	·9590	9595	9600	9605	9609	9614	9619	9624	9628	9633	0	1	1	2	2	3	3	4	4
92	·9638	9643	9647	9652	9657	9661	9666	9671	9675	9680	0	1	1	2	2	3	3	4	4
93	·9685	9689	9694	9699	9703	9708	9713	9717	9722	9727	0	1	1	2	2	3	3	4	4
94	·9731	9736	9741	9745	9750	9754	9759	9763	9768	9773	0	1	1	2	2	3	3	4	4
95	·9777	9782	9786	9791	9795	9800	9805	9809	9814	9818	0	1	1	2	2	3	3	4	4
96	·9823	9827	9832	9836	9841	9845	9850	9854	9859	9863	0	1	1	2	2	3	3	4	4
97	·9868	9872	9877	9881	9886	9890	9894	9899	9903	9908	0	1	1	2	2	3	3	4	4
98	·9912	9917	9921	9926	9930	9934	9939	9943	9948	9952	0	1	1	2	2	3	3	4	4
99	·9956	9961	9965	9969	9974	9978	9983	9987	9991	9996	0	1	1	2	2	3	3	3	4

26*

RECIPROCALS

SUBTRACT.

	0	1	2	3	4	5	6	7	8	9	1 2 3	4 5 6	7 8 9
10	10000	9901	9804	9709	9615	9524	9434	9346	9259	9174	9 18 28	37 46 55	64 73 83
11	9091	9009	8929	8850	8772	8696	8621	8547	8475	8403	8 15 23	31 38 46	54 61 69
12	8333	8264	8197	8130	8065	8000	7937	7874	7813	7752	6 13 19	26 32 39	45 52 58
13	7692	7634	7576	7519	7463	7407	7353	7299	7246	7194	5 11 17	22 28 33	39 44 50
14	7143	7092	7042	6993	6944	6897	6849	6803	6757	6711	5 10 14	19 24 29	34 38 43
15	6667	6623	6579	6536	6494	6452	6410	6369	6329	6289	4 8 13	17 21 25	29 34 38
16	6250	6211	6173	6135	6098	6061	6024	5988	5952	5917	4 7 11	15 18 22	26 29 33
17	5882	5848	5814	5780	5747	5714	5682	5650	5618	5587	3 7 10	13 16 20	23 26 29
18	5556	5525	5495	5464	5435	5405	5376	5348	5319	5291	3 6 9	12 15 18	20 23 26
19	5263	5236	5208	5181	5155	5128	5102	5076	5051	5025	3 5 8	11 13 16	18 21 24
20	5000	4975	4950	4926	4902	4878	4854	4831	4808	4785	2 5 7	10 12 14	17 19 21
21	4762	4739	4717	4695	4673	4651	4630	4608	4587	4566	2 4 7	9 11 13	15 17 19
22	4545	4525	4505	4484	4464	4444	4425	4405	4386	4367	2 4 6	8 10 12	14 16 18
23	4348	4329	4310	4292	4274	4255	4237	4219	4202	4184	2 4 5	7 9 11	13 15 16
24	4167	4149	4132	4115	4098	4082	4065	4049	4032	4016	2 3 5	7 8 10	12 13 15
25	4000	3984	3968	3953	3937	3922	3906	3891	3876	3861	2 3 5	6 8 9	11 12 14
26	3846	3831	3817	3802	3788	3774	3759	3745	3731	3717	1 3 4	6 7 9	10 11 13
27	3704	3690	3676	3663	3650	3636	3623	3610	3597	3584	1 3 4	5 7 8	9 11 12
28	3571	3559	3546	3534	3521	3509	3497	3484	3472	3460	1 2 4	5 6 7	9 10 11
29	3448	3436	3425	3413	3401	3390	3378	3367	3356	3344	1 2 3	5 6 7	8 9 10
30	3333	3322	3311	3300	3289	3279	3268	3257	3247	3236	1 2 3	4 5 6	8 9 10
31	3226	3215	3205	3195	3185	3175	3165	3155	3145	3135	1 2 3	4 5 6	7 8 9
32	3125	3115	3106	3096	3086	3077	3067	3058	3049	3040	1 2 3	4 5 6	7 8 9
33	3030	3021	3012	3003	2994	2985	2976	3967	2959	2950	1 2 3	4 4 5	6 7 8
34	2941	2933	2924	2915	2907	2899	2890	2882	2874	2865	1 2 3	3 4 5	6 7 8
35	2857	2849	2841	2833	2825	2817	2809	2801	2793	2786	1 2 2	3 4 5	6 6 7
36	2778	2770	2762	2755	2747	2740	2732	2725	2717	2710	1 2 2	3 4 5	5 6 7
37	2703	2695	2688	2681	2674	2667	2660	2653	2646	2639	1 1 2	3 4 4	5 6 6
38	2632	2625	2618	2611	2604	2597	2591	2584	2577	2571	1 1 2	3 3 4	5 5 6
39	2564	2558	2551	2545	2538	2532	2525	2519	2513	2506	1 1 2	3 3 4	4 5 6
40	2500	2494	2488	2481	2475	2469	2463	2457	2451	2445	1 1 2	2 3 4	4 5 5
41	2439	2433	2427	2421	2415	2410	2404	2398	2392	2387	1 1 2	2 3 3	4 5 5
42	2381	2375	2370	2364	2358	2353	2347	2342	2336	2331	1 1 2	2 3 3	4 4 5
43	2326	2320	2315	2309	2304	2299	2294	2288	2283	2278	1 1 2	2 3 3	4 4 5
44	2273	2268	2262	2257	2252	2247	2242	2237	2232	2227	1 1 2	2 3 3	4 4 5
45	2222	2217	2212	2208	2203	2198	2193	2188	2183	2179	0 1 1	2 2 3	3 4 4
46	2174	2169	2165	2160	2155	2151	2146	2141	2137	2132	0 1 1	2 2 3	3 4 4
47	2128	2123	2119	2114	2110	2105	2101	2096	2092	2088	0 1 1	2 2 3	3 3 4
48	2083	2079	2075	2070	2066	2062	2058	2053	2049	2045	0 1 1	2 2 3	3 3 4
49	2041	2037	2033	2028	2024	2020	2016	2012	2008	2004	0 1 1	2 2 2	3 3 4
50	2000	1996	1992	1988	1984	1980	1976	1972	1969	1965	0 1 1	2 2 2	3 3 4
51	1961	1957	1953	1949	1946	1942	1938	1934	1931	1927	0 1 1	2 2 2	3 3 3
52	1923	1919	1916	1912	1908	1905	1901	1898	1894	1890	0 1 1	1 2 2	3 3 3
53	1887	1883	1880	1876	1873	1869	1866	1862	1859	1855	0 1 1	1 2 2	2 3 3
54	1852	1848	1845	1842	1838	1835	1832	1828	1825	1821	0 1 1	1 2 2	2 3 3

SUBTRACT.

Find the position of the decimal point by inspection.

SUBTRACT.

	0	1	2	3	4	5	6	7	8	9	1	2	3	4	5	6	7	8	9
55	1818	1815	1812	1808	1805	1802	1799	1795	1792	1789	0	1	1	1	2	2	2	3	3
56	1786	1783	1779	1776	1773	1770	1767	1764	1761	1757	0	1	1	1	2	2	2	3	3
57	1754	1751	1748	1745	1742	1739	1736	1733	1730	1727	0	1	1	1	2	2	2	2	3
58	1724	1721	1718	1715	1712	1709	1706	1704	1701	1698	0	1	1	1	1	2	2	2	3
59	1695	1692	1689	1686	1684	1681	1678	1675	1672	1669	0	1	1	1	1	2	2	2	3
60	1667	1664	1661	1658	1656	1653	1650	1647	1645	1642	0	1	1	1	1	2	2	2	2
61	1639	1637	1634	1631	1629	1626	1623	1621	1618	1616	0	1	1	1	1	2	2	2	2
62	1613	1610	1608	1605	1603	1600	1597	1595	1592	1590	0	1	1	1	1	2	2	2	2
63	1587	1585	1582	1580	1577	1575	1572	1570	1567	1565	0	0	1	1	1	1	2	2	2
64	1563	1560	1558	1555	1553	1550	1548	1546	1543	1541	0	0	1	1	1	1	2	2	2
65	1538	1536	1534	1531	1529	1527	1524	1522	1520	1517	0	0	1	1	1	1	2	2	2
66	1515	1513	1511	1508	1506	1504	1502	1499	1497	1495	0	0	1	1	1	1	2	2	2
67	1493	1490	1488	1486	1484	1481	1479	1477	1475	1473	0	0	1	1	1	1	2	2	2
68	1471	1468	1466	1464	1462	1460	1458	1456	1453	1451	0	0	1	1	1	1	1	2	2
69	1449	1447	1445	1443	1441	1439	1437	1435	1433	1431	0	0	1	1	1	1	1	2	2
70	1429	1427	1425	1422	1420	1418	1416	1414	1412	1410	0	0	1	1	1	1	1	2	2
71	1408	1406	1404	1403	1401	1399	1397	1395	1393	1391	0	0	1	1	1	1	1	2	2
72	1389	1387	1385	1383	1381	1379	1377	1376	1374	1372	0	0	1	1	1	1	1	2	2
73	1370	1368	1366	1364	1362	1361	1359	1357	1355	1353	0	0	1	1	1	1	1	2	2
74	1351	1350	1348	1346	1344	1342	1340	1339	1337	1335	0	0	1	1	1	1	1	1	2
75	1333	1332	1330	1328	1326	1325	1323	1321	1319	1318	0	0	1	1	1	1	1	1	2
76	1316	1314	1312	1311	1309	1307	1305	1304	1302	1300	0	0	1	1	1	1	1	1	2
77	1299	1297	1295	1294	1292	1290	1289	1287	1285	1284	0	0	0	1	1	1	1	1	1
78	1282	1280	1279	1277	1276	1274	1272	1271	1269	1267	0	0	0	1	1	1	1	1	1
79	1266	1264	1263	1261	1259	1258	1256	1255	1253	1252	0	0	0	1	1	1	1	1	1
80	1250	1248	1247	1245	1244	1242	1241	1239	1238	1236	0	0	0	1	1	1	1	1	1
81	1235	1233	1232	1230	1229	1227	1225	1224	1222	1221	0	0	0	1	1	1	1	1	1
82	1220	1218	1217	1215	1214	1212	1211	1209	1208	1206	0	0	0	1	1	1	1	1	1
83	1205	1203	1202	1200	1199	1198	1196	1195	1193	1192	0	0	0	1	1	1	1	1	1
84	1190	1189	1188	1186	1185	1183	1182	1181	1179	1178	0	0	0	1	1	1	1	1	1
85	1176	1175	1174	1172	1171	1170	1168	1167	1166	1164	0	0	0	1	1	1	1	1	1
86	1163	1161	1160	1159	1157	1156	1155	1153	1152	1151	0	0	0	1	1	1	1	1	1
87	1149	1148	1147	1145	1144	1143	1142	1140	1139	1138	0	0	0	1	1	1	1	1	1
88	1136	1135	1134	1133	1131	1130	1129	1127	1126	1125	0	0	0	1	1	1	1	1	1
89	1124	1122	1121	1120	1119	1117	1116	1115	1114	1112	0	0	0	1	1	1	1	1	1
90	1111	1110	1109	1107	1106	1105	1104	1103	1101	1100	0	0	0	0	1	1	1	1	1
91	1099	1098	1096	1095	1094	1093	1092	1091	1089	1088	0	0	0	0	1	1	1	1	1
92	1087	1086	1085	1083	1082	1081	1080	1079	1078	1076	0	0	0	0	1	1	1	1	1
93	1075	1074	1073	1072	1071	1070	1068	1067	1066	1065	0	0	0	0	1	1	1	1	1
94	1064	1063	1062	1060	1059	1058	1057	1056	1055	1054	0	0	0	0	1	1	1	1	1
95	1053	1052	1050	1049	1048	1047	1046	1045	1044	1043	0	0	0	0	1	1	1	1	1
96	1042	1041	1040	1038	1037	1036	1035	1034	1033	1032	0	0	0	0	1	1	1	1	1
97	1031	1030	1029	1028	1027	1026	1025	1024	1022	1021	0	0	0	0	1	1	1	1	1
98	1020	1019	1018	1017	1016	1015	1014	1013	1012	1011	0	0	0	0	0	1	1	1	1
99	1010	1009	1008	1007	1006	1005	1004	1003	1002	1001	0	0	0	0	0	1	1	1	1

SUBTRACT.

Find the position of the decimal point by inspection.

	0	1	2	3	4	5	6	7	8	9	1	2	3	4	5	6	7	8	9
10	1000	1020	1040	1061	1082	1103	1124	1145	1166	1188	2	4	6	8	10	13	15	17	19
11	1210	1232	1254	1277	1300	1323	1346	1369	1392	1416	2	5	7	9	11	14	16	18	21
12	1440	1464	1488	1513	1538	1563	1588	1613	1638	1664	2	5	7	10	12	15	17	20	22
13	1690	1716	1742	1769	1796	1823	1850	1877	1904	1932	3	5	8	11	13	16	19	22	24
14	1960	1988	2016	2045	2074	2103	2132	2161	2190	2220	3	6	9	12	14	17	20	23	26
15	2250	2280	2310	2341	2372	2403	2434	2465	2496	2528	3	6	9	12	15	19	22	25	28
16	2560	2592	2624	2657	2690	2723	2756	2789	2822	2856	3	7	10	13	16	20	23	26	30
17	2890	2924	2958	2993	3028	3063	3098	3133	3168	3204	3	7	10	14	17	21	24	28	31
18	3240	3276	3312	3349	3386	3423	3460	3497	3534	3572	4	7	11	15	18	22	26	30	33
19	3610	3648	3686	3725	3764	3803	3842	3881	3920	3960	4	8	12	16	19	23	27	31	35
20	4000	4040	4080	4121	4162	4203	4244	4285	4326	4368	4	8	12	16	20	25	29	33	37
21	4410	4452	4494	4537	4580	4623	4666	4709	4752	4796	4	9	13	17	21	26	30	34	39
22	4840	4884	4928	4973	5018	5063	5108	5153	5198	5244	4	9	13	18	22	27	31	36	40
23	5290	5336	5382	5429	5476	5523	5570	5617	5664	5712	5	9	14	19	23	28	33	38	42
24	5760	5808	5856	5905	5954	6003	6052	6101	6150	6200	5	10	15	20	24	29	34	39	44
25	6250	6300	6350	6401	6452	6503	6554	6605	6656	6708	5	10	15	20	25	31	36	41	46
26	6760	6812	6864	6917	6970	7023	7076	7129	7182	7236	5	11	16	21	26	32	37	42	48
27	7290	7344	7398	7453	7508	7563	7618	7673	7728	7784	5	11	16	22	27	33	38	44	49
28	7840	7896	7952	8009	8066	8123	8180	8237	8294	8352	6	11	17	23	28	34	40	46	51
29	8410	8468	8526	8585	8644	8703	8762	8821	8880	8940	6	12	18	24	29	35	41	47	53
30	9000	9060	9120	9181	9242	9303	9364	9425	9486	9548	6	12	18	24	30	37	43	49	55
31	9610	9672	9734	9797	9860	9923	9986				6	13	19	25	31	38	44	50	57
31								1005	1011	1018	1	1	2	3	3	4	5	5	6
32	1024	1030	1037	1043	1050	1056	1063	1069	1076	1082	1	1	2	3	3	4	5	5	6
33	1089	1096	1102	1109	1116	1122	1129	1136	1142	1149	1	1	2	3	3	4	5	5	6
34	1156	1163	1170	1176	1183	1190	1197	1204	1211	1218	1	1	2	3	3	4	5	6	6
35	1225	1232	1239	1246	1253	1260	1267	1274	1282	1289	1	1	2	3	4	4	5	6	6
36	1296	1303	1310	1318	1325	1332	1340	1347	1354	1362	1	1	2	3	4	4	5	6	7
37	1369	1376	1384	1391	1399	1406	1414	1421	1429	1436	1	2	2	3	4	5	5	6	7
38	1444	1452	1459	1467	1475	1482	1490	1498	1505	1513	1	2	2	3	4	5	5	6	7
39	1521	1529	1537	1544	1552	1560	1568	1576	1584	1592	1	2	2	3	4	5	6	6	7
40	1600	1608	1616	1624	1632	1640	1648	1656	1665	1673	1	2	2	3	4	5	6	6	7
41	1681	1689	1697	1706	1714	1722	1731	1739	1747	1756	1	2	2	3	4	5	6	7	7
42	1764	1772	1781	1789	1798	1806	1815	1823	1832	1840	1	2	3	3	4	5	6	7	8
43	1849	1858	1866	1875	1884	1892	1901	1910	1918	1927	1	2	3	3	4	5	6	7	8
44	1936	1945	1954	1962	1971	1980	1989	1998	2007	2016	1	2	3	4	4	5	6	7	8
45	2025	2034	2043	2052	2061	2070	2079	2088	2098	2107	1	2	3	4	5	5	6	7	8
46	2116	2125	2134	2144	2153	2162	2172	2181	2190	2200	1	2	3	4	5	6	7	7	8
47	2209	2218	2228	2237	2247	2256	2266	2275	2285	2294	1	2	3	4	5	6	7	8	9
48	2304	2314	2323	2333	2343	2352	2362	2372	2381	2391	1	2	3	4	5	6	7	8	9
49	2401	2411	2421	2430	2440	2450	2460	2470	2480	2490	1	2	3	4	5	6	7	8	9
50	2500	2510	2520	2530	2540	2550	2560	2570	2581	2591	1	2	3	4	5	6	7	8	9
51	2601	2611	2621	2632	2642	2652	2663	2673	2683	2694	1	2	3	4	5	6	7	8	9
52	2704	2714	2725	2735	2746	2756	2767	2777	2788	2798	1	2	3	4	5	6	7	8	9
53	2809	2820	2830	2841	2852	2862	2873	2884	2894	2905	1	2	3	4	5	6	7	9	10
54	2916	2927	2938	2948	2959	2970	2981	2992	3003	3014	1	2	3	4	5	7	8	9	10

Find the position of the decimal point by inspection.

	0	1	2	3	4	5	6	7	8	9	1	2	3	4	5	6	7	8	9
55	3025	3036	3047	3058	3069	3080	3091	3102	3114	3125	1	2	3	4	6	7	8	9	10
56	3136	3147	3158	3170	3181	3192	3204	3215	3226	3238	1	2	3	5	6	7	8	9	10
57	3249	3260	3272	3283	3295	3306	3318	3329	3341	3352	1	2	3	5	6	7	8	9	10
58	3364	3376	3387	3399	3411	3422	3434	3446	3457	3469	1	2	4	5	6	7	8	9	11
59	3481	3493	3505	3516	3528	3540	3552	3564	3576	3588	1	2	4	5	6	7	8	10	11
60	3600	3612	3624	3636	3648	3660	3672	3684	3697	3709	1	2	4	5	6	7	8	10	11
61	3721	3733	3745	3758	3770	3782	3795	3807	3819	3832	1	2	4	5	6	7	9	10	11
62	3844	3856	3869	3881	3894	3906	3919	3931	3944	3956	1	3	4	5	6	7	9	10	11
63	3969	3982	3994	4007	4020	4032	4045	4058	4070	4083	1	3	4	5	6	8	9	10	11
64	4096	4109	4122	4134	4147	4160	4173	4186	4199	4212	1	3	4	5	6	8	9	10	12
65	4225	4238	4251	4264	4277	4290	4303	4316	4330	4343	1	3	4	5	7	8	9	10	12
66	4356	4369	4382	4396	4409	4422	4436	4449	4462	4476	1	3	4	5	7	8	9	11	12
67	4489	4502	4516	4529	4543	4556	4570	4583	4597	4610	1	3	4	5	7	8	9	11	12
68	4624	4638	4651	4665	4679	4692	4706	4720	4733	4747	1	3	4	5	7	8	10	11	12
69	4761	4775	4789	4802	4816	4830	4844	4858	4872	4886	1	3	4	6	7	8	10	11	13
70	4900	4914	4928	4942	4956	4970	4984	4998	5013	5027	1	3	4	6	7	8	10	11	13
71	5041	5055	5069	5084	5098	5112	5127	5141	5155	5170	1	3	4	6	7	9	10	11	13
72	5184	5198	5213	5227	5242	5256	5271	5285	5300	5314	1	3	4	6	7	9	10	12	13
73	5329	5344	5358	5373	5388	5402	5417	5432	5446	5461	1	3	4	6	7	9	10	12	13
74	5476	5491	5506	5520	5535	5550	5565	5580	5595	5610	1	3	4	6	7	9	10	12	13
75	5625	5640	5655	5670	5685	5700	5715	5730	5746	5761	2	3	5	6	8	9	11	12	14
76	5776	5791	5806	5822	5837	5852	5868	5883	5898	5914	2	3	5	6	8	9	11	12	14
77	5929	5944	5960	5975	5991	6006	6022	6037	6053	6068	2	3	5	6	8	9	11	12	14
78	6084	6100	6115	6131	6147	6162	6178	6194	6209	6225	2	3	5	6	8	9	11	13	14
79	6241	6257	6273	6288	6304	6320	6336	6352	6368	6384	2	3	5	6	8	10	11	13	14
80	6400	6416	6432	6448	6464	6480	6496	6512	6529	6545	2	3	5	6	8	10	11	13	14
81	6561	6577	6593	6610	6626	6642	6659	6675	6691	6708	2	3	5	7	8	10	11	13	15
82	6724	6740	6757	6773	6790	6806	6823	6839	6856	6872	2	3	5	7	8	10	12	13	15
83	6889	6906	6922	6939	6956	6972	6989	7006	7022	7039	2	3	5	7	8	10	12	13	15
84	7056	7073	7090	7106	7123	7140	7157	7174	7191	7208	2	3	5	7	8	10	12	14	15
85	7225	7242	7259	7276	7293	7310	7327	7344	7362	7379	2	3	5	7	9	10	12	14	15
86	7396	7413	7430	7448	7465	7482	7500	7517	7534	7552	2	3	5	7	9	10	12	14	16
87	7569	7586	7604	7621	7639	7656	7674	7691	7709	7726	2	4	5	7	9	10	12	14	16
88	7744	7762	7779	7797	7815	7832	7850	7868	7885	7903	2	4	5	7	9	11	12	14	16
89	7921	7939	7957	7974	7992	8010	8028	8046	8064	8082	2	4	5	7	9	11	13	14	16
90	8100	8118	8136	8154	8172	8190	8208	8226	8245	8263	2	4	5	7	9	11	13	14	16
91	8281	8299	8317	8336	8354	8372	8391	8409	8427	8446	2	4	5	7	9	11	13	15	16
92	8464	8482	8501	8519	8538	8556	8575	8593	8612	8630	2	4	6	7	9	11	13	15	17
93	8649	8668	8686	8705	8724	8742	8761	8780	8798	8817	2	4	6	7	9	11	13	15	17
94	8836	8855	8874	8892	8911	8930	8949	8968	8987	9006	2	4	6	8	9	11	13	15	17
95	9025	9044	9063	9082	9101	9120	9139	9158	9178	9197	2	4	6	8	10	11	13	15	17
96	9216	9235	9254	9274	9293	9312	9332	9351	9370	9390	2	4	6	8	10	12	14	15	17
97	9409	9428	9448	9467	9487	9506	9526	9545	9565	9584	2	4	6	8	10	12	14	16	18
98	9604	9624	9643	9663	9683	9702	9722	9742	9761	9781	2	4	6	8	10	12	14	16	18
99	9801	9821	9841	9860	9880	9900	9920	9940	9960	9980	2	4	6	8	10	12	14	16	18

Find the position of the decimal point by inspection.

	0	1	2	3	4	5	6	7	8	9	1 2 3	4 5 6	7 8 9
10	1000	1005	1010	1015	1020	1025	1030	1034	1039	1044	0 1 1	2 2 3	3 4 4
11	1049	1054	1058	1063	1068	1072	1077	1082	1086	1091	0 1 1	2 2 3	3 4 4
12	1095	1100	1105	1109	1114	1118	1122	1127	1131	1136	0 1 1	2 2 3	3 4 4
13	1140	1145	1149	1153	1158	1162	1166	1170	1175	1179	0 1 1	2 2 3	3 3 4
14	1183	1187	1192	1196	1200	1204	1208	1212	1217	1221	0 1 1	2 2 2	3 3 4
15	1225	1229	1233	1237	1241	1245	1249	1253	1257	1261	0 1 1	2 2 2	3 3 4
16	1265	1269	1273	1277	1281	1285	1288	1292	1296	1300	0 1 1	2 2 2	3 3 4
17	1304	1308	1311	1315	1319	1323	1327	1330	1334	1338	0 1 1	2 2 2	3 3 3
18	1342	1345	1349	1353	1356	1360	1364	1367	1371	1375	0 1 1	1 2 2	3 3 3
19	1378	1382	1386	1389	1393	1396	1400	1404	1407	1411	0 1 1	1 2 2	3 3 3
20	1414	1418	1421	1425	1428	1432	1435	1439	1442	1446	0 1 1	1 2 2	2 3 3
21	1449	1453	1456	1459	1463	1466	1470	1473	1476	1480	0 1 1	1 2 2	2 3 3
22	1483	1487	1490	1493	1497	1500	1503	1507	1510	1513	0 1 1	1 2 2	2 3 3
23	1517	1520	1523	1526	1530	1533	1536	1539	1543	1546	0 1 1	1 2 2	2 3 3
24	1549	1552	1556	1559	1562	1565	1568	1572	1575	1578	0 1 1	1 2 2	2 3 3
25	1581	1584	1587	1591	1594	1597	1600	1603	1606	1609	0 1 1	1 2 2	2 3 3
26	1612	1616	1619	1622	1625	1628	1631	1634	1637	1640	0 1 1	1 2 2	2 2 3
27	1643	1646	1649	1652	1655	1658	1661	1664	1667	1670	0 1 1	1 2 2	2 2 3
28	1673	1676	1679	1682	1685	1688	1691	1694	1697	1700	0 1 1	1 1 2	2 2 3
29	1703	1706	1709	1712	1715	1718	1720	1723	1726	1729	0 1 1	1 1 2	2 2 3
30	1732	1735	1738	1741	1744	1746	1749	1752	1755	1758	0 1 1	1 1 2	2 2 3
31	1761	1764	1766	1769	1772	1775	1778	1780	1783	1786	0 1 1	1 1 2	2 2 3
32	1789	1792	1794	1797	1800	1803	1806	1808	1811	1814	0 1 1	1 1 2	2 2 2
33	1817	1819	1822	1825	1828	1830	1833	1836	1838	1841	0 1 1	1 1 2	2 2 2
34	1844	1847	1849	1852	1855	1857	1860	1863	1865	1868	0 1 1	1 1 2	2 2 2
35	1871	1873	1876	1879	1881	1884	1887	1889	1892	1895	0 1 1	1 1 2	2 2 2
36	1897	1900	1903	1905	1908	1910	1913	1916	1918	1921	0 1 1	1 1 2	2 2 2
37	1924	1926	1929	1931	1934	1936	1939	1942	1944	1947	0 1 1	1 1 2	2 2 2
38	1949	1952	1954	1957	1960	1962	1965	1967	1970	1972	0 1 1	1 1 2	2 2 2
39	1975	1977	1980	1982	1985	1987	1990	1992	1995	1997	0 1 1	1 1 2	2 2 2
40	2000	2002	2005	2007	2010	2012	2015	2017	2020	2022	0 0 1	1 1 1	2 2 2
41	2025	2027	2030	2032	2035	2037	2040	2042	2045	2047	0 0 1	1 1 1	2 2 2
42	2049	2052	2054	2057	2059	2062	2064	2066	2069	2071	0 0 1	1 1 1	2 2 2
43	2074	2076	2078	2081	2083	2086	2088	2090	2093	2095	0 0 1	1 1 1	2 2 2
44	2098	2100	2102	2105	2107	2110	2112	2114	2117	2119	0 0 1	1 1 1	2 2 2
45	2121	2124	2126	2128	2131	2133	2135	2138	2140	2142	0 0 1	1 1 1	2 2 2
46	2145	2147	2149	2152	2154	2156	2159	2161	2163	2166	0 0 1	1 1 1	2 2 2
47	2168	2170	2173	2175	2177	2179	2182	2184	2186	2189	0 0 1	1 1 1	2 2 2
48	2191	2193	2195	2198	2200	2202	2205	2207	2209	2211	0 0 1	1 1 1	2 2 2
49	2214	2216	2218	2220	2223	2225	2227	2229	2232	2234	0 0 1	1 1 1	2 2 2
50	2236	2238	2241	2243	2245	2247	2249	2252	2254	2256	0 0 1	1 1 1	2 2 2
51	2258	2261	2263	2265	2267	2269	2272	2274	2276	2278	0 0 1	1 1 1	2 2 2
52	2280	2283	2285	2287	2289	2291	2293	2296	2298	2300	0 0 1	1 1 1	2 2 2
53	2302	2304	2307	2309	2311	2313	2315	2317	2319	2322	0 0 1	1 1 1	2 2 2
54	2324	2326	2328	2330	2332	2335	2337	2339	2341	2343	0 0 1	1 1 1	1 2 2

Find the first significant figure and the position of the decimal point by inspection.

	0	1	2	3	4	5	6	7	8	9	1 2 3	4 5 6	7 8 9
10	3162	3178	3194	3209	3225	3240	3256	3271	3286	3302	2 3 5	6 8 9	11 12 14
11	3317	3332	3347	3362	3376	3391	3406	3421	3435	3450	1 3 4	6 7 9	10 12 13
12	3464	3479	3493	3507	3521	3536	3550	3564	3578	3592	1 3 4	6 7 8	10 11 13
13	3606	3619	3633	3647	3661	3674	3688	3701	3715	3728	1 3 4	5 7 8	10 11 12
14	3742	3755	3768	3782	3795	3808	3821	3834	3847	3860	1 3 4	5 7 8	9 11 12
15	3873	3886	3899	3912	3924	3937	3950	3962	3975	3987	1 3 4	5 6 8	9 10 11
16	4000	4012	4025	4037	4050	4062	4074	4087	4099	4111	1 2 4	5 6 7	9 10 11
17	4123	4135	4147	4159	4171	4183	4195	4207	4219	4231	1 2 4	5 6 7	8 10 11
18	4243	4254	4266	4278	4290	4301	4313	4324	4336	4347	1 2 3	5 6 7	8 9 10
19	4359	4370	4382	4393	4405	4416	4427	4438	4450	4461	1 2 3	5 6 7	8 9 10
20	4472	4483	4494	4506	4517	4528	4539	4550	4561	4572	1 2 3	4 6 7	8 9 10
21	4583	4593	4604	4615	4626	4637	4648	4658	4669	4680	1 2 3	4 5 6	8 9 10
22	4690	4701	4712	4722	4733	4743	4754	4764	4775	4785	1 2 3	4 5 6	7 8 9
23	4796	4806	4817	4827	4837	4848	4858	4868	4879	4889	1 2 3	4 5 6	7 8 9
24	4899	4909	4919	4930	4940	4950	4960	4970	4980	4990	1 2 3	4 5 6	7 8 9
25	5000	5010	5020	5030	5040	5050	5060	5070	5079	5089	1 2 3	4 5 6	7 8 9
26	5099	5109	5119	5128	5138	5148	5158	5167	5177	5187	1 2 3	4 5 6	7 8 9
27	5196	5206	5215	5225	5235	5244	5254	5263	5273	5282	1 2 3	4 5 6	7 8 9
28	5292	5301	5310	5320	5329	5339	5348	5357	5367	5376	1 2 3	4 5 6	7 7 8
29	5385	5394	5404	5413	5422	5431	5441	5450	5459	5468	1 2 3	4 5 5	6 7 8
30	5477	5486	5495	5505	5514	5523	5532	5541	5550	5559	1 2 3	4 4 5	6 7 8
31	5568	5577	5586	5595	5604	5612	5621	5630	5639	5648	1 2 3	3 4 5	6 7 8
32	5657	5666	5675	5683	5692	5701	5710	5718	5727	5736	1 2 3	3 4 5	6 7 8
33	5745	5753	5762	5771	5779	5788	5797	5805	5814	5822	1 2 3	3 4 5	6 7 8
34	5831	5840	5848	5857	5865	5874	5882	5891	5899	5908	1 2 3	3 4 5	6 7 8
35	5916	5925	5933	5941	5950	5958	5967	5975	5983	5992	1 2 2	3 4 5	6 7 8
36	6000	6008	6017	6025	6033	6042	6050	6058	6066	6075	1 2 2	3 4 5	6 7 7
37	6083	6091	6099	6107	6116	6124	6132	6140	6148	6156	1 2 2	3 4 5	6 7 7
38	6164	6173	6181	6189	6197	6205	6213	6221	6229	6237	1 2 2	3 4 5	6 6 7
39	6245	6253	6261	6269	6277	6285	6293	6301	6309	6317	1 2 2	3 4 5	6 6 7
40	6325	6332	6340	6348	6356	6364	6372	6380	6387	6395	1 2 2	3 4 5	6 6 7
41	6403	6411	6419	6427	6434	6442	6450	6458	6465	6473	1 2 2	3 4 5	5 6 7
42	6481	6488	6496	6504	6512	6519	6527	6535	6542	6550	1 2 2	3 4 5	5 6 7
43	6557	6565	6573	6580	6588	6595	6603	6611	6618	6626	1 2 2	3 4 5	5 6 7
44	6633	6641	6648	6656	6663	6671	6678	6686	6693	6701	1 2 2	3 4 5	5 6 7
45	6708	6716	6723	6731	6738	6745	6753	6760	6768	6775	1 1 2	3 4 4	5 6 7
46	6782	6790	6797	6804	6812	6819	6826	6834	6841	6848	1 1 2	3 4 4	5 6 7
47	6856	6863	6870	6877	6885	6892	6899	6907	6914	6921	1 1 2	3 4 4	5 6 7
48	6928	6935	6943	6950	6957	6964	6971	6979	6986	6993	1 1 2	3 4 4	5 6 6
49	7000	7007	7014	7021	7029	7036	7043	7050	7057	7064	1 1 2	3 4 4	5 6 6
50	7071	7078	7085	7092	7099	7106	7113	7120	7127	7134	1 1 2	3 4 4	5 6 6
51	7141	7148	7155	7162	7169	7176	7183	7190	7197	7204	1 1 2	3 4 4	5 6 6
52	7211	7218	7225	7232	7239	7246	7253	7259	7266	7273	1 1 2	3 3 4	5 6 6
53	7280	7287	7294	7301	7308	7314	7321	7328	7335	7342	1 1 2	3 3 4	5 5 6
54	7348	7355	7362	7369	7376	7382	7389	7396	7403	7409	1 1 2	3 3 4	5 5 6

Find the first significant figure and the position of the decimal point by inspection.

	0	1	2	3	4	5	6	7	8	9	1 2 3	4 5 6	7 8 9
55	2345	2347	2349	2352	2354	2356	2358	2360	2362	2364	0 0 1	1 1 1	1 2 2
56	2366	2369	2371	2373	2375	2377	2379	2381	2383	2385	0 0 1	1 1 1	1 2 2
57	2387	2390	2392	2394	2396	2398	2400	2402	2404	2406	0 0 1	1 1 1	1 2 2
58	2408	2410	2412	2415	2417	2419	2421	2423	2425	2427	0 0 1	1 1 1	1 2 2
59	2429	2431	2433	2435	2437	2439	2441	2443	2445	2447	0 0 1	1 1 1	1 2 2
60	2449	2452	2454	2456	2458	2460	2462	2464	2466	2468	0 0 1	1 1 1	1 2 2
61	2470	2472	2474	2476	2478	2480 ·	2482	2484	2486	2488	0 0 1	1 1 1	1 2 2
62	2490	2492	2494	2496	2498	2500	2502	2504	2506	2508	0 0 1	1 1 1	1 2 2
63	2510	2512	2514	2516	2518	2520	2522	2524	2526	2528	0 0 1	1 1 1	1 2 2
64	2530	2532	2534	2536	2538	2540	2542	2544	2546	2548	0 0 1	1 1 1	1 2 2
65	2550	2551	2553	2555	2557	2559	2561	2563	2565	2567	0 0 1	1 1 1	1 2 2
66	2569	2571	2573	2575	2577	2579	2581	2583	2585	2587	0 0 1	1 1 1	1 2 2
67	2588	2590	2592	2594	2596	2598	2600	2602	2604	2606	0 0 1	1 1 1	1 2 2
68	2608	2610	2612	2613	2615	2617	2619	2621	2623	2625	0 0 1	1 1 1	1 2 2
69	2627	2629	2631	2632	2634	2636	2638	2640	2642	2644	0 0 1	1 1 1	1 2 2
70	2646	2648	2650	2651	2653	2655	2657	2659	2661	2663	0 0 1	1 1 1	1 2 2
71	2665	2666	2668	2670	2672	2674	2676	2678	2680	2681	0 0 1	1 1 1	1 1 2
72	2683	2685	2687	2689	2691	2693	2694	2696	2698	2700	0 0 1	1 1 1	1 1 2
73	2702	2704	2706	2707	2709	2711	2713	2715	2717	2718	0 0 1	1 1 1	1 1 2
74	2720	2722	2724	2726	2728	2729	2731	2733	2735	2737	0 0 1	1 1 1	1 1 2
75	2739	2740	2742	2744	2746	2748	2750	2751	2753	2755	0 0 1	1 1 1	1 1 2
76	2757	2759	2760	2762	2764	2766	2768	2769	2771	2773	0 0 1	1 1 1	1 1 2
77	2775	2777	2778	2780	2782	2784	2786	2787	2789	2791	0 0 1	1 1 1	1 1 2
78	2793	2795	2796	2798	2800	2802	2804	2805	2807	2809	0 0 1	1 1 1	1 1 2
79	2811	2812	2814	2816	2818	2820	2821	2823	2825	2827	0 0 1	1 1 1	1 1 2
80	2828	2830	2832	2834	2835	2837	2839	2841	2843	2844	0 0 1	1 1 1	1 1 2
81	2846	2848	2850	2851	2853	2855	2857	2858	2860	2862	0 0 1	1 1 1	1 1 2
82	2864	2865	2867	2869	2871	2872	2874	2876	2877	2879	0 0 1	1 1 1	1 1 2
83	2881	2883	2884	2886	2888	2890	2891	2893	2895	2897	0 0 1	1 1 1	1 1 2
84	2898	2900	2902	2903	2905	2907	2909	2910	2912	2914	0 0 1	1 1 1	1 1 2
85	2915	2917	2919	2921	2922	2924	2926	2927	2929	2931	0 0 1	1 1 1	1 1 2
86	2933	2934	2936	2938	2939	2941	2943	2944	2946	2948	0 0 1	1 1 1	1 1 2
87	2950	2951	2953	2955	2956	2958	2960	2961	2963	2965	0 0 1	1 1 1	1 1 2
88	2966	2968	2970	2972	2973	2975	2977	2978	2980	2982	0 0 1	1 1 1	1 1 2
89	2983	2985	2987	2988	2990	2992	2993	2995	2997	2998	0 0 1	1 1 1	1 1 2
90	3000	3002	3003	3005	3007	3008	3010	3012	3013	3015	0 0 0	1 1 1	1 1 1
91	3017	3018	3020	3022	3023	3025	3027	3028	3030	3032	0 0 0	1 1 1	1 1 1
92	3033	3035	3036	3038	3040	3041	3043	3045	3046	3048	0 , 0 0	1 1 1	1 1 1
93	3050	3051	3053	3055	3056	3058	3059	3061	3063	3064	0 0 0	1 1 1	1 1 1
94	3066	3068	3069	3071	3072	3074	3076	3077	3079	3081	0 0 0	1 1 1	1 1 1
95	3082	3084	3085	3087	3089	3090	3092	3094	3095	3097	0 0 0	1 1 1	1 1 1
96	3098	3100	3102	3103	3105	3106	3108	3110	3111	3113	0 0 0	1 1 1	1 1 1
97	3114	3116	3118	3119	3121	3122	3124	3126	3127	3129	0 0 0	1 1 1	1 1 1
98	3130	3132	3134	3135	3137	3138	3140	3142	3143	3145	0 0 0	1 1 1	1 1 1
99	3146	3148	3150	3151	3153	3154	3156	3158	3159	3161	0 0 0	1 1 1	1 1 1

Find the first significant figure and the position of the decimal point by inspection.

	0	1	2	3	4	5	6	7	8	9	1 2 3	4 5 6	7 8 9
55	7416	7423	7430	7436	7443	7450	7457	7463	7470	7477	1 1 2	3 3 4	5 5 6
56	7483	7490	7497	7503	7510	7517	7523	7530	7537	7543	1 1 2	3 3 4	5 5 6
57	7550	7556	7563	7570	7576	7583	7589	7596	7603	7609	1 1 2	3 3 4	5 5 6
58	7616	7622	7629	7635	7642	7649	7655	7662	7668	7675	1 1 2	3 3 4	5 5 6
59	7681	7688	7694	7701	7707	7714	7720	7727	7733	7740	1 1 2	3 3 4	5 5 6
60	7746	7752	7759	7765	7772	7778	7785	7791	7797	7804	1 1 2	3 3 4	4 5 6
61	7810	7817	7823	7829	7836	7842	7849	7855	7861	7868	1 1 2	3 3 4	4 5 6
62	7874	7880	7887	7893	7899	7906	7912	7918	7925	7931	1 1 2	3 3 4	4 5 6
63	7937	7944	7950	7956	7962	7969	7975	7981	7987	7994	1 1 2	3 3 4	4 5 6
64	8000	8006	8012	8019	8025	8031	8037	8044	8050	8056	1 1 2	2 3 4	4 5 6
65	8062	8068	8075	8081	8087	8093	8099	8106	8112	8118	1 1 2	2 3 4	4 5 5
66	8124	8130	8136	8142	8149	8155	8161	8167	8173	8179	1 1 2	2 3 4	4 5 5
67	8185	8191	8198	8204	8210	8216	8222	8228	8234	8240	1 1 2	2 3 4	4 5 5
68	8246	8252	8258	8264	8270	8276	8283	8289	8295	8301	1 1 2	2 3 4	4 5 5
69	8307	8313	8319	8325	8331	8337	8343	8349	8355	8361	1 1 2	2 3 4	4 5 5
70	8367	8373	8379	8385	8390	8396	8402	8408	8414	8420	1 1 2	2 3 4	4 5 5
71	8426	8432	8438	8444	8450	8456	8462	8468	8473	8479	1 1 2	2 3 4	4 5 5
72	8485	8491	8497	8503	8509	8515	8521	8526	8532	8538	1 1 2	2 3 3	4 5 5
73	8544	8550	8556	8562	8567	8573	8579	8585	8591	8597	1 1 2	2 3 3	4 5 5
74	8602	8608	8614	8620	8626	8631	8637	8643	8649	8654	1 1 2	2 3 3	4 5 5
75	8660	8666	8672	8678	8683	8689	8695	8701	8706	8712	1 1 2	2 3 3	4 5 5
76	8718	8724	8729	8735	8741	8746	8752	8758	8764	8769	1 1 2	2 3 3	4 5 5
77	8775	8781	8786	8792	8798	8803	8809	8815	8820	8826	1 1 2	2 3 3	4 4 5
78	8832	8837	8843	8849	8854	8860	8866	8871	8877	8883	1 1 2	2 3 3	4 4 5
79	8888	8894	8899	8905	8911	8916	8922	8927	8933	8939	1 1 2	2 3 3	4 4 5
80	8944	8950	8955	8961	8967	8972	8978	8983	8989	8994	1 1 2	2 3 3	4 4 5
81	9000	9006	9011	9017	9022	9028	9033	9039	9044	9050	1 1 2	2 3 3	4 4 5
82	9055	9061	9066	9072	9077	9083	9088	9094	9099	9105	1 1 2	2 3 3	4 4 5
83	9110	9116	9121	9127	9132	9138	9143	9149	9154	9160	1 1 2	2 3 3	4 4 5
84	9165	9171	9176	9182	9187	9192	9198	9203	9209	9214	1 1 2	2 3 3	4 4 5
85	9220	9225	9230	9236	9241	9247	9252	9257	9263	9268	1 1 2	2 3 3	4 4 5
86	9274	9279	9284	9290	9295	9301	9306	9311	9317	9322	1 1 2	2 3 3	4 4 5
87	9327	9333	9338	9343	9349	9354	9359	9365	9370	9375	1 1 2	2 3 3	4 4 5
88	9381	9386	9391	9397	9402	9407	9413	9418	9423	9429	1 1 2	2 3 3	4 4 5
89	9434	9439	9445	9450	9455	9460	9466	9471	9476	9482	1 1 2	2 3 3	4 4 5
90	9487	9492	9497	9503	9508	9513	9518	9524	9529	9534	1 1 2	2 3 3	4 4 5
91	9539	9545	9550	9555	9560	9566	9571	9576	9581	9586	1 1 2	2 3 3	4 4 5
92	9592	9597	9602	9607	9612	9618	9623	9628	9633	9638	1 1 2	2 3 3	4 4 5
93	9644	9649	9654	9659	9664	9670	9675	9680	9685	9690	1 1 2	2 3 3	4 4 5
94	9695	9701	9706	9711	9716	9721	9726	9731	9737	9742	1 1 2	2 3 3	4 4 5
95	9747	9752	9757	9762	9767	9772	9778	9783	9788	9793	1 1 2	2 3 3	4 4 5
96	9798	9803	9808	9813	9818	9823	9829	9834	9839	9844	1 1 2	2 3 3	4 4 5
97	9849	9854	9859	9864	9869	9874	9879	9884	9889	9894	1 1 2	2 3 3	4 4 5
98	9899	9905	9910	9915	9920	9925	9930	9935	9940	9945	0 1 1	2 2 3	3 4 4
99	9950	9955	9960	9965	9970	9975	9980	9985	9990	9995	0 1 1	2 2 3	3 4 4

Find the first significant figure and the position of the decimal point by inspection.

£3-50